AM PREPARATION & PRACTICE GUIDE

John Owen
David Martin
Michael Haese
Robert Haese
Sandra Haese

second edition

Haese & Harris Publications

# MATHEMATICS FOR THE INTERNATIONAL STUDENT
**Mathematics SL**
**EXAM PREPARATION & PRACTICE GUIDE second edition**


| | |
|---|---|
| John Owen | B.Sc., Dip.T. |
| David Martin | B.A., B.Sc., M.A., M.Ed.Admin. |
| Michael Haese | B.Sc.(Hons), Ph.D. |
| Robert Haese | B.Sc. |
| Sandra Haese | B.Sc. |



Haese & Harris Publications
3 Frank Collopy Court, Adelaide Airport, SA 5950, AUSTRALIA
Telephone: +61 8 8355 9444, Fax: + 61 8 8355 9471
Email: info@haeseandharris.com.au
Web: www.haeseandharris.com.au

National Library of Australia Card Number & ISBN 978-1-921500-11-4





Published by Raksar Nominees Pty Ltd
3 Frank Collopy Court, Adelaide Airport, SA 5950, AUSTRALIA

First Edition 2006
Second Edition 2009

Artwork by Piotr Poturaj.
Cover design by Piotr Poturaj.

Typeset in Australia by Susan Haese and Charlotte Sabel (Raksar Nominees).

Typeset in Times Roman 9/10.





**Acknowledgements**: While every attempt has been made to trace and acknowledge copyright, the authors and publishers apologise for any accidental infringement where copyright has proved untraceable. They would be pleased to come to a suitable agreement with the rightful owner.

The authors and publishers would like to thank all those teachers who have read the proofs of this book and offered advice and encouragement.

Special thanks to John Bush for his detailed advice and criticism in the early stages of planning the Exam Preparation & Practice Guides. Others who offered to read and comment on the proofs include: Irene Owen, Jane Kerr, Paula Waldman, Genny Green, Margie Karbassioun, Susan Cox, Andrew Spray, Mark Banner-Martin, Brendan Watson, Jeff Jones, Wallis Green, Andrzej Cichy, Peter Blythe, Robert Sloan, Mark Willis, Edward Kemp, Peter Joseph, Jim Napolitano, Sonja Bartholomew, Myrricia Holmann, Rema George, Peter Hamer-Hodges. To anyone we may have missed, we offer our apologies.

The publishers wish to make it clear that acknowledging these teachers does not imply any endorsement of this book by any of them, and all responsibility for the content rests with the authors and publishers.

# FOREWORD

The aim of this Guide is to help you prepare for the Mathematics SL final examinations.

In this second edition, the overall number of questions has been increased and questions throughout are divided into two categories: 'no calculators' and 'calculators' in response to the introduction of a calculator-free examination paper.

This Guide should be used in conjunction with other material suggested by your teacher. Past examination papers, for example, are invaluable aids. Ensure you frequently refer to the information booklet. It is essential that you become familiar with the layout and content of the booklet.

This Guide covers all seven Topics in the Mathematics SL syllabus. The main elements within each Topic are summarised in a way that highlights the important facts and concepts. These summaries are intended to complement your textbook and information booklet. When a formula can be found in the information booklet, it may not be repeated in this Guide.

Two sets of Skill Builder Questions appear at the end of each Topic, the first set categorised as 'no calculators', the second as 'calculators'. Skill Builder Questions can be used as a warm-up and should help to consolidate your understanding of each Topic. The best way to consolidate your understanding is to be active: to summarise concepts concisely and accurately, and to practise answering questions.

Following the coverage of all seven Topics, the Guide has six Examination Practice Sets: three are categorised as 'no calculators' and three as 'calculators'. There are twenty questions in each set. Full solutions are provided but it is recommended that you work through a full set before checking the solutions.

Try to complete the sets under examination conditions. Getting into good habits will reduce pressure during the examination.

- It is important that you persevere with a question, but sometimes it is a good strategy to move on to other questions and return later to ones you have found challenging. Time management is very important during the examination and too much time spent on a difficult question may mean that you do not leave yourself sufficient time to complete other questions.
- Use a pen rather than a pencil, except for graphs and diagrams.
- If you make a mistake draw a single line through the work you want to replace. Do not cross out work until you have replaced it with something you consider better.
- Set out your work clearly with full explanations. Do not take shortcuts.
- Diagrams and graphs should be sufficiently large, well labelled and clearly drawn.
- Remember to leave answers correct to three significant figures unless an exact answer is more appropriate or a different level of accuracy is requested in the question.

Get used to reading the questions carefully.

- Check for key words. If the word "hence" appears, then you must use the result you have just obtained. "Hence, or otherwise" means that you can use any method you like, although it is likely that the best method uses the previous result.
- Rushing into a question may mean that you miss subtle points. Underlining key words may help.
- Often questions in the examination are set so that, even if you cannot get through one part, the question can still be picked up in a later part.

After completing a practice set, identify areas of weakness.

- Return to your notes or textbook and review the Topic.
- Ask your teacher or a friend for help if further explanation is needed.
- Summarise each Topic. Summaries that you make yourself are the most valuable.
- Test yourself, or work with someone else to help improve your knowledge of a Topic.
- If you have had difficulty with a question, try it again later. Do not just assume that you know how to do it once you have read the solution. It is important that you work on areas of weakness, but do not neglect the other areas.

In addition to the information booklet, your graphics display calculator is an essential aid.

- Make sure you are familiar with the model you will be using.
- In trigonometry questions remember to check whether the graphics calculator should be in degrees or radians.
- Become familiar with common error messages and how to respond to them.
- Important features of graphs may be revealed by zooming in or out.
- Asymptotic behaviour is not always clear on a graphics calculator screen; don't just rely on appearances. As with all aspects of the graphics calculator, reflect on the reasonableness of the results.
- Are your batteries fresh?

We hope this guide will help you structure your revision program effectively. Remember that good examination techniques will come from good examination preparation.

We welcome your feedback:

web: http://haeseandharris.com.au

email: info@haeseandharris.com.au

# TABLE OF CONTENTS

# TOPIC 1: ALGEBRA

## SEQUENCES AND SERIES

A **number sequence** is a set of numbers defined by a rule which is valid for positive integers. Often, the rule is a formula for the **general term** or **$n$th term** of the sequence.

### Arithmetic Sequences

In an **arithmetic sequence**, each term differs from the previous one by the same fixed number.

$u_{n+1} - u_n = d$ for all $n$, where $d$ is a constant called the **common difference**.

For an arithmetic sequence with first term $u_1$ and common difference $d$, $u_n = u_1 + (n-1)\,d$.

### Geometric Sequences

In a **geometric sequence**, each term is obtained from the previous one by multiplying by the same non-zero constant.

$\dfrac{u_{n+1}}{u_n} = r$ for all $n$, where $r$ is a constant called the **common ratio**.

For a geometric sequence with first term $u_1$ and common ratio $r$, $u_n = u_1 r^{n-1}$.

### Series

A **series** is the addition of the terms of a sequence. Given a series which includes the first $n$ terms of a sequence, its sum is $S_n = u_1 + u_2 + .... + u_n$.

Using **sigma notation** we can write

$u_1 + u_2 + u_3 + .... + u_n$ as $\sum\limits_{k=1}^{n} u_k$.

For an **arithmetic series**, $S_n = \frac{n}{2}(u_1 + u_n)$.

For a **geometric series**, $S_n = \dfrac{u_1(r^n - 1)}{r - 1}$.

The sum of an **infinite geometric series** is

$S = \dfrac{u_1}{1-r}$ provided $|r| < 1$.

If $|r| > 1$ the series is **divergent**.

For compound interest problems we have a geometric sequence. If the interest rate is $i\%$ per time period then the common ratio is $\left(1 + \frac{i}{100}\right)$ and the number of compounding periods is $n$.

## EXPONENTIALS AND LOGARITHMS

Exponential and logarithmic functions are inverses of each other. The graph of $y = \log_a x$ is the reflection in the line $y = x$ of the graph of $y = a^x$.

| Index or Exponent Laws | |
|---|---|
| $a^x \times a^y = a^{x+y}$ | $a^{-x} = \dfrac{1}{a^x}$ and $\dfrac{1}{a^{-x}} = a^x$ |
| $\dfrac{a^x}{a^y} = a^{x-y}$ | $a^{\frac{1}{n}} = \sqrt[n]{a}$ |
| $(a^x)^y = a^{xy}$ | $a^{\frac{m}{n}} = \sqrt[n]{a^m} = (\sqrt[n]{a})^m$ |
| $a^0 = 1 \ (a \neq 0)$ | |

If $a^x = a^k$ then $x = k$. So, if the base numbers are the same, we can **equate indices**.

If $b = a^x$, $a \neq 1$, $a > 0$, we say that $x$ is the **logarithm** of $b$ in base $a$, and that $b = a^x \Leftrightarrow x = \log_a b$, $b > 0$.

The **natural logarithm** is the logarithm in base $e$. $\ln x \equiv \log_e x$

| Logarithm Laws | |
|---|---|
| **Base $a$** | **Base $e$** |
| $\log_a xy = \log_a x + \log_a y$ | $\ln xy = \ln x + \ln y$ |
| $\log_a \left(\dfrac{x}{y}\right) = \log_a x - \log_a y$ | $\ln \left(\dfrac{x}{y}\right) = \ln x - \ln y$ |
| $\log_a x^y = y \log_a x$ | $\ln x^y = y \ln x$ |
| $\log_a 1 = 0$ | $\ln 1 = 0$ |
| $\log_a a = 1$ | $\ln e = 1$ |

To change the base of a logarithm, use the rule $\log_b x = \dfrac{\log_c x}{\log_c b}$.

$x = \log_a a^x$ and $x = a^{\log_a x}$ provided $x > 0$.

## THE BINOMIAL THEOREM

$a + b$ is called a **binomial** as it contains two terms.

Any expression of the form $(a+b)^n$ is called a **power of a binomial**.

The **general binomial expansion** is

$$(a+b)^n = \binom{n}{0}a^n + \binom{n}{1}a^{n-1}b + \binom{n}{2}a^{n-2}b^2 + .... + \binom{n}{r}a^{n-r}b^r + .... + \binom{n}{n}b^n$$

where $\binom{n}{r}$ is the binomial coefficient of $a^{n-r}b^r$ and $r = 0, 1, 2, 3, ...., n$.

The **general term** in the binomial expansion is

$T_{r+1} = \binom{n}{r}a^{n-r}b^r$, so $(a+b)^n = \sum\limits_{r=0}^{n} \binom{n}{r}a^{n-r}b^r$.

You should know how to calculate binomial coefficients from Pascal's triangle and using your calculator.

## SKILL BUILDER QUESTIONS (NO CALCULATORS)

**1** Find the 20th term of:

**a** $51, 45, 39, 33, ....$ **b** $0.125, 0.5, 2, 8, ....$

**2** Find the sum of the infinite geometric series with first term 27 and fourth term 8.

**3** The 7th and 15th terms of an arithmetic sequence are 1 and $-23$ respectively. Find:

**a** the 27th term

**b** the sum of the first 27 terms of the sequence.

**4** Find the 10th term of:

**a** $x^2, 3x^2, 5x^2, ....$ **b** $x^{-\frac{1}{2}}, x, x^{2\frac{1}{2}}, ....$

**5** The first term of a finite arithmetic series is 18 and the sum of the series is $-210$. If the common difference is $-3$, find the number of terms in the series.

**6** Simplify:

**a** $(5x^2)^3 \times \left(\dfrac{x}{4}\right)^2 \times \dfrac{8}{25x^5}$ **b** $\dfrac{24a^3b^8}{15(a^2b)^3} \div \dfrac{5ab^3}{12a^6b}$

**c** $\dfrac{8x^{-2}y^3}{3(xy^2)^0} \times \dfrac{9x^0y^{-1}}{4x^{-3}}$ **d** $\dfrac{4x^{\frac{1}{2}} \times x^{-1\frac{1}{2}}}{8x^2}$

**e** $\sqrt[5]{a^3} \times \sqrt{a^5}$

**7** Find:

**a** $16^{-\frac{1}{2}}$ **b** $81^{\frac{1}{4}}$ **c** $32^{\frac{2}{5}}$

**d** $27^{-\frac{4}{3}}$ **e** $\left(\frac{1}{9}\right)^{\frac{3}{2}}$ **f** $(0.008)^{-\frac{5}{3}}$

**8** Factorise:

**a** $9^x - 6(3^x) + 8$ **b** $25^x + 5^{x+1} + 6$

**9** Write in the form $\log A$:

**a** $\log 2 + \log 12$ **b** $\log 36 - \log 12$

**c** $3\log 5 + 2\log 3$ **d** $\frac{1}{4}\log 81$

**10** Find $x$ if $8^{2x-3} = 16^{2-x}$.

**11** Simplify: $\dfrac{3^{x+1} - 3^x}{2(3^x) - 3^{x-1}}$

**12** Solve for $x$: $4^x + 4 = 17(2^{x-1})$

**13** If $A = \log_{10} P$, $B = \log_{10} Q$ and $C = \log_{10} R$, express in terms of $A$, $B$ and $C$:

**a** $\log_{10}\left(P^2Q\sqrt{R}\right)$ **b** $\log\left(\dfrac{R^3}{(PQ^2)^4}\right)$

**14** If $\log_5(2x-1) = -1$, find $x$.

**15** Write $\dfrac{8}{\log_5 9}$ in the form $a\log_3 b$ where $a, b \in \mathbb{Z}$.

**16** Write $2\ln x + \ln(x-1) - \ln(x-2)$ as a single logarithm.

**17** Solve for $x$: $\log_3 x + \log_3(x-2) = 1$.

**18** If $\log_a 5 = x$, find in terms of $x$:

**a** $\log_a(5a)$ **b** $\log_a\left(\dfrac{a^2}{25}\right)$.

**19** Write as a logarithmic equation in base $b$:

**a** $M = ab^3$ **b** $D = \dfrac{a}{b^2}$

**20** Write without logarithms:

**a** $\log_{10} M = 2x - 1$ **b** $\log_a N = 2\log_a d - \log_a c$

**21** Use Pascal's triangle to help expand and simplify $\left(x + \dfrac{1}{x}\right)^5$.

## SKILL BUILDER QUESTIONS (CALCULATORS)

**1** Find the first term in the arithmetic sequence 100, 130, 160, 190, .... to exceed 1200.

**2** If the 5th and 8th terms of a geometric sequence are 18 and 486 respectively, find the 12th term.

**3** Maria invested €800 on Jan 1st 1996.

**a** If her investment earns interest of 7% per annum, what was it worth on Jan 1st 2004?

**b** How many years will it take for her investment to reach €4000?

**4** Ying is training to run a marathon. In one week she ran 10 km on the first day and increased the distance by 10% on each subsequent day.

**a** How far did she run on the seventh day?

**b** What was the total distance she ran during the week?

**5** Find the sum of the series:

**a** $10 + 14 + 18 + 22 + \ldots. + 138$

**b** $6 - 12 + 24 - 48 + 96 - \ldots. + 1536$

**6** The sum of an infinite geometric series is 1.5, and its first term is 1. Find:

**a** the common ratio

**b** the sum of its first 7 terms in rational form.

**7** A sequence is defined by $u_n = 12\left(\frac{2}{3}\right)^{n-1}$.

**a** Prove that the sequence is geometric.

**b** Find the 5th term in rational form.

**c** Find: **i** $\sum_{n=1}^{\infty} u_n$

**ii** $\sum_{n=1}^{20} u_n$ correct to 4 decimal places.

**8** Stan invests £3500 for 33 months at an interest rate of 8% p.a. compounded quarterly. Find its maturing value.

**9** Solve for $x$:

**a** $3^x = 243$ **b** $5 \times 2^x = 160$ **c** $e^x = 27$

**d** $(1.25)^x = 10$ **e** $7e^x = 100$

**10** Solve for $t$:

**a** $200 \times e^{\frac{t}{4}} = 1500$ **b** $0.15e^{0.012t} = 2.18$

**c** $20e^{0.2t} = 250$

**11** Solve for $x$: $x^2 > e^{-x}$.

**12** Find the constant term in the expansion of $\left(x + \dfrac{3}{x^2}\right)^9$.

**13** Find the coefficient of $x^4y^9$ in the expansion of $\left(x + 2y^3\right)^7$.

**14** Consider the binomial expansion of $\left(2x - \dfrac{1}{x^2}\right)^{12}$. Find:

**a** the coefficient of $x^3$ **b** the constant term.

**15** Find $k$ given that the constant term of $\left(kx + \dfrac{1}{\sqrt{x}}\right)^9$ is $-10\frac{1}{2}$.

**16** Find the coefficient of $x^5$ in the expansion of $(x+2)(1-x)^{10}$.

**17** If $A = 125e^{-kt}$ and $A = 200$ when $t = 3$, find the value of $k$.

**18** Twins Pierre and Francesca were each given 100 dollars on their 15th birthday. They immediately put their money into their individual money boxes.
Each week throughout the next year they added a portion of their weekly pocket money. Pierre added \$10 each week. Francesca added 50 cents the first week, \$1 the next, \$1.50 the next, and so on, adding an extra 50 cents each subsequent week.

**a** Find the amount that each had added to his or her money box after 8 weeks.

**b** How much did Francesca add to her money box on her 16th birthday?

**c** Calculate the total amount they each had in their money boxes after one year.

**19** Hayley and Patrick are training for a road cycling race. During the first week Hayley cycles 60 km and Patrick does likewise. Hayley cycles an additional 20 km each subsequent week, whereas Patrick increases his distance by 20% each subsequent week.

**a** How far does each of them cycle in the 5th week of training?

**b** Who is the first to cycle 210 km in one week?

**c** What total distance does each cycle in the first 12 weeks?

**20** Kapil invested 2000 rupees in a bank account on Jan 1st 2002. Each year thereafter, he invested another 2000 rupees into the same account which pays 8.25% per annum compounded annually.

**a** Find the total value of his investment immediately after he invested 2000 rupees on Jan 1st 2009.

**b** Would it have been a better option for Kapil to invest his money each year into an account paying 9% per annum simple interest? Justify your answer.

**21** At the beginning of 2000 the number of koalas on an island was 2400. The numbers steadily increase each year according to $N(t) = 2400 + 250t$ where $t$ is the number of years since 2000. The population of kangaroos on the same island is given by $K(t) = 3200 \times (0.85)^t$.

**a** What was the kangaroo population at the beginning of 2000?

**b** How many kangaroos were on the island at the beginning of 2005?

**c** How many koalas were on the island at the beginning of 2005?

**d** After how many years will the kangaroo population fall below 1000?

**e** When will the number of koalas exceed the number of kangaroos?

# TOPIC 2: FUNCTIONS AND EQUATIONS

## FUNCTIONS $f : x \mapsto f(x)$ OR $y = f(x)$

A **relation** is any set of points on the Cartesian plane.

A **function** is a relation in which no two different ordered pairs have the same $x$-coordinate or first member. For each value of $x$ there is only one value of $y$ or $f(x)$. We sometimes refer to $y$ or $f(x)$ as the **image value** of $x$.

We **test for functions** using the vertical line test. A graph is a function if no vertical line intersects the graph more than once.

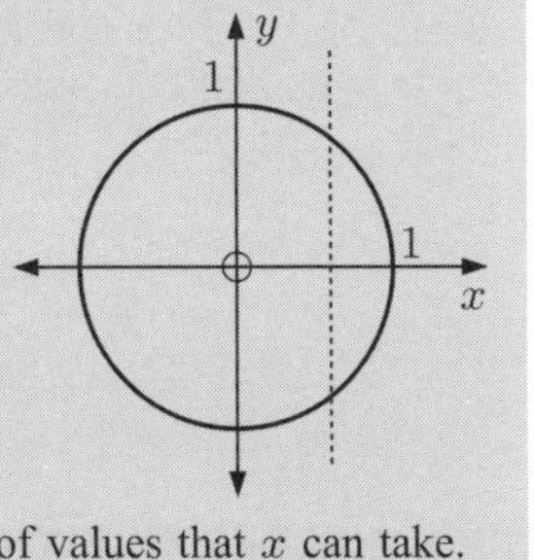


For example, a circle such as $x^2 + y^2 = 1$ has a graph which is not a function.

The **domain** of a function is the set of values that $x$ can take.

To find the domain of a function, remember that we cannot:

- divide by zero
- take the square root of a negative number
- take the logarithm of a non-positive number.

The **range** of a function is the set of values that $y$ or $f(x)$ can take.

Given $f : x \mapsto f(x)$ and $g : x \mapsto g(x)$, the **composite function** of $f$ and $g$ is $f \circ g : x \mapsto f(g(x))$.

In general, $f(g(x)) \neq g(f(x))$, so $f \circ g \neq g \circ f$.

The **identity function** is $f(x) = x$.

If $y = f(x)$ has an **inverse function** $y = f^{-1}(x)$, then the inverse function:

- must satisfy the vertical line test
- is a reflection of $y = f(x)$ in the line $y = x$
- satisfies $(f \circ f^{-1})(x) = (f^{-1} \circ f)(x) = x$
- has range equal to the domain of $f(x)$
- has domain equal to the range of $f(x)$.

The **reciprocal function** is $f(x) = \dfrac{1}{x}$, $x \neq 0$.

The reciprocal function is a **self-inverse function**, as $f^{-1}(x) = f(x) = \dfrac{1}{x}$.

## GRAPHS OF FUNCTIONS

The **$x$-intercepts** of a function are the values of $x$ for which $y = 0$. They are the **zeros** of the function.

The **$y$-intercept** of a function is the value of $y$ when $x = 0$.

An **asymptote** is a line that the graph *approaches* or begins to look like as it tends to infinity in a particular direction.

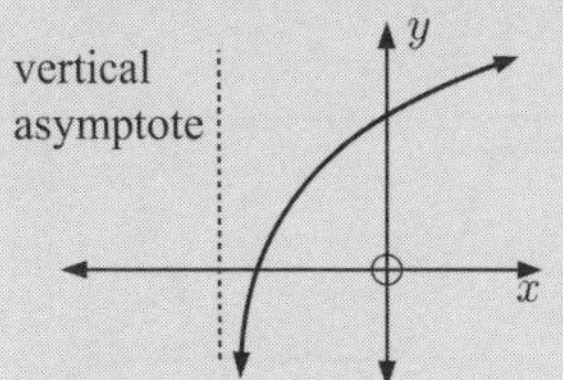


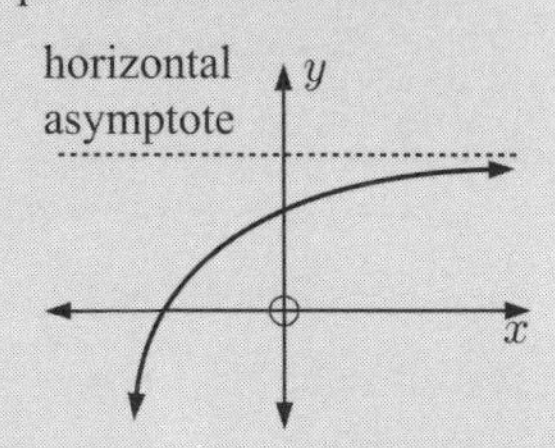


To find vertical asymptotes, look for values of $x$ for which the function is undefined:

- if $y = \dfrac{f(x)}{g(x)}$ find where $g(x) = 0$
- if $y = \log_a(f(x))$ find where $f(x) = 0$.

To find horizontal asymptotes, consider the behaviour as $x \to \pm\infty$.

**Transformations of graphs**

- $y = f(x) + b$ **translates** $y = f(x)$ vertically $b$ units.
- $y = f(x - a)$ **translates** $y = f(x)$ horizontally $a$ units.
- $y = f(x - a) + b$ **translates** $y = f(x)$ by the vector $\begin{pmatrix} a \\ b \end{pmatrix}$.
- $y = pf(x)$, $p > 0$ is a **vertical stretch** of $y = f(x)$ with dilation factor $p$.
- $y = f\left(\dfrac{x}{q}\right)$, $q > 0$ is a **horizontal stretch** of $y = f(x)$ with dilation factor $q$.
- $y = -f(x)$ is a **reflection** of $y = f(x)$ in the $x$-axis.
- $y = f(-x)$ is a **reflection** of $y = f(x)$ in the $y$-axis.
- $y = f^{-1}(x)$ is a **reflection** of $y = f(x)$ in the line $y = x$.

## LINEAR FUNCTIONS

A **linear function** has the form $f(x) = ax + b$, $a \neq 0$.

Its graph is a straight line with gradient $a$ and $y$-intercept $b$.

**Perpendicular lines** have gradients which are the negative reciprocals of each other.

## QUADRATIC FUNCTIONS

A **quadratic function** has the form $f(x) = ax^2 + bx + c$, $a \neq 0$.

The graph is a parabola with the following properties:

- it is *concave up* if $a > 0$

and *concave down* if $a < 0$

- its axis of symmetry is $x = \dfrac{-b}{2a}$
- its vertex is at $\left(\dfrac{-b}{2a}, f\left(\dfrac{-b}{2a}\right)\right)$.

A quadratic function written in the form:

- $f(x) = a(x-h)^2 + k$ has vertex $(h, k)$
- $f(x) = a(x-p)(x-q)$ has $x$-intercepts $p$ and $q$.

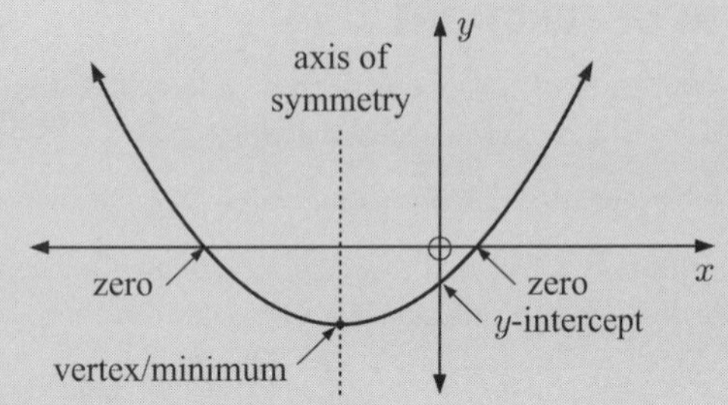


| | |
|---|---|
| $\boldsymbol{y = a(x-p)(x-q)}$<br>$x$-intercepts $p$, $q$<br>axis of symmetry $x = \dfrac{p+q}{2}$ | 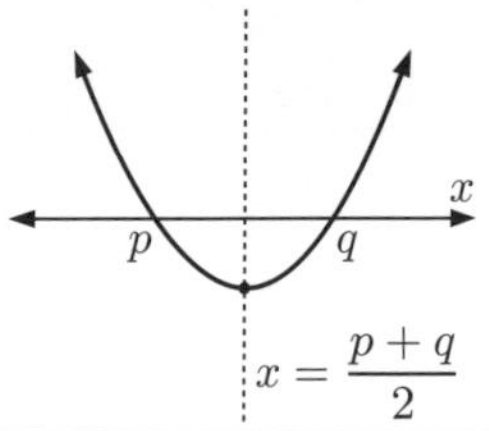 |
| $\boldsymbol{y = a(x-p)^2}$<br>touches $x$-axis at $p$<br>vertex $(p, 0)$<br>axis of symmetry $x = p$ | 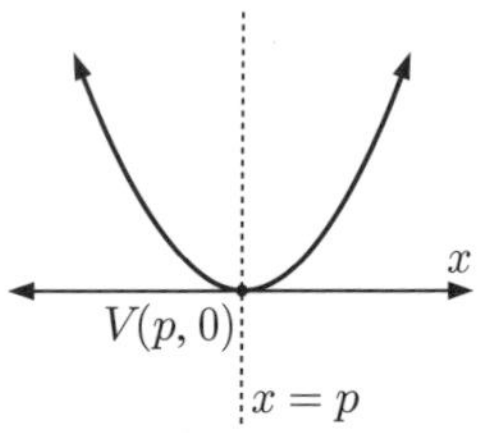 |
| $\boldsymbol{y = a(x-h)^2 + k}$<br>vertex $(h, k)$<br>axis of symmetry $x = h$ | 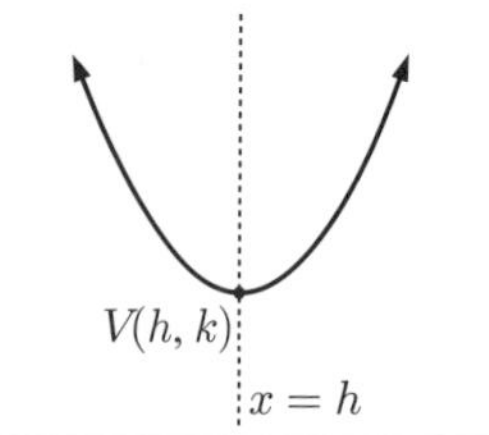 |
| $\boldsymbol{y = ax^2 + bx + c}$<br>axis of symmetry $x = \dfrac{-b}{2a}$<br>$x$-intercepts $\dfrac{-b \pm \sqrt{\Delta}}{2a}$<br>where $\Delta = b^2 - 4ac \geqslant 0$ | 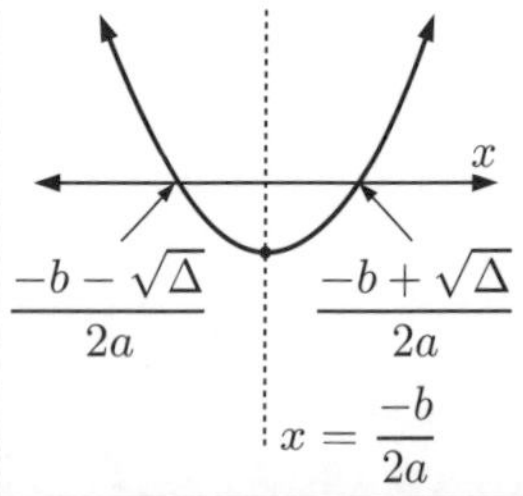 |

## QUADRATIC EQUATIONS

A quadratic equation of the form $ax^2 + bx + c = 0$, $a \neq 0$, can be solved by:

- factorisation
- completing the square
- the quadratic formula $x = \dfrac{-b \pm \sqrt{b^2 - 4ac}}{2a}$.

The **discriminant** of the quadratic equation is $\Delta = b^2 - 4ac$.

The quadratic equation has:

- *no real solutions* if $\Delta < 0$
- *one real (repeated) solution* if $\Delta = 0$
- *two real solutions* if $\Delta > 0$.

The number of solutions indicates whether the graph of the corresponding quadratic function *does not meet*, *touches*, or *cuts* the $x$-axis.

A quadratic function is **positive definite** if $a > 0$ and $\Delta < 0$.
A quadratic function is **negative definite** if $a < 0$ and $\Delta < 0$.

## EXPONENTIAL AND LOGARITHMIC FUNCTIONS

The simplest **exponential function** is $f(x) = b^x$, $b > 0$.

If $b > 1$ we have *growth*.

If $0 < b < 1$ we have *decay*.

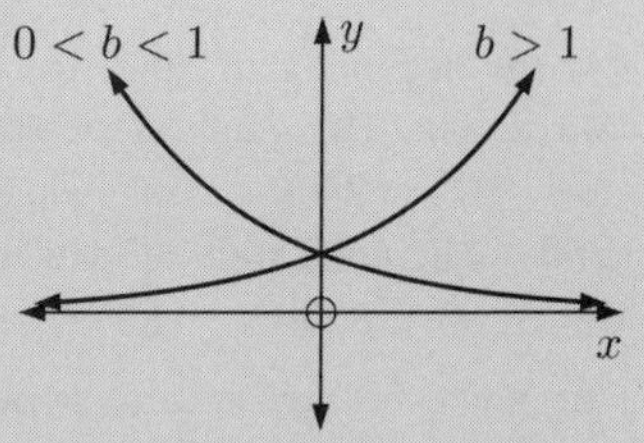


The graph of $y = b^x$ has the horizontal asymptote $y = 0$.

$b^x > 0$ and $b^{-x} > 0$ for all $x \in \mathbb{R}$.

The inverse function of $f(x) = b^x$ is the **logarithmic function** $f^{-1}(x) = \log_b x$, $x > 0$.

The graph of $y = \log_b x$ has the vertical asymptote $x = 0$.

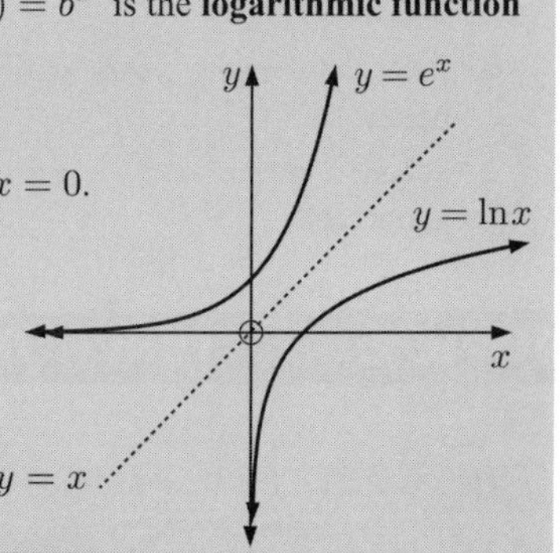


## EXPONENTIAL EQUATIONS

- If we can make the base numbers the same then we can equate indices.

  So, if $a^x = a^k$ then $x = k$.
- If the bases cannot be made the same then we take the logarithm of both sides.

  For example: If $2^x = 30$

  then $\log(2^x) = \log 30$

  $\therefore \; x \log 2 = \log 30$

  $\therefore \; x = \dfrac{\log 30}{\log 2} \approx 4.91$

## SKILL BUILDER QUESTIONS (NO CALCULATORS)

**1** Which of these relations are functions?

**a**

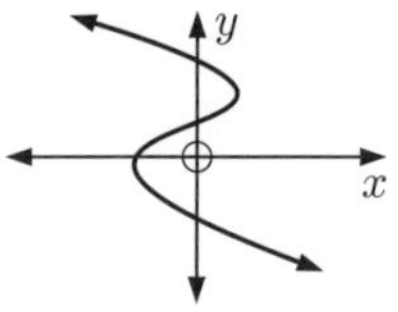


**b**

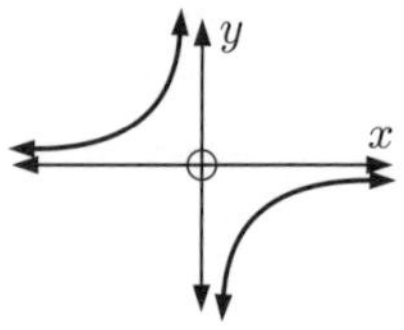


**c**

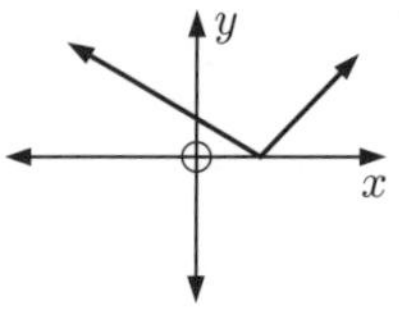


**d**

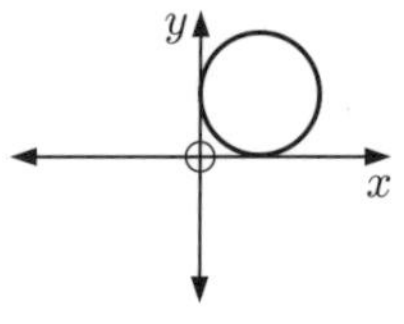


**e**

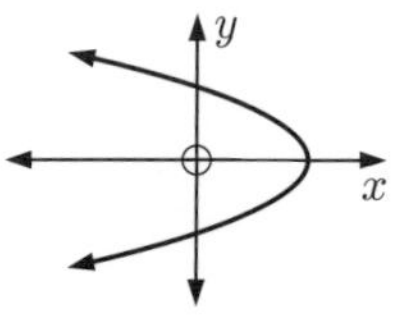


**f**

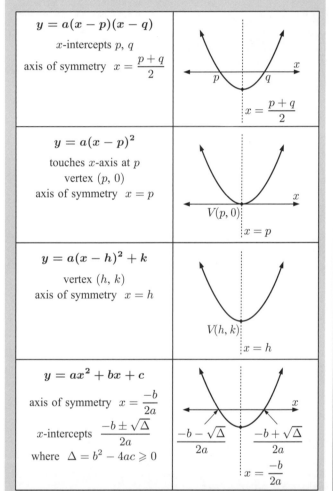

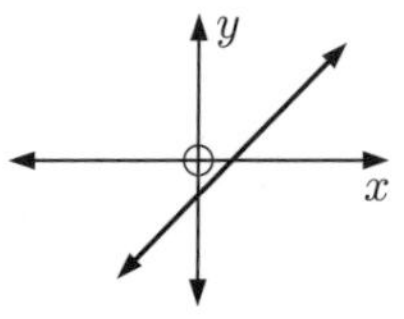

**2** Given that $G(x) = 3 - x - 2x^2$, find:

**a** $G(-1)$ **b** $G(3)$ **c** $G(a^3)$ **d** $G(a-2)$

**3** Given $f : x \mapsto 5x - 2$ and $g : x \mapsto 2x + 7$, find in simplest form:

**a** $(f \circ g)(x)$ **b** $(g \circ f)(x)$ **c** $g^{-1}(x)$

**4** State the domain of $f(x) = \dfrac{1}{x-1} + \sqrt{x+1}$.

**5** State the domain and range of $g : x \mapsto 4 - \ln(x-2)$.

**6** Functions $f$ and $g$ are defined by $f : x \mapsto 3x + 1$ and $g : x \mapsto 4 - x$.
Find: **a** $f(g(x))$ **b** $(g \circ f)(-4)$ **c** $f^{-1}\left(\frac{1}{2}\right)$

**7** Consider $f(x) = 2^{x-1}$.

**a** Graph $y = f(x)$ and its inverse function on the same set of axes.

**b** Find $f^{-1}(x)$.

**8** Copy each of these graphs of $y = f(x)$ and include the graphs of $y = x$ and $y = f^{-1}(x)$.

**a**

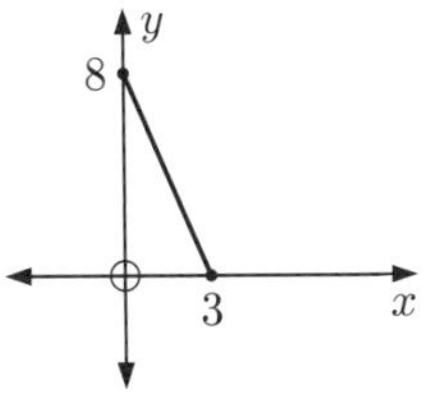


**b**

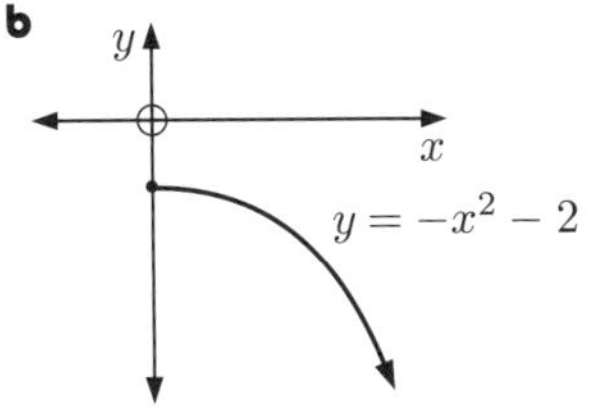


**9** Copy this graph of $y = f(x)$.
Draw graphs of:

**a** $y = f(x+2)$

**b** $y = 2f(x) - 3$

**c** $y = 4 - f(x)$

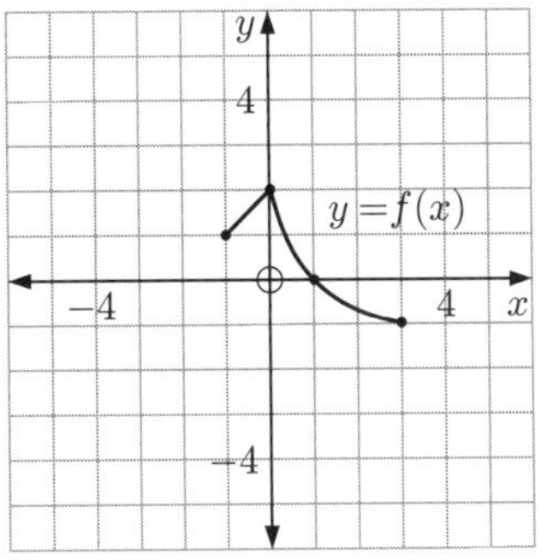


**10** Copy this graph of $y = g(x)$.
Draw graphs of:

**a** $y = g(-x)$

**b** $y = g(2x)$

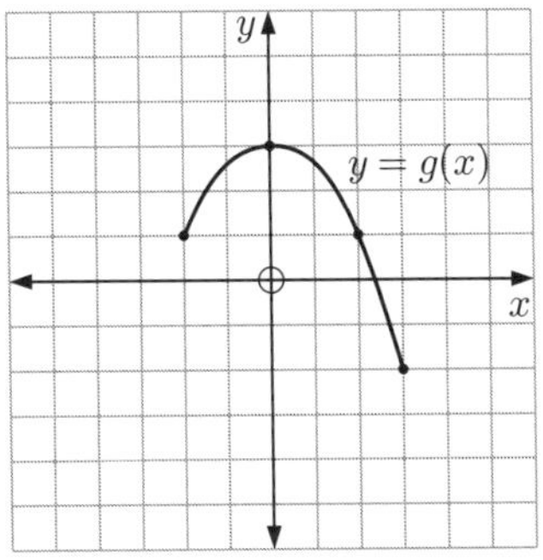


**11** Find the equation of the straight line which passes through:

**a** $(-7, 2)$ and $(3, -3)$

**b** $(4, -1)$ and has gradient $\frac{3}{5}$

**c** $(-2, 8)$ and is perpendicular to the line with equation $8x + 3y = 10$

**d** $(4, 7)$ and is parallel to the $y$-axis.

**12** On separate axes, sketch the graphs of these functions:

**a** $y = 5 - 2x$

**b** $f(x) = 2(x-4)(x+2)$

**c** $f : x \mapsto 3(x-2)^2 + 5$

**d** $y = -4(x+1)^2$

**13** For each of the following functions:

**i** find the $x$-intercepts

**ii** find the equation of the axis of symmetry

**iii** find the coordinates of the vertex

**iv** state the $y$-intercept

**v** sketch the graph.

**a** $y = -4x(x+3)$ **b** $y = \frac{1}{2}(x+6)(x-4)$

**c** $y = -3(x-2)^2$ **d** $y = 2(x+5)^2 - 4$

**14** Write each of these quadratic functions in the form $y = f(x)$.

**a**

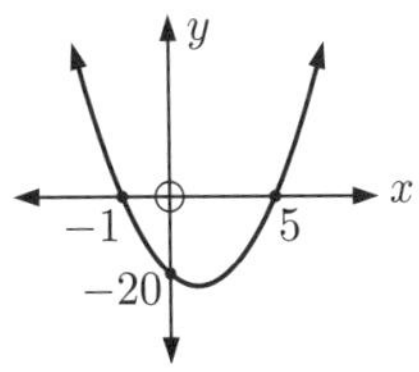


**b**

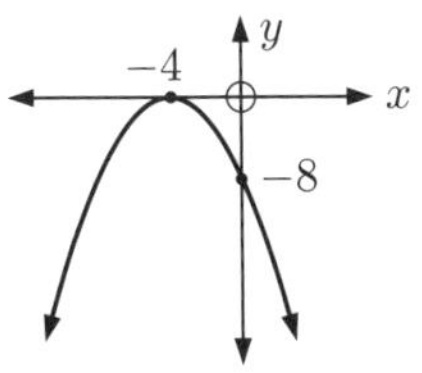


**c**

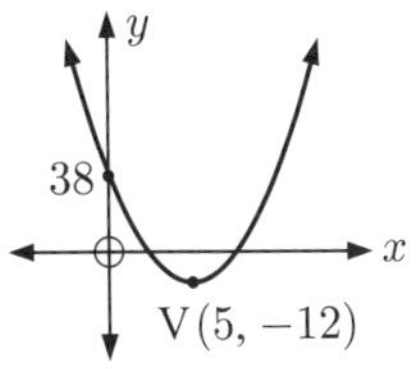


**15** Write these quadratics in the form $y = a(x-h)^2 + k$.
Sketch each function, showing the coordinates of its vertex.

**a** $y = x^2 - 4x + 9$ **b** $y = x^2 - 6x - 2$

**c** $y = 4x^2 + 16x + 11$ **d** $y = -3x^2 + 12x - 10$

**16** Use the quadratic formula to find the exact roots of:

**a** $x^2 + 12x + 8 = 0$ **b** $3x^2 - 4x - 1 = 0$

**17** Determine the discriminant of $x^2 + 8x + k = 0$.
Hence, find the values of $k$ for which the equation has:

**a** no real roots **b** two distinct real roots.

**18** For what values of $m$ would the graph of $y = mx^2 + 4x + 6$ lie entirely above the $x$-axis?

**19** Find $m$ given that $mx^2 + (m-2)x + m = 0$ has a repeated root.

**20** $-2$ is a solution of $x^2 + bx + (b-2) = 0$. Find $b$ and the other root.

**21** Consider the function $f(x) = 4 - \dfrac{1}{x-2}$.

**a** State the domain of $y = f(x)$.

**b** State the range of $y = f(x)$.

**c** What are the axes intercepts of $y = f(x)$?

**d** Write down the equations of the asymptotes of $y = f(x)$.

**22** Consider the function $f(x) = x^2$.

**a** On the same set of axes, sketch the graphs of $y = f(x-1) + 2$ and $y = \frac{1}{2}f(x) - 1$.

**b** For each graph in **a**, describe the transformations which map $y = f(x)$ onto the graph.

**23** Consider the function $f(x) = \sqrt{x}$.

**a** On the same set of axes, sketch the graphs of $y = -f(x)$, $y = f(-x)$ and $y = f(\frac{1}{2}x)$.

**b** For each graph in **a**, describe the transformation which maps $y = f(x)$ onto the graph.

## SKILL BUILDER QUESTIONS (CALCULATORS)

**1** State the domain and range of these functions:

**a** $f : x \mapsto \sqrt{x+3}$ **b** $f(x) = x^2 + 4$

**c** $f(x) = x^2 - 6x$ **d** $f : x \mapsto \ln(x-2)$

**e** $f(x) = \dfrac{1}{\sqrt{x-4}}$

**2** Find the range of these functions:

**a** $f : x \mapsto 25 - 7x - 5x^2$ **b** $y = e^{\sin x}$

**c** $f(x) = 2x + \dfrac{2}{x}$

**3** Find the inverse function of $f : x \mapsto e^{2x+1}$ and hence find $f^{-1}(7)$.

**4** On the same axes, sketch the graphs of $y = e^{x-2}$ and $y = 2 - e^x$ for $-1 \leqslant x \leqslant 5$.
Hence find, correct to 3 decimal places, any points of intersection of the graphs.

**5** For $f : x \mapsto \ln x$ and $g : x \mapsto x^3$, find the value of:

**a** $(f \circ g)(2)$ **b** $(g \circ f)(2)$

**c** $(f^{-1} \circ g)(1.2)$ **d** $(g \circ f)^{-1}(8)$

**6** Consider $f : x \mapsto \ln(x+2) - 5$, $x > -2$.

**a** Find the defining equation of $f^{-1}$.

**b** On the same set of axes, sketch the graphs of $f$ and $f^{-1}$.

**c** State the domain and range of $f$ and $f^{-1}$.

**7** Solve to 5 decimal places:

**a** $7x^2 - 10x + 2 = 0$ **b** $2x^2 = 11x + 15$

**8** Consider the quadratic $y = 2x^2 - 9x + 3$.

**a** Find the equation of the axis of symmetry.

**b** Find the coordinates of the vertex.

**c** Find the axes intercepts.

Hence sketch the function.

**9** Find the asymptotes of $f : x \mapsto \dfrac{6-2x}{x+4}$.
Sketch the graph of the function, clearly showing the asymptotes and the axes intercepts.

**10** Find the asymptotes of:

**a** $f(x) = \dfrac{2x+9}{x^2 - 5x - 6}$ **b** $f(x) = \dfrac{2}{\sqrt{25 - x^2}}$

**11** Graph $y = -1 + 2^{-x}$ and include on your graph any axes intercepts and asymptotes.

**12** **a** Graph $f : x \mapsto e^{x-1}$.

**b** State the domain and range of $f$.

**13** The current in an electrical circuit $t$ milliseconds after it is switched off is given by $I(t) = 40e^{-0.1t}$ amps.

**a** What current was flowing in the circuit initially?

**b** What current is still flowing in the circuit after $t = 100$ milliseconds?

**c** Sketch $I(t)$ and $I = 1$ on the same set of axes.

**d** How long will it take for the current to fall to 1 amp?

**14** Andreas is making an aquarium in the shape of an equilateral triangular prism. The sum of all side lengths of the prism must be 1.8 m.
What dimensions should he choose for the aquarium to maximise its surface area?

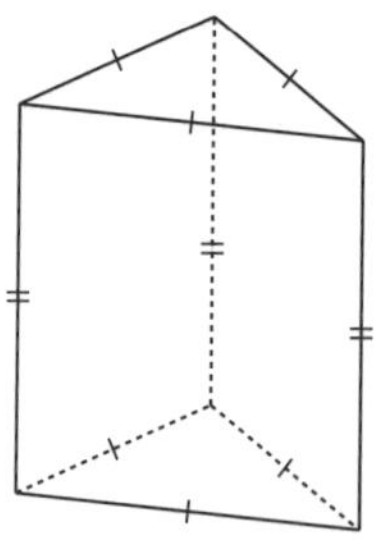

## TOPIC 3: CIRCULAR FUNCTIONS AND TRIGONOMETRY

The **unit circle** is the circle centred at the origin O and with radius 1 unit.

The coordinates of any point P on the unit circle, where the angle $\theta$ is made by [OP] and the positive $x$-axis, are $(\cos\theta, \sin\theta)$.

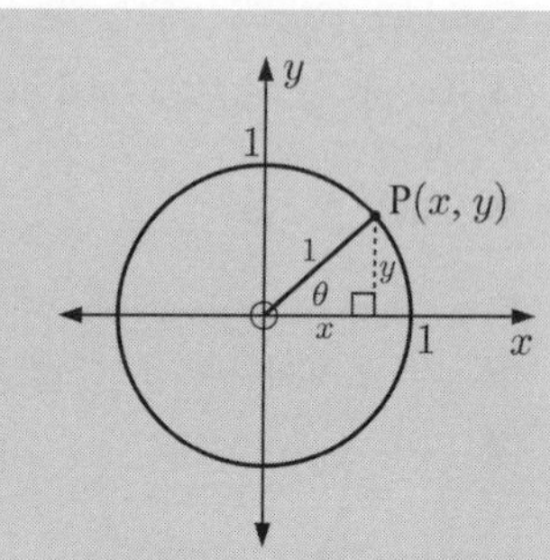


$\theta$ is **positive** when measured in an **anticlockwise** direction from the positive $x$-axis.

From the unit circle we can see that:

- $\cos^2\theta + \sin^2\theta = 1$
- $-1 \leqslant \cos\theta \leqslant 1$ and $-1 \leqslant \sin\theta \leqslant 1$ for all $\theta$
- $\tan\theta = \dfrac{\sin\theta}{\cos\theta}$ provided $\cos\theta \neq 0$.

$2\pi$ radians is equivalent to $360°$.

To convert from degrees to radians, multiply by $\frac{\pi}{180}$.

To convert from radians to degrees, multiply by $\frac{180}{\pi}$.

For $\theta$ in radians:

- the length of an arc of radius $r$ and angle $\theta$ is $l = \theta r$
- the area of a sector of radius $r$ and angle $\theta$ is $A = \frac{1}{2}\theta r^2$.

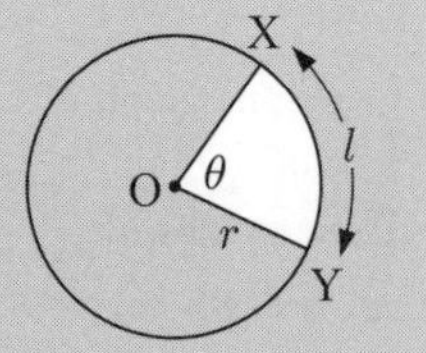


### MULTIPLES OF 45° OR $\frac{\pi}{4}$

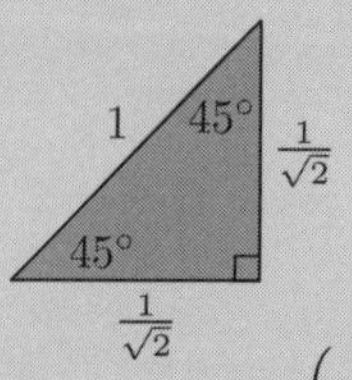


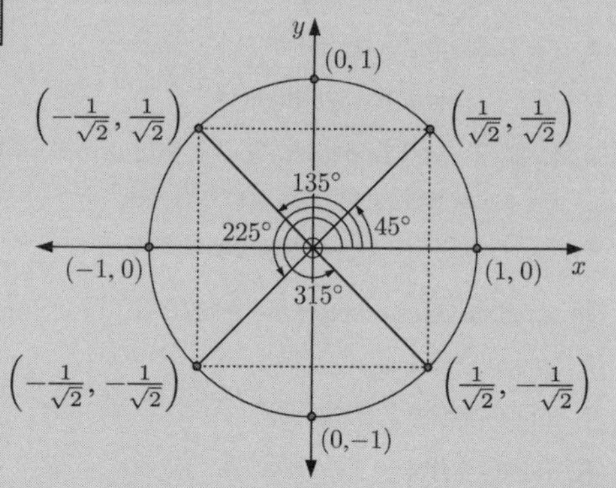

**MULTIPLES OF 30° OR $\frac{\pi}{6}$**

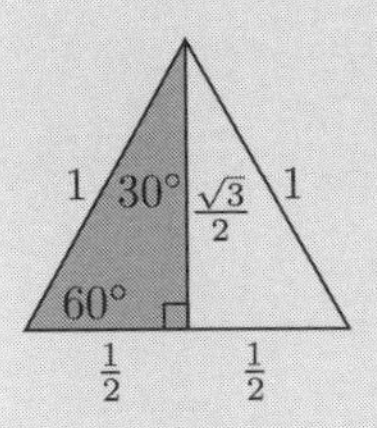


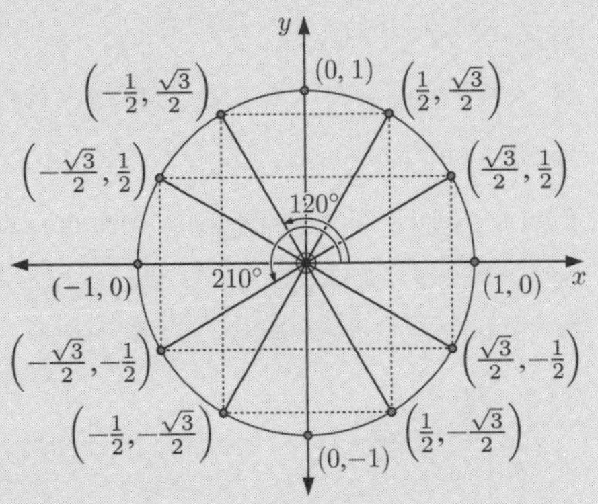


If a straight line makes an angle of $\theta$ with the positive $x$-axis, then its gradient is $m = \tan\theta$.

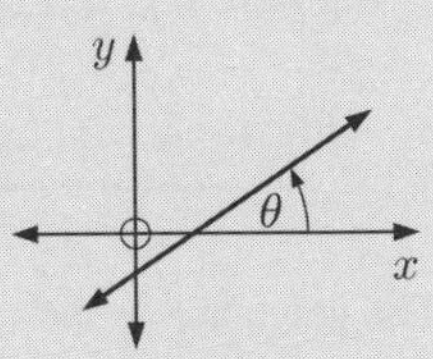


## NON-RIGHT ANGLED TRIANGLE TRIGONOMETRY

For the triangle alongside:

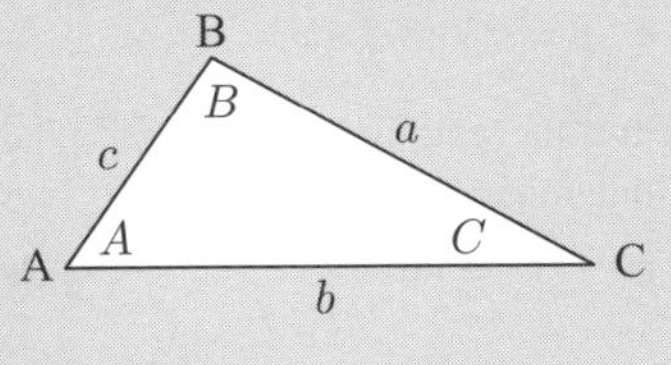


**Area formula**

Area $= \frac{1}{2}ab\sin C$

**Cosine rule**

$a^2 = b^2 + c^2 - 2bc\cos A$

**Sine rule** $\quad \dfrac{\sin A}{a} = \dfrac{\sin B}{b} = \dfrac{\sin C}{c}$

If you have the choice of rules to use, use the cosine rule to avoid the **ambiguous case**.

## PERIODIC FUNCTIONS

A **periodic function** is one which repeats itself over and over in a horizontal direction.

The **period** of a periodic function is the length of one cycle.

For example, a **wave** oscillates about a horizontal line called the **principal axis**.

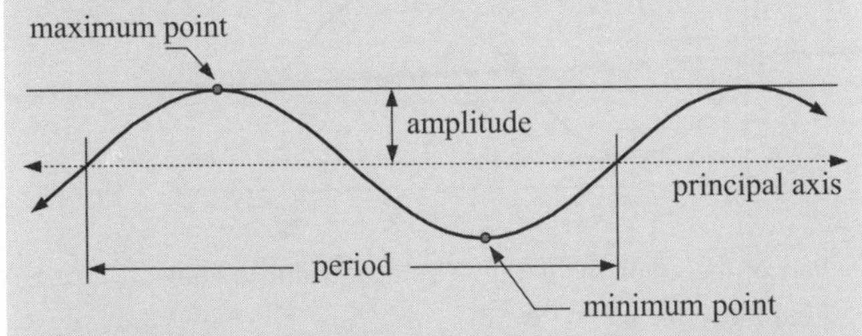


The **amplitude** is the distance between a maximum or minimum point and the principal axis.

## TRANSFORMING $y = \sin x$

- $y = a\sin x$ is a **vertical stretch** of $y = \sin x$ with dilation factor $a$.

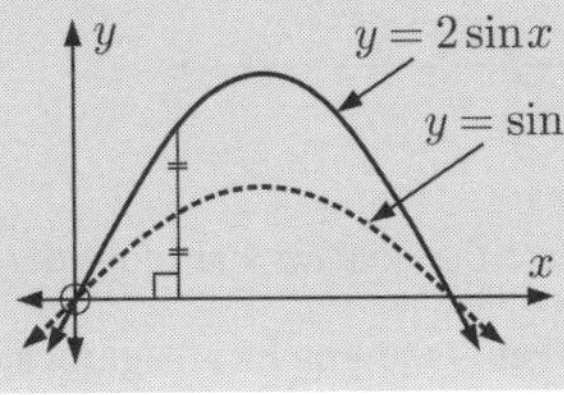


- $y = \sin bx$ is a **horizontal stretch** of $y = \sin x$ with dilation factor $\frac{1}{b}$.

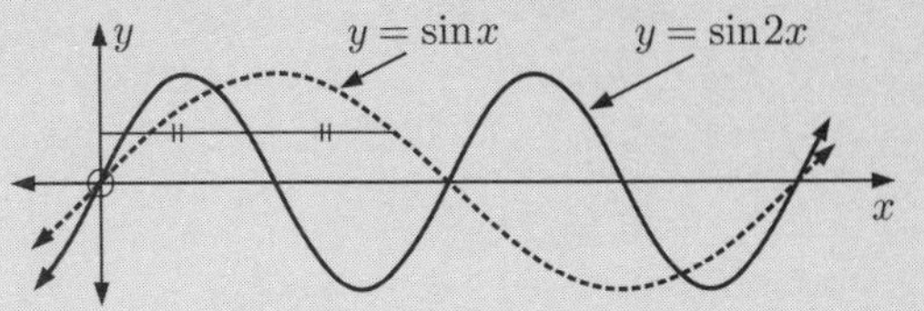


- $y = \sin(x - c)$ is a **horizontal translation** of $y = \sin x$ through $c$ units.
- $y = \sin x + d$ is a **vertical translation** of $y = \sin x$ through $d$ units.

## THE GENERAL SINE FUNCTION

If we begin with $y = \sin x$, we can perform transformations to produce the **general sine function** $f(x) = a\sin b(x - c) + d$.

We have a vertical stretch with factor $a$ and a horizontal stretch with factor $\frac{1}{b}$, followed by a translation with vector $\begin{pmatrix} c \\ d \end{pmatrix}$.

The general sine function has the following properties:

- the **amplitude** is $|a|$
- the **principal axis** is $y = d$
- the **period** is $\frac{2\pi}{b}$.

## THE COSINE FUNCTION

Since $\cos x = \sin\left(x + \frac{\pi}{2}\right)$, the graph of $y = \cos x$ is a horizontal translation of $y = \sin x$, $\frac{\pi}{2}$ units to the left.

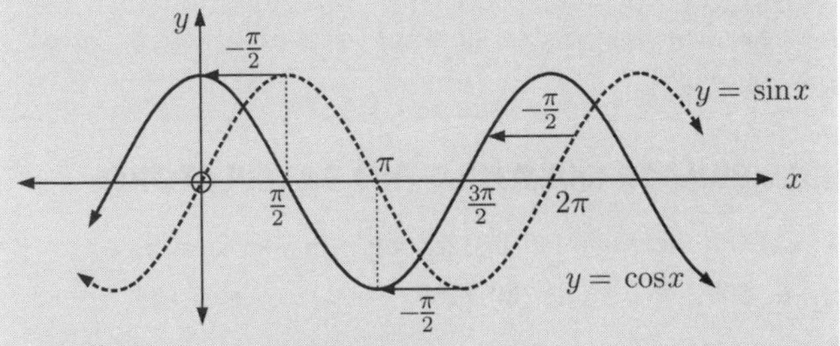


## THE TANGENT FUNCTION

$y = \tan x = \dfrac{\sin x}{\cos x}$ is undefined when $\cos x = 0$.

$\therefore$ there are vertical asymptotes when $x = \frac{\pi}{2} + k\pi$, $k \in \mathbb{Z}$.

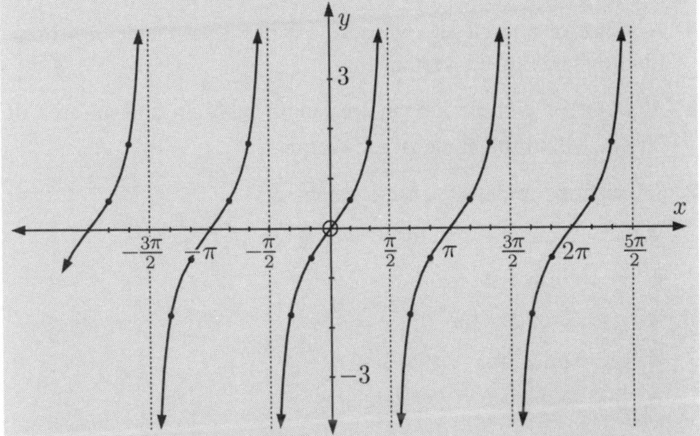


## TRIGONOMETRIC IDENTITIES

$\cos^2\theta + \sin^2\theta = 1$

$\cos(\theta + 2k\pi) = \cos\theta$ and $\sin(\theta + 2k\pi) = \sin\theta$ for all $k \in \mathbb{Z}$

$\cos(-\theta) = \cos\theta$, $\sin(-\theta) = -\sin\theta$ and $\tan(-\theta) = -\tan\theta$

$\cos\left(\frac{\pi}{2} - \theta\right) = \sin\theta$ and $\sin\left(\frac{\pi}{2} - \theta\right) = \cos\theta$

$\cos(\pi - \theta) = -\cos\theta$ and $\sin(\pi - \theta) = \sin\theta$

$\sin 2A = 2\sin A\cos A$

$$\cos 2A = \begin{cases} \cos^2 A - \sin^2 A \\ 1 - 2\sin^2 A \\ 2\cos^2 A - 1 \end{cases}$$

$\cos^2 x = \frac{1}{2} + \frac{1}{2}\cos 2x$ and $\sin^2 x = \frac{1}{2} - \frac{1}{2}\cos 2x$

## TRIGONOMETRIC EQUATIONS

To solve trigonometric equations we can either use graphs from technology, or algebraic methods involving the trigonometric identities. In either case we must make sure to include all solutions on the specified domain.

We need to use the inverse trigonometric functions to invert sin, cos and tan.

| *Equation* | *Function* | *Domain* | *Range* |
|---|---|---|---|
| $\sin x = k$ | $x = \sin^{-1} k$ | $-1 \leqslant k \leqslant 1$ | $-\frac{\pi}{2} \leqslant x \leqslant \frac{\pi}{2}$ |
| $\cos x = k$ | $x = \cos^{-1} k$ | $-1 \leqslant k \leqslant 1$ | $0 \leqslant x \leqslant \pi$ |
| $\tan x = k$ | $x = \tan^{-1} k$ | $k \in \mathbb{R}$ | $-\frac{\pi}{2} \leqslant x \leqslant \frac{\pi}{2}$ |

The ranges of these functions are important because our calculator will only give us the one answer in the range. Sometimes other solutions may also be possible. For example, when using $\sin^{-1}$ our calculator will always give us an acute angle answer, but the obtuse angle with the same sine may also be valid.

An equation of the form $a\sin x = b\cos x$ can always be solved as $\tan x = \frac{b}{a}$.

## SKILL BUILDER QUESTIONS (NO CALCULATORS)

**1** Convert these into radians, leaving $\pi$ in your answer:

**a** $60^o$ **b** $210^o$ **c** $-135^o$

**2** Convert these to degrees:

**a** $\frac{2\pi}{3}$ **b** $\frac{5\pi}{4}$ **c** $\frac{-11\pi}{6}$

**3** Find the exact value of:

**a** $\sin\left(\frac{5\pi}{3}\right)$ **b** $\cos\left(\frac{3\pi}{4}\right)$ **c** $\tan\left(-\frac{\pi}{3}\right)$

**4** A sector of a circle of radius 10 cm has a perimeter of 40 cm. Find the area of the sector.

**5** A sector of a circle has an arc length of 6 cm and an area of 20 $cm^2$. Find the angle of the sector.

**6** On separate grids, sketch the graphs of:

**a** $y = 2\sin(x - \frac{\pi}{3})$ for $0 \leqslant x \leqslant 2\pi$

**b** $y = \sin x + 2$ for $-\pi \leqslant x \leqslant \pi$

**c** $y = 3\cos 2x$ for $0 \leqslant x \leqslant 2\pi$

**d** $y = \tan x$ for $-\pi \leqslant x \leqslant \pi$

**e** $y = \cos(\frac{x}{2}) - 1$ for $0 \leqslant x \leqslant 2\pi$

**7** For each of the following state:

**i** the period **ii** the amplitude (if applicable)

**a** $y = \sin 2x + 2$ **b** $y = 4\cos x$

**c** $y = 5\tan 3x$ **d** $y = 10 - 6\sin 3x$

**8** In triangle PQR, PR = 12 cm, RQ = 11 cm, and $R\hat{P}Q = 60^o$. Find the length of [PQ], giving your answer in radical form.

**9** What consecutive transformations map the graph of $y = \sin x$ onto:

**a** $y = 2\sin\left(\frac{x}{3}\right)$ **b** $y = \sin\left(x + \frac{\pi}{3}\right) - 4$?

**10** Find the period of:

**a** $y = -\sin 3x$ **b** $y = 2\sin\left(\frac{x}{2}\right) + 1$

**c** $y = \sin^2 x + 5$.

**11** Find the exact solutions of these equations for $0 \leqslant x \leqslant 2\pi$:

**a** $\sqrt{2}\cos x + 1 = 0$ **b** $2\sin x = \sqrt{3}$

**c** $2\sin^2 x + 3\cos x = 3$ **d** $\sin 2x + \sin x = 0$

**12**

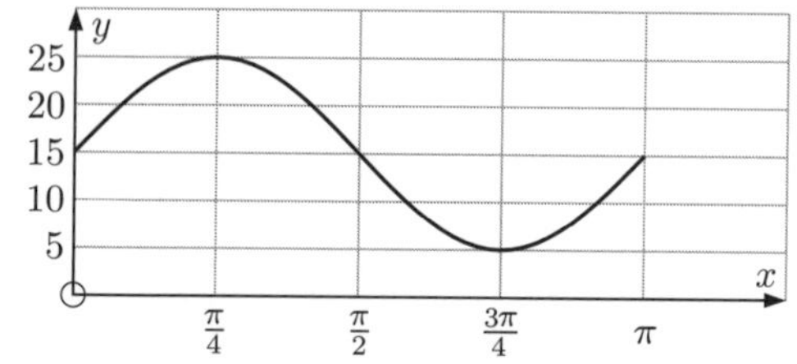


The graph above shows $y = a\sin(bx) + c$ for $0 \leqslant x \leqslant \pi$. Find the values of $a$, $b$ and $c$.

**13** Sketch these graphs on $-\pi \leqslant x \leqslant \pi$:

**a** $y = 2 - 3\cos x$ **b** $y = \cos 3x + 2$

**14** Find the amplitude, principal axis, and period of the following functions:

**a** $f(x) = \sin 4x$ **b** $f(x) = -2\sin\left(\frac{x}{2}\right) - 1$.

**15** $\theta$ is an acute angle and $\cos\theta = \frac{3}{8}$. Find the value of:

**a** $\sin\theta$ **b** $\sin 2\theta$

**16** $\alpha$ is an obtuse angle and $\sin\alpha = \frac{2}{3}$. Find the value of:

**a** $\cos\alpha$ **b** $\cos 2\alpha$

**17** If $\alpha$ is acute and $\cos 2\alpha = \frac{5}{13}$, find the value of $\sin\alpha$.

**18** Given that $\sin\theta = -\frac{1}{2}$ and $\cos\theta = -\frac{\sqrt{3}}{2}$ where $0^o < \theta < 360^o$, find the exact value of:

**a** $\theta$ **b** $\tan\theta$

**19**

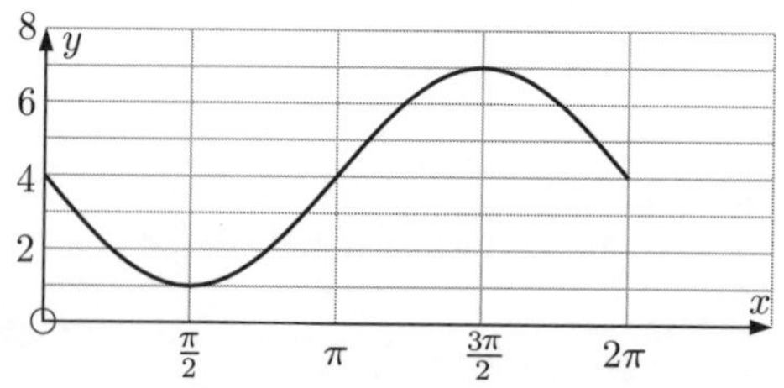


Part of the graph of $y = a + b\sin x$ is drawn above.
Find the value of: **a** $a$ **b** $b$

**20** Find the equations of these straight lines:

**a**

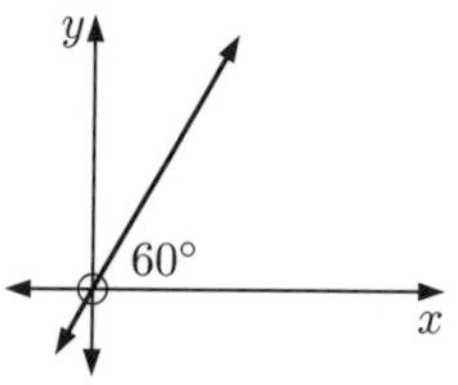


**b**

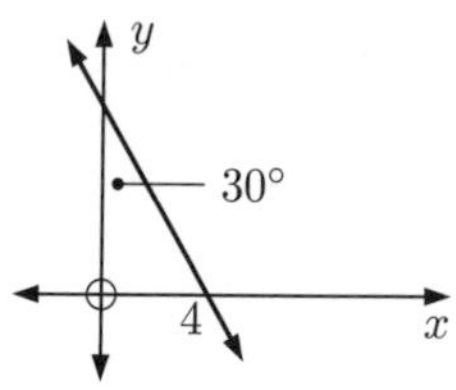


**21** **a** State the domain and range for $f(x) = \dfrac{1}{\sin x}$.

**b** What is the graphical significance of your answers in **a**?

**22** Consider $f(x) = 1 - 3\sin 2x$.

**a** Find the period of $y = f(x)$.

**b** Find the amplitude of $y = f(x)$.

**c** Sketch the graph of $y = 1 - 3\sin 2x$ for $-\frac{\pi}{2} \leqslant x \leqslant \pi$.

**23** **a** What quadrant contains $\theta$ if $\tan\theta > 0$ and $\cos\theta < 0$?

**b** Find the exact value of $\cos\theta$ if $\tan\theta = 2$ and $180^o < \theta < 270^o$.

**24** What transformation maps:

**a** $y = \sin x$ onto $y = -\sin x$

**b** $y = \cos x$ onto $y = 2\cos x$

**c** $y = \cos x$ onto $y = \cos 2x$

**d** $y = \sin x$ onto $y = \sin(x + \frac{\pi}{6}) + 2$?

**25**

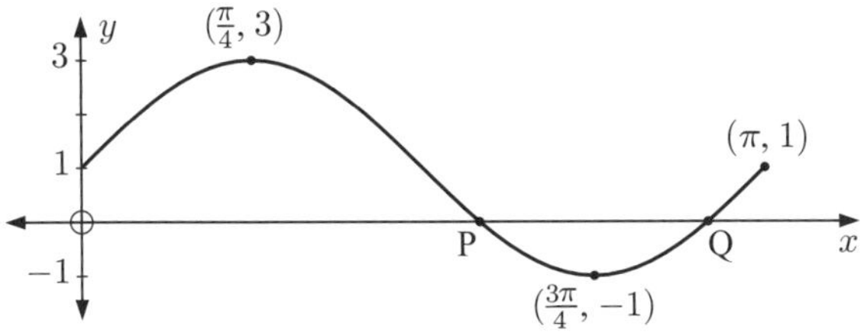


**a** Find the equation of the illustrated sine function.

**b** Find the coordinates of P and Q.

**26** Find $\cos\theta$ if $\sin\theta = -\frac{4}{5}$ and $\tan\theta = -\frac{4}{3}$.

**27**

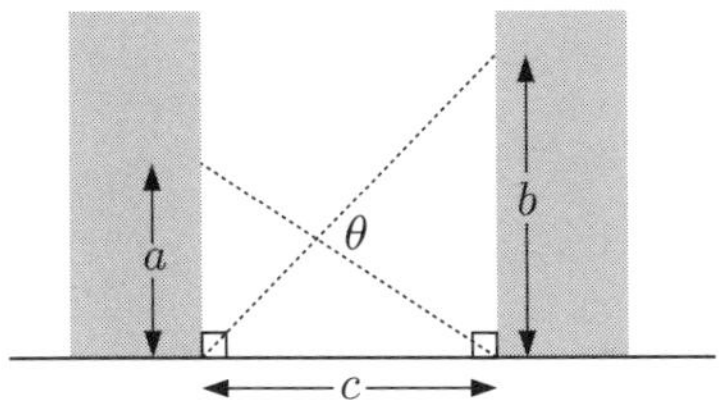


Show that $\theta = \tan^{-1}\left(\frac{a}{c}\right) + \tan^{-1}\left(\frac{b}{c}\right)$.

**28** Express $\theta$ in terms of $x$:

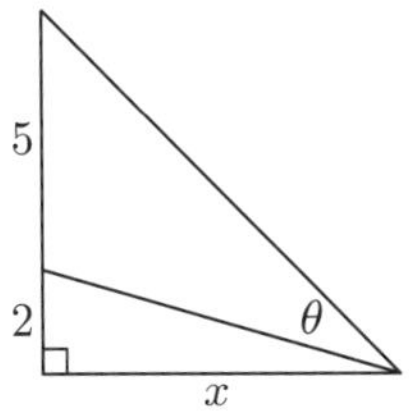


**29** Simplify $1 - \dfrac{\sin^2\theta}{1 + \cos\theta}$.

**30** If $\cos 2x = \frac{5}{8}$, find the exact value of $\sin x$.

**31** $\theta$ is obtuse and $\sin\theta = \frac{2}{3}$. Find the exact value of $\sin 2\theta$.

**32** Find $x$ if $(\sin x + \cos x)^2 = \sin^2 x + \cos^2 x$, $0 \leqslant x \leqslant \pi$.

**33** Simplify:

**a** $\tan(-\frac{\pi}{6})$

**b** $\dfrac{\sqrt{2}}{\sin(\frac{3\pi}{4})}$

**34** Sketch graphs of:

**a** $f(x) = \sqrt{3}\cos x$ for $-2\pi \leqslant x \leqslant 2\pi$

**b** $f(x) = -2\sin 2x$ for $-2\pi \leqslant x \leqslant 2\pi$

**35** At what points does the graph of $y = 2^{-x}\sin 2x$ cut the $x$-axis for $0 \leqslant x \leqslant 3\pi$?

**36** Prove that $\tan t = \dfrac{\sqrt{1 - \cos^2 t}}{\cos t}$, $0 < t < \pi$.

**37**

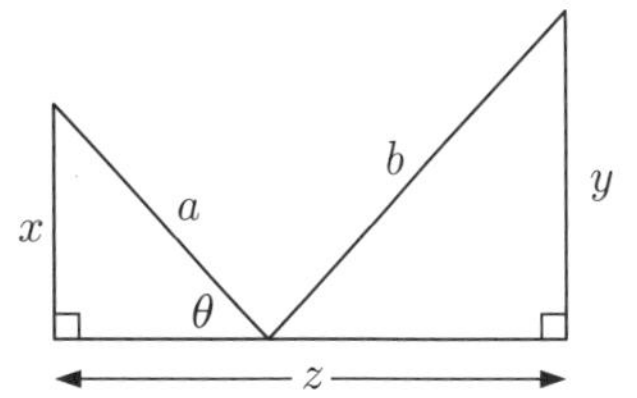


Find $a + b$ in terms of $x$, $y$, $z$ and $\theta$.

**38** Solve for $x$: $\sin^{-1}(3x^2 - 2x) = \frac{5\pi}{6}$

**39** Find $\theta$ if $0 < \theta < \frac{\pi}{2}$ and $\dfrac{1 - \cos 2\theta}{\sin 2\theta} = \sqrt{3}$.

**40** Find $\theta$ where $-2\pi \leqslant \theta \leqslant 2\pi$ and:

**a** $2\sin\theta \leqslant \sqrt{3}$

**b** $\sqrt{2}\cos\theta \leqslant -1$

**41** Find the exact solutions of $\sin x + \sqrt{3}\cos x = 0$, $0 \leqslant x \leqslant 2\pi$.

**42** Show that $\dfrac{\sin^2\theta}{1 + \cos\theta} = 1 - \cos\theta$ for all $\theta$ except where $\cos\theta = -1$.

**43** Given that $\tan 2A = \sin A$ where $\sin A \neq 0$, find $\cos A$ in simplest radical form.

## SKILL BUILDER QUESTIONS (CALCULATORS)

**1** Convert these radian measures to degrees (to the nearest tenth of a degree):

**a** 0.815

**b** 2.7

**2** Convert these to radians, correct to 3 decimal places:

**a** $48^o$

**b** $203^o$

**3** Find the perimeter and area of a sector of:

**a** radius 8 cm and angle $40^o$

**b** radius 12 cm and angle 2.4 radians.

**4** O is the centre of a circle of radius 32 cm. Chord [AB] is 50 cm long. Find the area of the shaded segment.

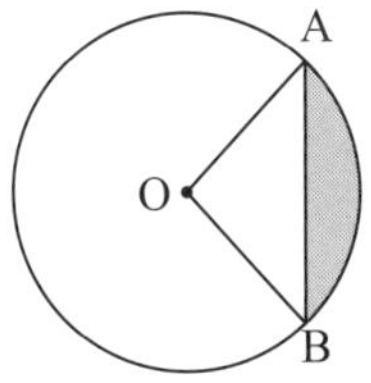


**5** Find the area of:

**a**

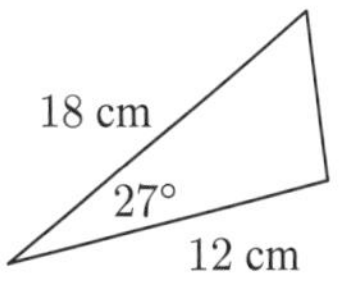


**b**

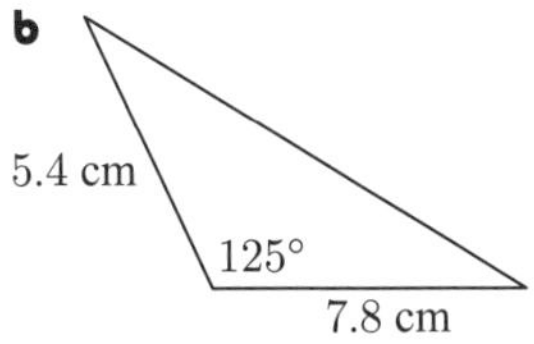


**6** Find $a$ in:

**a**

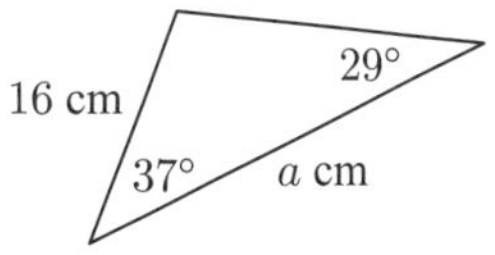


**b**

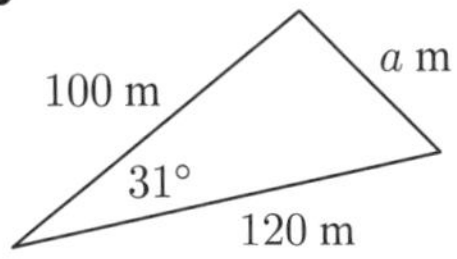


**7** Find the largest angle of the triangle with sides 11 cm, 9 cm and 7 cm.

**8** In triangle ABC, AB = 15 cm, AC = 12 cm, and angle ABC measures $30^o$. Find the size of angle ACB.

**9**

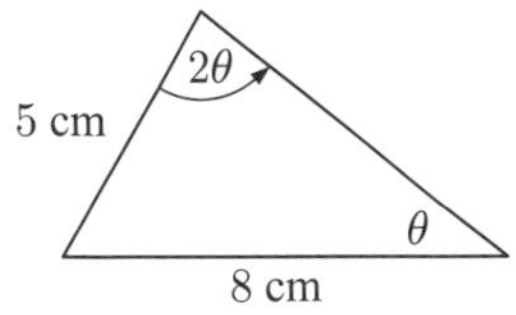


Find: **a** $\cos\theta$ **b** the area of the triangle.

**10** Solve for $x$ if $0 \leqslant x \leqslant 2\pi$:

**a** $\sin x = 0.785$ **b** $2\cos x = 5\sin x$

**c** $\tan 3x = 0.9$

**11** Solve for $t$ if $0 \leqslant t \leqslant 12$:

**a** $5\sin(2t - 3) = 2$ **b** $15 + 3\cos(\frac{t}{2} + 1) = 14.5$

**12** The depth of water in a tidal river $t$ hours after midnight may be represented by a function of the form

$d = a + b\sin\left(\frac{2\pi t}{k}\right)$ metres where $a$, $b$ and $k$ are constants.

The water is at a maximum depth of 22.5 m at 3 am and again at 3 pm. It is at a minimum depth of 8.7 m at 9 am and 9 pm. Find the values of $a$, $b$ and $k$.

**13** [PT] is a tangent to the circle at T. If the circle has radius 9 cm and OP = 30 cm, find the area of the shaded region.

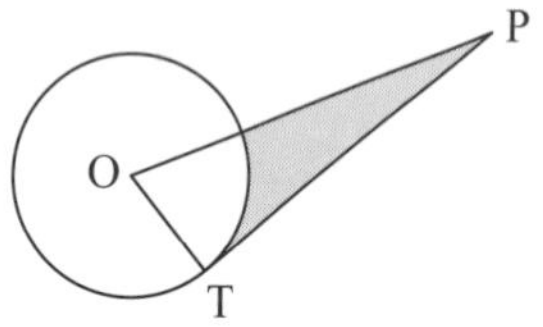


**14** Solve these equations for $0^o \leqslant \theta \leqslant 360^o$, giving answers to the nearest degree:

**a** $4\cos^2\theta = 1$ **b** $4\sin^2\theta = \cos^2\theta$

**15** An aeroplane averaging 400 $\text{km h}^{-1}$ travels directly north from an airport for 45 minutes, then changes its course to north-east for 90 minutes. What is the direct distance between the plane's present position and the airport?

**16** A ship leaves a port at 2:00 pm and sails in the direction $034^o$ at a speed of 16 $\text{km h}^{-1}$. Another ship leaves the port at 2:30 pm and sails in the direction $107^o$ at a speed of 19 $\text{km h}^{-1}$. How far apart are the ships at 4:00 pm?

**17** Find the solutions of $\dfrac{\sin x}{x^2+1} = 0.3$ to 3 decimal places.

**18** Solve for $x$:

**a** $2\cos 2x + 1 = 0,\ 0 \leqslant x \leqslant 2\pi$

**b** $\cos 2x = 2\cos x,\ 0 \leqslant x \leqslant 3\pi$

**19** Solve for $x$ given that $2^{-x}\sin x = \frac{1}{2}x - 1$ and $x > 0$.

**20** Find $\theta$ given that $\tan\theta = 2\cos\theta,\ 0 < \theta < \frac{\pi}{2}$.

**21** Sketch the graph of $y = \sin x + x - 1$ for $0 \leqslant x \leqslant 6$.

# TOPIC 4: MATRICES

A **matrix** is a rectangular array of numbers arranged in **rows** and **columns**.

If a matrix has $m$ rows and $n$ columns, its **order** is $m \times n$.

Two matrices are **equal** if they have the same order and the elements in corresponding positions are equal.

## MATRIX OPERATIONS

To **add** two matrices of the same order, we **add** the elements in corresponding positions.

To **subtract** two matrices of the same order, we **subtract** the elements in corresponding positions.

A **zero matrix O** is a matrix in which all elements are zero.

To multiply a matrix by a **scalar**, we multiply every element by that scalar.

The **negative** of matrix **A** is $-\mathbf{A}$ or $-1\mathbf{A}$. It is obtained by reversing the signs of every element in **A**.

If **A**, **B** and **C** are matrices of the same order then:

- $\mathbf{A} + \mathbf{B}$ is a matrix of the same order
- $\mathbf{A} + \mathbf{B} = \mathbf{B} + \mathbf{A}$
- $(\mathbf{A} + \mathbf{B}) + \mathbf{C} = \mathbf{A} + (\mathbf{B} + \mathbf{C})$
- $\mathbf{A} + \mathbf{O} = \mathbf{O} + \mathbf{A} = \mathbf{A}$
- $\mathbf{A} + (-\mathbf{A}) = (-\mathbf{A}) + \mathbf{A} = \mathbf{O}$
- a half of **A** is $\frac{1}{2}\mathbf{A}$, not $\dfrac{\mathbf{A}}{2}$

## MATRIX MULTIPLICATION

We can only **multiply** matrix **A** by matrix **B** if the number of columns in **A** equals the number of rows in **B**.

If **A** is $m \times p$ and **B** is $p \times n$ then the product matrix **AB** is $m \times n$. The element in the $r$th row and $c$th column of **AB** is the sum of the products of the elements in the $r$th row of **A** with the corresponding elements in the $c$th column of **B**.

For example:

If $\mathbf{A} = \begin{pmatrix} a & b \\ c & d \end{pmatrix}$ and $\mathbf{B} = \begin{pmatrix} p & q \\ r & s \end{pmatrix}$

then $\mathbf{AB} = \begin{pmatrix} ap+br & aq+bs \\ cp+dr & cq+ds \end{pmatrix}$.

If $\mathbf{C} = \begin{pmatrix} a & b & c \\ d & e & f \end{pmatrix}$ and $\mathbf{D} = \begin{pmatrix} x \\ y \\ z \end{pmatrix}$

$2 \times 3$ $3 \times 1$

then $\mathbf{CD} = \begin{pmatrix} ax+by+cz \\ dx+ey+fz \end{pmatrix}$.

$2 \times 1$

In general, $\mathbf{AB} \neq \mathbf{BA}$.

$\mathbf{A} + \mathbf{O} = \mathbf{O} + \mathbf{A} = \mathbf{A}$ for all matrices **A** of the same order.

An **identity matrix I** is a square matrix with 1s along the leading diagonal and zeros everywhere else.

$\mathbf{AI} = \mathbf{IA} = \mathbf{A}$ for all square matrices **A** of the same order.

$\mathbf{A}(\mathbf{B} + \mathbf{C}) = \mathbf{AB} + \mathbf{AC}$

## MATRIX DETERMINANTS

The **determinant** of the matrix $\mathbf{A} = \begin{pmatrix} a & b \\ c & d \end{pmatrix}$ is $\det\mathbf{A}$ or $|\mathbf{A}| = ad - bc$.

The determinant of the matrix $\mathbf{A} = \begin{pmatrix} a & b & c \\ d & e & f \\ g & h & k \end{pmatrix}$

is $|\mathbf{A}| = \begin{vmatrix} a & b & c \\ d & e & f \\ g & h & k \end{vmatrix} = a\begin{vmatrix} e & f \\ h & k \end{vmatrix} - b\begin{vmatrix} d & f \\ g & k \end{vmatrix} + c\begin{vmatrix} d & e \\ g & h \end{vmatrix}$.

## MATRIX INVERSES

The **inverse** of square matrix **A** is the matrix $\mathbf{A}^{-1}$ such that $\mathbf{AA}^{-1} = \mathbf{A}^{-1}\mathbf{A} = \mathbf{I}$.

If $|\mathbf{A}| = 0$ then $\mathbf{A}^{-1}$ does not exist and **A** is **singular**.

If $|\mathbf{A}| \neq 0$ then **A** is **invertible**.

If $\mathbf{A} = \begin{pmatrix} a & b \\ c & d \end{pmatrix}$ then $\mathbf{A}^{-1} = \dfrac{1}{|\mathbf{A}|}\begin{pmatrix} d & -b \\ -c & a \end{pmatrix}$.

You should be able to find $|\mathbf{A}|$ and $\mathbf{A}^{-1}$ for $3 \times 3$ matrices using your calculator.

$|\mathbf{AB}| = |\mathbf{A}|\,|\mathbf{B}|$ for all square matrices **A** and **B** of equal size.

If **A** and **B** are invertible then
$(\mathbf{A}^{-1})^{-1} = \mathbf{A}$ and $(\mathbf{AB})^{-1} = \mathbf{B}^{-1}\mathbf{A}^{-1}$.

Any system of linear equations can be written as a matrix equation of the form $\mathbf{AX} = \mathbf{B}$ where **A** is a square matrix of coefficients, **X** is a column matrix of unknowns, and **B** is a column matrix of constants.

If **A** is **invertible** then the unique solution to the system is $\mathbf{X} = \mathbf{A}^{-1}\mathbf{B}$.

## SKILL BUILDER QUESTIONS (NO CALCULATORS)

**1** Given $\mathbf{A} = \begin{pmatrix} 2 & -1 \\ 3 & 4 \end{pmatrix}$ and $\mathbf{B} = \begin{pmatrix} -3 & 2 \\ 6 & -5 \end{pmatrix}$, find:

**a** $\mathbf{A} + 2\mathbf{B}$ **b** $3\mathbf{A} - 6\mathbf{I}$ **c** $\mathbf{AB}$

**d** $\det\mathbf{B}$ **e** $\mathbf{A}^{-1}$ **f** $\mathbf{A}^2$

**2** Given $\mathbf{M} = \begin{pmatrix} 7 & 2 & 1 \\ -3 & 4 & 4 \\ 2 & 1 & 6 \end{pmatrix}$ and $\mathbf{N} = \begin{pmatrix} 2 & 8 & -3 \\ 1 & 2 & 1 \\ 4 & -2 & 5 \end{pmatrix}$,

find: **a** $3\mathbf{M} - 2\mathbf{N}$ **b** $\mathbf{MN}$

**3** Find the inverse of $\begin{pmatrix} 3 & 2 \\ 5 & 4 \end{pmatrix}$.

Hence, solve the system of equations $\begin{cases} 3x + 2y = 14 \\ 5x + 4y = 22. \end{cases}$

**4** For $\mathbf{S} = \begin{pmatrix} 7 & 1 & 5 \\ 2 & -3 & 3 \end{pmatrix}$ and $\mathbf{T} = \begin{pmatrix} 8 & -2 \\ 4 & -1 \\ 3 & 2 \end{pmatrix}$, find **ST**.

**5** $\mathbf{A} = \begin{pmatrix} 7 & 2 \\ 4 & -1 \end{pmatrix}$, $\mathbf{B} = \begin{pmatrix} 8 & 2 \\ 3 & -4 \end{pmatrix}$ and $\mathbf{X} = \begin{pmatrix} a & 2 \\ 1 & -a \end{pmatrix}$.

Find $a$ if $2\mathbf{A} + \mathbf{X} = 3\mathbf{B}$.

**6** State the conditions for $m$, $n$, $p$, and $q$ if we can evaluate $2\mathbf{A} - 3\mathbf{B}$ where **A** is a matrix of order $m \times n$ and **B** is a matrix of order $p \times q$.

**7** State the 2 conditions under which the equation $\mathbf{A} = \mathbf{B}$ is true for matrices **A** and **B**.

**8** Suppose **A** has order $m \times n$ and **B** has order $p \times q$.

**a** Under what conditions does matrix $\mathbf{C} = \mathbf{AB}$ exist?

**b** If **C** does exist, what is its order?

**9** Under what conditions will $\mathbf{A} + \mathbf{O} = \mathbf{O} + \mathbf{A}$? What matrix will they be equal to?

**10** Under what conditions will $\mathbf{AI} = \mathbf{IA} = \mathbf{A}$? State clearly the order of each matrix and the elements in **I**.

**11** **a** If $\mathbf{A} = \begin{pmatrix} 2 & 4 \\ 3 & 2 \end{pmatrix}$, find $\mathbf{A}^{-1}$ then use it to solve

$\mathbf{A}\begin{pmatrix} x \\ y \end{pmatrix} = \begin{pmatrix} 15 \\ -5 \end{pmatrix}$.

**b** Let $\mathbf{N} = \begin{pmatrix} a & b \\ a^2 & b^2 \end{pmatrix}$ where $a, b \neq 0$.

Determine the relationship between $a$ and $b$ if **N** does *not* have an inverse.

**12** If $\mathbf{A} = \begin{pmatrix} a & 4 \\ 2 & a+2 \end{pmatrix}$, for what values of $a$ does the inverse matrix $\mathbf{A}^{-1}$ exist?

**13** Find $a$ and $b$ if:

$3\begin{pmatrix} a & 4 \\ 1 & b \end{pmatrix} = \begin{pmatrix} a & 1 \\ 0 & b \end{pmatrix}\begin{pmatrix} 1 & 2 \\ -1 & 1 \end{pmatrix} + \begin{pmatrix} 3 & 9 \\ 2 & -2 \end{pmatrix}$

**14** Given $\mathbf{A} = \begin{pmatrix} 2 & -1 \\ -4 & 3 \end{pmatrix}$, find $\mathbf{A}^{-1}$.

Hence, solve the matrix equation

$$\begin{pmatrix} 2 & -1 \\ -4 & 3 \end{pmatrix}\begin{pmatrix} x \\ y \end{pmatrix} = \begin{pmatrix} 6 \\ -2 \end{pmatrix}.$$

**15** Find $n$ given that $\begin{vmatrix} 8 & -1 \\ n & 4 \end{vmatrix} = \begin{vmatrix} 1 & n & 0 \\ 3 & -1 & n \\ 2 & 1 & 4 \end{vmatrix}$.

**16** For what values of $x$ is the matrix $\mathbf{P} = \begin{pmatrix} 2 & x & -1 \\ -1 & 0 & 4 \\ 2 & 3 & -1 \end{pmatrix}$ non-singular?

**17** Show that the matrix $\mathbf{A} = \begin{pmatrix} 0 & -2 \\ -1 & 1 \end{pmatrix}$

satisfies the equation $\mathbf{A}^2 = \mathbf{A} + 2\mathbf{I}$ where **I** is the multiplicative identity for $2 \times 2$ matrices. Use this equation to show, without evaluating $\mathbf{A}^4$, that $\mathbf{A}^4 = 5\mathbf{A} + 6\mathbf{I}$.

**18** Let $\mathbf{A} = \begin{pmatrix} 1 & 5 \\ 1 & 4 \end{pmatrix}$, $\mathbf{B} = \begin{pmatrix} 1 & -2 \\ 0 & 1 \end{pmatrix}$,

$\mathbf{C} = \begin{pmatrix} 3 & 2 \\ -1 & 1 \end{pmatrix}$, $\mathbf{I} = \begin{pmatrix} 1 & 0 \\ 0 & 1 \end{pmatrix}$.

**a** Show, by direct calculation, that $(\mathbf{AB})^{-1} = \mathbf{B}^{-1}\mathbf{A}^{-1}$.

**b** Verify that **C** satisfies the equation $\mathbf{C}^2 - 4\mathbf{C} = -5\mathbf{I}$.

**c** Show that $\mathbf{C}^{-1} = \frac{1}{5}(4\mathbf{I} - \mathbf{C})$.

**19** Write this system of equations in the form $\mathbf{AX} = \mathbf{B}$. $\begin{cases} x - y = 3 \\ 2x + cy = 6 \end{cases}$

For what values of $c$ does $\mathbf{A}^{-1}$ exist? For these values of $c$, find $\mathbf{A}^{-1}$, then use it to find the unique solution of these equations.

**20** If $\mathbf{A} = \begin{pmatrix} -8 & -6 & -6 \\ 2 & 0 & 2 \\ 8 & 8 & 6 \end{pmatrix}$, find $\mathbf{A}^2$ and *hence* $\mathbf{A}^{-1}$.

**21** **a** Consider the matrix $\mathbf{M} = \begin{pmatrix} n-1 & 4 \\ 3 & n-2 \end{pmatrix}$.

Find $\det\mathbf{M}$, and find two distinct values of $n$ such that $\det\mathbf{M} = 0$. When does $\mathbf{M}^{-1}$ exist?

**b** Given $\mathbf{P} = \begin{pmatrix} -4 & 2 \\ 1 & -3 \\ -2 & 6 \end{pmatrix}$ and $\mathbf{Q} = \begin{pmatrix} 3 & -2 \\ 1 & -4 \end{pmatrix}$,

find **PQ**, and explain why **QP** cannot be found.

**22** Let $\mathbf{A} = \begin{pmatrix} 2 & 0 & 0 \\ 0 & 3 & 1 \\ 0 & 1 & 3 \end{pmatrix}$. Find $\mathbf{A}^2$, and show that $\mathbf{A}^2 - 6\mathbf{A} = -8\mathbf{I}$.

*Hence* verify that $\mathbf{A}^{-1} = \frac{1}{8}(6\mathbf{I} - \mathbf{A})$.

**23** Let $\mathbf{A} = \begin{pmatrix} 1 & 2 & k \\ 2 & -1 & 1 \\ k & -1 & 2 \end{pmatrix}$. Find $k$ such that $\det\mathbf{A} = 0$.

**24** If $\mathbf{A} = \begin{pmatrix} 1 & 1 & 1 \\ x & 2 & 3 \\ x^2 & 4 & 9 \end{pmatrix}$, find all $x$ such that $\det\mathbf{A} = 0$.

**25** Find the inverse of the matrix $\begin{pmatrix} 2 & 4 \\ -1 & -3 \end{pmatrix}$.

Hence, solve the system $\begin{cases} 2x + 4y = 2 \\ -x - 3y = 1. \end{cases}$

**26** Let $\mathbf{A} = \begin{pmatrix} 3 & 4 \\ -2 & -3 \end{pmatrix}$.

**a** Find $\mathbf{A}^{-1}$ and $\mathbf{A}^2$.

**b** Hence, or otherwise, simplify $\mathbf{A}^3 + 4\mathbf{A}^2 - 2\mathbf{A} - 3\mathbf{I}$, and show that this matrix has no inverse.

**27** Let $\mathbf{A} = \begin{pmatrix} 3 & 0 \\ 0 & 4 \end{pmatrix}$, $\mathbf{B} = \begin{pmatrix} 1 & -2 \\ -1 & 1 \end{pmatrix}$, $\mathbf{C} = \begin{pmatrix} 2 & -2 \\ 3 & 1 \end{pmatrix}$.

**a** Find the inverse matrices $\mathbf{A}^{-1}$ and $\mathbf{B}^{-1}$.

**b** *Hence* find the matrix $\mathbf{X}$ which satisfies $\mathbf{AXB} = \mathbf{C}$.

**28** Let $\mathbf{A} = \begin{pmatrix} x & 0 & 2 \\ 1 & -1 & 0 \end{pmatrix}$ and $\mathbf{B} = \begin{pmatrix} 0 & 1 \\ 2 & x \\ 0 & -1 \end{pmatrix}$.

Find $x$ such that $\det(\mathbf{AB}) = \det(\mathbf{BA})$.

**29** Evaluate the determinant $\begin{vmatrix} a & -a & a \\ -a & a & -a \\ a & -a & a \end{vmatrix}$.

**30** If $\mathbf{A}$, $\mathbf{B}$ and $\mathbf{C}$ are invertible square matrices and $\mathbf{ABC} = 2\mathbf{I}$, find:

**a** $\mathbf{A}^{-1}$ in terms of $\mathbf{B}$ and $\mathbf{C}$

**b** $\mathbf{B}^{-1}$ in terms of $\mathbf{A}$ and $\mathbf{C}$

**c** $\mathbf{C}^{-1}$ in terms of $\mathbf{A}$ and $\mathbf{B}$.

## SKILL BUILDER QUESTIONS (CALCULATORS)

**1** Given $\mathbf{P} = \begin{pmatrix} -3 & 2 \\ 6 & 8 \end{pmatrix}$ and $\mathbf{Q} = \begin{pmatrix} 7 & -2 & 3 \\ 4 & 2 & 1 \\ 0 & -3 & 5 \end{pmatrix}$, find:

**a** $\det\mathbf{P}$ **b** $\det\mathbf{Q}$ **c** $\mathbf{P}^{-1}$ **d** $\mathbf{Q}^{-1}$

**2** Use technology to find the inverse of $\begin{pmatrix} 3 & 1 & 2 \\ 2 & 4 & 1 \\ 1 & -2 & 1 \end{pmatrix}$.

Hence, solve the system of equations $\begin{cases} 3x + y + 2z = 18 \\ 2x + 4y + z = 8 \\ x - 2y + z = 9. \end{cases}$

**3** School $A$ bought 2 soccer balls, one softball and 3 basketballs for a total of \$90, school $B$ bought 3 soccer balls, 2 softballs and 1 basketball for a total of \$81 and school $C$ bought 5 soccer balls and 2 basketballs for a total of \$104.
Write this information down as a matrix equation that will enable you to calculate the cost of each soccer ball, softball and basketball. Find the cost of each type of ball.

**4** Erica, Wu and Yasmina went shopping together. Erica bought 10 bread rolls, 8 apples, and 4 bags of chips for a total cost of €17.20. Wu purchased 5 bread rolls, 12 apples, and 1 bag of chips for a total cost of €9.80. Yasmina paid €13.60 for 12 bread rolls, 6 apples, and 2 bags of chips.
Represent this information using a system of linear equations, explaining carefully what each variable represents.
Use an inverse matrix to find the individual costs of the three items the girls purchased.

**5** **a** Let $\mathbf{A} = \begin{pmatrix} 1 & 2 & 1 \\ 3 & -2 & 0 \end{pmatrix}$ and $\mathbf{B} = \begin{pmatrix} 1 & 2 \\ -1 & 1 \\ 0 & 2 \end{pmatrix}$.

Find $\mathbf{C}$ if $\mathbf{AB} - 2\mathbf{C} = \begin{pmatrix} -1 & -4 \\ 3 & 8 \end{pmatrix}$.

**b** Let $\mathbf{D} = \begin{pmatrix} 0 & 2 \\ -2 & 0 \end{pmatrix}$.

Show that $-\frac{1}{4}\mathbf{D}^2 = \mathbf{I}$, where $\mathbf{I}$ is the identity matrix.

Hence state $\mathbf{D}^{-1}$ in terms of $\mathbf{D}$.

**6** Compute $\mathbf{AB}$ where

$\mathbf{A} = \begin{pmatrix} 2 & 1 & -1 \\ 0 & 1 & 0 \\ 0 & 0 & 1 \end{pmatrix}$ and $\mathbf{B} = \begin{pmatrix} 0 & 1 & 1 \\ 1 & 1 & 0 \\ 1 & 2 & 1 \end{pmatrix}$.

Hence or otherwise, obtain the matrix $\mathbf{A}^{10}\mathbf{B}$, giving reasons for your answer.

**7** Let $\mathbf{A} = \begin{pmatrix} 4 & 1 \\ 3 & 2 \end{pmatrix}$ and $\mathbf{B} = \begin{pmatrix} 2 & 0 \\ 7 & 1 \end{pmatrix}$. Find:

**a** $\mathbf{A}^{-1}$ **b** $\det(\mathbf{AB})^{-1}$

**8** **a** Let $\mathbf{A} = \begin{pmatrix} 1 & 2 & 4 \\ 4 & 3 & 8 \\ -4 & -4 & -9 \end{pmatrix}$.

**i** Calculate $\mathbf{B} = \mathbf{A} + 4\mathbf{I}$. **ii** Calculate $\mathbf{AB}$.

**iii** Deduce the matrix $\mathbf{A}^{-1}$.

**b** Find all values of $k$ for which the determinant

$$\begin{vmatrix} k & 2 \\ 2 & k-3 \end{vmatrix} = 0.$$

**9** Find the solution of the system of equations: $\begin{cases} x - 2y + 3z = 3 \\ 3x - 8y + 5z = -5 \\ -2x + 3y - 2z = 2. \end{cases}$

**10** $\mathbf{A} = \begin{pmatrix} 2 & 0 & -1 \\ 0 & 2 & 1 \\ -1 & 1 & 2 \end{pmatrix}$ and $\mathbf{B} = \begin{pmatrix} 15 & -1 & -4 \\ -1 & 15 & 4 \\ -4 & 4 & 16 \end{pmatrix}$.

Find the matrix $(\mathbf{B} - 6\mathbf{A})$ and show that $\mathbf{A}(\mathbf{B} - 6\mathbf{A}) = k\mathbf{I}$ where $k$ is some number and $\mathbf{I}$ is the identity matrix. Hence find the inverse $\mathbf{A}^{-1}$.

**11** **a** Solve the system of equations $\begin{cases} -x + y - z = 1 \\ 3x - 2y + z = -2 \\ 3x + y = -4. \end{cases}$

**b** The cubic polynomial $f(t) = at^3 + bt^2 + ct + d$ has the following properties:

$f(0) = 0$, $f(-1) = 1$, $f'(-1) = -2$, $f''(1) = -8$.

Use **a** to determine the coefficients of $f(t)$.

**12** Because of overhunting, the population of Sei whales in the Indian Ocean decreased rapidly last century. The biologists modelling this decrease chose a variable $t$ such that $t = 1$ corresponds to the year 1950, $t = 2$ to 1960, $t = 3$ to 1970, and so on. Estimates of the population size $P(t)$, in thousands of whales, are shown below for these times.

| $t$ | 1 | 2 | 3 |
|---|---|---|---|
| $P(t)$ | 23 | 21 | 17 |

The biologists model the relationship between $t$ and $P(t)$ using a quadratic $P(t) = a + bt + ct^2$ where $a$, $b$ and $c$ are constants.

**a** Explain why the data and relationship above produce the equations: $a + b + c = 23$
$a + 2b + 4c = 21$
$a + 3b + 9c = 17$

**b** Solve the system in **a** for $a$, $b$, and $c$.

**c** In 1980 (when $t = 4$) the population was 3000 whales. Determine whether the biologists' model overestimates or underestimates the population, and by how much.

**13** Let $\mathbf{A} = \begin{pmatrix} 3 & -2 & 10 \\ 0 & 1 & -3 \\ -1 & 1 & -4 \end{pmatrix}$.

**a** Find $\mathbf{A}^2$.

**b** Verify that $\mathbf{A}^3 = \mathbf{I}$ and hence deduce that $\mathbf{A}^2 = \mathbf{A}^{-1}$.

**14** A nut wholesaler prepares three different 1 kg packs of mixed nuts: Premium, Deluxe and Special.

By weight, the Premium packs consist of 40% hazelnuts, 30% cashews, and 30% peanuts. The Deluxe packs consist of 30% hazelnuts, 20% cashews, and 50% peanuts. The Special packs consist of 30% hazelnuts, 10% cashews, and 60% peanuts.

The company has an order to produce 3000 packets of Premium mix, 4000 of Deluxe mix, and 7000 of Special mix. Determine the number of kilograms of each nut variety needed to fill the order.

**15** The points $(2, 4)$, $(2, -6)$ and $(-1, 3)$ lie on a circle with equation $x^2 + y^2 + ax + by + c = 0$.

**a** Write three equations in the unknowns $a$, $b$ and $c$.

**b** Find the values of $a$, $b$ and $c$ and hence find the equation of the circle.

# TOPIC 5: VECTORS

A **scalar** is a quantity which has only size or **magnitude**.

A **vector** is a quantity with both **magnitude** and **direction**.

Two vectors are **equal** if they have the same magnitude *and* direction.

## VECTORS IN GEOMETRIC FORM

Given two vectors **v** and **w**, to find $\mathbf{v} + \mathbf{w}$ we first start by drawing **v**, and then from the end of **v** we draw **w**. The vector $\mathbf{v} + \mathbf{w}$ starts at the beginning of **v** and ends at the end of **w**.

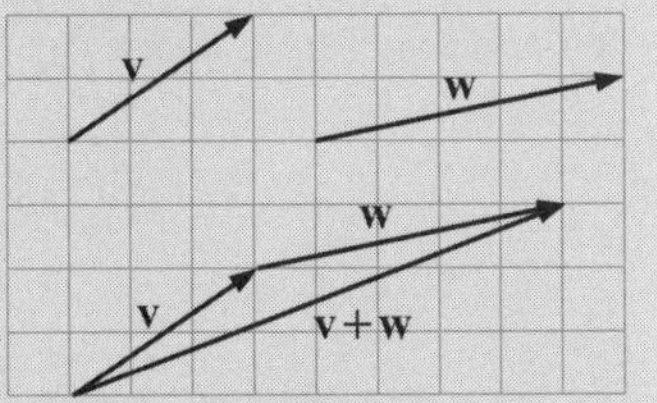


To find $\mathbf{v} - \mathbf{w}$ we find $\mathbf{v} + (-\mathbf{w})$. We start by drawing **v**, then from the end of **v** we draw $-\mathbf{w}$.

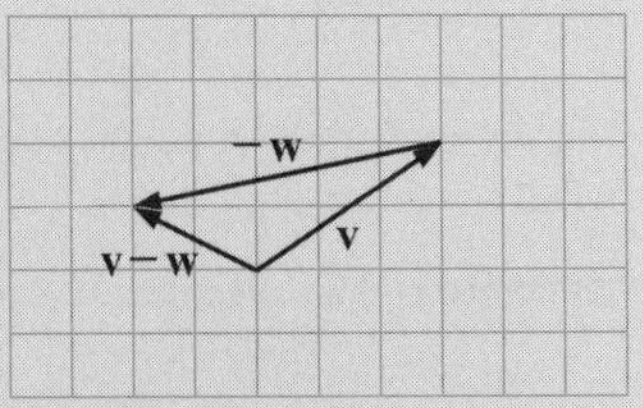


So, $\mathbf{v} + \mathbf{w}$ and $\mathbf{v} - \mathbf{w}$ are represented by the diagonals of a parallelogram with defining vectors **v** and **w**.

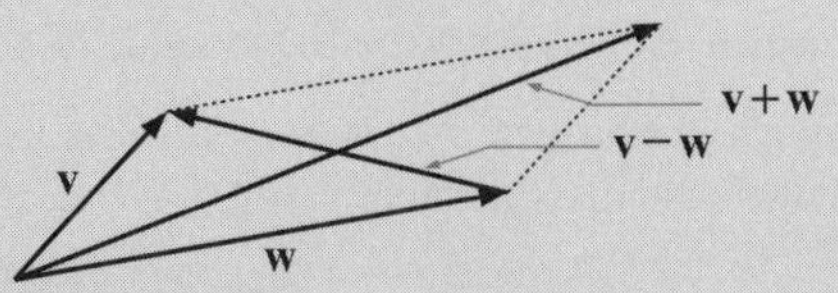


The **zero vector 0**, is a vector of length 0. It is the only vector with no direction.

In the diagram alongside,

$\mathbf{a} + \mathbf{b} = \mathbf{c}$

or $\mathbf{a} + \mathbf{b} - \mathbf{c} = \mathbf{0}$.

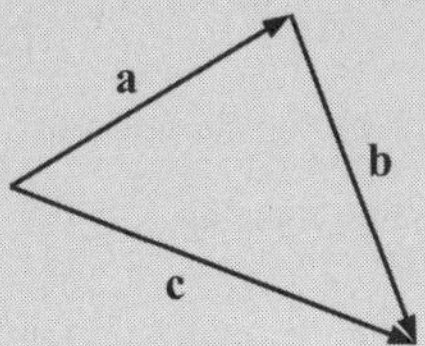


## VECTORS IN COMPONENT FORM

The basic unit vectors with magnitude 1 are:

in 2-D: $\mathbf{i} = \begin{pmatrix} 1 \\ 0 \end{pmatrix}$ and $\mathbf{j} = \begin{pmatrix} 0 \\ 1 \end{pmatrix}$

in 3-D: $\mathbf{i} = \begin{pmatrix} 1 \\ 0 \\ 0 \end{pmatrix}$, $\mathbf{j} = \begin{pmatrix} 0 \\ 1 \\ 0 \end{pmatrix}$ and $\mathbf{k} = \begin{pmatrix} 0 \\ 0 \\ 1 \end{pmatrix}$.

The **zero vector 0** is $\begin{pmatrix} 0 \\ 0 \end{pmatrix}$ in 2-D and $\begin{pmatrix} 0 \\ 0 \\ 0 \end{pmatrix}$ in 3-D.

The general 2-D vector $\mathbf{v} = \begin{pmatrix} v_1 \\ v_2 \end{pmatrix} = v_1\mathbf{i} + v_2\mathbf{j}$

The general 3-D vector $\mathbf{v} = \begin{pmatrix} v_1 \\ v_2 \\ v_3 \end{pmatrix} = v_1\mathbf{i} + v_2\mathbf{j} + v_3\mathbf{k}$.

In examinations, scalars are written in italics, for example $a$, and vectors are written in bold type, for example **a**. On paper you should write vector **a** as $\vec{a}$.

You should understand the following for vectors in component form:

- vector equality
- vector addition
  - $\mathbf{a} + \mathbf{b} = \mathbf{b} + \mathbf{a}$
  - $(\mathbf{a} + \mathbf{b}) + \mathbf{c} = \mathbf{a} + (\mathbf{b} + \mathbf{c})$
  - $\mathbf{a} + \mathbf{0} = \mathbf{0} + \mathbf{a} = \mathbf{a}$
  - $\mathbf{a} + (-\mathbf{a}) = (-\mathbf{a}) + \mathbf{a} = \mathbf{0}$
- vector subtraction $\mathbf{v} - \mathbf{w} = \mathbf{v} + (-\mathbf{w})$
- multiplication by a scalar $k$ to produce vector $k\mathbf{v}$ which is parallel to **v**
  - if $k > 0$, $k\mathbf{a}$ and **a** have the same direction
  - if $k < 0$, $k\mathbf{a}$ and **a** have opposite directions
  - if $k = 0$, $k\mathbf{a} = \mathbf{0}$
- the magnitude of vector **v**, $|\mathbf{v}| = \sqrt{v_1^2 + v_2^2 + v_3^2}$
- the distance between two points in space is the magnitude of the vector which joins them
- $|k\mathbf{a}| = |k|\,|\mathbf{a}|$

## POSITION VECTORS IN 2-D

The **position vector** of $\mathrm{A}(x, y)$ is $\overrightarrow{\mathrm{OA}}$ or $\mathbf{a} = \begin{pmatrix} x \\ y \end{pmatrix}$.

The position vector of B relative to A is

$\overrightarrow{\mathrm{AB}} = \overrightarrow{\mathrm{OB}} - \overrightarrow{\mathrm{OA}} = \mathbf{b} - \mathbf{a}$.

Given $\mathrm{A}(x_1, y_1)$ and $\mathrm{B}(x_2, y_2)$:

- the length of $\overrightarrow{\mathrm{AB}}$ is $\mathrm{AB} = \sqrt{(x_2 - x_1)^2 + (y_2 - y_1)^2}$
- the midpoint of $\overrightarrow{\mathrm{AB}}$ is $\left(\dfrac{x_1 + x_2}{2}, \dfrac{y_1 + y_2}{2}\right)$.

## POSITION VECTORS IN 3-D

The **position vector** of $\mathrm{A}(x, y, z)$ is $\overrightarrow{\mathrm{OA}}$ or $\mathbf{a} = \begin{pmatrix} x \\ y \\ z \end{pmatrix}$.

Given $\mathrm{A}(x_1, y_1, z_1)$ and $\mathrm{B}(x_2, y_2, z_2)$:

- the length of $\overrightarrow{\mathrm{AB}}$ is
  $\mathrm{AB} = \sqrt{(x_2 - x_1)^2 + (y_2 - y_1)^2 + (z_2 - z_1)^2}$
- the midpoint of $\overrightarrow{\mathrm{AB}}$ is $\left(\dfrac{x_1 + x_2}{2}, \dfrac{y_1 + y_2}{2}, \dfrac{z_1 + z_2}{2}\right)$.

## PROPERTIES OF VECTORS

If X divides [AB] in the ratio $a:b$ then $\overrightarrow{AX}:\overrightarrow{XB} = a:b$.

A, B and C are **collinear** if $\overrightarrow{AB} = k\overrightarrow{BC}$ for some scalar $k$.

Two vectors **a** and **b** are parallel if $\mathbf{a} = k\mathbf{b}$ for some constant $k \neq 0$.

The unit vector in the direction of **a** is $\frac{1}{|\mathbf{a}|}\mathbf{a}$.

A vector **b** of length $k$ in the same direction as **a** is $\mathbf{b} = \frac{k}{|\mathbf{a}|}\mathbf{a}$.

A vector **b** of length $k$ which is *parallel* to **a** could be $\mathbf{b} = \pm\frac{k}{|\mathbf{a}|}\mathbf{a}$.

**The scalar or dot product of two vectors**

$\mathbf{v} \bullet \mathbf{w} = |\mathbf{v}||\mathbf{w}|\cos\theta$ where $\theta$ is the angle between the vectors.

$\mathbf{v} \bullet \mathbf{w} = v_1w_1 + v_2w_2 + v_3w_3$

For non-zero vectors **v** and **w**:

- $\mathbf{v} \perp \mathbf{w} \Leftrightarrow \mathbf{v} \bullet \mathbf{w} = 0$
- $\mathbf{v} \parallel \mathbf{w} \Leftrightarrow \mathbf{v} = k\mathbf{w}$ or $\mathbf{v} \bullet \mathbf{w} = \pm|\mathbf{v}||\mathbf{w}|$

The angle $\theta$ between vectors **v** and **w** emanating from the same point is given by $\cos\theta = \frac{\mathbf{v} \bullet \mathbf{w}}{|\mathbf{v}||\mathbf{w}|}$.

If $\mathbf{v} \bullet \mathbf{w} > 0$ then $\theta$ is acute.

If $\mathbf{v} \bullet \mathbf{w} < 0$ then $\theta$ is obtuse.

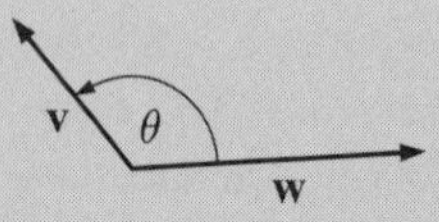


## LINES

The **vector equation of a line** is $\mathbf{r} = \mathbf{a} + t\mathbf{b}$ where **a** is the position vector of any point on the line, **b** is a vector parallel to the line, and $t \in \mathbb{R}$.

For example, if an object has initial position vector **a** and moves with constant velocity **b**, its position at time $t$ is given by $\mathbf{r} = \mathbf{a} + t\mathbf{b}$ for $t \geqslant 0$.

If $\mathbf{r} = \begin{pmatrix} x \\ y \\ z \end{pmatrix}$, $\mathbf{a} = \begin{pmatrix} x_0 \\ y_0 \\ z_0 \end{pmatrix}$ and $\mathbf{b} = \begin{pmatrix} l \\ m \\ n \end{pmatrix}$, the **parametric form** for the equation of a line is $x = x_0 + tl$, $y = y_0 + tm$, $z = z_0 + tn$

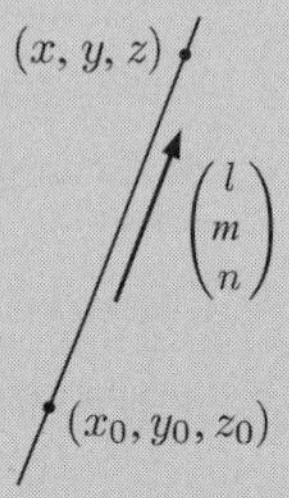


The **acute angle $\theta$ between two lines** is given by $\cos\theta = \frac{|\mathbf{a} \bullet \mathbf{b}|}{|\mathbf{a}||\mathbf{b}|}$ where **a** and **b** are the direction vectors of the lines.

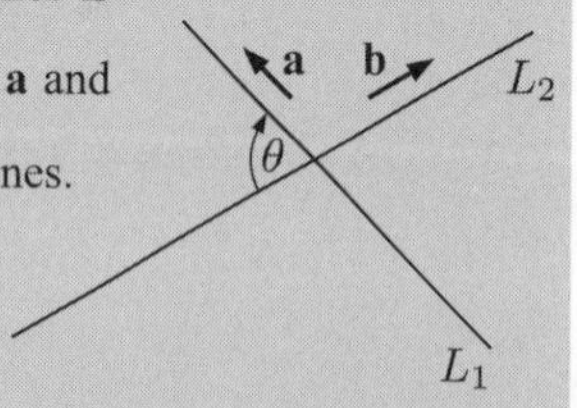


Lines are:

- **parallel** if their direction vectors are parallel: $\mathbf{a} = k\mathbf{b}$
- **coincident** if they are parallel and have a common point
- **intersecting** if you can solve them simultaneously to find a unique common point that fits both equations
- **skew** if they are not parallel and do not have a point of intersection; there are no solutions when the equations are solved simultaneously.

The shortest distance from point A to a line with direction vector **b** occurs at the point P on the line such that $\overrightarrow{AP}$ is perpendicular to **b**.

## SKILL BUILDER QUESTIONS (NO CALCULATORS)

**1** For $\mathbf{p} = \begin{pmatrix} -4 \\ 1 \end{pmatrix}$ and $\mathbf{q} = \begin{pmatrix} 2 \\ 3 \end{pmatrix}$, geometrically construct:

**a** $\mathbf{p} + \mathbf{q}$ **b** $\mathbf{p} - \mathbf{q}$

**2** Given $\mathbf{a} = \begin{pmatrix} 3 \\ -1 \end{pmatrix}$ and $\mathbf{b} = \begin{pmatrix} -1 \\ 2 \end{pmatrix}$, geometrically construct $2\mathbf{a} - 3\mathbf{b}$.

**3** Find a vector equation for:

**a**

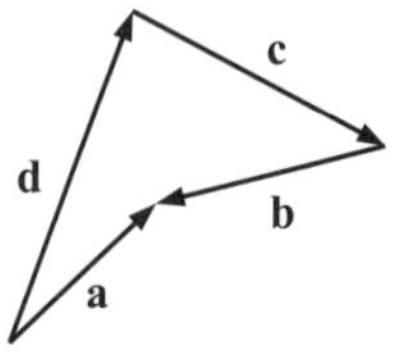


**b**

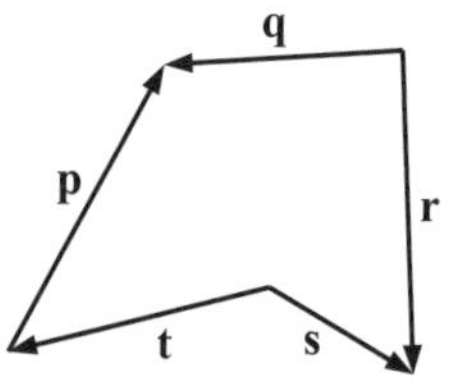


**4** Consider the *position vector* $\mathbf{a} = \begin{pmatrix} 1 \\ -2 \\ 3 \end{pmatrix}$

**a** Write **a** in terms of the base vectors **i**, **j**, and **k**.

**b** Find the magnitude of **a**.

**c** Write down a unit vector in the opposite direction to **a**.

**5** On grid paper, illustrate how to find the vector $2\mathbf{a} - \mathbf{b} + 3\mathbf{c}$ where $\mathbf{a} = \begin{pmatrix} 4 \\ -3 \end{pmatrix}$, $\mathbf{b} = \begin{pmatrix} -5 \\ 7 \end{pmatrix}$ and $\mathbf{c} = \begin{pmatrix} 1 \\ 2 \end{pmatrix}$.

Check your answer algebraically.

**6** Find the value(s) of $k$ for which $\begin{pmatrix} k \\ 1 \\ 3 \end{pmatrix}$ and $\begin{pmatrix} 4 \\ k \\ 3k \end{pmatrix}$ are:

**a** parallel to each other

**b** perpendicular to each other.

**7**

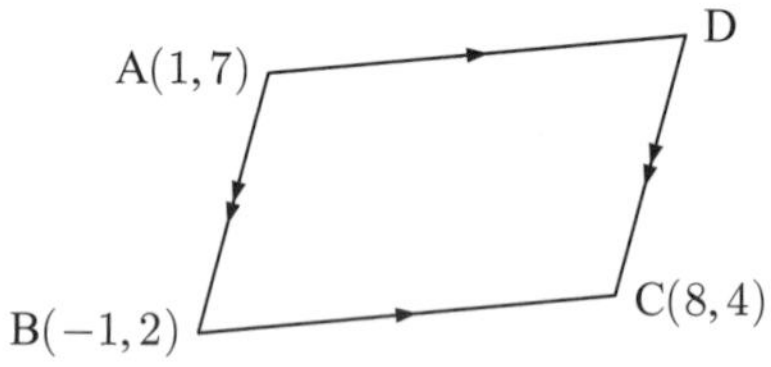


Use vector methods to find the coordinates of D for parallelogram ABCD.

**8** **a** Draw a clear diagram of a parallelogram ABCD formed by two vectors $\overrightarrow{AB} = \mathbf{a}$ and $\overrightarrow{AD} = \mathbf{b}$ along its sides.

**b** Write the vectors $\overrightarrow{BC}$, $\overrightarrow{CD}$ and the diagonals $\overrightarrow{AC}$ and $\overrightarrow{BD}$ in terms of **a** and **b**.

**c** Calculate the product $\overrightarrow{AC} \bullet \overrightarrow{BD}$ in terms of **a** and **b**.

**d** Explain clearly why $\overrightarrow{AC}$ is perpendicular to $\overrightarrow{BD}$ when the parallelogram is a rhombus.

**9** Find scalars $r$ and $s$ such that $r\begin{pmatrix} 3 \\ -6 \end{pmatrix} + s\begin{pmatrix} 7 \\ 2 \end{pmatrix} = \begin{pmatrix} 5 \\ 22 \end{pmatrix}$.

**10** Find $t$ if $\begin{pmatrix} t \\ 1 \end{pmatrix}$ and $\begin{pmatrix} t-4 \\ -5 \end{pmatrix}$ are perpendicular vectors.

**11** Find the vector equation of:

**a** the line through $(1, 6)$ and parallel to $\begin{pmatrix} 4 \\ 2 \end{pmatrix}$

**b** the line through the points $(-3, 2)$ and $(5, -2)$.

**12** A line passes through the point $(-5, -2)$ and has a direction parallel to $\begin{pmatrix} 2 \\ 3 \end{pmatrix}$. Find:

**a** the vector equation of the line

**b** the parametric equations of the line.

**13** Vectors $\mathbf{v}$ and $\mathbf{w}$ are given by $\mathbf{v} = 5\mathbf{i} - 2\mathbf{j}$ and $\mathbf{w} = \mathbf{i} + 3\mathbf{j}$. Find scalars $r$ and $s$ such that $r(\mathbf{v} - \mathbf{w}) = (r + s)\,\mathbf{i} - 20\mathbf{j}$.

**14** Find the vector equation of the line through $(6, -2)$ and $(-3, 5)$. Give your answer in the form $\mathbf{r} = \mathbf{a} + t\mathbf{b}$ where $t \in \mathbb{R}$.

**15** Find the vector equation of the line through $(0, 4)$ which is parallel to the vector $3\mathbf{i} + \mathbf{j}$.

**16** Triangle ABC is defined by the following information:

$\overrightarrow{OA} = \begin{pmatrix} -2 \\ 4 \end{pmatrix}$, $\overrightarrow{AB} \bullet \overrightarrow{OA} = 0$, $\overrightarrow{CA} = \begin{pmatrix} -6 \\ 2 \end{pmatrix}$,

and $\overrightarrow{CB}$ is parallel to $\begin{pmatrix} 0 \\ 1 \end{pmatrix}$.

**a** On grid paper, draw an accurate diagram of $\Delta$ABC.

**b** Write down the vector $\overrightarrow{OB}$.

**17** The vector equations of two lines are:

$L_1$: $\mathbf{r}_1 = \begin{pmatrix} 4 \\ -2 \end{pmatrix} + t\begin{pmatrix} 3 \\ 2 \end{pmatrix}$ and $L_2$: $\mathbf{r}_2 = \begin{pmatrix} -1 \\ -1 \end{pmatrix} + s\begin{pmatrix} 5 \\ -1 \end{pmatrix}$

Use vector methods to find the coordinates of the point where $L_1$ meets $L_2$.

**18** Solve for $\mathbf{x}$: $\mathbf{r} - 3\mathbf{x} = \mathbf{q}$.

**19** For $\mathbf{m} = 3\mathbf{i} + \mathbf{j} + 2\mathbf{k}$ and $\mathbf{n} = -2\mathbf{i} + 5\mathbf{j} - 4\mathbf{k}$ find:

**a** $3\mathbf{m} - \mathbf{n}$ **b** $\mathbf{m} \bullet \mathbf{n}$

**c** $|\mathbf{m} + \mathbf{n}|$ **d** $\mathbf{m} \bullet (2\mathbf{i} + \mathbf{k})$

**20** Suppose $\mathbf{a} = \begin{pmatrix} 4 \\ -2 \\ 1 \end{pmatrix}$ and $\mathbf{b} = \begin{pmatrix} 3 \\ 2 \\ -4 \end{pmatrix}$.

Find $\mathbf{x}$ such that $\mathbf{a} - 4\mathbf{x} = 2\mathbf{b}$.

**21** Find scalars $a$ and $b$ given that $\begin{pmatrix} 4 \\ -1 \\ 5 \end{pmatrix}$ and $\begin{pmatrix} a \\ b \\ -15 \end{pmatrix}$ are parallel.

**22** **a** Find a unit vector that is parallel to $3\mathbf{i} + \mathbf{j} - \mathbf{k}$.

**b** Find a vector of length 4 units which is parallel to $3\mathbf{i} + \mathbf{j} - \mathbf{k}$.

**23** Find $t$ given that $\begin{pmatrix} 2t \\ -4 \\ 7 \end{pmatrix}$ and $\begin{pmatrix} 3 \\ t \\ -8 \end{pmatrix}$ are perpendicular vectors.

**24** Consider the points A$(1, -1, 2)$ and B$(5, -1, -1)$.

**a** Find the equation of the line $L$ through A and B.

**b** Find a point on $L$ which is 20 units from A.

**25** Consider P$(4, -2, 11)$, Q$(13, -8, 14)$ and R$(19, -12, 16)$.

**a** Prove that P, Q and R are collinear.

**b** Find the ratio in which Q divides [PR].

**26** Find the vector equations of these lines:

**a** parallel to $\begin{pmatrix} 1 \\ 2 \\ 3 \end{pmatrix}$ and passing through the point $(5, 0, -2)$

**b** parallel to $2\mathbf{i} - 3\mathbf{j} + 4\mathbf{k}$ and passing through the point $(-2, 5, 4)$

**c** perpendicular to the $XOZ$ plane and passing through the point $(2, -4, 1)$.

**27** Find the parametric equations of these lines:

**a** passing through $(5, -1, 2)$ and parallel to $\begin{pmatrix} 7 \\ 2 \\ -3 \end{pmatrix}$

**b** passing through $(0, 2, -6)$ and parallel to $2\mathbf{i} - 3\mathbf{j} + \mathbf{k}$

**c** passing through $(2, 5, 1)$ and $(8, 6, 2)$.

**28** At what point does the line

$\begin{pmatrix} x \\ y \\ z \end{pmatrix} = \begin{pmatrix} -1 \\ 4 \\ 3 \end{pmatrix} + t\begin{pmatrix} 3 \\ 2 \\ -1 \end{pmatrix}$ meet the $YOZ$ plane?

**29** **a** The position vectors of A and B are $\mathbf{a}$ and $\mathbf{b}$ respectively. If P lies on [AB] such that $\overrightarrow{AP} = t\overrightarrow{AB}$, show that the position vector of P is given by $\mathbf{p} = (1 - t)\mathbf{a} + t\mathbf{b}$.

**b** For A$(2, -1, 4)$ and B$(-3, 1, -1)$, find P on [AB] such that $\overrightarrow{AP} : \overrightarrow{PB} = 2 : 5$.

**30** A is $(-1, 2, 1)$ and B is $(0, 1, 3)$.

**a** Find the equation of the line (AB) in the form $\mathbf{r} = \mathbf{a} + t\mathbf{b}$, $t \in \mathbb{R}$.

**b** Find the angle between (AB) and the line $L$ given by

$$\begin{pmatrix} x \\ y \\ z \end{pmatrix} = \begin{pmatrix} 1 \\ -1 \\ 2 \end{pmatrix} + s\begin{pmatrix} 2 \\ 0 \\ -1 \end{pmatrix}.$$

**31** Suppose $\mathbf{a} = \begin{pmatrix} 1 \\ 3 \\ k \end{pmatrix}$, $\mathbf{b} = \begin{pmatrix} 2 \\ 0 \\ -1 \end{pmatrix}$ and $\mathbf{c} = \begin{pmatrix} -1 \\ 2 \\ 3 \end{pmatrix}$, and $\mathbf{b}$ is perpendicular to $\mathbf{c} - 2\mathbf{a}$. Find the value of $k$.

## SKILL BUILDER QUESTIONS (CALCULATORS)

**1** For $\mathbf{v} = \begin{pmatrix} -4 \\ 3 \end{pmatrix}$ and $\mathbf{w} = \begin{pmatrix} 2 \\ 6 \end{pmatrix}$ find:

**a** $|\mathbf{v}|$ **b** $|\mathbf{v} + \mathbf{w}|$ **c** $3\mathbf{w} - 2\mathbf{v}$

**d** $\mathbf{v} \bullet \mathbf{w}$ **e** $\mathbf{w} \bullet \mathbf{w}$

**2** A is $(2, 10)$, B is $(-2, 2)$ and C is $(16, 6)$. Find:

**a** $\overrightarrow{AC}$ **b** $\overrightarrow{AM}$ where M is the midpoint of [BC]

**c** the size of angle BAC.

**3** For $\mathbf{p} = 4\mathbf{i} - 9\mathbf{j}$ and $\mathbf{q} = -12\mathbf{i} + 5\mathbf{j}$ find:

**a** $|\mathbf{q}|$ **b** $\mathbf{p} \bullet \mathbf{q}$

**c** the angle between $\mathbf{p}$ and $\mathbf{q}$

**d** a unit vector parallel to $\mathbf{p}$.

**4** For points P$(6, -4)$, Q$(4, 11)$ and R$(2, 1)$, find the size of angle PQR.

**5** Find the size of the acute angle between the lines with equations $y = 2x + 5$ and $3x + 4y = 20$.

**6** Find, to the nearest degree, the angle between $\mathbf{a} = 3\mathbf{i} - 3\mathbf{j}$ and $\mathbf{b} = 5\mathbf{i} - \mathbf{j}$.

**7** **a** Given $\mathbf{a} \bullet \mathbf{b} < 0$, what conclusion can you draw about the angle between $\mathbf{a}$ and $\mathbf{b}$?

**b** Find $\mathbf{a} \bullet \mathbf{b}$ for the vectors $\mathbf{a} = \begin{pmatrix} -2 \\ 1 \\ 3 \end{pmatrix}$ and $\mathbf{b} = \begin{pmatrix} 3 \\ -1 \\ 1 \end{pmatrix}$. Hence find the angle between these vectors in degrees, correct to one decimal place.

**8** Quadrilateral ABCD has vertices A(2, 10), B(12, 8), C(11, 5) and D(−1, 2).

Find the acute angle between the diagonals $\overrightarrow{AC}$ and $\overrightarrow{BD}$.

**9** A boat moves in a straight line defined by the parametric equations $x = 3 + t$ and $y = 4t - 3$, where $t$ is the time in seconds, $t \geqslant 0$, and $x$ and $y$ are measured in metres.

Find: **a** the initial position of the boat

**b** the velocity vector of the boat

**c** the speed of the boat.

**10** Suppose $\begin{pmatrix} 1 \\ 0 \end{pmatrix}$ represents a 1 km displacement due east and $\begin{pmatrix} 0 \\ 1 \end{pmatrix}$ represents a 1 km displacement due north. A lighthouse is at the point (0, 10). A ship is moving in a straight line according to the parametric equations $x = 3 - 2t$, $y = 3t + 1$, $t \geqslant 0$ where $t$ is the number of hours after 8:30 am.

**a** What was the initial position of the ship?

**b** Find the ship's: **i** velocity vector **ii** speed.

**c** Find the distance between the ship and the lighthouse at 10:30 am.

**d** Find the time when the ship is directly west of the lighthouse.

**e** At what time (to the nearest minute) will the ship be closest to the lighthouse?

**11** Write vector equations in the form $\mathbf{r} = \mathbf{a} + t\mathbf{b}$ to define the position at time $t$ for these remote controlled toy racing cars. All distances are in metres and time is in seconds.

**a** Car $A$ is initially at (10, 6), and is travelling at 13 m s$^{-1}$ in the direction $5\mathbf{i} + 12\mathbf{j}$.

**b** Car $B$ is initially at (−5, 3), and is travelling parallel to $\begin{pmatrix} 4 \\ -3 \end{pmatrix}$ at 15 m s$^{-1}$.

**c** Car $C$ is initially at (−1, 4), and travels at a constant velocity for 3 seconds to (5, 7).

**12** Triangle PQR is formed by these lines:

(PQ): $\begin{pmatrix} x \\ y \end{pmatrix} = \begin{pmatrix} 11 \\ 13 \end{pmatrix} + r\begin{pmatrix} 4 \\ -6 \end{pmatrix}$

(QR): $\begin{pmatrix} x \\ y \end{pmatrix} = \begin{pmatrix} 9 \\ 3 \end{pmatrix} + t\begin{pmatrix} 3 \\ 2 \end{pmatrix}$

(PR): $\begin{pmatrix} x \\ y \end{pmatrix} = \begin{pmatrix} 2 \\ 7 \end{pmatrix} + u\begin{pmatrix} 5 \\ 12 \end{pmatrix}$

where $r$, $t$ and $u$ are scalars.

**a** Accurately draw the three lines on a grid and hence find the coordinates of P, Q and R.

**b** Prove that ΔPQR is right angled.

**c** Find the area of ΔPQR.

**13** For the points A(2, 0, 5), B(−3, 1, 7) and C(4, −2, 9), find:

**a** the distance AB **b** the distance BC

**c** $\overrightarrow{AC}$ **d** $\overrightarrow{AB}$ **e** the size of $B\widehat{A}C$.

**14** For $\mathbf{p} = \begin{pmatrix} 3 \\ 1 \\ 3 \end{pmatrix}$, $\mathbf{q} = \begin{pmatrix} -4 \\ 2 \\ 4 \end{pmatrix}$ and $\mathbf{r} = \begin{pmatrix} -4 \\ -3 \\ 2 \end{pmatrix}$, find:

**a** $\mathbf{p} + 2\mathbf{q} - \mathbf{r}$ **b** $|\mathbf{r} + \mathbf{q}|$

**c** a unit vector parallel to $\mathbf{q}$ **d** $\mathbf{p} \bullet \mathbf{q}$ **e** $(\mathbf{p} + \mathbf{q}) \bullet \mathbf{q}$

**15** A(2, −5, 3), B(7, −3, −1), C(1, 3, 0) and D(−4, 1, 4) are vertices of a quadrilateral.

**a** Prove that ABCD is a parallelogram.

**b** Find the size of the smallest angles of the parallelogram.

**16** Find the angle between the $Z$-axis and the vector $\begin{pmatrix} 4 \\ -1 \\ 3 \end{pmatrix}$.

**17** Given the points K(4, −2, 7), L(6, 1, −1) and M(3, −2, 5), find the measure of $K\widehat{L}M$.

**18** Given $\overrightarrow{AB} = \begin{pmatrix} 4 \\ -6 \\ 2 \end{pmatrix}$ and $\overrightarrow{AC} = \begin{pmatrix} -2 \\ 7 \\ -3 \end{pmatrix}$ find:

**a** $\overrightarrow{BC}$ **b** the size of $B\widehat{A}C$.

**19** Find the shortest distance from the point (1, 4, 6) to the line with parametric equations
$x = 3 + t$, $y = -1 + 2t$, $z = 2 + t$, $t \in \mathbb{R}$.

**20** Lines $L_1$, $L_2$ and $L_3$ are defined by:

$$L_1 : \begin{pmatrix} x \\ y \\ z \end{pmatrix} = \begin{pmatrix} 2 \\ 1 \\ -1 \end{pmatrix} + t\begin{pmatrix} 3 \\ -6 \\ -3 \end{pmatrix}$$

$L_2 : x = 5 - r,\ y = -4 + 2r,\ z = 1 + r$

$L_3 : x = 5 - 3s,\ y = 5 + 4s,\ z = 1 + 2s$

**a** Show that $L_1$ is parallel to $L_2$.

**b** Show that $L_1$ and $L_3$ intersect and find the angle between them.

# TOPIC 6: STATISTICS AND PROBABILITY

## POPULATIONS AND SAMPLES

The **population** is the set of all members under consideration.

A **sample** is any subset of the population.

A **random sample** is a sample for which each member of the population has an equal chance of being selected. Random samples are used to ensure the sample reflects the true population.

## TYPES OF DATA AND ITS REPRESENTATION

**Discrete data** can take any of a set of distinct values $x_1, x_2, x_3, \ldots$. It is normally **counted**.

**Continuous data** can take any value on a particular domain of the number line. It is normally **measured**.

**Grouped data** refers to data which is collected in groups or classes, often for presentation purposes. The **interval width** of a class is its upper score minus its lower score.

For both discrete and continuous data we can plot the data value on the horizontal axis and the frequency on the vertical axis. For discrete data this is a **column graph**, and the columns have spaces between them. For continuous data this is a **frequency histogram**, and there are no spaces between the columns; the classes are all of equal width.

A **relative frequency histogram** uses relative frequency on the vertical axis. It enables us to compare distributions of different sample size.

Data may be symmetric, positively skewed, or negatively skewed.

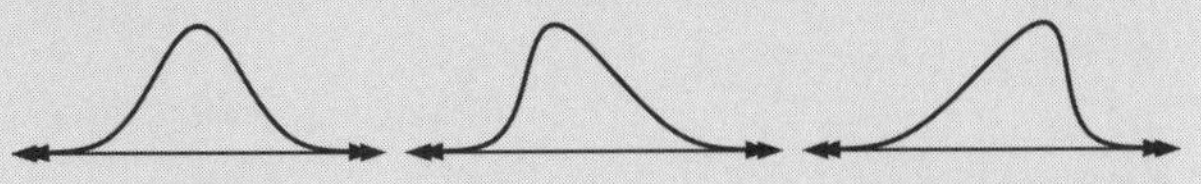


We use a **cumulative frequency graph** or **ogive** to display the cumulative frequency for each data value in a distribution. This enables us to read off the values at each percentile.

## DESCRIPTIVE STATISTICS

The **mean** of a set of scores is their arithmetic average.

For a large population, the **population mean** $\mu$ is generally unknown. The **sample mean** $\overline{x}$ is used as an **unbiased estimate** of $\mu$.

For ungrouped data, $\overline{x} = \dfrac{\sum_{i=1}^{n} x_i}{n}$

For grouped data, $\overline{x} = \dfrac{\sum fx}{\sum f}$ where $f$ is the frequency of each value.

The **median** is the middle score of an ordered sample.

For an **odd number** of data, the median is one of the original data values.

For an **even number** of data, the median is the average of the two middle values, and may not be in the original data set.

The **mode** is the most frequently occurring score. If there are two modes we say the data is **bimodal**. For continuous data we refer to a **modal class**.

If a data set is symmetric, both the mode and the median should accurately measure the centre of the distribution.

The ***k*th percentile** is the score $a$ such that $k\%$ of the scores are less than $a$.

The **lower quartile** $Q_1$ corresponds to the 25th quartile.

The **median** $Q_2$ corresponds to the 50th percentile.

The **upper quartile** $Q_3$ corresponds to the 75th quartile.

A **box-and-whisker plot** indicates the 5 key statistics for the set of data: minimum value, $Q_1$, $Q_2$, $Q_3$ and maximum value.

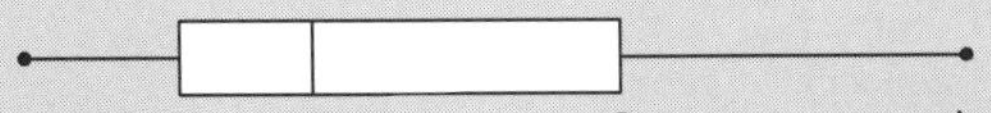


You should know how to generate a **cumulative frequency graph** and use it to estimate $Q_1$, $Q_2$ and $Q_3$.

**Measures of the spread of a distribution**

The **range** measures the spread from the highest to lowest score.

The **interquartile range** $\text{IQR} = Q_3 - Q_1$. It is the width of the box in a box and whisker plot.

The **sample variance** $s_n^2$ measures the **spread** of the scores about the sample mean.

The **sample standard deviation** $s_n$ is the square root of the variance. You will find formulae for the standard deviation in your information booklet.

When a sample of size $n$ is used to draw inference about a population:

- the sample mean $\overline{x}$ is used as an unbiased estimate of $\mu$
- $s_n$ is used to estimate the population standard deviation $\sigma$.

## PROBABILITY

A **trial** occurs each time we perform an experiment.

The possible results from each trial of an experiment are called its **outcomes**. If the outcomes have the same probability of occurring, we say they are **equally likely**.

The **sample space** $U$ is the set of all possible outcomes from one trial of the experiment.

**Experimental Probability**

In many situations, we can only measure the probability of an event by experimentation.
Experimental probability = relative frequency.

**Theoretical Probability**

If all outcomes are equally likely, the probability of event $A$ occurring is $\text{P}(A) = \dfrac{n(A)}{n(U)}$.

For any event $A$, $0 \leqslant \text{P}(A) \leqslant 1$.

For any event $A$, $A'$ is the event that $A$ does not occur. $A$ and $A'$ are **complementary events**, and $\text{P}(A) + \text{P}(A') = 1$.

$A \cup A' = U$ and $A \cap A' = \varnothing$

The **union** $A$ *or* $B$ is $A \cup B$.

The **intersection** $A$ *and* $B$ is $A \cap B$.

$\text{P}(A \cup B) = \text{P}(A) + \text{P}(B) - \text{P}(A \cap B)$.

For **disjoint** or **mutually exclusive** events, $\text{P}(A \cap B) = 0$.

Two events are **independent** if the occurrence of each of them does not affect the probability that the other occurs. An example of this is sampling **with replacement**. For independent events $A$ and $B$, $\text{P}(A \cap B) = \text{P}(A)\text{P}(B)$.

Two events are **dependent** if the occurrence of one of them *does* affect the probability that the other occurs. An example of this is sampling **without replacement**.

You should be able to use **Venn diagrams** and **tree diagrams** to calculate probabilities. You should also be able to use Venn diagrams to verify set identities.

**Binomial Probabilities**

If $A$ is an event with probability $p$ of occurring, and its complement $A'$ has probability $q = 1 - p$ of occurring, then the probability generator for the various outcomes over $n$ **independent** trials is $(p+q)^n$.

$$\text{P}(A \text{ occurs exactly } x \text{ times}) = \binom{n}{x} p^x q^{n-x} = \binom{n}{x} p^x (1-p)^{n-x}$$

**Conditional Probability**

For any two events $A$ and $B$, $\text{P}(A \mid B) = \dfrac{\text{P}(A \cap B)}{\text{P}(B)}$.

For independent events: $\text{P}(A) = \text{P}(A \mid B) = \text{P}(A \mid B')$

$\text{P}(A \cap B) = \text{P}(A)\text{P}(B)$.

## DISCRETE RANDOM VARIABLES

A **random variable** represents the possible numerical outcomes of an experiment.

A **discrete random variable** can take any of a set of distinct values, each of which corresponds to exactly one outcome in the sample space.

For a discrete random variable where $p_i$ is the probability of the $i$th outcome: $0 \leqslant p_i \leqslant 1$ and $\sum p_i = 1$.

The probabilities $p_i$ may be given as a **probability mass function** $P(x)$ where $x$ can take discrete values.

If there are $n$ trials of an experiment, and an event has probability $p$ of occurring in each of the trials, then the number of times we **expect** the event to occur is $np$.

The **expectation** of a random variable is $\text{E}(X) = \mu = \sum_{i=1}^{n} p_i x_i$.

In a gambling game, suppose $X$ represents the gain of a player from each game. The game is **fair** if $\text{E}(X) = 0$.

### The Binomial Distribution

In a **binomial experiment** there are two possible results: success and failure.

The random variable $X$ has a **binomial distribution** if there are $n$ independent trials of the same experiment with the probability of success being a constant $p$ for each trial. We write $X \sim \text{B}(n, p)$.

The **binomial probability distribution function** is $\text{P}(X = r) = \binom{n}{r} p^r (1-p)^{n-r}$ where $r = 0, 1, 2, ...., n$ and $X$ is the number of successes in $n$ trials of the experiment.

You should be able to use your calculator to find:

- $\text{P}(X = r)$ using the binomial probability distribution function
- $\text{P}(X \leqslant r)$ using the binomial cumulative distribution function.

$\text{E}(X) = \mu = np$

## CONTINUOUS RANDOM VARIABLES

A **continuous random variable** takes on all possible *measured* values. We consider measurements that are in a particular *range* rather than taking a particular value. For example, we do not consider $X = 3.7$ kg but rather $3.65 \leqslant X < 3.75$ kg.

A **continuous probability density function** is a function $f(x)$ such that $f(x) \geqslant 0$ on a given interval $a \leqslant x \leqslant b$ and $\int_a^b f(x)\,dx = 1$. The area under the graph of $f(x)$ over which $f(x)$ is defined is 1.

$\text{P}(c \leqslant X \leqslant d) = \int_c^d f(x)\,dx$

The **mean** or **expectation** is $\text{E}(X) = \mu = \int_a^b x f(x)\,dx$.

The **mode** is the value of $x$ on $a \leqslant x \leqslant b$ for which $f(x)$ is maximised.

### The Normal Distribution

If the random variable $X$ has a normal distribution with mean $\mu$ and variance $\sigma^2$, we write $X \sim \text{N}(\mu, \sigma^2)$.

The probability density function is $f(x) = \dfrac{1}{\sigma\sqrt{2\pi}} e^{-\frac{1}{2}\left(\frac{x-\mu}{\sigma}\right)^2}$ for $x \in \mathbb{R}$.

$f(x)$ is a bell-shaped curve which is symmetric about $x = \mu$. It has the property that:

- $\approx 68\%$ of all scores lie within one $\sigma$ of $\mu$
- $\approx 95\%$ of all scores lie within two $\sigma$s of $\mu$
- $\approx 99.7\%$ of all scores lie within three $\sigma$s of $\mu$.

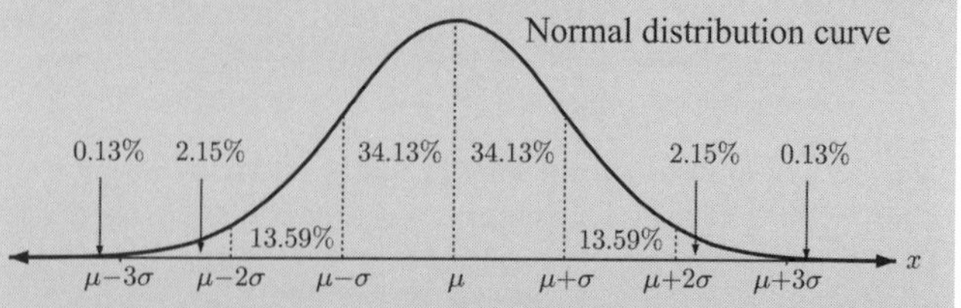


### The Standard Normal Distribution

Every normal $X$-distribution can be transformed into the **standard normal distribution** or **$Z$-distribution** using the transformation $z = \dfrac{x-\mu}{\sigma}$.

The standard normal distribution has mean 0 and variance 1, so $Z \sim \text{N}(0, 1)$.

The probability density function is $f(z) = \dfrac{1}{\sqrt{2\pi}} e^{-\frac{1}{2}z^2}$ for $z \in \mathbb{R}$.

We use $Z$-distributions when:

- we are looking for an unknown mean $\mu$ or variance $\sigma^2$
- we are comparing scores from two different normal distributions

You should be able to use your calculator to find normal probabilities for the situations:

- $\text{P}(Z \leqslant a)$
- $\text{P}(Z \geqslant a)$
- $\text{P}(a \leqslant Z \leqslant b)$

You should also be able to use your calculator or inverse normal tables to find the scores corresponding to particular probabilities, or **quantiles**.

## SKILL BUILDER QUESTIONS (NO CALCULATORS)

**1** A frequency table for the speeds of cars travelling through a country town one Sunday morning is given alongside.

| *Speed* (km h$^{-1}$) | *Frequency* |
|---|---|
| $30 \leqslant v < 40$ | 4 |
| $40 \leqslant v < 50$ | 11 |
| $50 \leqslant v < 60$ | 15 |
| $60 \leqslant v < 70$ | 18 |
| $70 \leqslant v < 80$ | 12 |
| $80 \leqslant v < 90$ | 6 |
| $90 \leqslant v < 100$ | 4 |
| $100 \leqslant v < 110$ | 2 |

**a** Construct a frequency histogram for the data. What is the modal class?

**b** Construct a cumulative frequency graph for the data and use it to estimate:

**i** the median **ii** the interquartile range

**iii** the 40th percentile of the data.

**2** After seven netball matches, Kai has averaged 11 goals per game. How many goals will she need to score in the next game to improve her overall average to 12?

**3** After a 10 minute run, a class of 24 students measured their pulse rates. The results were:

85 106 148 112 105 96 100 108 135 126 144 156
98 108 112 128 148 140 120 123 133 144 118 125

**a** Find:

**i** the lower quartile **ii** the median

iii the upper quartile   iv the interquartile range

v the range of the data.

**b** Draw a box-and-whisker plot to represent the data.

**4** A box-and-whisker plot has been drawn to show the heights of some petunia seedlings, in centimetres.

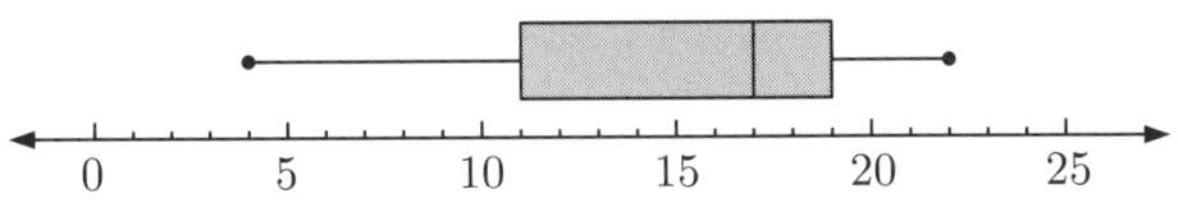


**a** What was the:

**i** tallest height   **ii** smallest height

**iii** 75th percentile   **iv** median height?

**b** What was the:

**i** range   **ii** interquartile range?

**c** How many seedlings were taller than 11 cm?

**d** Was the distribution of seedlings symmetrical?

**5** A cumulative frequency graph for the selling price of units sold at Sunset Beach last year is given below.

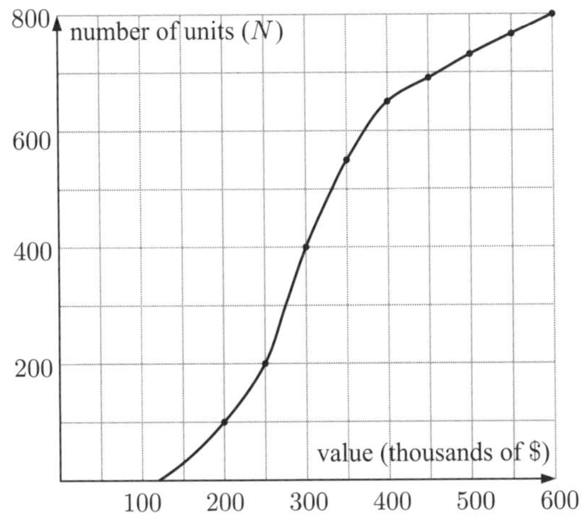


**a** How many units sold for less than $200 000?

**b** What was the median selling price?

**c** What was the interquartile range of the selling prices?

**d** What was the 60th percentile of the selling prices?

**6** Two unbiased dice are rolled and the difference between the scores is noted. Using a table of outcomes, find the probability that the difference between the scores is 3.

**7** In the town of Expiet 71% of the population are right-handed, 44% are either right-handed or have blonde hair but not both, and 21% do not have blonde hair.
If a member of this population is selected at random, what is the likelihood that the person:

**a** is right-handed but not blonde

**b** is both right-handed and has blonde hair

**c** is right-handed or has blonde hair?

**8** $f(x)$ is the probability density function of a continuous random variable $X$.

**a** What two properties must $f(x)$ have?

**b** How is $P(x_1 \leqslant X \leqslant x_2)$ found?

**9** A random variable $X$ has the following distribution table:

| $x$ | $-2$ | $0$ | $3$ | $5$ |
|---|---|---|---|---|
| $P(X = x)$ | $\frac{1}{3}$ | $\frac{1}{6}$ | $k$ | $\frac{1}{12}$ |

**a** Is the random variable discrete or continuous?

**b** Find $k$.   **c** Find $E(X)$.

**10** When two dice are rolled, find the probability that the sum of the two results is:

**a** $> 8$   **b** more than 3 but less than 8   **c** exactly 6.

**11** With the aid of a tree diagram, find the probability of getting:

**a** a tail and either a 2 or 5 when you toss a coin and roll a die

**b** at least one child of each sex if you have 3 children, assuming $P(\text{boy}) = P(\text{girl}) = 0.5$.

**12** Twins Tom and Jerry are keen archers. The probability that Tom successfully hits a target is 0.7. The probability that Jerry successfully hits a target is 0.6. Whenever they both shoot at a target, what is the probability that:

**a** only one of them is successful

**b** at least one of them is successful?

**13** A box of chocolates contains 6 dark brown, 4 light brown and 2 white truffles.

**a** Complete the following tree diagram displaying the probabilities if two truffles are selected from the box without replacement.

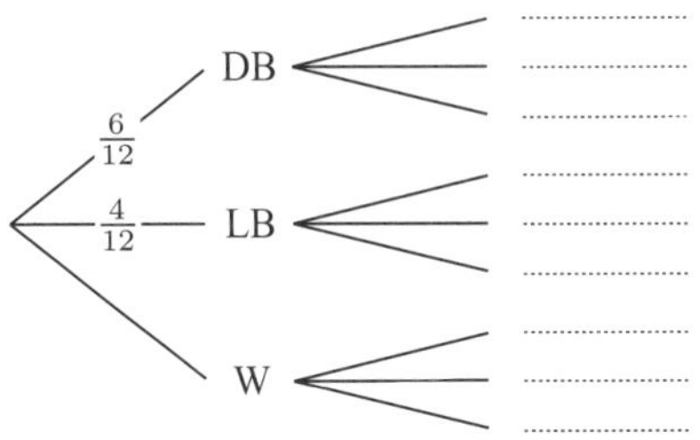


**b** If you chose 2 truffles from the box at random, what is the probability that you would get:

**i** 2 white truffles

**ii** 2 different coloured truffles?

**14** This Venn diagram illustrates the number of students in a particular class who play hockey ($H$) and tennis ($T$).

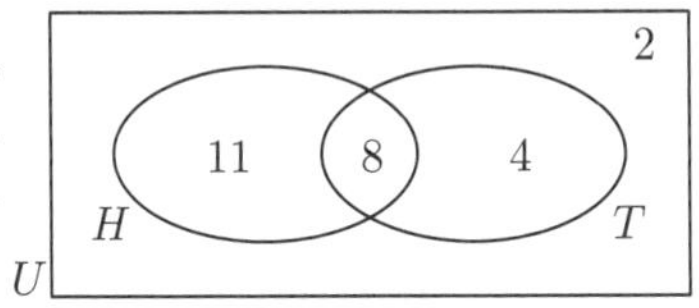


If a student from the class is picked at random, find the probability that he or she:

**a** plays hockey   **b** does not play tennis

**c** plays at least one of the two sports

**d** plays tennis if it is known that he or she plays hockey.

**15** In a class of 30 students, 17 have brown hair, 12 have blue eyes, and 4 have neither brown hair nor blue eyes.

**a** How many of the students have both brown hair and blue eyes?

**b** If a student is randomly selected, find the probability that the student:

**i** has blue eyes but not brown hair

**ii** has brown hair if it is known that he or she has blue eyes.

## SKILL BUILDER QUESTIONS (CALCULATORS)

**1** This table shows the distribution of marks for a spelling test.

| *Mark* | 4 | 5 | 6 | 7 | 8 | 9 | 10 |
|---|---|---|---|---|---|---|---|
| *Frequency* | 2 | 3 | 1 | 4 | 8 | 3 | 4 |

Calculate the mean mark.

**2** For each of the following sets of data, find the:

**i** mean **ii** median **iii** mode.

**a** 37, 43, 50, 50, 51, 55, 58, 59, 60

**b** 26, 23, 18, 21, 28, 30, 27, 21, 23, 21

**c**

| *Score* | *Frequency* |
|---|---|
| 7 | 15 |
| 8 | 23 |
| 9 | 16 |
| 10 | 11 |
| 11 | 8 |
| 12 | 7 |

**3**

| $x$ | 0 | 1 | 2 | 3 | 4 |
|---|---|---|---|---|---|
| *frequency* | 6 | 4 | 3 | $a$ | 2 |

Find the value of $a$ if $\overline{x} = 1.65$.

**4** Calculate the mean and standard deviation of the following sets of data:

**a** Birth weights of babies (in kg)

4.0 3.8 2.8 3.7 2.8 3.1 4.5 3.9
3.2 3.8 4.3 3.3 3.6 3.2 2.9 4.0

**b** Test scores

| *Score* | 10 | 12 | 15 | 16 | 17 | 18 | 19 | 20 |
|---|---|---|---|---|---|---|---|---|
| *Frequency* | 3 | 4 | 1 | 3 | 2 | 8 | 4 | 3 |

**c** Heights of basketballers

| *Height (cm)* | 178 | 180 | 182 | 184 | 186 | 188 | 190 |
|---|---|---|---|---|---|---|---|
| *Frequency* | 4 | 5 | 11 | 23 | 17 | 6 | 1 |

**d** Times to swim 50 metres backstroke

| *Time* (secs) | *Frequency* |
|---|---|
| $40 \leqslant t < 50$ | 3 |
| $50 \leqslant t < 60$ | 8 |
| $60 \leqslant t < 70$ | 13 |
| $70 \leqslant t < 80$ | 12 |
| $80 \leqslant t < 90$ | 4 |
| $90 \leqslant t < 100$ | 2 |

**5** A random sample of the distances of drives hit by a golfer was recorded in the table alongside:

Use the results in the table to answer the following questions:

| *Distance (m)* | *Frequency (f)* |
|---|---|
| $225 \leqslant d < 230$ | 1 |
| $230 \leqslant d < 235$ | 3 |
| $235 \leqslant d < 240$ | 5 |
| $240 \leqslant d < 245$ | 7 |
| $245 \leqslant d < 250$ | 3 |
| $250 \leqslant d < 255$ | 6 |
| $255 \leqslant d < 260$ | 4 |
| $260 \leqslant d < 265$ | 1 |

**a** How many drives were chosen in the sample?

**b** Construct a frequency histogram of the data using technology.

**c** Using technology, find estimates of the mean and median, and find the modal class of this sample. Use these answers to comment on the symmetry of the data.

**d** Construct a cumulative frequency table of the data.

**e** How many of the drives sampled travelled further than 235 metres?

**f** What percentage of the drives sampled travelled less than 250 metres?

**6** The mean average rainfall in Adelaide for October is 58 mm with a standard deviation of 4 mm. Over a 100 year period, assuming the rainfall distribution is normal, how many times would you expect there to be:

**a** more than 60 mm **b** between 50 mm and 60 mm

of rainfall in Adelaide during October?

**7** 38% of the students in a Year 12 IB Mathematics class are female. Of the female students in this class, 13% are left-handed whereas 24% of the male students are left-handed.

**a** Find the probability that a randomly chosen student from this class is left-handed.

**b** Find the probability that a randomly chosen student is female, given that the student is left-handed.

**8** Events $A$ and $B$ are independent.
Given that $\text{P}(A \cup B) = 0.63$ and $\text{P}(B) = 0.36$, find $\text{P}(A)$.

**9** Given that $\text{P}(A) = 0.46$, $\text{P}(B) = \frac{5}{7}$ and $\text{P}(A \cup B)' = \frac{1}{12}$, find $\text{P}(A \cap B)$.

**10** The mean contents of a certain brand of soft drink bottle is 310 mL with a standard deviation of 5 mL. Assuming the contents are normally distributed, find:

**a** the percentage of bottles which contain between 300 and 310 mL of drink

**b** the percentage of bottles which contain at least 304 mL of drink

**c** the probability that a randomly selected bottle contains less than 300 mL of drink.

**11** At a school sports carnival the mean distance for the discus throw was 40 m with a standard deviation of 8 m. Standardise the distances thrown by the students in the table.

| *Student* | *Distance* | $z$-score |
|---|---|---|
| Ashleigh | 44 m | |
| Bart | 32 m | |
| Carissa | 37 m | |
| David | 47 m | |
| Ethan | 53 m | |

**12** A student scored 80 for an English exam and 72 for a History exam. The class mean and standard deviation for English were 75 and 8 respectively, and for History were 60 and 15 respectively. In which subject did the student achieve a higher standard, and what percentage of others achieved higher marks in each subject?

**13** The marks obtained by some students in a mathematics test had mean $\mu$ and standard deviation $\sigma$. 12% of the students gained a mark greater than 90 but 20% of the students scored a mark less than 60.
Find $\mu$ and $\sigma$ correct to 1 decimal place.

**14** Ben scored 74 in his Chemistry exam. Alice scored 70 in her Mathematics exam.

**a** The scores in Chemistry were normally distributed with mean 70 and standard deviation 12. Find the proportion of students who scored 74 or greater.

**b** The scores in Mathematics were normally distributed with mean 65 and standard deviation 11. Find the proportion of students who scored 70 or greater.

**c** Can Ben or Alice claim to have performed better in their respective subjects? Explain your answer.

**d** What mark in Mathematics would be comparable to 74 in Chemistry?

**15** Four fifths of the residents in a particular street oppose the construction of traffic lights at the end of the street. One of the residents decides to carry out a formal survey and randomly samples 20 people who live in the street. Find the probability that:

**a** exactly 16 residents **b** 16 or more residents

oppose the construction of the lights.

**16** Robert takes a multiple choice test. There are 15 questions and each question has four alternative answers. The pass mark is 8, and Robert must score 10 or better in order to achieve an A in the subject overall.

Robert is confident that he knows the answer to 5 of the questions, but he has to guess the remainder of the answers.

Assuming that Robert does correctly answer the 5 questions that he is confident about, determine the probability that he will:

**a** fail the test

**b** answer exactly 8 out of 15 correctly

**c** achieve an A in the subject.

**17** A radar speed detection device is used to measure the speed of approaching vehicles. It is found to produce normally distributed errors with mean zero and standard deviation 1 $\text{km h}^{-1}$.

**a** Find the probability that a speed registered is no more than 1 $\text{km h}^{-1}$ higher than the actual speed.

**b** Find the probability that a speed registered is within 0.5 $\text{km h}^{-1}$ of the actual speed.

**c** If this device measures 850 speeds on a certain day, how many would you expect to exceed the actual speeds by more than 2 $\text{km h}^{-1}$?

**18** The lengths in centimetres of a certain species of fish are described by the variable $X \sim \text{N}(40,\ 5^2)$, where the mean is 40 cm and the standard deviation is 5 cm.

**a** Find the probability that a fish is longer than 45 cm.

**b** Find the probability that a fish is between 35 and 50 cm long.

**c** Determine the minimum length of the longest 10% of this species of fish.

**19** A machine fills bottles with tomato sauce. Each bottle is filled independently of all other bottles. The volume of sauce in each bottle is normally distributed with mean 500 mL and standard deviation 2.5 mL. Bottles are deemed to require extra sauce if the machine delivers less than 495 mL.

**a** Calculate the probability that a randomly selected bottle requires extra sauce.

**b** For a day in which 1000 bottles are produced, calculate:

**i** the expected number of bottles that require extra sauce

**ii** the expected total cost of the extra sauce if it costs an extra 4 cents for each bottle when extra sauce is given.

**20** During sleep, the reduction of a person's oxygen consumption has a normal distribution with a mean of 38.4 millilitres per minute ($\text{mL min}^{-1}$) and a standard deviation of 4.6 $\text{mL min}^{-1}$. Determine the probability that during sleep a person's oxygen consumption will be reduced by:

**a** more than 43.5 $\text{mL min}^{-1}$

**b** at most 36.4 $\text{mL min}^{-1}$

**c** anywhere from 30 to 40 $\text{mL min}^{-1}$.

**d** If 90% of people reduce their oxygen consumption by more than $k$ $\text{mL min}^{-1}$, determine $k$.

**21** The continuous random variable $X$ is normally distributed with $\text{P}(X < 56) = 0.8$.

**a** How many standard deviations from the mean is a score of 56?

**b** If the standard deviation of $X$ is 4, find the mean of the distribution. Give your answer correct to one decimal place.

**22** Containers of a particular brand of ice cream have a capacity of 1050 mL. They are advertised as containing 1 litre of ice cream. If the quantity is normally distributed with a mean of 1020 mL and a standard deviation of 15 mL, determine:

**a** the probability that the container has less than the advertised capacity

**b** the percentage of containers that overflow

**c** the number from a sample of 1500 that you would expect to contain between 1 litre and 1.03 litres.

**23** For a student to pass a particular course they must pass at least 8 of 10 tests. For each test the probability of the student passing is 0.88. Determine the probability that the student:

**a** passes exactly 8 of the 10 tests

**b** passes the course.

**24** 5% of all items coming off a production line are defective. The manufacturer packages his items in boxes of six and guarantees "double your money back" if more than two items in a box are defective. On what percentage of the boxes will the manufacturer have to pay double money back?

**25** A tinned food company examined a sample of its corn and pineapple tins for defects. The results are summarised in the table below.

| | *Defective* | *Not defective* |
|---|---|---|
| *Corn* | 37 | 581 |
| *Pineapple* | 24 | 617 |

**a** How many tins were included in the sample?

**b** Estimate the probability that the next randomly selected tin:

**i** is a pineapple tin **ii** is defective

**iii** is a corn tin given it is defective

**iv** is defective given it is a corn tin.

**26** A hospital recorded the age and sex of its melanoma patients over one year. The data is shown alongside.

| | $< 50$ | $\geqslant 50$ |
|---|---|---|
| *Male* | 136 | 469 |
| *Female* | 155 | 310 |

**a** How many melanoma patients were treated at the hospital that year?

**b** Find the probability that a randomly selected melanoma patient:

**i** was male **ii** was younger than 50

**iii** was male, given they were 50 years or older

**iv** was 50 years or older, given they were female.

**27** A penicillin injection causes an allergic reaction in one out of ten people. Find the probability that fewer than 470 reactions will occur among 5000 people injected with penicillin.

**28** The lengths of wooden chopsticks produced by a machine are normally distributed with a standard deviation of 0.5 cm. It is found that 1% of all these chopsticks are less than 24 cm long. Find the mean length of the chopsticks produced by the machine.

**29** The lengths of steel rods cut by a machine are normally distributed with mean 13.8 cm. It is found that 1.5% of all rods are less than 13.2 cm long. Find the standard deviation of rod lengths produced by this machine.

**30** Consider the probability distribution function defined by $\text{P}(X = x) = \frac{1}{24}(x + 6)$ for $x \in \{1,\ 2,\ 3\}$.

**a** Find $\text{P}(x)$ for $x = 1$, 2 and 3.

**b** Find the mean value of $X$.

**31** Josephine's number of safe hits at each softball match has the probability distribution opposite.

| $x$ | 0 | 1 | 2 | 3 |
|---|---|---|---|---|
| $P(x)$ | 0.05 | $k$ | 0.5 | 0.3 |

Find:

**a** the value of $k$

**b** Josephine's expected average number of safe hits in a game.

**32** The table alongside shows the probability distribution for $X$.

| $x$ | 0 | 1 | 2 | 3 |
|---|---|---|---|---|
| $P(X = x)$ | 0.3 | 0.2 | 0.15 | 0.35 |

Calculate $E(X)$, the mean value of $X$.

**33** A salesman contacts eight randomly selected people in the hope of selling them units in a property trust. History shows that the probability of him making a sale is 0.4.

**a** What is the random variable being studied here?

**b** List all possible values that this variable could take.

**c** Draw an accurate distribution of the possible results and describe its shape. How would the shape of the distribution change if the number of people contacted was increased?

**d** **i** Find the probability that he makes exactly five sales.

**ii** Find the probability that he makes at least two sales.

**e** The salesman makes \$100 commission per sale plus a special bonus of \$30 for every sale after the second. The cost involved in the exercise is \$200. Find the probability that he makes a profit of \$450 or greater.

**34** If $P(X) = 0.8$, $P(Y) = 0.6$ and $X$ and $Y$ are independent events, determine the probability of the occurrence of:

**a** both $X$ and $Y$ **b** $X$ or $Y$ but not both $X$ and $Y$

**c** $X$ given that $Y$ did not occur **d** neither $X$ nor $Y$.

**35** Given $X \sim N(13, \sigma^2)$ and $P(X \leqslant 15) = 0.613$, find $\sigma$.

**36** Suppose $X$ is normally distributed with $P(X \leqslant 24) = 0.035$ and $P(X \geqslant 33) = 0.262$.

Find the mean and standard deviation of $X$ correct to 3 significant figures.

## TOPIC 7: CALCULUS

### LIMITS

If $f(x)$ can be made as close as we like to some real number $A$ by making $x$ sufficiently close to $a$, we say that $f(x)$ approaches a **limit** as $x$ approaches $a$, and we write $\lim_{x \to a} f(x) = A$.

We say that as $x$ approaches $a$, $f(x)$ **converges** to $A$.

We can use the idea of limits as $x \to \pm\infty$ and as $f(x) \to \pm\infty$ to find asymptotes.

For example, if $f(x)$ and $g(x)$ are polynomials then for the rational function $F(x) = \dfrac{f(x)}{g(x)}$:

- $f(x) = 0$ gives the $x$-intercepts
- $F(0)$ gives the $y$-intercept
- $g(x) = 0$ gives the equations of vertical asymptotes
- if degree of $f <$ degree of $g$, the horizontal asymptote is $y = 0$
- if degree of $f =$ degree of $g$, the horizontal asymptote is $y = a$ where $a$ is the quotient of $\dfrac{f(x)}{g(x)}$.

A graph will never cross its vertical asymptotes, but may cross its horizontal asymptotes.

**The tangent to a curve**

The **instantaneous rate of change** of a variable at a particular instant is given by the gradient of the tangent to the graph at that point.

### DIFFERENTIATION

The **derivative function** is $f'(x) = \lim_{h \to 0} \dfrac{f(x+h) - f(x)}{h}$.

It provides the gradient of $f(x)$ or the rate of change of $f$ with respect to $x$. $f'(x)$ also gives the gradient of the tangent to $y = f(x)$ for any value of $x$.

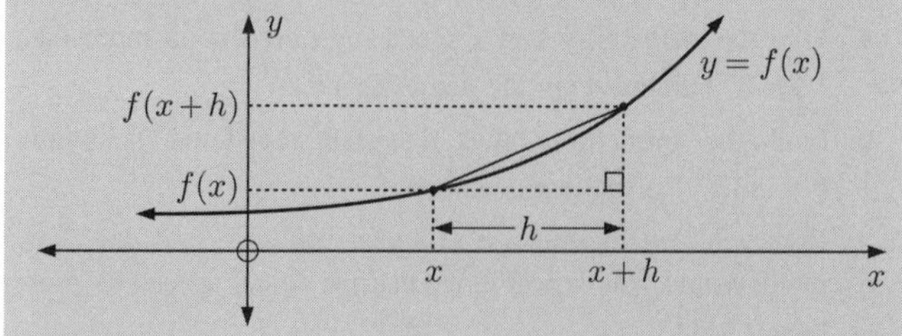


When we use the limit definition to find a derivative, we call this the **method of first principles**.

| $f(x)$ | $f'(x)$ | *Name of rule* |
|---|---|---|
| $c$ | $0$ | |
| $x^n$ | $nx^{n-1}$ | |
| $cu(x)$ | $cu'(x)$ | |
| $u(x)+v(x)$ | $u'(x)+v'(x)$ | addition rule |
| $u(x)v(x)$ | $u'(x)v(x)+u(x)v'(x)$ | product rule |
| $\dfrac{u(x)}{v(x)}$ | $\dfrac{u'(x)v(x)-u(x)v'(x)}{[v(x)]^2}$ | quotient rule |
| $e^{f(x)}$ | $e^{f(x)}f'(x)$ | exponentials |
| $\ln f(x)$ | $\dfrac{f'(x)}{f(x)}$ | logarithms |
| $\sin x$ | $\cos x$ | |
| $\cos x$ | $-\sin x$ | trigonometric functions |
| $\tan x$ | $\dfrac{1}{\cos^2 x}$ | |

**Chain rule**

If $y = g(u)$ where $u = f(x)$ then $\dfrac{dy}{dx} = \dfrac{dy}{du}\dfrac{du}{dx}$.

**Tangents and normals**

For the curve $y = f(x)$, the gradient of the **tangent** at $x = a$ is $m_T = f'(a)$.

The equation of the tangent to the curve at the point $A(a, b)$ is $\dfrac{y-b}{x-a} = f'(a)$.

The gradient of the **normal** at $x = a$ is $m_N = -\dfrac{1}{f'(a)}$.

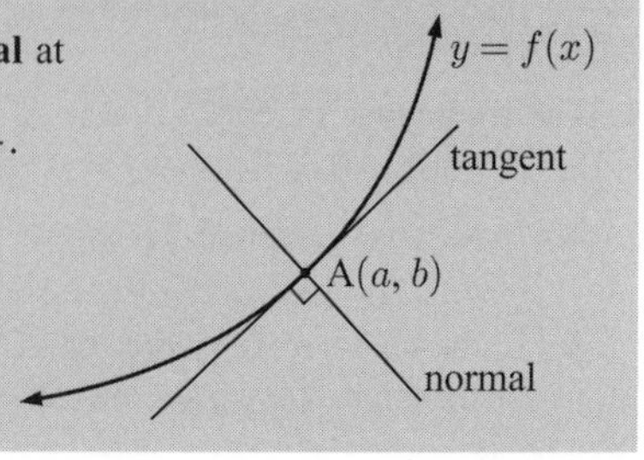

**Second derivative**

The second derivative of the function $f(x)$ is the derivative of $f'(x)$.

$$f''(x) = \frac{d}{dx}(f'(x))$$

**Rates of change**

$\frac{dy}{dx}$ gives the rate of change in $y$ with respect to $x$.

If $\frac{dy}{dx}$ is positive, then as $x$ increases, $y$ also increases.

If $\frac{dy}{dx}$ is negative, then as $x$ increases, $y$ decreases.

## KINEMATIC PROBLEMS

An object moves along a straight line. Its position from the origin at time $t$ is given by a displacement function $s(t)$.

Its instantaneous velocity is given by $v = \frac{ds}{dt}$,

and its instantaneous acceleration by $a = \frac{d^2s}{dt^2}$ or $a = v\frac{dv}{ds}$.

You should understand the difference between *instantaneous* velocity or acceleration, and *average* velocity or acceleration over a time period.

You should also understand the physical meaning of the different combinations of signs of velocity and acceleration.

**Signs of $s(t)$:**

| $s(t)$ | *Interpretation* |
|---|---|
| $= 0$ | P is at O |
| $> 0$ | P is located to the right of O |
| $< 0$ | P is located to the left of O |

**Signs of $v(t)$:**

| $v(t)$ | *Interpretation* |
|---|---|
| $= 0$ | P is instantaneously at rest |
| $> 0$ | P is moving to the right |
| $< 0$ | P is moving to the left |

**Signs of $a(t)$:**

| $a(t)$ | *Interpretation* |
|---|---|
| $> 0$ | velocity is increasing |
| $< 0$ | velocity is decreasing |
| $= 0$ | velocity may be a max. or min. |

The **speed** at any instant is the magnitude of the object's velocity. If $S(t)$ represents the speed then $S = |v|$.

If the signs of $v(t)$ and $a(t)$ are the same then the speed of the object is increasing.

If the signs of $v(t)$ and $a(t)$ are different then the speed of the object is decreasing.

## PROPERTIES OF CURVES

$f(x)$ is **increasing** on an interval $S$ $\Leftrightarrow$ $f(a) < f(b)$ for all $a, b \in S$ such that $a < b$.

$f(x)$ is increasing on $S \Leftrightarrow f'(x) \geqslant 0$ for all $x$ in $S$.

$f(x)$ is **decreasing** on $S$ $\Leftrightarrow$ $f(a) > f(b)$ for all $a, b \in S$ such that $a < b$.

$f(x)$ is decreasing on $S \Leftrightarrow f'(x) \leqslant 0$ for all $x$ in $S$.

Functions which have the same behaviour for all $x \in \mathbb{R}$ are called **monotone increasing** or **monotone decreasing**.

A **stationary point** of a function is a point such that $f'(x) = 0$.

You should be able to identify and explain the significance of local and global maxima and minima, and inflections both horizontal and non-horizontal.

| **Stationary point** | **Sign diagram of $f'(x)$ near $x = a$** | **Shape of curve near $x = a$** |
|---|---|---|
| local maximum | $+$ \| $-$ (at $a$, axis $x$) | 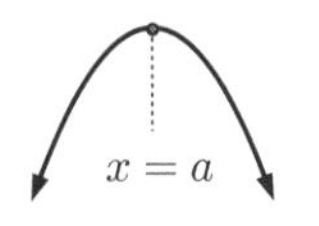 |
| local minimum | $-$ \| $+$ (at $a$, axis $x$) | 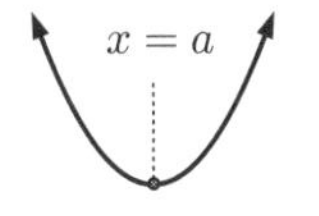 |
| horizontal inflection | $+$ \| $+$ (at $a$, axis $x$) *or* $-$ \| $-$ (at $a$, axis $x$) | 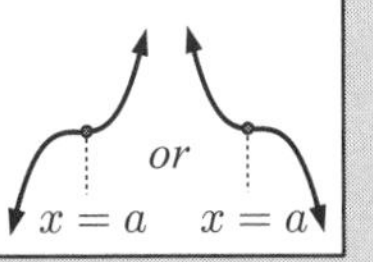 |

There is a **point of inflection** at $x = a$ if $f''(a) = 0$ **and** the sign of $f''(x)$ changes on either side of $x = a$. It corresponds to a change in *shape* of the curve.

If the tangent at a point of inflection is horizontal, we say we have a **horizontal** or **stationary inflection**.

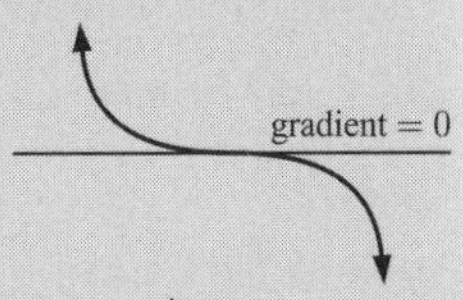


If the tangent at a point of inflection is *not* horizontal, we say we have a **non-horizontal** or **non-stationary inflection**.

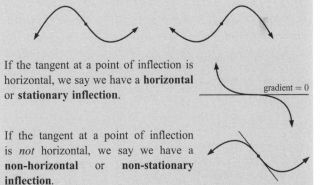

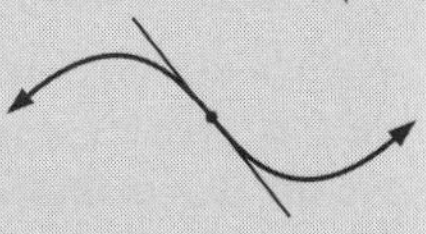

If $f''(x) \leqslant 0$ for all $x \in S$, the curve is **concave downwards** on the interval $S$.

If $f''(x) \geqslant 0$ for all $x \in S$, the curve is **concave upwards** on the interval $S$.

## OPTIMISATION PROBLEMS

It is important to remember that a local minimum or maximum does not always give the minimum or maximum value of the function in a particular domain. You must check for other turning points in the domain and whether the end values of the domain give higher or lower values.

**Optimisation problem solving method**

1. Draw a large, clear diagram of the situation.
2. Construct an equation with the variable to be optimised as the subject. It should be written in terms of **one** other variable such as $x$.
   Write down any restrictions on the value of $x$.
3. Find the first derivative of the formula, and the values of $x$ which make it zero.
4. Show, using a sign diagram or second derivative test, that you have a maximum or minimum stationary point. Test the stationary points and end points of the domain to find the optimal solution.

Consider the graph:

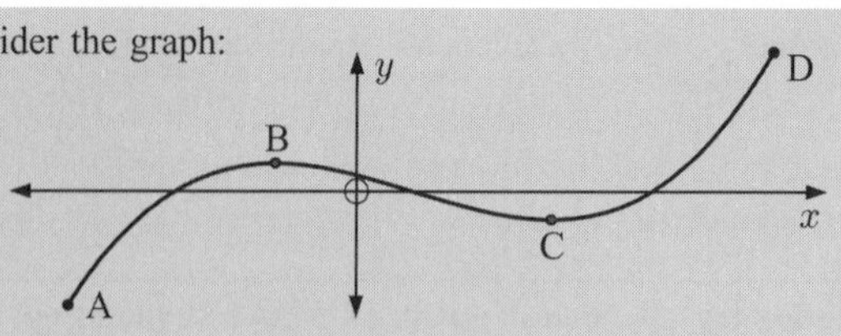


A is a **global minimum** as it is the minimum value of $y$ anywhere on the domain.
B is a **local maximum** as $f'(x) = 0$ and the curve is concave downwards at that point.
C is a **local minimum** as $f'(x) = 0$ and the curve is concave upwards at that point.
D is a **global maximum** as it is the maximum value of $y$ anywhere on the domain.

## INTEGRATION

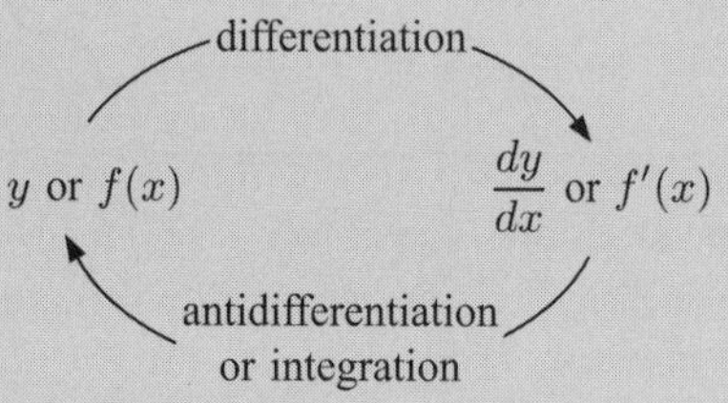


If $F(x)$ is a function where $F'(x) = f(x)$, then $F(x)$ is the **antiderivative** of $f(x)$.

**Fundamental theorem of calculus**

For a continuous function $f(x)$ with antiderivative $F(x)$, $\int_a^b f(x)\,dx = F(b) - F(a)$.

**Area under a curve**

You should be able to use the idea of **upper** and **lower rectangles** to approximate the area under a curve.

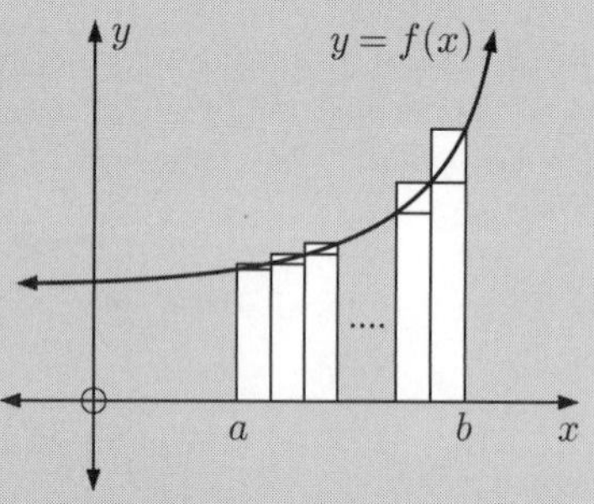


You should know the difference between a definite integral and the area under a curve, but also how they are related.

If $f(x)$ is a continuous *positive* function on the interval $a \leqslant x \leqslant b$ then the area under the curve between $x = a$ and $x = b$ is $\int_a^b f(x)\,dx$.

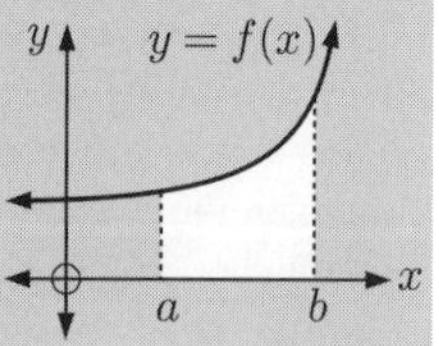


To find the total area enclosed by $y = f(x)$ and the $x$-axis between $x = a$ and $x = b$, we need to be careful about where $f(x) < 0$.

On an interval $c \leqslant x \leqslant d$ where $f(x) < 0$, the area is $-\int_c^d f(x)\,dx$.

For example:

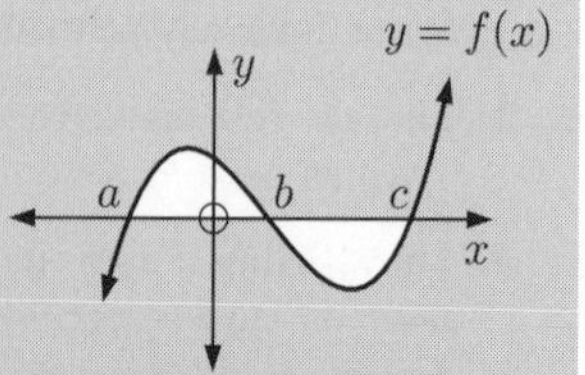


The total shaded area

$= \int_a^b f(x)\,dx - \int_b^c f(x)\,dx$

$\neq \int_a^c f(x)\,dx$.

The area *between* two functions is given by

$$A = \int_a^b (y_U - y_L)\,dx$$

where $y_U \geqslant y_L$ on the domain $a \leqslant x \leqslant b$.

**Indefinite integrals**

When performing an indefinite integral, we use the rules for differentiation in reverse. Do not forget to include the **constant of integration**.

If $F'(x) = f(x)$ then $\int f(x)\,dx = F(x) + c$.

$\int f(x)\,dx$ is the **indefinite integral** of $f(x)$ with respect to $x$.

| *Function* | *Integral* |
|---|---|
| $k$ | $kx + c$ |
| $x^n$ | $\dfrac{x^{n+1}}{n+1} + c, \ n \neq -1$ |
| $e^x$ | $e^x + c$ |
| $\dfrac{1}{x}$ | $\ln x + c, \ x > 0$ |
| $e^{ax+b}$ | $\dfrac{1}{a}e^{ax+b} + c$ |
| $(ax+b)^n$ | $\dfrac{(ax+b)^{n+1}}{a(n+1)} + c, \ n \neq -1$ |
| $\dfrac{1}{ax+b}$ | $\dfrac{1}{a}\ln(ax+b), \ ax+b > 0$ |
| $\cos(ax+b)$ | $\dfrac{1}{a}\sin(ax+b) + c$ |
| $\sin(ax+b)$ | $-\dfrac{1}{a}\cos(ax+b) + c$ |

Trigonometric identities are often useful for integration, in particular:

- $\cos^2 x = \frac{1}{2} + \frac{1}{2}\cos 2x$
- $\sin^2 x = \frac{1}{2} - \frac{1}{2}\cos 2x$

**Definite integrals**

- $\int_a^a f(x)\,dx = 0$
- $\int_b^a f(x)\,dx = -\int_a^b f(x)\,dx$
- $\int_a^b f(x)\,dx + \int_b^c f(x)\,dx = \int_a^c f(x)\,dx$
- $\int_a^b cf(x)\,dx = c\int_a^b f(x)\,dx$
- $\int_a^b [f(x) \pm g(x)]\,dx = \int_a^b f(x)\,dx \pm \int_a^b g(x)\,dx$

**Motion in a straight line**

The displacement function is determined by the integral $s(t) = \int v(t)\,dt$.

To find the total distance travelled given $v(t) = s'(t)$ on $a \leqslant t \leqslant b$, we:

- draw a sign diagram for $v(t)$ so we can determine when any changes in direction occur
- determine $s(t)$ by integration
- find $s(a)$, $s(b)$, and $s(t)$ at each time the direction changes
- draw a motion diagram
- determine the total distance travelled from the motion diagram.

## SOLIDS OF REVOLUTION

When the region enclosed by $y = f(x)$, the $x$-axis, and the vertical lines $x = a$, $x = b$ is rotated about the $x$-axis to generate a solid, the volume of the solid is given by

$V = \pi \int_a^b y^2 dx$

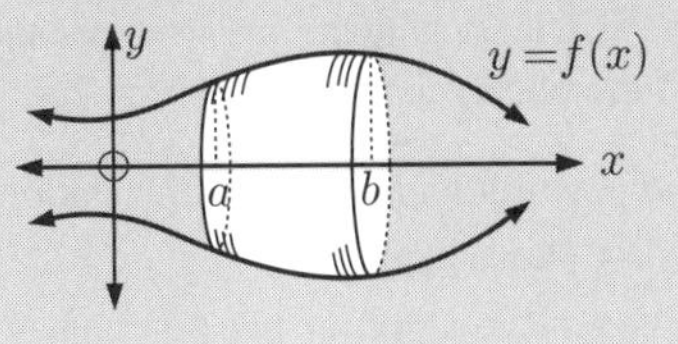


## SKILL BUILDER QUESTIONS (NO CALCULATORS)

**1** The derivative of $f(x)$ is defined by

$$f'(x) = \lim_{h \to 0} \frac{f(x+h) - f(x)}{h}.$$

Use this definition to find $f'(x)$ for $f(x) = 7x - x^2$.

**2** Find $\dfrac{dy}{dx}$ for:

**a** $y = \dfrac{3x+1}{\sqrt{x}}$ **b** $y = \dfrac{1}{x^4+9}$ **c** $y = x^2\sqrt{1-x^2}$

**3** Differentiate with respect to $x$:

**a** $(2x+3)^5$ **b** $\sqrt{x^2+x+1}$

**4** For the first 6 seconds of its motion, a particle moving in a straight line has velocity given by $v = t^3 - 9t^2 + 24t$ m s$^{-1}$, where $t$ is the time in seconds. Find the greatest velocity of the particle in this time.

**5** A man standing on a cliff above the ocean throws a ball high in the air. The height of the ball above the water $t$ seconds after release is given by $h(t) = 100 + 32t - 4t^2$ m.
How high above the water will the ball reach?

**6** Find, with reasons, the greatest and least values of the function $f(x) = x^3 - 2x^2$ on the interval $-1 \leqslant x \leqslant 1$.

**7** Show that the curves whose equations are $y = \sqrt{3x+1}$ and $y = \sqrt{5x - x^2}$ have the same gradient at their intersection point. Find the equation of the common tangent at this point.

**8** Find the equation of the tangent to the curve $y = x^3 - 5$ at the point $(1, -4)$. Where does this tangent cut the $x$-axis?

**9** A manufacturer makes a batch of $N$ articles, the cost of each being $N^2 - 6N + 35$ cents. If he sells each article for 50 cents, find an expression representing his profit, $P$ cents, for the entire batch. How many articles should be in the batch to maximise $P$? Is it true that $P$ is greatest when the cost *per article* is least?

**10** Find, from first principles, the derivative of $y = -2x^3 + 3x^2 - 1$.

**11** Find $\dfrac{dy}{dx}$ for: **a** $y = \dfrac{1-2x}{\sqrt[3]{x}}$ **b** $y = 2x(1+2x)^4$

**12** Find $\dfrac{d^2y}{dx^2}$ for: **a** $y = \dfrac{3}{x^2}$ **b** $y = x^2 \sin 3x$

**13** Find the equation of the tangent to $f(x) = \dfrac{x-4}{x+2}$ at the point where $x = 3$.

**14** Find the equation of the normal to $y = x^2 - 2x - 4$ at the point where $x = -1$.

**15** Find where the tangent to $y = x^3 + 2x + 1$ at the point where $x = -1$ meets the curve again.

**16** A particle moves in a straight line with displacement function $s(t) = 12t - 3t^3 + 1$ cm where $t \geqslant 0$ is in seconds.

**a** Find the velocity and acceleration functions for the particle's movement.

**b** When is the particle's:

**i** speed decreasing **ii** velocity decreasing?

**17** Differentiate with respect to $x$:

**a** $(2+x)\sqrt{3-x}$ **b** $\left(x + \dfrac{1}{x}\right)^4$

**18** **a** Sketch the graph of $y = x(x^2 - 12x + 45)$, indicating the turning points and their coordinates.

**b** For what range of values of $a$ does the equation $x^3 - 12x^2 + 45x - a = 0$ have three distinct real roots?

**19** Find intervals where the function $f(x) = x^3 - 3x^2 - 9x + 5$ is:

**a** increasing **b** concave up.

**20** **a** Find the derivatives with respect to $x$ of:

**i** $\dfrac{x}{e^x}$ **ii** $x^2 e^{-(x+2)}$ **iii** $\dfrac{e^{2x}+1}{e^{2x}-1}$

**b** Without simplifying, find $\int (x^2 + e^{2x+1})\, dx$.

**21** Consider the polynomial $p(x) = x^3 + ax^2 + b$.

**a** Show that $p(x)$ has a stationary point at $x = 0$.

**b** If $p(x)$ also has a stationary point at $(-2, 6)$, find the values of $a$ and $b$, and the nature of both stationary points.

**c** If the second stationary point of $p(x)$ is at $(h, k)$ with $h \neq 0$, show that $a = -\frac{3}{2}h$ and $b = k + \frac{1}{2}h^3$.

**22** Find the equation of the normal to the curve $y = x^2$ at the point P(2, 4). At what other point does this normal intersect the curve $y = x^2$?

**23** The area of the figure shown is given by $A = xy + (0.6)x^2$.
If its perimeter is fixed at 48 m, express $y$ in terms of $x$.
Hence find the maximum possible area of the figure.

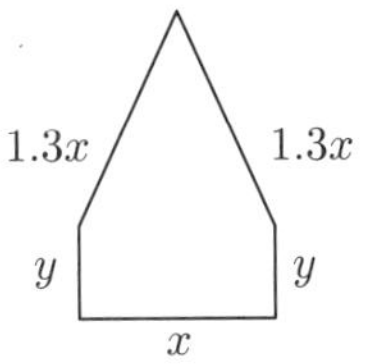


**24** Find the equation of the normal to the curve $y = \dfrac{8}{x^2}$ at the point where $x = 2$.

**25** The diagram below shows an *open* trough in which the cross-section is an isosceles right-angled triangle. The total outside surface area is fixed at 27 square metres.

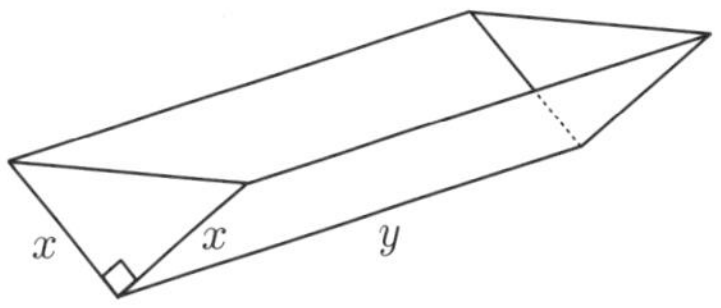


**a** By considering the total outside surface area of the trough, show that $x^2 + 2xy = 27$.

**b** Find an expression for the volume $V$ of the trough in terms of $x$ only.

**c** Hence show that the dimensions of the trough which yield the maximum volume are $x = y = 3$ metres.

**26** Obtain $\dfrac{dy}{dx}$ for $y = \sqrt{1+x}$.

**27** On the graph of $y = f(x)$ shown, A and B are stationary points, and C is a point of inflection.

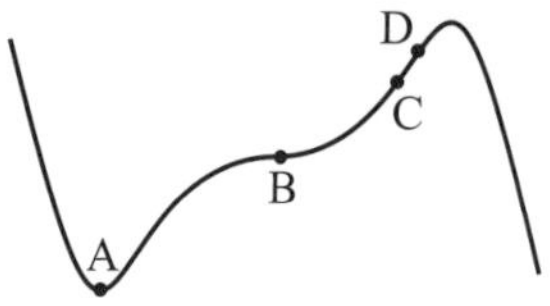


For each of the points A, B, C, and D, state whether each of $f'(x)$ and $f''(x)$ is zero, positive, or negative.

**28** Consider $f(x) = x + 5 + \dfrac{4}{x}$.

**a** Find the zeros of $f(x)$.

**b** Find the stationary points of $y = f(x)$ and their nature.

**c** Sketch the graph of $y = f(x)$, clearly labelling the information in **a** and **b** above.

**29** **a** Write down the derivative with respect to $x$ of:

**i** $f(x) = \ln x$ **ii** $F(x) = x \ln x - x$.

What is the relationship between $f(x)$ and $F(x)$?

**b** Sketch the graph of the curve $C$ whose equation is $y = \ln x$. Let O be the origin, and let P be a point on $C$ with $x$-coordinate $t$, $1 < t \leqslant e$.

**i** Show that the area bounded by [OP], the curve $C$, and the $x$-axis, is $t - \frac{1}{2} t \ln t - 1$ units$^2$. For what values of $t$ will this area be maximised?

**ii** Write down the equation of the tangent to the curve $C$ at the point P$(t, \ln t)$. Find the condition on $t$ for this tangent to pass through the origin.

**30** An offshore oil rig is at point R, 8 km from a straight shore. The point P is on the shore directly opposite the rig. A refinery is on the shore at S which is 11 km from P.

A pipeline is to be constructed under the sea from R to reach the shore at the point Q. From Q a pipeline is to be taken overland to S. The cost of the pipeline is \$5 million per km under the sea and \$3 million per km overland.

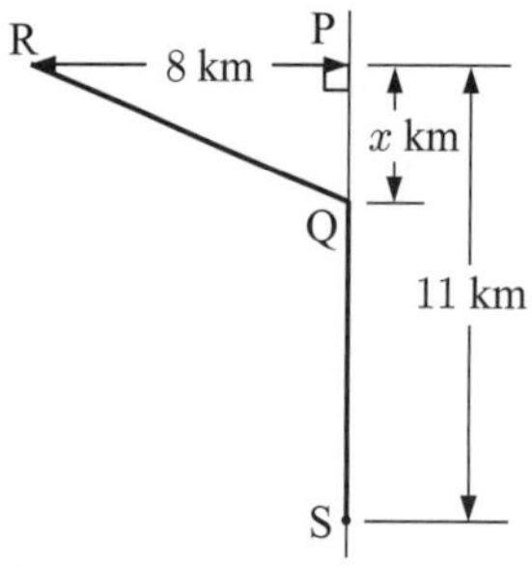


If Q is $x$ km from P, show that the cost to construct the pipeline from R to S is

$C(x) = 5\sqrt{x^2 + 64} + 33 - 3x$ million dollars.

What is the minimum cost of the pipeline?

**31** OAB is a triangle with a right angle at O. OA = 2 cm and OB = 4 cm. OPQR is a rectangle as shown, with OP = $x$ cm.

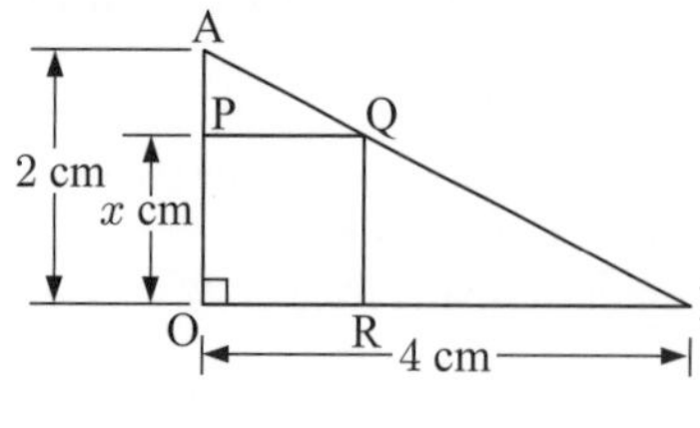


Show that the area of OPQR is equal to $4x - 2x^2$ cm$^2$.

Hence, or otherwise, find the value of $x$ for which the area of the rectangle is a maximum.

**32**

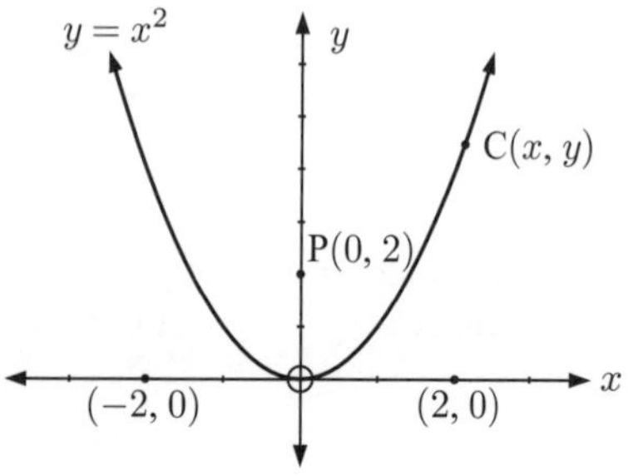


A comet travels in an orbit which can be described by the equation $y = x^2$ as shown in the diagram.

**a** Show that the distance of the comet at C$(x, y)$ from an observer at the point P$(0, 2)$ is given by

$s(x) = \sqrt{x^4 - 3x^2 + 4}$.

**b** Find the least and the greatest distance between the comet and the observer for $-2 \leqslant x \leqslant 2$.

**33** Find the position and nature of the stationary points of $y = 3x^4 + 16x^3 + 24x^2 + 1$.

Hence sketch the graph of the function.

**34** A manufacturer has a factory capable of producing up to 150 chairs a week. The cost of the materials and labour needed to produce $x$ chairs is $(26x + x^{\frac{3}{2}})$ dollars, where $x > 0$. Fixed weekly costs including rent and insurance total \$500.

Suppose $x$ chairs are made and sold each week and the selling price of *each* chair is $\left(44 + \dfrac{600}{x}\right)$ dollars.

**a** Show that the manufacturer's weekly profit is

$P(x) = -x^{\frac{3}{2}} + 18x + 100$ dollars.

**b** How many chairs should be made and sold each week to maximise the profit?

**c** What is the maximum weekly profit?

**35** Terry wants to fence off a rectangular garden plot of area 48 m$^2$. Three sides will be fenced with strong wire mesh costing \$18 per metre, and the remaining side will be fenced with corrugated iron costing \$30 per metre.

**a** By letting $x$ be the length in metres of the side fenced with corrugated iron, show that the cost of fencing is

$C = 48\left(\dfrac{36}{x} + x\right)$ dollars.

**b** Find the dimensions of the garden plot which will minimise the cost of fencing.

**36** **a** For the graph of $y = 4x^3 - 3x^4$ find:

**i** the intercepts on the axes

**ii** the coordinates and nature of the stationary points

**iii** the coordinates of the non-stationary point of inflection.

Sketch the graph of $y = 4x^3 - 3x^4$ showing this information.

**b** Find values of $k$ for which the equation $4x^3 - 3x^4 = k$ has exactly two distinct positive solutions.

**37** Find $\dfrac{dy}{dx}$ for:

**a** $y = x \ln(x + 1)$, $x > -1$ **b** $y = x \ln x^2$, $x > 0$

**c** $y = \dfrac{e^{2x}}{2x + 1}$, $x \neq -\frac{1}{2}$

**38** Show that if $f(x) = \ln\left(\dfrac{1 - 2x}{x^2 + 2}\right)$, then

$f'(x) = \dfrac{2x^2 - 2x - 4}{(1 - 2x)(x^2 + 2)}$.

On what intervals is $f(x)$ decreasing?

**39** Find $\dfrac{dy}{dx}$ for:

**a** $y = xe^{4x}$ **b** $y = \dfrac{x^3 + 2}{\sqrt{x - 3}}$, $x > 3$

**c** $y = \dfrac{e^{5x}}{x^2 + 1}$ **d** $y = \ln\left(\dfrac{x - 4}{x^2 + 4}\right)$, $x > 4$

**40** $f(x) = 1 - \dfrac{4x}{x^2+4}$

**a** Find the axes intercepts.

**b** Find the position and nature of the stationary points of the graph of $f(x)$.

**c** Sketch the graph of $y = f(x)$. Clearly show the information found above.

**41** An ornamental pond of area $A$ is to be built with straight sides and semi-circular ends as shown. The cost of tiling per unit length is 25% more along the rounded ends than along the straight walls. Show that the total cost of tiling the walls is least when the shaded area is $\frac{2}{3}A$.

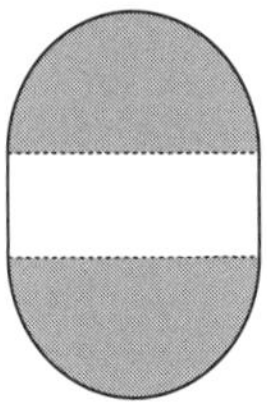

**42** For the function shown, find:

**a** $\int_2^5 f(x)\,dx$

**b** $\int_5^8 f(x)\,dx$

**c** $\int_2^8 f(x)\,dx$

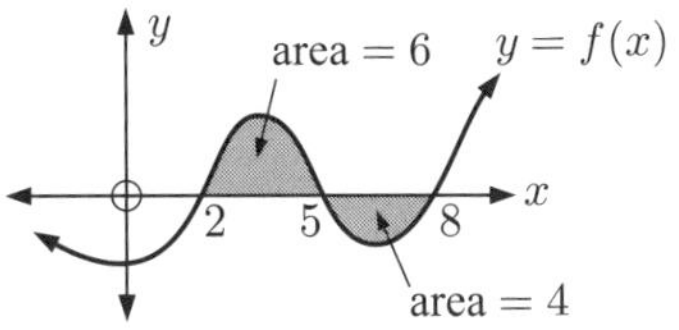


**43** Given that

$\int_0^a f(x)\,dx = 4,$

find $a$.

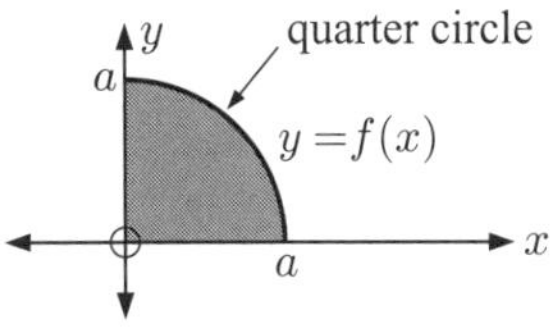


**44** Find the integrals:

**a** $\int (2x^2 + x - 3)\,dx$

**b** $\int_0^1 \sqrt{5x+4}\,dx$

**c** $\int (x + \dfrac{1}{x})^2\,dx.$

**45** A particle undergoing straight line motion has velocity

$v = \dfrac{10}{\sqrt{5t+4}}$ m s$^{-1}$ at time $t$ seconds, $t \geqslant 0$.

**a** If its position at time $t = 0$ is $s = 0$, find its position at time $t$.

**b** What is the acceleration at time $t$?

**46** If $f(x) = x(3-2x)^{\frac{1}{2}}$, find $f'(x)$, and write your answer in the form $\dfrac{k(1-x)}{(3-2x)^{\frac{1}{2}}}$. Hence, find $\displaystyle\int \frac{x-1}{(3-2x)^{\frac{1}{2}}}\,dx.$

**47** Find:

**a** $\displaystyle\int \frac{2x^2 - x - 3}{x^2}\,dx$

**b** $\displaystyle\int_1^5 \frac{2x^3+1}{x^2}\,dx$

**c** $\int \sin^2 3x\,dx$

**48** Find the area of the region lying below the parabola $y = 1 - x^2$ and above the line $y = -3$.

**49** If $y = x\sqrt{4-x}$, find $\dfrac{dy}{dx}$ and simplify your answer.

Hence, evaluate $\displaystyle\int_0^2 \frac{8-3x}{\sqrt{4-x}}\,dx.$

**50** Consider the graph of $f(x) = x^3 - x^2 - 4x + 4$.

**a** Find $\int_{-2}^2 f(x)\,dx$.

**b** Does the value obtained in **a** represent the shaded area?

Explain your answer.

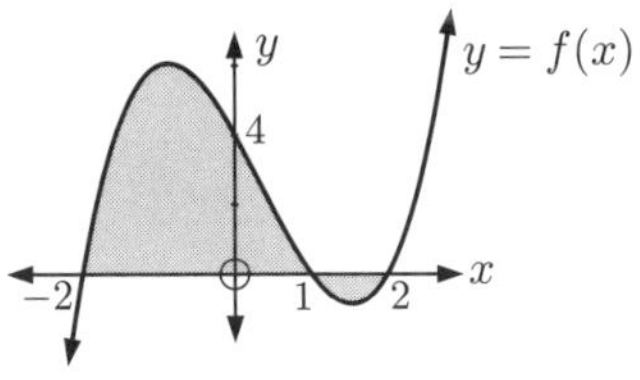


**51** Find the exact value of $\displaystyle\int_0^4 \frac{1}{\sqrt{x+4}}\,dx.$

**52** By considering $\dfrac{d}{dx}(x^2 \ln x)$, find $\int x \ln x\,dx.$

**53** A particle moves on a straight line with acceleration given by $2 - 3t$ m s$^{-2}$.

**a** Express its distance $s$ m from point O in terms of $t$, given that $s = 3$ when $t = 0$, and that the particle is momentarily at rest when $t = 1$ s.

**b** At what other time is the particle's velocity zero?

**54** Calculate the area enclosed by the curves whose equations are $y = 4 - x^2$ and $y = -2x - 4$.

**55** At time $t$ seconds, the velocity of a particle moving in a straight line is given by $v = 2t - 3t^2$ m s$^{-1}$. Find the *total distance* moved by the particle in the interval from $t = 0$ to $t = 1$.

**56** The line $y = x - 2$ is a tangent to the curve $y = x^3 - 2x$.

**a** Show that the point of contact T occurs when $x = 1$. Find the coordinates of T, and the other point of intersection P of the line and the curve.

**b** Find the axes intercepts of $y = x^3 - 2x$.

**c** Use the results of **a** and **b** to sketch $y = x - 2$ and $y = x^3 - 2x$ on the same set of axes.

**d** Find the area of the region bounded by the curve and the segment [PT] of the given straight line.

**57** Find the volume of the solid formed when the region enclosed by the graph of $y = x^2 - 2x$ and the $x$-axis is rotated about the $x$-axis. Give your answer as an exact value.

**58** In the figure, AEB is an arc of the parabola $y = 4 - x^2$, and ABCD is a rectangle. The area of the rectangle ABCD is equal to the area enclosed by the arc AEB and the line segment [AB].

Find the dimensions of the rectangle.

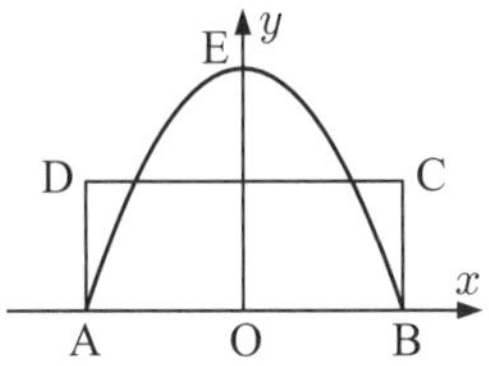


**59** Sketch the graphs of $y = x^2 - 3x + 3$ and $y = x + 3$ for the interval $-2 \leqslant x \leqslant 5$. Find the area contained between the curve and the line.

Find $\int_{-2}^4 (4x - x^2)\,dx$ and interpret the result geometrically.

**60** Integrate with respect to $x$:

**a** $(x^2 + 2)^2$

**b** $\sqrt{4x+5}$

**61** Find:

**a** $\displaystyle\int_0^1 \frac{1}{2x+1}\,dx$

**b** $\int (e^x - 1)^2\,dx$

**62** Find the area of the region enclosed between the curves with equations $y = x^2$ and $y = x$.

**63** A parabola passes through the points $(-\pi, 0)$, $(\pi, 0)$, and $(0, \alpha)$. The area between the parabola and the $x$-axis is 4 units$^2$. Calculate the possible values of $\alpha$.

**64** A particle moves along the $x$-axis with velocity $v(t) = 1 + 2t - 2t^3$ metres per second. When $t = 2$ seconds the particle is 4 m to the right of the origin. Where will the particle be when $t = 4$ seconds?

**65** If $y = x^2e^{-x^2}$, show that $\dfrac{dy}{dx} = 2x(1-x^2)e^{-x^2}$.

Hence find $\displaystyle\int x(1-x^2)e^{-x^2}\,dx$.

**66** Find the area bounded by the graphs of $y = x^2 + 2x - 3$ and $y = x - 1$.

**67** A particle moves along the $x$-axis with velocity $v(t) = t - 4t^3$ metres per second, $t \geqslant 0$. Find the total distance travelled by the particle in the first second.

**68** The diagram shows a line $y = \sqrt{3}x$ and an arc of the circle $x^2 + y^2 = r^2$, $r > 0$.

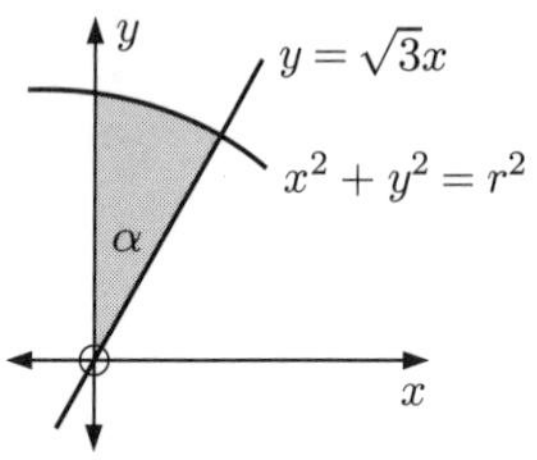


**a** Show that $\alpha = \frac{\pi}{6}$.

Hence state the arc length $l$ and area $A$ of the sector shown.

**b** By considering $A$ as the area between the two curves $x^2 + y^2 = r^2$ and $y = \sqrt{3}x$, show that

$$A = \int_0^{\frac{r}{2}} \sqrt{r^2 - x^2}\,dx - \frac{\sqrt{3}r^2}{8}.$$

**c** Using parts **a** and **b** above, show that

$$\int_0^{\frac{r}{2}} \sqrt{r^2 - x^2}\,dx = \frac{\pi r^2}{12} + \frac{\sqrt{3}r^2}{8}.$$

**d** Hence show that $\int_0^1 \sqrt{36 - 9x^2}\,dx = \pi + \frac{3\sqrt{3}}{2}$.

**69** Show that $\dfrac{2}{x+1} + \dfrac{1}{1-x} = \dfrac{x-3}{x^2-1}$

and hence show that $\displaystyle\int_0^{\frac{1}{2}} \frac{x-3}{x^2-1}\,dx = 2\ln 3 - \ln 2$.

**70** Find the volume of the solid formed when the graph of the function $y = x^2$ for $0 \leqslant x \leqslant 2$ is revolved about the $x$-axis.

**71** Let $f(x) = \dfrac{x+2}{\sqrt{x-1}}$.

**a** State the values of $x$ for which $f(x)$ is a real number.

**b** Find the equation of the normal to the curve $y = f(x)$ at $x = 10$.

**72** A piece of wire 40 cm long is bent to form the boundary OPQ of a sector of a circle with centre O and radius $x$ cm.

The angle of the sector is $\theta$ radians and the length of the arc is $s$ cm.

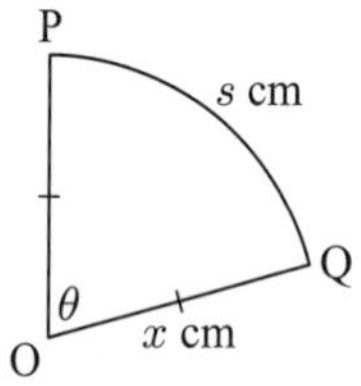


**a** Show that $s = 40 - 2x$.

**b** Given that $s = \theta x$ and the area of the sector is given by $A = \frac{1}{2}\theta x^2$, show that $A = 20x - x^2$ cm$^2$.

**c** Find the value of $x$ for which the area $A$ is a maximum.

**d** Hence find $\theta$ when the area is a maximum.

**73** A particle undergoing straight line motion has velocity $v(t) = e^{2t} - 3e^t$ metres per second at time $t$ seconds, $t \geqslant 0$.

**a** Find the initial velocity, and show that the particle is stationary when $t = \ln 3$ seconds.

**b** If the initial position of the particle is 1 metre to the right of the origin, show that its position at $t = \ln 5$ seconds is also 1 metre to the right of the origin.

**c** Find the distance travelled by the particle in the first $\ln 5$ seconds.

**d** Find the times for which the velocity is increasing.

**74** Find $f'(x)$ for these functions:

**a** $f(x) = 3\sin(x-4)$

**b** $f(x) = 12x - 2\cos(\frac{x}{3})$

**c** $f(x) = \sin 2x \cos 3x$

**d** $f(x) = \sqrt{\sin(2x+1)}$

**e** $f(x) = e^{2\sin x}$

**f** $f(x) = \tan(3x-4)$

**75** Find the volume of revolution when the shaded region is revolved about the $x$-axis.

**a**

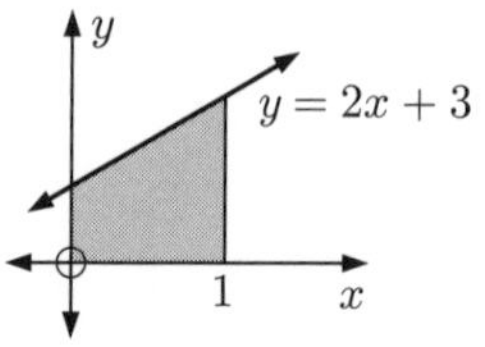


**b**

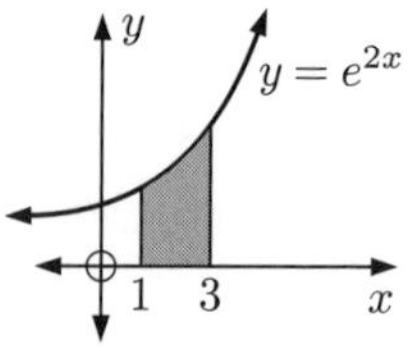


**76** Obtain $\dfrac{dy}{dx}$ for $y = \dfrac{\sin 2x}{1+x}$.

**77** Let $f(x) = \ln(\cos x)$ on the domain $0 \leqslant x \leqslant \pi$.

**a** For what values of $x$ in the domain is $f(x)$ undefined?

**b** Find $f'(x)$.

**78** Write down the derivatives of the following functions. Do not simplify your answers.

**a** $\dfrac{\sin x + \cos x}{\sin x - \cos x}$

**b** $e^{\tan x}$

**c** $x^{\frac{7}{2}} \sin 3x$

**79** Find:

**a** $\int_0^{\pi} \sin x\,dx$

**b** $\int_0^{8\pi} \sin x\,dx$

**c** $\displaystyle\int_{-\frac{\pi}{4}}^{\frac{\pi}{4}} \cos 2x\,dx$

**80** On the same set of axes, sketch the two functions $f(x) = \sin x$ and $g(x) = \sin 2x$ for $0 \leqslant x \leqslant 2\pi$.

Show the zeros and turning points of both $f$ and $g$.

Find the areas of each of the four regions bounded by these two graphs.

**81** $f(x)$ is said to be *odd* if $f(-x) = -f(x)$ for all $x$.

**a** Sketch the graph of one odd function.

**b** Evaluate $\int_{-1}^{1} f(x)\,dx$ for any odd function $f(x)$.

**c** Show that $f(x) = x^3 \cos 2x$ is an odd function.

**d** Evaluate $\int_{-1}^{1} (e^{-2x} + x^3 \cos 2x)\,dx$.

**82** Obtain $\dfrac{dy}{dx}$ for $y = \dfrac{\cos 3x}{2+x}$.

**83** The coordinate of a point moving on a straight line is given by $x = \sin t + \frac{1}{2}\sin 2t$ cm at any time $t \geqslant 0$ s.

Determine the position and velocity of the point at $t = 0$ s and $t = 2\pi$ s, the times when it comes to rest for $0 \leqslant t \leqslant 2\pi$, and the acceleration at each of these instants.

Hence describe the motion of the point during the time interval $0 \leqslant t \leqslant 2\pi$.

**84** Let $f(\theta) = \dfrac{2 - \cos\theta}{\sin\theta}$, $0 < \theta \leqslant \frac{\pi}{2}$.

Show that $f'(\theta) = \dfrac{1 - 2\cos\theta}{\sin^2\theta}$.

Find the minimum value of $f(\theta)$.

**85** Let $f(\theta) = \cos\theta \sin^2\theta,\ 0 < \theta \leqslant \frac{\pi}{2}$.
Show that $f'(\theta) = \sin\theta(3\cos^2\theta - 1)$.
Find the maximum value of $f(\theta)$.

**86** **a** Sketch the graph of $f(x) = \sin(x+\frac{\pi}{6})$ for $-2\pi \leqslant x \leqslant 2\pi$.

**b** Find the area that lies above the line $y = \frac{1}{2}$ and below the graph of $y = f(x)$ for $-2\pi \leqslant x \leqslant 2\pi$.

**87** Find $\displaystyle\int_0^{\frac{\pi}{2}} (\sin 3x + 5\cos x)\,dx$

**88** **a** If $y = \ln(\tan x),\ 0 < x < \frac{\pi}{2}$, find the constant $k$ for which $\dfrac{dy}{dx} = \dfrac{k}{\sin 2x}$.

**b** Alongside is a graph of $y = \dfrac{1}{\sin 2x}$. Using the result of **a**, or otherwise, find the shaded area enclosed by the curve, the $x$-axis, and the lines $x = \frac{\pi}{6}$ and $x = \frac{\pi}{3}$.

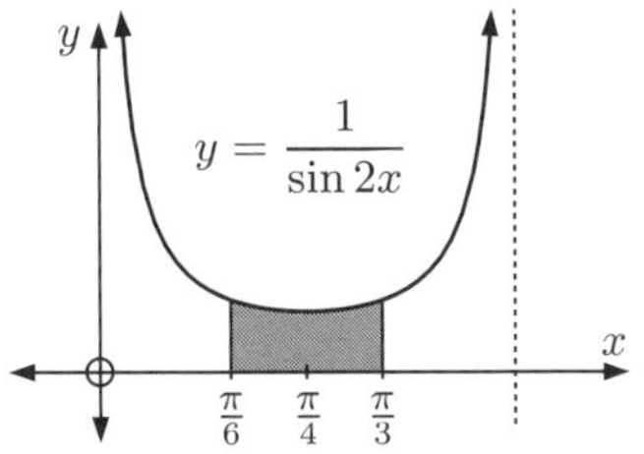


**89**

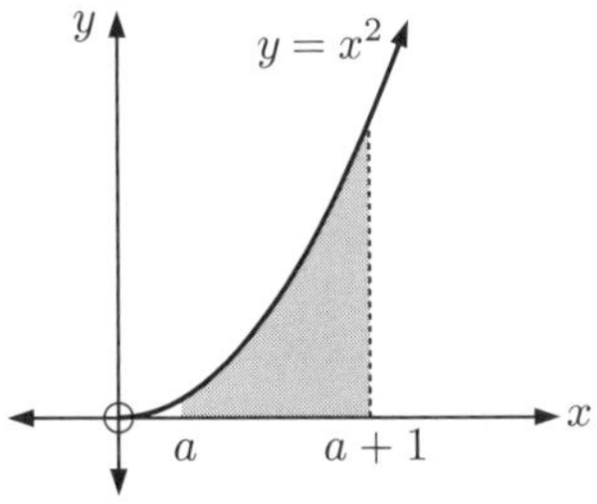


The shaded area is $\frac{1}{2}$ units$^2$.
Find $a$, where $a > 0$.

**90** In the diagram alongside, O is the centre of two concentric circles. The larger circle has radius 1, and the smaller circle has radius $x$. [AB] and [CD] are parallel chords of the larger circle and tangents to the smaller circle. The length of [AB] is $2y$, and $\text{A}\widehat{\text{O}}\text{B} = 2\theta$.

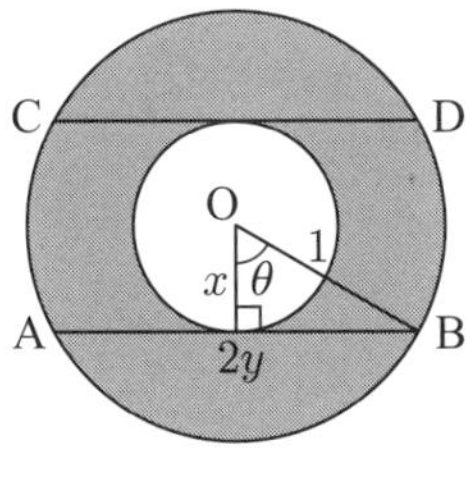


**a** Let $S$ be the area of the shaded region.
Show that $S = \pi y^2 = \pi \sin^2\theta$.

**b** Find the area of the shaded region that is *below* [AB]. Use this to show that the shaded area that is *between* [AB] and [CD] is $f(\theta) = \pi\sin^2\theta + \sin 2\theta - 2\theta$.

**c** Let $g(\theta) = \pi\sin 2\theta + 2\cos 2\theta$.
Show that $f'(\theta) = g(\theta) - 2$.

**d** The diagram below shows the graph of $g(\theta)$.

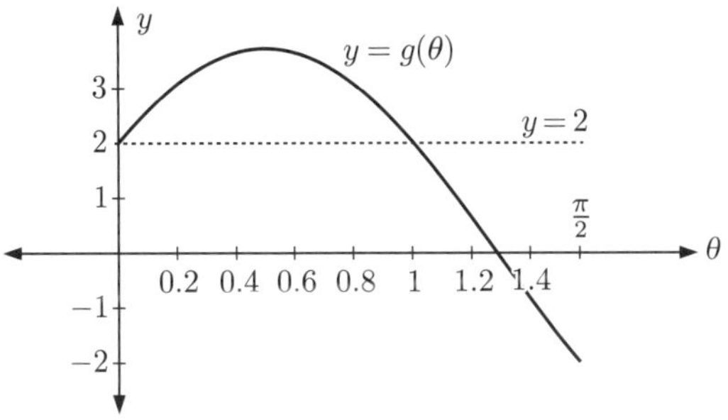


**i** Read the solution of $f'(\theta) = 0$ from this graph for $0 < \theta < \frac{\pi}{2}$.

**ii** Show that this value of $\theta$ maximises $f(\theta)$.

## SKILL BUILDER QUESTIONS (CALCULATORS)

**1** **a** Find $\displaystyle\lim_{h\to 0} \frac{(x+h)^3 - x^3}{h}$.

**b** Evaluate $\dfrac{(5+h)^3 - 5^3}{h}$ for $h = 0.01$.

**c** What does $\dfrac{(5+h)^3 - 5^3}{h}$ approach as $h \to 0$?

**2**

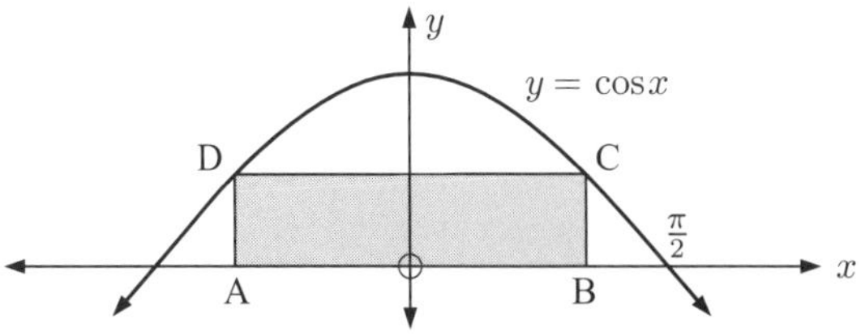


Rectangle ABCD is inscribed under one arch of $y = \cos x$. Find the coordinates of C such that ABCD has maximum area.

**3** An open cylindrical bin is to be made from PVC plastic and is to have a capacity of 500 litres. Find the dimensions of the bin which minimise the amount of PVC plastic used.

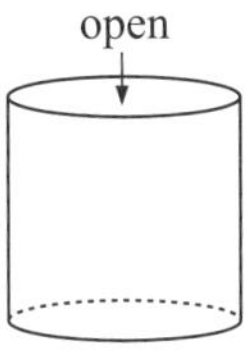


**4** Consider the graph of $y = f(x)$, where $f(x) = 3x^3 + 3x^2 - 3x - 1$.

**a** Find the $y$-intercept.

**b** Find the stationary points and their nature.

**c** Sketch the graph of $y = f(x)$, $-2 \leqslant x \leqslant 1$, clearly labelling the information in **a** and **b** above.

**d** Use technology to find the $x$-intercepts.

**5** The weight of a radioactive substance is given by the equation $W_t = 100 \times e^{-\frac{t}{20}}$ grams where $t$ is the time in days, $t \geqslant 0$.

**a** Find the weight at times $t = 0$, 10, 20, 30 and 40 days.

**b** Find the time necessary for half of the mass to decay.

**c** Find $\dfrac{dW}{dt}$ and interpret its sign.

**d** Discuss $W$ as $t$ increases.

**e** Sketch the graph of $W$ against $t$ showing the information obtained above.

**6** The current in an electrical circuit $t$ seconds after the power is switched on is given by $I(t) = 80(1 - e^{-5t})$ amps, $t \geqslant 0$.

**a** Find the current when: **i** $t = 0$ **ii** $t = 0.2$ **iii** $t = 1$

**b** What happens to the current as $t \to \infty$?

**c** Find $I'(t)$ and draw a sign diagram for the rate of change of current. Explain your result.

**d** Sketch the graph of $I(t)$ against $t$.

**7** A psychologist proposes that the ability of a child to memorize during the first four years can be modelled by the continuous function $f(x) = x\ln x + 1$, where $x$ is the age in years, $0 < x \leqslant 4$.

**a** During which month is the ability at a minimum in the first four years?

**b** When is it a maximum during this period?

**8** The size $f(t)$ of a population at time $t$ may be described by the function $f(t) = \dfrac{N}{1 + 2e^{-\frac{t}{2}}}$ where $N$ is a positive constant.

**a** Find $f'(t)$ and show that $f'(t) > 0$ for all values of $t$.

**b** Find $f''(t)$ and show that the maximum rate of growth of the population occurs when $t = \ln 4$. Find the size of the population at this time.

**c** Sketch the graph of $f(t)$ for $t \geqslant 0$, showing its asymptotes and axes intercepts.

**9** The function $f$ is defined by $f(x) = x - \dfrac{1}{\sqrt{x}}$.

**a** For what values of $x$ is the function defined?

**b** Find $f'(x)$ and hence explain why $f'(x) > 0$ for all $x$.

**c** Find any axes intercepts.

**d** Discuss $f(x)$ as $x \to 0$ and as $x \to \infty$.

**e** Sketch the graph of $y = f(x)$.

**f** Find the area enclosed by the function, the $x$-axis and the line $x = 4$.

**10** Suppose $A(t) = 20e^{at}$ where $a$ is a constant. If $A(2) = 25$, find the value of $a$. Evaluate $A(10)$ to three decimal places.

**11** Let $f(x) = xe^{-2x^2}$ on the interval $0 \leqslant x \leqslant 2$.

**a** Find the stationary point of $f(x)$ on this interval.

**b** *Hence* determine the maximum and minimum values of $f(x)$ on this interval.

**12** An open cylindrical container is to hold 16 $m^3$ of grain.

**a** If the radius of the container is $x$ metres and its height is $y$ metres, show that $y = \dfrac{16}{\pi x^2}$.

Hence show that the surface area of the container including the sides and base is $\pi x^2 + \dfrac{32}{x}$ $m^2$.

**b** A conical cover of height $\frac{3}{4}x$ metres is placed on top to form a silo. Given that the surface area of an open cone of radius $r$ and slant height $s$ is $\pi rs$, show that the surface area of this cover is $\frac{5\pi}{4}x^2$ $m^2$.

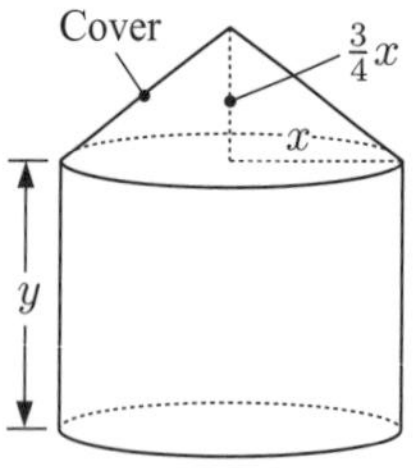


**c** If the sides and base cost $k$ dollars per square metre, and the cost per unit area of the cover is 50% more, show that the total cost of the silo including cover, sides, and base, is given by $C = k\left(\frac{23}{8}\pi x^2 + \dfrac{32}{x}\right)$ dollars.

**d** Find the value of $x$ which minimises the total cost.

**13** Let $g(x) = \dfrac{\ln x}{x}$ for $0 < x \leqslant 5$.

**a** Find the point where the graph of $g(x)$ cuts the $x$-axis.

**b** Find $g'(x)$ and $g''(x)$, and hence show that the graph of $g(x)$ has one stationary point and one point of inflection. Find the coordinates of these points and find the gradient of the graph at the point of inflection.

**c** Describe the behaviour of $g(x)$ for $x$ close to 0.

**d** Sketch the graph of $g(x)$, showing all the above information.

**e** By using your graph, or otherwise, explain why:

**i** $\ln x \leqslant \dfrac{x}{e}$ for $x > 0$ **ii** $\ln x > \dfrac{x}{3}$ for $2 \leqslant x \leqslant 4$.

**14** If $f(x) = \ln(x\sqrt{1-2x})$, show that $f'(x) = \dfrac{1-3x}{x(1-2x)}$.

At what point(s) on the graph of $y = f(x)$ does the normal have gradient $-\frac{6}{5}$?

**15** At time $t$ years, the mass of a material decaying radioactively is given by $M = 5e^{-0.1t}$.

**a** If at time $t_1$ the mass is $M_1$ and at time $t_2$ the mass is $\frac{1}{2}M_1$, show that $t_2 - t_1 = 10\ln 2$.

**b** Calculate the time taken for the mass to reduce to $\frac{1}{32}$ of its original size.

**16** Consider the function $f(x) = \left(2 - \dfrac{1}{x}\right)e^{-x}$, $x > 0$.

**a** Find the zero of $f(x)$.

**b** Discuss the behaviour of $f(x)$ near $x = 0$ and as $x \to \infty$.

**c** Find the position and nature of the stationary point.

**d** Sketch the graph of $y = f(x)$, showing all the above information.

**e** Use technology to find the point of inflection.

**17** Let $f(x) = 1 + \dfrac{1}{2x-1}$.

**a** Find $f'(x)$, and show that the graph of $f(x)$ has no turning points.

**b** Draw the graphs of $f(x)$ and $g(x) = e^x$ on the same set of axes.

Hence determine the *number* of real roots of the equation $(2x-1)e^x - 2x = 0$.

**c** Solve the equation in **b**.

**18** Let $f$ be the function defined by $f(x) = \dfrac{1}{x} - \dfrac{4}{x-2}$.

**a** Find the value of $x$ for which $f(x) = 0$.

**b** Find the coordinates and the nature of the stationary points of $f$.

**c** Show that if $f''(x) = 0$ then $(x-2)^3 = 4x^3$.

Hence find the coordinates of the point on the graph for which $f''(x) = 0$. Give your answer accurate to two decimal places.

**d** Draw the graph of $f$, showing all the above information.

**e** Find algebraically, the area enclosed by the graph, the $x$-axis, and the lines $x = \frac{1}{2}$ and $x = 1\frac{1}{2}$.

**19** For each of these graphs:

**i** find the equations of any asymptotes

**ii** find the position and nature of any stationary points.

**iii** find any axes intercepts.

**iv** sketch the graph, clearly showing the information from **i**, **ii** and **iii**.

**a** $y = \dfrac{2x+6}{1-x}$ **b** $y = \dfrac{3x-12}{x^2-4}$ **c** $y = \dfrac{5x}{(x+2)^2}$

**20** A particle moves from rest along a straight line. Its velocity is given by $v = 2\sqrt{t} - t$ $m\,s^{-1}$, where $t \geqslant 0$ is the time in seconds.

**a** Show that the direction of motion changes at $t = 4$ seconds.

**b** Find the total distance travelled in the first nine seconds.

**21** **a** Determine algebraically, the area of the region bounded by the curve $y = \dfrac{1}{\sqrt{x}}$, the $x$-axis, and the lines $x = 1$ and $x = 9$.

**b** Find the area bounded by $y = \dfrac{1}{\sqrt{x}}$, the $x$-axis, $x = 1.3$ and $x = 3.5$ .

**22** Find the exact area of the region enclosed by the graph of $y = 8x - x^2$ and the $x$-axis.

**23** Find the exact area of the region enclosed by the graphs of $y = x^2 - 3x$ and the line $y = x$.

**24**

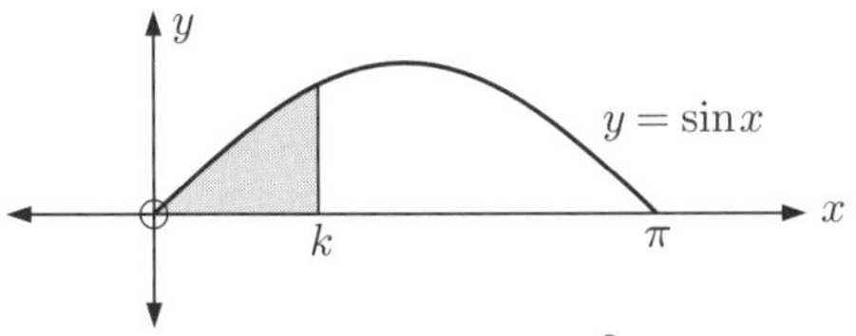


The shaded region has area 0.42 units$^2$. Find $k$.

**25** Sketch the curve $y = 3x^2 + 1$ for $0 \leqslant x \leqslant 3$.

**a** Find the area between the curve and the $x$-axis for $0 \leqslant x \leqslant 3$.

**b** Find a constant $k$ such that the area between the curve and the $x$-axis for $0 \leqslant x \leqslant k$ is 10 units$^2$.

**26** O is a point on a straight line. A particle moving on the straight line has a velocity of 27 cm s$^{-1}$ as it starts from O. Its acceleration $t$ seconds later is $(6t - 30)$ cm s$^{-2}$. Find the *total* distance that the particle has travelled when it comes momentarily to rest for the *second* time.

**27** **a** Evaluate $\int_0^4 (2t+1)^{\frac{1}{2}}\,dt$.

**b** Find the indefinite integral $\int (x^3 + 2)^2\,dx$.

**28** Consider the graph of $y = f(x)$ where $f(x) = 3x^4 + 8x^3 + 6x^2 - 8$.

**a** Show that $x = -2$ is a zero of $f(x)$, and that there is at least one other real zero between $x = 0$ and $x = 1$.

**b** Find the position and nature of the stationary points of $f(x)$.

**c** Sketch the graph of the function for $-2 \leqslant x \leqslant 1$, clearly showing the information from **a** and **b**.

**d** Write down the equation of the straight line which cuts the graph at $x = -2$ and at $x = 1$.

**e** Find the area bounded by the straight line found in **d** and the curve $y = f(x)$.

**29** A particle moves along the $x$-axis with velocity $v(t) = e^{-2t}$ metres per second.

**a** Find the value of $t$ for which the acceleration of the particle is $-\frac{1}{4}$ metres per second per second. Give your answer to 3 significant figures.

**b** At time $t = 0$, the particle is 2 metres to the right of the origin. Find the position of the particle at time $t = 1$ second.

**30** The velocity of a boat travelling in a straight line is given by $v(t) = 30 - 20e^{-0.2t}$ m s$^{-1}$, $t \geqslant 0$.

**a** What is the boat's initial velocity?

**b** What is the velocity after 2 seconds? Give your answer correct to two decimal places.

**c** How long does it take for the boat's velocity to reach 20 ms$^{-1}$? Give your answer correct to one decimal place.

**d** What happens to $v(t)$ as $t \to \infty$?

**e** Calculate $v'(t)$ and show that the acceleration is always positive.

**f** Graph $v(t)$ against $t$, showing the information from **a** to **d**.

**g** Find the formula for the boat's displacement $s(t)$ if its initial position is 10 m in the positive direction.

**31** Find $a$ given that $\int_a^{2a} \sqrt{x}\,dx = 2$.

**32** Two industrial plants, Cinder and Puff-Out, are situated 2 km apart on a straight road. Each plant emits pollutants into the atmosphere.

At a point $x$ km from Cinder, on the road towards Puff-Out, the total concentration of pollutants is given by

$$C(x) = \frac{8}{x^2} + \frac{1}{(2-x)^2} \text{ units}, \quad 0 < x < 2.$$

**a** Find $C'(x)$.

**b** Show that $C'(x) = 0$ when $\left(\frac{x}{2-x}\right)^3 = 8$.

**c** Find the value of $x$ for which the total concentration of pollutants is minimised.

**33** The number of bacteria found in a sample of human tissue $t$ hours after infection occurred, is modelled by the function $N = (8-t)e^{t-6}$ millions, $0 < t \leqslant 8$.

The graph of this function is shown alongside, and takes into account the effect of the body's immune system, which eventually kills the bacteria.

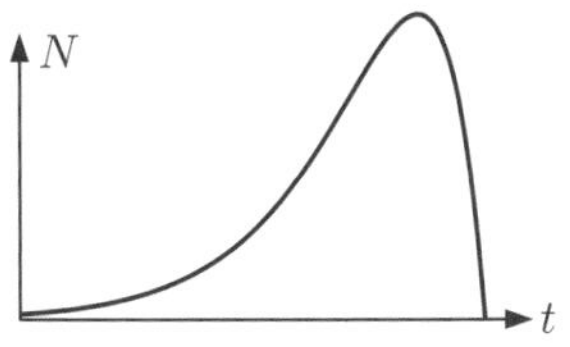


**a** Show that $\frac{dN}{dt} = (7-t)e^{t-6}$.

**b** Find the coordinates of the

**i** turning point **ii** point of inflection **iii** $t$-intercept.

**c** Use these coordinates to state:

**i** the time when all the bacteria are dead

**ii** the maximum number of bacteria reached in the sample

**iii** the time at which the rate of increase of the bacteria is a maximum.

**d** Copy the graph and indicate clearly which points on the graph represent your answers to **c**.

**34** Find:

**a** the gradient of the tangent to $y = \sin(2x+3)$ at the point where $x = 0.4$

**b** $\int_{0.1}^{0.9} e^{\cos^2 x}\,dx$

**35** Find the volume of revolution when the region between $y = \sin x$ and the lines $x = \frac{\pi}{4}$ and $x = \frac{5\pi}{6}$ is rotated about the $x$-axis.

**36** Consider $f(x) = x + \sin x$, $x \geqslant 0$.

**a** Sketch $y = f(x)$ for $0 \leqslant x \leqslant 2\pi$.

**b** Find the area enclosed by the curve, the $x$-axis, and $x = \frac{\pi}{2}$.

**c** Suppose $f(x) = x + \sin x$ and $g(x) = x^2$ meet at $x = a$, $a > 0$. Find $a$ correct to 3 decimal places.

**d** Find the area enclosed by $y = x + \sin x$ and $y = x^2$.

**37** Consider $f(t) = \sin^2 t - \sin t$ where $0 \leqslant t \leqslant 2$.

**a** Sketch the graph of $y = f(t)$ over the given domain.

**b** Find the area enclosed by the curve, the $t$-axis, and $t = 2$.

**38** The shaded area is 24 units$^2$. Find $k$.

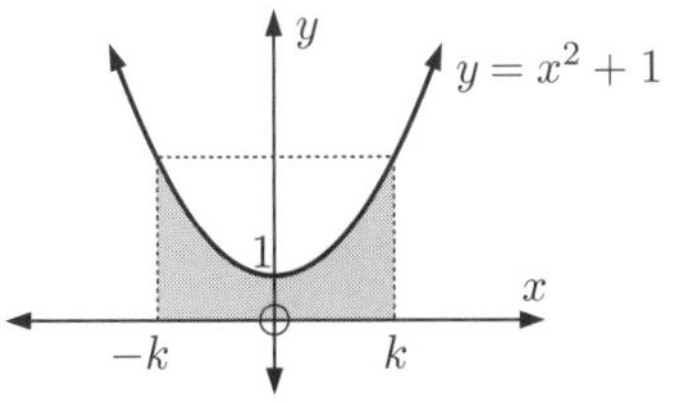

**39** At time $t$ seconds a particle is moving in a straight line with acceleration $4\cos t$ m s$^{-2}$. At $t = 0$ its velocity is $2$ m s$^{-1}$.

**a** Find the velocity at $t = 4$ seconds.

**b** Find the total distance travelled in the interval $t = 0$ to $t = 5$ seconds. Give your answers to two decimal places.

**40** Let $f(x) = 2\cos x - \sin x + 2x\sin x,\ 0 \leqslant x \leqslant 2$.

**a** Show that $f'(x) = (2x - 1)\cos x$.

**b** Find the minimum value of $f(x)$ for $0 \leqslant x \leqslant 2$.

**41** Find $a$ given that $0 < a < 2\pi$ and $\int_a^{a+2} \sin x\, dx = 0.3$.

## EXAM PRACTICE SET 1 NO CALCULATORS

**1** **a** Differentiate with respect to $x$:

**i** $y = 3e^{x^2} + 3(2 - x)$ **ii** $y = \ln(2x + 5)$

**b** Find: **i** $\int \sin(\pi - x)\, dx$ **ii** $\int x(1 + x)\, dx$

**2** A bag contains 4 green, 6 blue, and 2 yellow balls. Two balls are drawn at random from the bag without replacement. What is the probability that they are of different colours?

**3** Given that $\log_7 A = x$, express each of the following in terms of $x$:

**a** $\log_7 A^3$ **b** $\log_7 \dfrac{1}{\sqrt{A}}$ **c** $\log_{49} A$

**4** **a** Line $L$ has the vector equation $\mathbf{r} = \begin{pmatrix} 1 \\ 2 \end{pmatrix} + t\begin{pmatrix} 4 \\ -1 \end{pmatrix}$.

Which of the following are also vector equations for the same line?

**A** $\mathbf{r} = \begin{pmatrix} 5 \\ 1 \end{pmatrix} + t\begin{pmatrix} 4 \\ -1 \end{pmatrix}$ **B** $\mathbf{r} = \begin{pmatrix} -7 \\ 4 \end{pmatrix} + t\begin{pmatrix} 4 \\ -1 \end{pmatrix}$

**C** $\mathbf{r} = \begin{pmatrix} 1 \\ -2 \end{pmatrix} + t\begin{pmatrix} -4 \\ -1 \end{pmatrix}$ **D** $\mathbf{r} = \begin{pmatrix} 1 \\ 2 \end{pmatrix} + t\begin{pmatrix} 12 \\ -3 \end{pmatrix}$

**b** A rocket is travelling with a speed of 800 km min$^{-1}$ in the direction $\begin{pmatrix} 0 \\ 3 \\ 4 \end{pmatrix}$.

At the time $t = 0$, the rocket was launched from the point P(2, 5, 0.05). Find the position vector $\mathbf{r}$ of the rocket at time $t$.

**5** Consider the function $f(x) = \dfrac{4}{\sqrt{4 - x^2}},\ -2 < x < 2$.

**a** Write down the equation of each vertical asymptote.

**b** Find the minimum value of the function $f$ on the given domain.

**c** Sketch the graph of $y = f(x)$.

**6** Copy the graph of $y = f(x)$ alongside.
On the same diagram, draw the graph of $y = 2f(x - 1) - 3$.

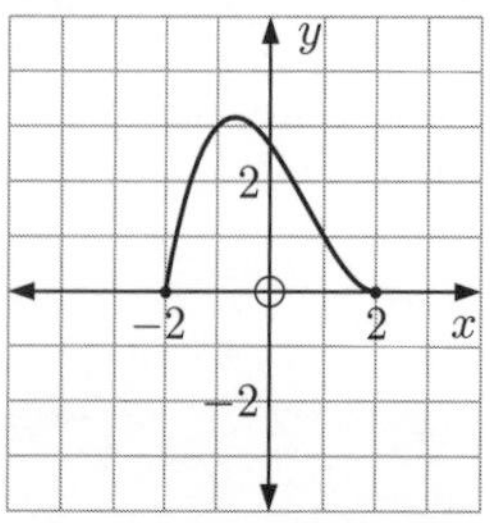


**7** The graph of the function $y = ax^2 + bx + c$ is shown alongside.
Complete the table to show whether each expression is positive, zero, or negative.

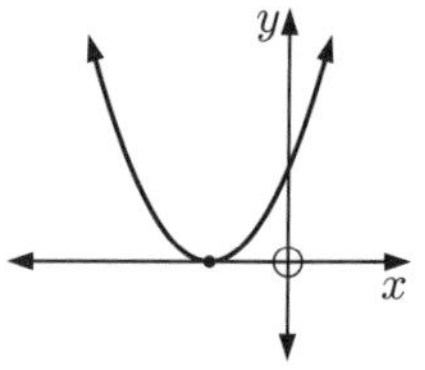


| *expression* | *positive* | *negative* | *zero* |
|---|---|---|---|
| $a$ | | | |
| $b$ | | | |
| $c$ | | | |
| $b^2 - 4ac$ | | | |

**8** Given $f : x \mapsto x + \dfrac{1}{x}$ and $g : x \mapsto e^{-x}$, find:

**a** $g^{-1}(x)$ **b** $(f \circ g)(x)$

**9** The diagram alongside shows the graph of $y = f(x)$.
On the same set of axes sketch the graph of $y = f'(x)$.

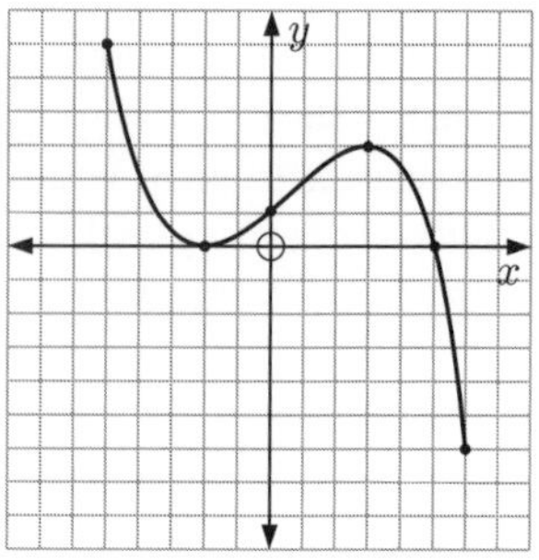


**10** **a** The equation $kx^2 - 7x + 4 = 0$ has exactly one solution. Find the value of $k$.

**b** For what values of $n$ will the equation $3\sin(2x - \pi) = n$ have no solutions?

**c** Find the gradient of the tangent to the curve $y = 2\cos(4x + \pi)$ at the point $(\frac{\pi}{8}, 0)$.

**11** Given $\mathbf{a} = \begin{pmatrix} -2 \\ 6 \end{pmatrix}$ and $\mathbf{b} = \begin{pmatrix} 4 \\ -5 \end{pmatrix}$, find:

**a** $|\mathbf{a}|$ **b** $2\mathbf{a} - 3\mathbf{b}$ **c** $\mathbf{a} \bullet \mathbf{b}$

**d** the vector equation of the line parallel to $\mathbf{b}$ that passes through $(1, 5)$.

**12** **a** The quadratic equation $2x^2 - 3mx + 8 = 0,\ m > 0$ has exactly one solution for $x$. Find the value of $m$.

**b** The function $h$ is defined by $h : x \mapsto \sqrt{4x + 9}$, $x \geqslant -2\frac{1}{4}$. Evaluate $h^{-1}(10)$.

**13** In a survey, 80 students were asked "Do you prefer computer games or playing sport?". The results are partially displayed in the following table.

| | *Girls* | *Boys* | *Total* |
|---|---|---|---|
| *Computer Games* | 10 | 12 | |
| *Sport* | | | |
| *Total* | | 36 | |

By completing the table, or otherwise, find the probability that a student selected at random:

**a** prefers to play sport

**b** prefers to play sport, given that the student is a girl.

**14** Complete the following expansion
$(ax - 3)^4 = a^4x^4 +$ ....................... $+ 81$

**15** **a** Suppose $\mathbf{A}$ is the $3 \times 2$ matrix $\begin{pmatrix} 2 & 4 \\ 3 & 2 \\ -1 & 2 \end{pmatrix}$ and $\mathbf{AB} = \mathbf{C}$.

**i** State the possible orders of matrices **B** and **C**.

**ii** Find **C**, given that $\mathbf{B} = \begin{pmatrix} -2 \\ 3 \end{pmatrix}$.

**b** Expand $(\mathbf{A} + 2\mathbf{I})(\mathbf{A} - 3\mathbf{I})$ where **A** is a square matrix and **I** is the identity matrix.
Rewrite the equation $(\mathbf{A} + 2\mathbf{I})(\mathbf{A} - 3\mathbf{I}) = \mathbf{O}$ in the form $\mathbf{AB} = 6\mathbf{I}$. Hence write $\mathbf{A}^{-1}$ in terms of **A** and **I**.

**16** **a** A water tank is to have a rectangular cross-section with dimensions $2x$ m by $x$ m.

**i** If the volume of the tank must be 9 $\text{m}^3$, find an expression for the height $y$ in terms of $x$.

**ii** Assuming the tank is closed at the top, show that the total surface area $A$ of the tank is given by
$A = 4x^2 + \dfrac{27}{x}\ \text{m}^2$.

**iii** Find the dimensions of the tank for which the surface area is minimised.

**b** Let $f(x) = 1 - \dfrac{1}{1+x^2}$.

**i** Find the position and nature of the stationary point of the graph of $y = f(x)$.

**ii** Find the position of any points of inflection.

**iii** By using a sign diagram or otherwise, state the values of $x$ for which $f(x) \geqslant 0$.

**iv** Using all the information obtained above, sketch the graph of $y = f(x)$.

**17** **a** At a book sale Josie bought five books by Jane Austen and two books by Catherine Cookson. She randomly selects two of the books to take with her on a holiday. Calculate the probability that both books are by the same author.

**b** This Venn diagram shows a sample space $U$ and events $X$ and $Y$.
$n(U) = 100$, $n(X) = 60$, $n(Y) = 70$, and $n(X \cap Y) = 42$.

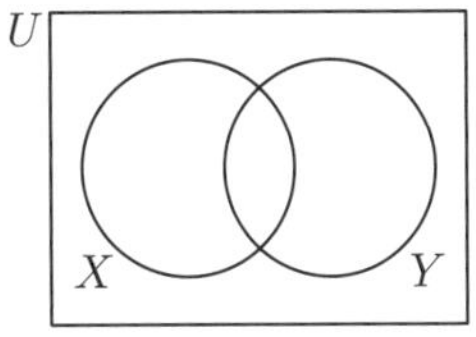


**i** Find:
**(1)** $n(X \cup Y)$ **(2)** $P(X')$ **(3)** $P(Y \mid X')$

**ii** Explain why events $X$ and $Y$ are independent.

**18** **a** The graph of $y = 10 - 3x$ intersects the $x$-axis at P and the $y$-axis at Q.

**i** Find the coordinates of P and Q.

**ii** Find the area of $\Delta$OPQ where O is the origin.

**b** Find the equation of the line perpendicular to [AB] which passes through M, the midpoint of [AB].

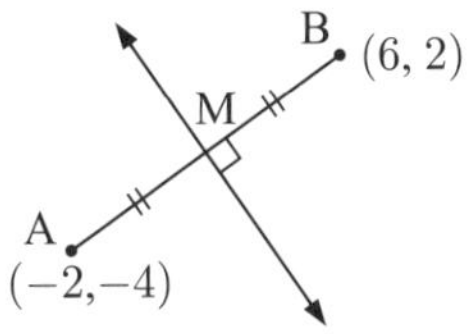


**c** The sketch shows part of the graph of $y = x + \dfrac{2}{x-3}$.
Find the area of the shaded region from $x = 1$ to $x = 2$. Give your answer in the form $a + b(\ln 2)$ where $a$ and $b$ are constants.

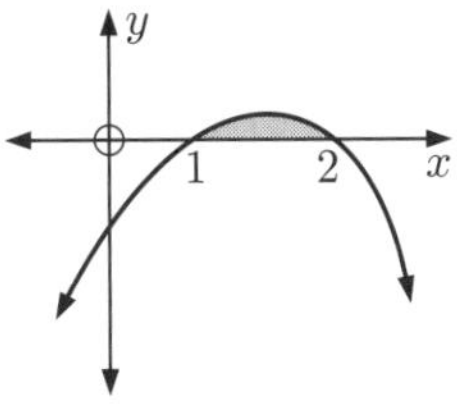


**19** **a** Given $\mathbf{v} = 3\mathbf{i} - 7\mathbf{j}$ and $\mathbf{w} = 5\mathbf{i} + 2\mathbf{j}$, find:

**i** $\mathbf{v} + 2\mathbf{w}$ **ii** a unit vector perpendicular to **v**

**iii** $(\mathbf{v} + \mathbf{w}) \bullet (\mathbf{v} - \mathbf{w})$ **iv** $|3\mathbf{w}|$

**b** **i** Find vector equations for the following lines:

$L_1$ : passing through $(4, -11, 5)$ in the direction $\begin{pmatrix} 1 \\ 2 \\ -1 \end{pmatrix}$

$L_2$ : passing through $(10, -4, -2)$ and $(-2, 2, 16)$.

**ii** Find the coordinates of the point P where lines $L_1$ and $L_2$ intersect.

**iii** Find the cosine of the acute angle between the lines $L_1$ and $L_2$.

**20** A circle of radius $r$ encloses a regular octagon as shown.

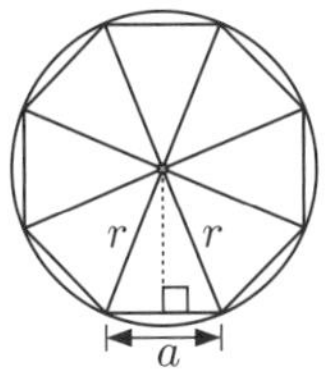


**a** Show that $a$ and $r$ are related by $a = 2r\sin\left(\frac{\pi}{8}\right)$.

**b** Show that the area of the octagon is $8r^2\sin\left(\frac{\pi}{8}\right)\cos\left(\frac{\pi}{8}\right)$.

**c**

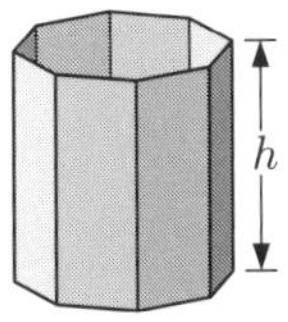


Octagonal waste paper bins are to be made of fixed volume $V$. The radius $r$ (shown in the first diagram) and height $h$ are to be determined.

**i** Show that the area of material needed for the base and sides is given by $A = 8r\left(2h + r\cos\left(\frac{\pi}{8}\right)\right)\sin\left(\frac{\pi}{8}\right)$ and that the volume $V = 8r^2h\sin\left(\frac{\pi}{8}\right)\cos\left(\frac{\pi}{8}\right)$

**ii** Show that $A = \dfrac{2V}{r\cos\left(\frac{\pi}{8}\right)} + 8r^2\sin\left(\frac{\pi}{8}\right)\cos\left(\frac{\pi}{8}\right)$.

**iii** Show that A is a minimum when

$$r = \left(\frac{V}{8\sin\left(\frac{\pi}{8}\right)\cos^2\left(\frac{\pi}{8}\right)}\right)^{\frac{1}{3}}.$$

## EXAM PRACTICE SET 2 CALCULATORS

**1** In an arithmetic sequence the first term is 8 and the thirtieth term is 124.

**a** Find the 12th term.

**b** Find the sum of the first twelve terms.

**2** Given $\mathbf{A} = \begin{pmatrix} 2 & 7 & 6 \\ -1 & 3 & 2 \\ 4 & -2 & 0 \end{pmatrix}$ and $\mathbf{B} = \begin{pmatrix} -3 & 1 & 2 \\ 2 & 1 & -5 \\ -2 & 4 & 3 \end{pmatrix}$ find:

**a** $\mathbf{A} - \mathbf{B}$ **b** $\mathbf{AB}$ **c** $|\mathbf{A}|$ **d** $\mathbf{B}^{-1}$

**3** Find:

**a** $a$

**b** the area of $\Delta$ABC

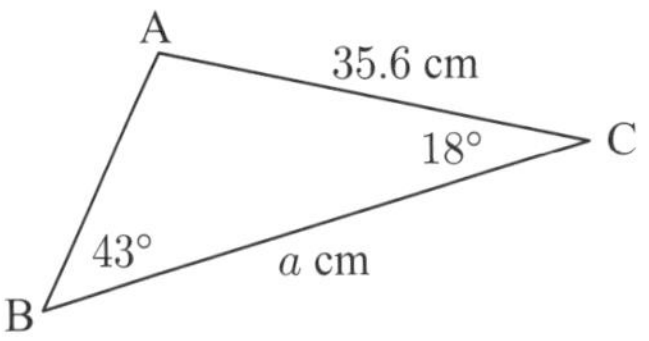


**4** Find the coefficient of the $x^6$ term in the expansion of $(2x+5)^{10}$.

**5** **a** Solve $\begin{pmatrix} 1 & -3 \\ -2 & 1 \end{pmatrix}\begin{pmatrix} x \\ y \end{pmatrix} = \begin{pmatrix} -3 \\ -4 \end{pmatrix}$.

**b** **i** Find the possible values of $p$ such that $\begin{pmatrix} 1 & p-2 \\ 2p & p^2 \end{pmatrix}$ has an inverse.

**ii** State this inverse in terms of $p$.

**6** The heights of trees in a plantation are normally distributed with mean 3.18 metres and standard deviation 19.5 cm.

**a** Find the probability that a randomly selected tree will be:

**i** taller than 3 metres

**ii** between 2.8 and 3.3 metres tall.

**b** What height must a tree be to be in the tallest 20%?

**7** **a** Given $f(x) = 3\sin(2x+1)$, find:

**i** $f'(x)$ **ii** $\int f(x)\,dx$

**b** Find $\int e^x(1-e^{2x})\,dx$

**8** The diagram shows a rectangular prism in which M is the midpoint of [BC]. Suppose A is at $(0, 0, 0)$ and B is at $(5, 0, 0)$.

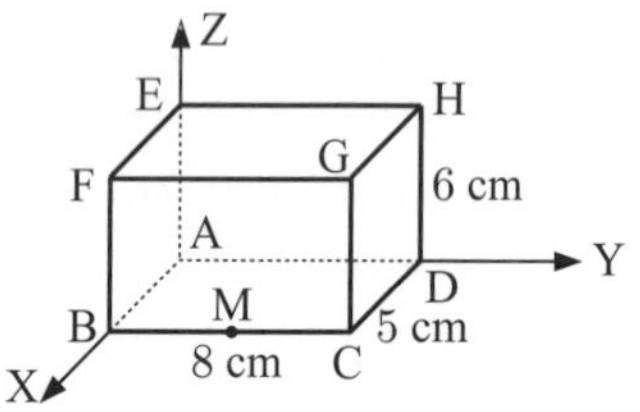


**a** State the coordinates of E, M and G.

**b** Find:

**i** $\overrightarrow{ME}$ **ii** $\overrightarrow{MG}$

**c** Use a vector method to find the measure of $\widehat{EMG}$.

**9** Consider $f(x) = \dfrac{1}{x^2-4}$, $-3 \leqslant x \leqslant 3$.

**a** Sketch a graph of $y = f(x)$.

**b** Write down the equation of each vertical asymptote.

**c** State the range of $f(x)$ on the given domain.

**10** **a** Sketch the graphs of $y = \ln x$ and $y = 2 - x$ for $-1 \leqslant x \leqslant 4$.

**b** The equation $\ln x = 2 - x$ has a solution between $-1$ and 4. Find this solution.

**11** **a** Factorise the expression $3\cos^2\theta - 10\cos\theta + 3$.

**b** Solve the equation $3\cos^2\theta - 10\cos\theta + 3 = 0$ for $0^o \leqslant \theta \leqslant 360^o$, giving your answers correct to the nearest degree.

**12** A sum of 12 000 euros is invested at a compound interest rate of 7.2% per annum.

**a** Write down an expression for the value of the investment after $t$ complete years.

**b** What will be the value of the investment at the end of 4 years?

**c** How long will it take before the value of the investment is 25 000 euros?

**13** Consider the points A$(-2, 0, 3)$, B$(1, -3, 5)$ and C$(7, 2, -1)$. Find:

**a** $|\overrightarrow{AC}|$ **b** a unit vector parallel to $\overrightarrow{AB}$

**c** the measure of $\widehat{CAB}$.

**14** O is the centre of a circle that has a radius of 16 cm. Chord [AB] subtends an angle of $110^o$ at the centre of the circle.

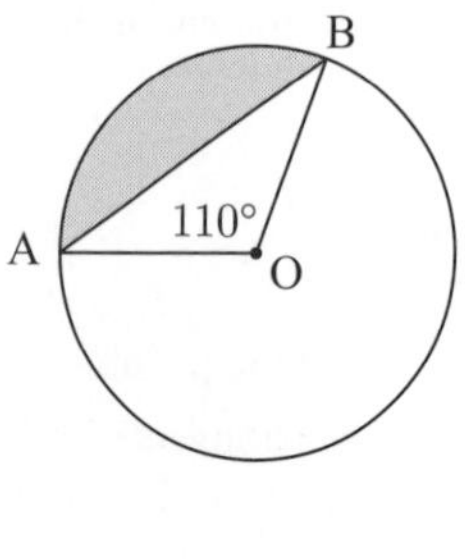


**a** Find the length of [AB].

**b** Find the shaded area.

**15** Let $f(x) = 4 - \sin 2x + 2\cos\left(\frac{x}{2}\right)$, where $x$ is in radians. For the domain $0 \leqslant x \leqslant 4$:

**a** sketch the curve of $y = f(x)$

**b** solve $f(x) = 5$

**c** find the minimum value of $f(x)$.

**16** **a** If $\det\mathbf{A} = 0$ where $\mathbf{A} = \begin{pmatrix} 1 & 2 & -1 \\ 1 & k & 2 \\ 2 & -1 & 1 \end{pmatrix}$, find $k$.

**b** A circular railway line is to pass through the three points shown in the diagram.

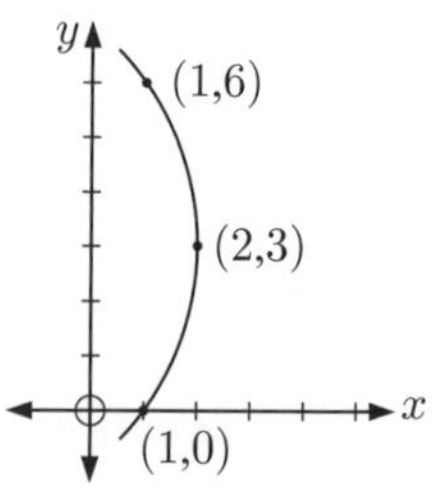


**i** By substituting each point into the equation of the circle $x^2 + y^2 + px + qy + s = 0$, show that $p$, $q$ and $s$ satisfy the system of equations:

$$\begin{cases} p + s = -1 \\ 2p + 3q + s = -13 \\ p + 6q + s = -37. \end{cases}$$

**ii** Find the values of $p$, $q$ and $s$.

**17** **a** The times taken by 200 students to complete a 400 metre run were recorded. The cumulative frequency graph for the times is given below.

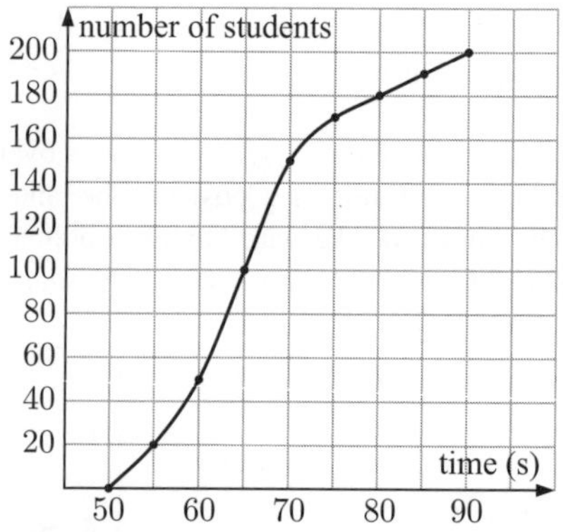


**i** How many students took less than 60 seconds to complete the 400 metre run?

**ii** Find the median and interquartile range for the times taken by the 200 students.

**iii** Find the 90th percentile of the times taken by the 200 students.

**b** An agent for a football club contacts nine large corporations seeking sponsorships of $10 000 each. The agent's record suggests the probability that she will obtain sponsorship from any given company is 0.3.

**i** What is the random variable in this case?

**ii** List the possible outcomes that could occur.

**iii** Find the probability that the agent gets:

**(1)** exactly 4 sponsorships

**(2)** at least 3 sponsorships.

**iv** The agent earns a commission of 2.5% per sponsorship plus a bonus of 1% for each sponsorship after the first. Her total costs are $150. Calculate the probability that she makes a profit of $1150 or greater.

**v** Now suppose the agent approaches 40 corporations instead of nine. Her costs increase to $300. Calculate the probability that she makes a profit less than $6600.

**18** **a** If $f(x) = e^{3x}\sin 2x$, show that $f'(x) = 0$ when $\tan 2x = -\frac{2}{3}$.

**b** The graph of $f(x) = e^{3x}\sin 2x$ for $x \geqslant 0$ is shown below.

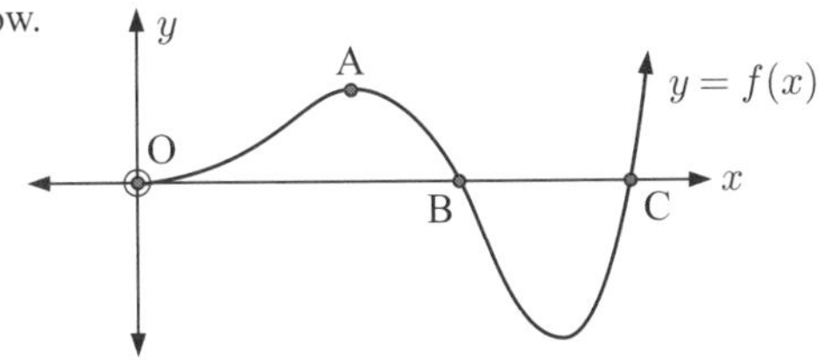


The graph intersects the $x$-axis at the points B and C. The point A is a local maximum.

**i** Find the $x$-coordinates of B and C.

**ii** Find the $x$-coordinate of A.

**c** **i** If $g(x) = \frac{1}{13}(3e^{3x}\sin 2x - 2e^{3x}\cos 2x)$, show that $g'(x) = e^{3x}\sin 2x$.

**ii** Using **c i** or otherwise, find the area between the graph of $f(x) = e^{3x}\sin 2x$ and the $x$-axis from O to B.

**19** A garage is illustrated below on a set of three-dimensional coordinate axes.

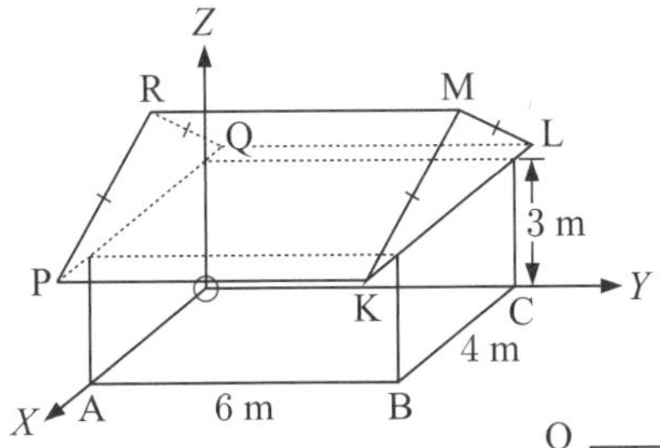


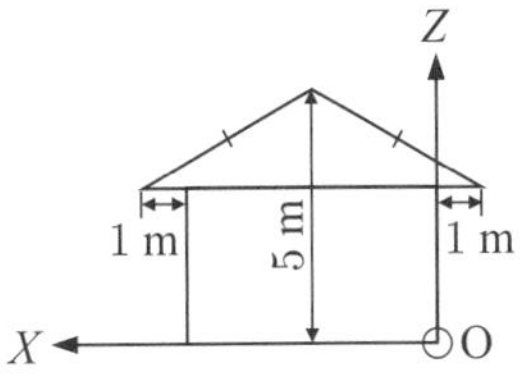


right end view

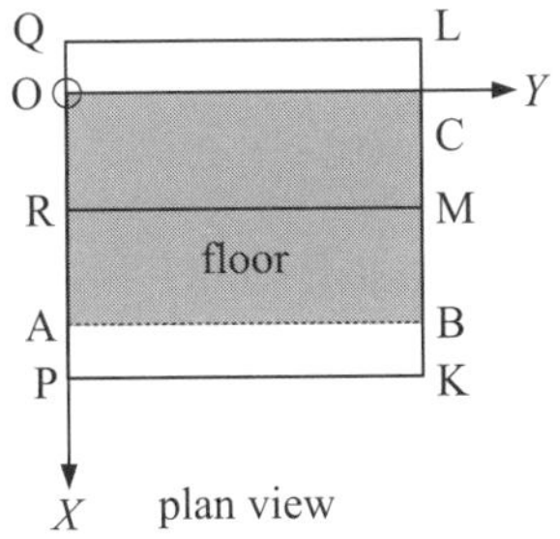


plan view

**a** Find the 3-dimensional coordinates of:
A, B, C, P, Q, R, K, L, M.

**b** Find the vector equation of [MK].

**c** Find the acute angle that (MK) makes with (AC).

**d** An electric light pole has base $(6, 2, 0)$ and is 5 m high. Find point N on [MK] such that N is 5.05 m from the top of the pole.

**20** **a** Consider the following normal distribution graph which models the weight of mice.

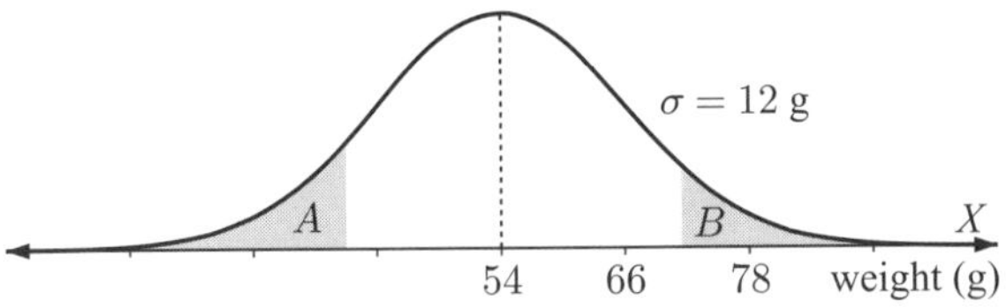


**i** Complete the $X$-scale, and add a $Z$-scale to the graph.

**ii** The shaded region $A$ corresponds to 12% of the population. What is the greatest weight of any mouse in the lightest 12% of the population?

**iii** The shaded region $B$ corresponds to 8% of the population. Find the lowest weight of a mouse in the heaviest 8% of the population.

**b** A random variable $X$ is normally distributed so that $X \sim N(\mu, \sigma^2)$. If 20% of the values are below 6 and the mean is 9, find $\sigma$.

**c** Whenever Pele takes a penalty shot for goal he has an 80% chance of being successful. If he takes twenty penalty shots at goal, find:

**i** the expected number of successes

**ii** the probability that he scores with all but two shots

**iii** the probability that he scores with at least 18 shots.

## EXAM PRACTICE SET 3 NO CALCULATORS

**1** The function $f$ is defined by $f(x) = 2\cos(3x+1)$.
Find: **a** $f''(x)$ **b** $\int f(x)\, dx$

**2** State the domain of each of the following functions:

**a** $y = \sqrt{x-4}$ **b** $y = \sqrt{\dfrac{1}{x-4}}$ **c** $y = \sqrt{\ln(x-4)}$

**3** The equation of this curve can be written in the form $y = a(x-p)(x-q)$.

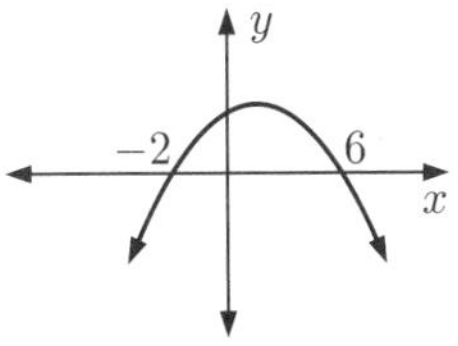


**a** Write down the values of $p$ and of $q$.

**b** Given that the point $(4, 3)$ lies on the curve, find the value of $a$.

**c** Write the equation of the curve in the form $y = ax^2 + bx + c$.

**4** If $A$ is an obtuse angle and $\sin A = \frac{8}{15}$, calculate $\sin 2A$.

**5** Consider the functions $f : x \mapsto 6 - 2x$ and $g : x \mapsto x^2 + 3$.
Find: **a** $f^{-1}(4)$ **b** $(g \circ f)(-2)$

**6** Solve:

**a** $3x^2 + 12x - 5 = 0$

**b** $2\sin x + \sqrt{3} = 0, \quad 0 \leqslant x \leqslant 2\pi$

**7** The coordinates of A, B and C are $(2, -1, 2)$, $(4, -2, 5)$ and $(5, 2, 1)$ respectively.

**a** Find $\overrightarrow{AB}$.

**b** Prove that the triangle ABC is right angled at A.

**8** Let $\log_b M = x$, $\log_b N = y$ and $\log_b P = z$.

Express $\log_b \dfrac{N^3}{M\sqrt{P}}$ in terms of $x$, $y$ and $z$.

**9** The velocity of a moving object at time $t$ seconds is given by $v = 30 - 6t^2$ m s$^{-1}$.

**a** Find its acceleration at the moment when $t = 5$ seconds.

**b** The initial displacement $s$ is 15 metres. Find an expression for $s$ in terms of $t$.

**10** The diagram shows the graph of $y = a\cos(bx) + c$ for $0 \leqslant x \leqslant \pi$.

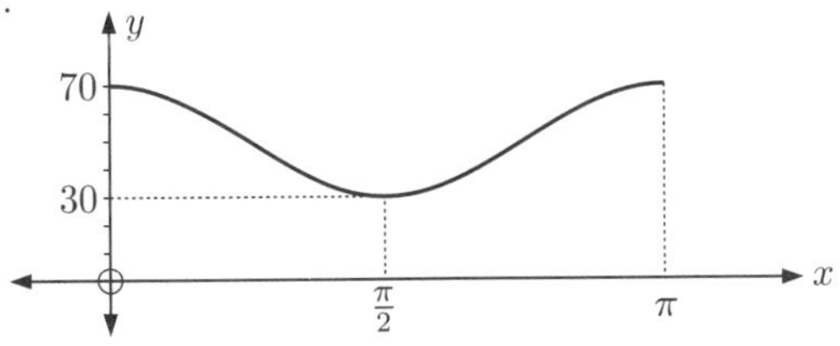


Find the values of $a$, $b$ and $c$.

**11** **a** Let $\mathbf{M} = \begin{pmatrix} 1 & a \\ b & c \end{pmatrix}$ and $\mathbf{N} = \begin{pmatrix} a & 2 \\ d & 0 \end{pmatrix}$.

Find: **i** $\mathbf{M} + \mathbf{N}$ **ii** $\mathbf{MN}$

**b** Let $\mathbf{A} = \begin{pmatrix} 1 & 2 & a \\ b & 1 & c \\ 3 & 0 & 1 \end{pmatrix}$ and $\mathbf{B} = \begin{pmatrix} a & 0 & b \\ 1 & b & c \\ a & 1 & 1 \end{pmatrix}$.

Find: **i** $\mathbf{A} - \mathbf{B}$ **ii** the 3rd column of $\mathbf{AB}$.

**12** Consider the points A(−3, 4), B(6, −1), and C(−1, 12).
Find:

**a** **i** $\overrightarrow{BA}$ **ii** $\overrightarrow{BC}$ **b** $\overrightarrow{BA} \bullet \overrightarrow{BC}$ **c** $|\overrightarrow{AC}|$

**d** the coordinates of D if ABCD is a parallelogram.

**13** The two lines $ax + by = 32$ and $2x - 3y = 4$ are perpendicular and intersect at (8, 4).
Find the values of $a$ and $b$.

**14** Bin A contains 3 red balls and 4 blue balls. Bin B contains 3 red balls and 1 blue ball. A die with 4 faces marked A and 2 faces marked B is rolled and used to select bin A or B. A ball is then randomly selected from this bin.
Determine the probability that:

**a** the ball is blue

**b** the ball was chosen from bin B given that it is blue.

**15** Find the point of intersection between the lines:

$$L_1: \begin{pmatrix} x \\ y \\ z \end{pmatrix} = \begin{pmatrix} 2 \\ 3 \\ -1 \end{pmatrix} + t\begin{pmatrix} -1 \\ 2 \\ 1 \end{pmatrix}$$

and $$L_2: \begin{pmatrix} x \\ y \\ z \end{pmatrix} = \begin{pmatrix} -3 \\ 1 \\ 4 \end{pmatrix} + s\begin{pmatrix} 1 \\ 2 \\ -1 \end{pmatrix}.$$

**16** A parabola with equation $y = a + bx + x^2$ passes through the points A, B, and C shown in the following graph:

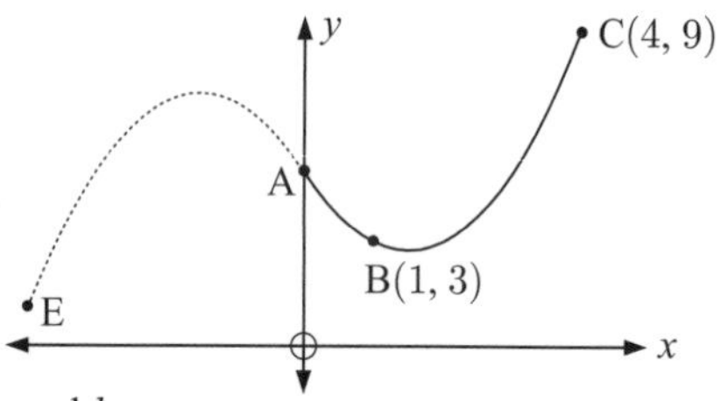


**a** Find $a$ and $b$.

**b** A second parabola passes through the points E and A, and has equation $y = p + qx - x^2$.
Find $p$ such that the two curves meet at A.

**c** Find the gradient of the parabola ABC at A.

**d** Find an expression for the gradient of the parabola AE at A.

**e** Find the value of $q$ so that the two curves join smoothly at A without a change of gradient.

**17** Consider this graph of $y = \sin ax$ for $0 \leqslant x \leqslant 2$.

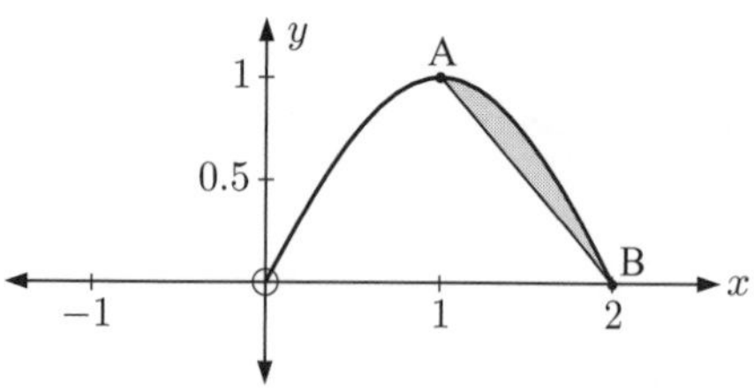


Find:

**a** the value of $a$

**b** the equation of (AB)

**c** the area of the shaded region which is enclosed by $y = \sin ax$ and (AB).

**18**

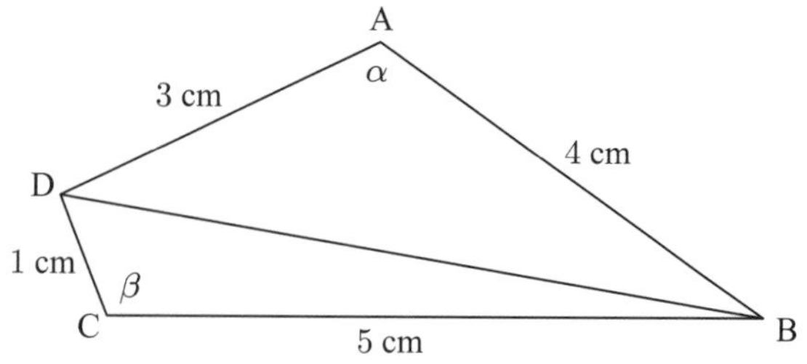


**a** If $\alpha = \beta$, find the length of [BD].

**b** If the triangles ABD and BCD have equal areas, find the ratio of $\sin\alpha$ to $\sin\beta$.

**19** Solve for $x$:

**a** $\log_x 2 = -\frac{1}{3}$

**b** $\log_2 5 = 3\log_x 5$

**c** $e^x = \dfrac{2}{e^x + 1}$

**d** $\displaystyle\int_0^x \frac{1}{2t+1}\,dt = 2$

**20** The function $f$ is defined by $f : x \mapsto 3x^4 - 8x^3 - 6x^2 + 24x$.

**a** Find any zero of the function.

**b** Show that $f'(2) = 0$. Hence find the coordinates and nature of *all* stationary points of $y = f(x)$.

**c** Find the intervals where the function is concave up and concave down.

**d** Sketch the graph of $y = f(x)$, showing the information found above.

## EXAM PRACTICE SET 4 CALCULATORS

**1** **a** Find $\dfrac{dy}{dx}$ if $y = \sqrt{x^2 + 9}$.

**b** Find: **i** $\displaystyle\int \left(x - \frac{4}{x}\right)^2 dx$ **ii** $\displaystyle\int \frac{3}{2x+4}\,dx$

**c** Evaluate $\int_0^2 e^{-x^2}\,dx$ correct to 4 decimal places.

**2** O is the centre of a circle with radius 1 m.
Chord [PQ] has length 120 cm.
Find the area of the shaded region.

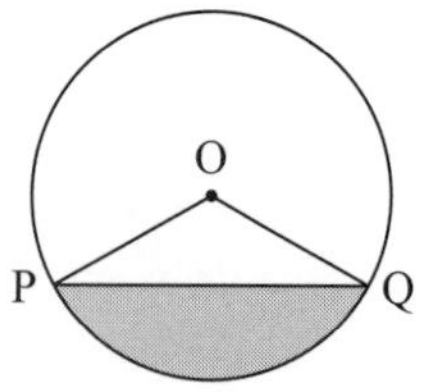


**3** **a** Solve for $x$: $2\sin x = 6\cos x$, $0 \leqslant x \leqslant 2\pi$.

**b** Solve for $\theta$: $3\sin 2\theta = 4\cos\theta$, $0° \leqslant \theta \leqslant 360°$.

**4** **a** The diameter of optical fibre produced by a manufacturer is normally distributed with mean 0.502 mm and standard deviation 0.0025 mm.
The specifications require the diameter of the fibre to be 0.5 mm ± 0.005 mm.
What proportion of the manufacturer's production will fail to meet the specification?

**b** A coin is unbalanced so that the probability $p$ of a head is 0.2. The coin is tossed 6 times. Let $X$ be the number of heads observed.

**i** List all possible outcomes that could occur.

**ii** Find the probability of obtaining:

**(1)** exactly three heads

**(2)** two heads or fewer

**(3)** a head on the first toss only

**5** Write down the inverse of $\mathbf{M} = \begin{pmatrix} 3 & -7 & 2 \\ 1 & 4 & -3 \\ -2 & -1 & 4 \end{pmatrix}$.

Hence solve the system of equations: $\begin{cases} 3a - 7b + 2c = 25 \\ a + 4b - 3c = -20 \\ -2a - b + 4c = 21 \end{cases}$

**6** **a** Find the sum of the infinite geometric series $6 - 3 + 1\frac{1}{2} - \frac{3}{4} + ....$

**b** The number of students at Petersfield High School has increased by 5.2% each year. At present there are 1250 students. How many students were there two years ago?

**7** **a** State the domain of:

**i** $f(x) = \dfrac{x^2}{3x-2}$ **ii** $g(x) = \sqrt{2x+16}$

**b** State the range of:

**i** $y = 20 - 2e^{-0.1x}$ **ii** $y = x^3 + \dfrac{3}{x}$

**8** Suppose $\mathbf{a} = 2\mathbf{i} - 7\mathbf{j}$ and $\mathbf{b} = 3\mathbf{i} + 4\mathbf{j}$.

**a** Construct $\mathbf{a} - \mathbf{b}$ geometrically and hence find $\mathbf{a} - \mathbf{b}$.

**b** Find $\mathbf{a} \bullet \mathbf{b}$ and use your answer to find the angle between **a** and **b**.

**9** The depth of the sea at Hikuai Point this Tuesday is given by $D = 4.7 + 3.4\cos nt$ metres, $t$ hours after midnight.

**a** Find $n$ given that successive low tides are 12.6 hours apart.

**b**

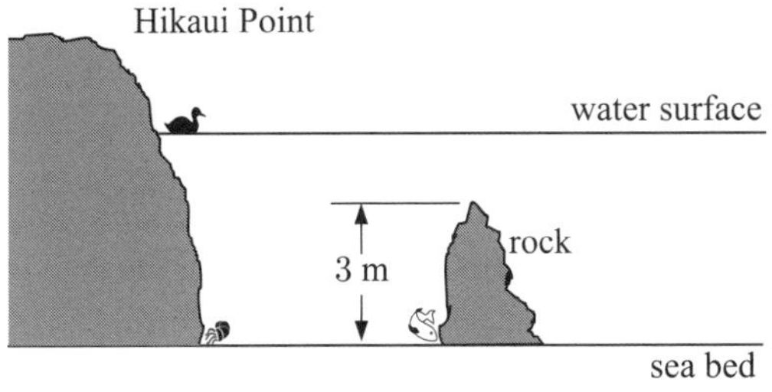


A jagged rock on the sea bed is 3 m high.
Between what times will the rock be visible above the surface if the weather is calm on Tuesday?

**10** For the following frequency distribution table, find:

**a** the median **b** the mode **c** the mean

| *Score (x)* | 10 | 11 | 12 | 13 | 14 | 15 |
|---|---|---|---|---|---|---|
| *Frequency* | 2 | 9 | 11 | 18 | 12 | 8 |

**11** The function $h$ is defined by $h(x) = x^2 + 8x - 2$.

**a** Write $h(x)$ in the form $(x+a)^2 - b$.

**b** Find the coordinates of the vertex of $h(x)$.

**c** Find the $x$-intercepts of $h(x)$.

**12** A glass of water at temperature $T_0$ °C is placed in a refrigerator. The temperature of the water $t$ minutes later is given by $T = T_0 e^{-0.02t}$ °C.

**a** Find the time when the temperature of the water has reduced by 30%. Give your answer correct to the nearest minute.

**b** Find an expression for $\dfrac{dT}{dt}$ in terms of $T$.

Hence, evaluate $\dfrac{dT}{dt}$ when the temperature of the water reaches 20°C.

**13** The diagram shows a metal strip 10 cm long and $2x$ cm wide, with two semicircular ends. A circular hole $x$ cm in diameter has been drilled in the centre.

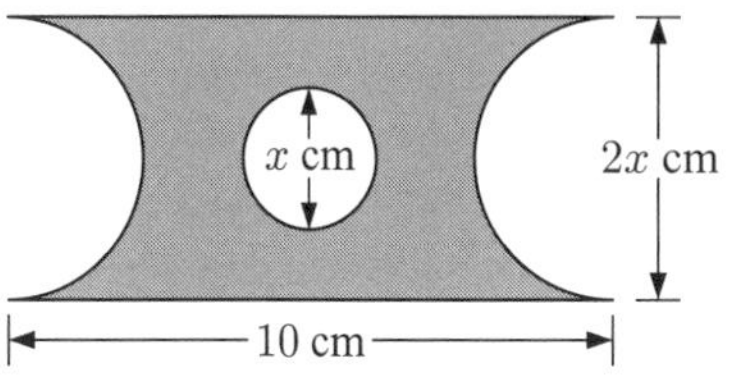


**a** Show that the area of the shaded region is given by $A = 20x - \frac{5\pi}{4}x^2$ cm$^2$.

Hence, find the value of $x$ for which $A$ is a maximum.

**b** Find the largest value $x$ can have.

**14** The functions $f$ and $g$ are defined by $f : x \mapsto 2x + 1$ and $g : x \mapsto x - 2$.

**a** Find $(f \circ g)(x)$. **b** Find $(f \circ f)(x)$.

**c** For what values of $x$ is $f^{-1}(x) = g^{-1}(x)$?

**15** Find the coefficient of $x$ in the expansion of $\left(2x - \dfrac{1}{2x}\right)^5$.

**16** Quadrilateral ABCD is formed by the following lines:

$L_1$ (AB): $\begin{pmatrix} x \\ y \end{pmatrix} = \begin{pmatrix} 2 \\ -11 \end{pmatrix} + r\begin{pmatrix} -2 \\ 11 \end{pmatrix}$

$L_2$ (BC): $\begin{pmatrix} x \\ y \end{pmatrix} = \begin{pmatrix} 0 \\ 12 \end{pmatrix} + s\begin{pmatrix} 2 \\ 1 \end{pmatrix}$

$L_3$ (CD): $\begin{pmatrix} x \\ y \end{pmatrix} = \begin{pmatrix} 10 \\ 5 \end{pmatrix} + t\begin{pmatrix} 2 \\ -11 \end{pmatrix}$

$L_4$ (AD): $\begin{pmatrix} x \\ y \end{pmatrix} = \begin{pmatrix} 12 \\ 6 \end{pmatrix} + u\begin{pmatrix} -2 \\ -1 \end{pmatrix}$

where $r$, $s$, $t$ and $u$ are scalars.

**a** Given A is (0, 0), construct the 4 lines on a grid and determine the coordinates of B, C and D.

**b** Find: **i** $\overrightarrow{AC}$ **ii** $\overrightarrow{DB}$ **iii** $\overrightarrow{AC} \bullet \overrightarrow{DB}$

**c** Find: **i** $|\overrightarrow{BC}|$ **ii** $|\overrightarrow{BA}|$ **iii** the measure of $\widehat{CBA}$

**d** Find: **i** $\overrightarrow{AB}$ **ii** $\overrightarrow{DC}$

**e** What do your answers to **b**, **c** and **d** imply about the quadrilateral ABCD? Explain your answer.

**17** The UV radiation rate from the sun $t$ hours after sunrise on January 7 was modelled by
$R(t) = 8.4 + 6.1\sin[\frac{\pi}{12}(t-1)]$ units, $0 \leqslant t \leqslant 12$.

**a** What was the UV radiation rate at sunrise?

**b** Find the greatest UV radiation rate.

**c** When was the UV radiation rate 10?

**d** Sunrise was at 6:13 am. What was the UV radiation rate at noon?

**e** A UV radiation rate of 12 or more is considered dangerous. Between what times did this level occur?

**18** **a** Find the mean and standard deviation for the class marks recorded in the following frequency distribution table.

| *Mark* | 10 | 12 | 14 | 16 | 18 | 20 |
|---|---|---|---|---|---|---|
| *Frequency* | 2 | 7 | 4 | 9 | 3 | 1 |

**b** The diameters of oranges grown in the valley are normally distributed with a standard deviation of 7 mm. It is found that 98% of all oranges have a diameter greater than 68 mm. Find the mean diameter of the oranges.

**c** It is known that 160 out of 800 students at St Parry High School play football. If a random sample of 20 students is selected with replacement, find the probability that:

**i** 7 or fewer play football **ii** 3 or more play football.

**d** A bus company has established that its buses arrive at their destinations on average 6.72 minutes late, with a standard deviation of 2.31 minutes.

**i** Show that the probability of one randomly chosen bus arriving more than 15 minutes late is extremely small.

**ii** What is the probability of one randomly chosen bus arriving late by between 2 and 5 minutes?

**19** Raymond is training for a triathlon. In the first week he swims 2000 metres, cycles 5000 metres, and runs 4000 metres. Each week thereafter he swims 200 metres more than the previous week, cycles 500 metres more than the previous week, and increases his running by 10% of the previous week's distance.

**a** How far does Raymond swim in the fifth week?

**b** How far does Raymond cycle in the tenth week?

**c** How far does Raymond run in the fourth week?

**d** In total, how far has Raymond cycled after 10 weeks?

**e** In total, how far has Raymond run after 10 weeks?

**20** Consider the function $f(x) = x + 1 + \dfrac{4}{x-1}$.

**a** **i** Find the local maximum and local minimum of $f(x)$

**ii** Find the $y$-intercept of the graph $y = f(x)$.

**iii** Indicate the information obtained in **i** and **ii** on the following graph:

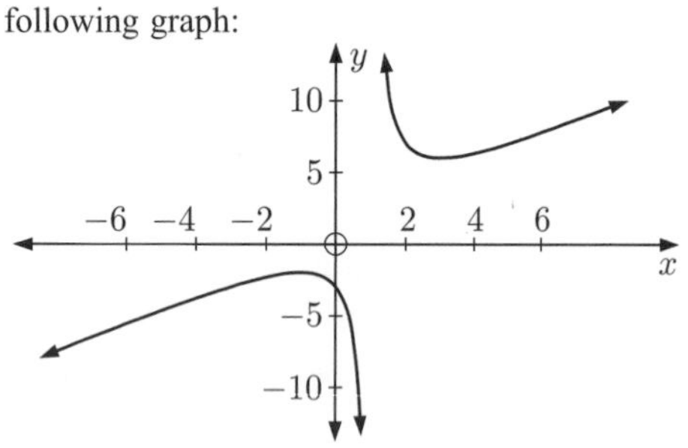


**iv** Find the area enclosed between the graph of $f(x)$ and the line $y = -3$.

**b**

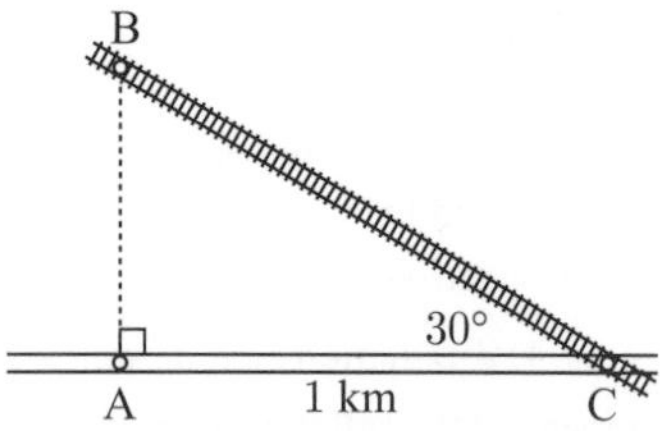


The diagram shows a railway (BC) crossing a road (AC) at an angle of 30° at the point C. A is 1 km from C, and $B\widehat{A}C$ is 90°. At the time $t = 0$ minutes, a train is at B, travelling at a constant speed of 2 km min$^{-1}$ towards C. At the same time, a car is at A travelling towards C. The car accelerates at the rate $a(t) = 2e^{-2t}$ km min$^{-2}$. When $t = 0$, the car has a speed of 1 km min$^{-1}$.

**i** Show that the velocity of the car at time $t$ minutes is $v(t) = 2 - e^{-2t}$ km min$^{-1}$. Sketch the graph of $v(t)$, indicating what happens when $t$ is large.

**ii** How long does the train take to reach the crossing C?

**iii** Does the train reach the crossing C before or after the car? Give reasons for your answer.

## EXAM PRACTICE SET 5 NO CALCULATORS

**1** Sketch the graph of $g(x) = (x-2)(x-5)$ for $0 \leqslant x \leqslant 6$ on the set of axes given.

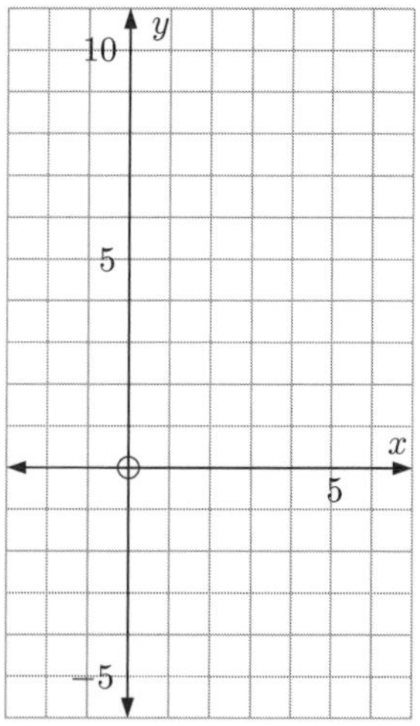


**2** The function $f$ is defined by $f : x \mapsto \dfrac{5}{1-x}$.

Find: **a** $f''(x)$ **b** $\int f(x)\,dx$

**3** Let $\mathbf{A} = \begin{pmatrix} -1 & -1 \\ 3 & 3 \end{pmatrix}$.

**a** Show that $\mathbf{A}^2 = 2\mathbf{A}$, and hence find the matrix $\frac{1}{8}\mathbf{A}^4$.

**b** Solve $\left(\frac{1}{8}\mathbf{A}^4 + 2\mathbf{I}\right)\begin{pmatrix} x \\ y \end{pmatrix} = \begin{pmatrix} 2 \\ 7 \end{pmatrix}$ where $\mathbf{I}$ is the $2 \times 2$ identity matrix.

**4** A basket contains 20 tickets that are numbered $1, 2, 3, \ldots, 20$. Two tickets are chosen at random from the basket, without replacement. Suppose $A$ is the event that a ticket numbered 9 or more is chosen.

**a** Complete the tree diagram:

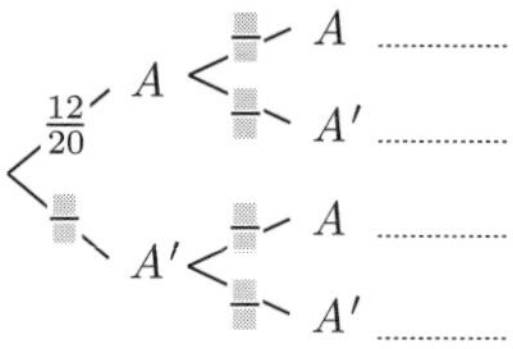


**b** What is the probability that both tickets drawn are numbered less than 9?

**c** Given that the second ticket was 9 or more, what is the probability of the first ticket being less than 9?

**5** Solve for $x$:

**a** $\log_2 x = 8$

**b** $\log_6 x + \log_6(x+6) = \log_6 16$

**c** $\log_8 64 + \log_8 2 + \log_8(\frac{1}{4}) = \log_8 x$

**6** **a** The graph shows the function $f(x) = ax^2 + bx + c$. Find the values of $a$, $b$ and $c$.

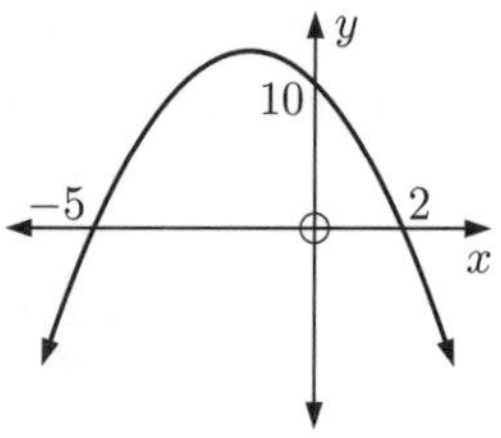


**b** This graph shows the parabola $g(x) = 2(x+3)(x-7)$. Find the coordinates of A, B, C and D.

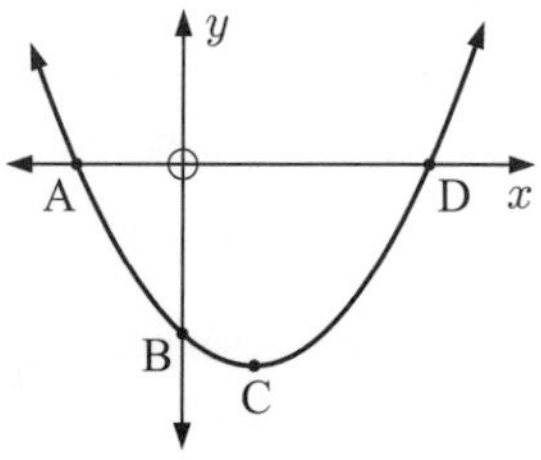

**7** Let $f(x) = 2^x$ and $g(x) = x + 2$.
Solve the equation $(g^{-1} \circ f)(x) = 6$.

**8** Solve for $x$:
**a** $4\sin^2 x = 1,\ 0 < x < 2\pi$ **b** $e^{2x} = 4e^x$

**9** Write the equations $\begin{cases} 2x - 3y = -2 \\ 5x - 2y = 5 \end{cases}$

in the matrix form $\mathbf{BX} = \mathbf{C}$.
Find $\mathbf{B}^{-1}$ and use it to solve for $x$ and $y$.

**10** The following diagrams show how the graph of $y = x^2$ is transformed into the graph of $y = f(x)$ in four steps. For each diagram give the equation of the curve.

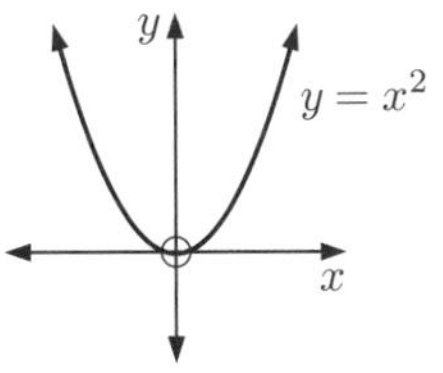


**a**

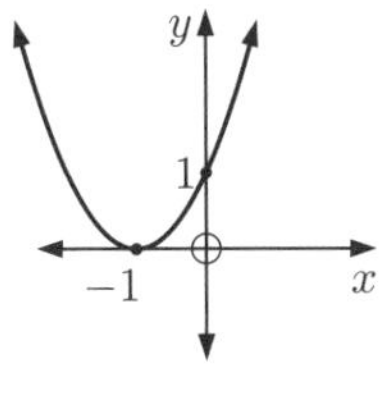


**b**

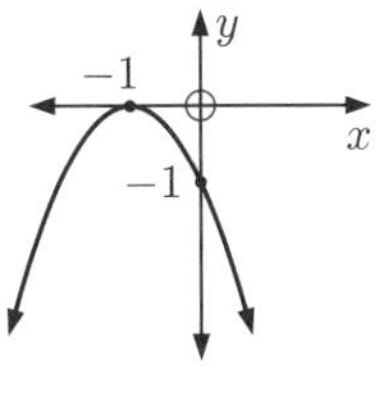


**c**

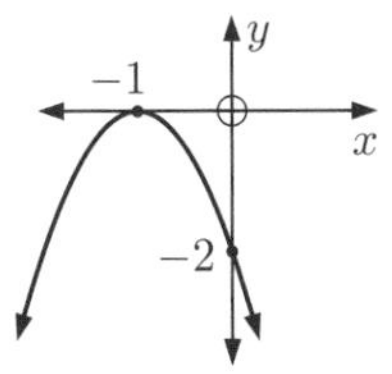


**d**

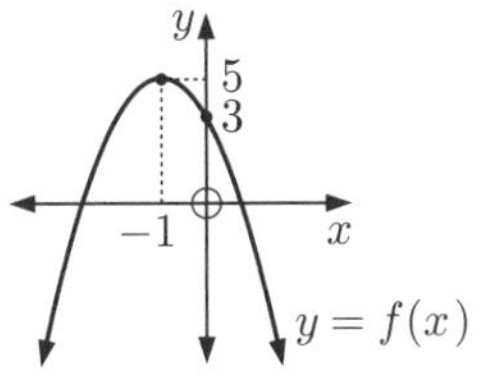


**11** **a** A train starts from rest. Its acceleration after $t$ seconds is $(c - \frac{1}{10}t)$ m s$^{-2}$, where $c$ is a constant. At the end of the first minute its speed is 30 ms$^{-1}$. Find the distance travelled in the first minute.

**b** **i** Find the area contained between the curve $y = 12 - x - x^2$ and the line $y = x + 4$.

**ii** Illustrate by shading regions on a diagram the geometric meaning of the definite integral $\int_{-5}^{2} (8 - 2x - x^2)\,dx$.

**12** Let $\mathbf{A} = \begin{pmatrix} 3 & 2 \\ -2 & -1 \end{pmatrix}$.

**a** Find $\mathbf{A}^2$.
**b** Find constants $a$ and $b$ such that $\mathbf{A}^2 = a\mathbf{A} + b\mathbf{I}$.
**c** Show that $\mathbf{A}^{-1}$ exists.
**d** Find $\mathbf{A}^{-1}$ in terms of $\mathbf{A}$ and $\mathbf{I}$.

**13** A bin contains 4 green balls and 3 red balls. Two balls are chosen at random from the bin, without replacement. Let $X$ denote the number of green balls chosen.

**a** Complete the following table to show the probability distribution for $X$.

| $x$ | 0 | 1 | 2 |
|---|---|---|---|
| $\text{P}(X = x)$ | | | |

**b** Calculate $\text{E}(X)$, the mean number of green balls chosen.

**14** $3x - 6y = 10$ and $x + ky = 4$ are two straight lines.
Find the value of $k$ if the lines are:
**a** parallel **b** perpendicular.

**15** The function $f$ is composed of the arcs of two circles.

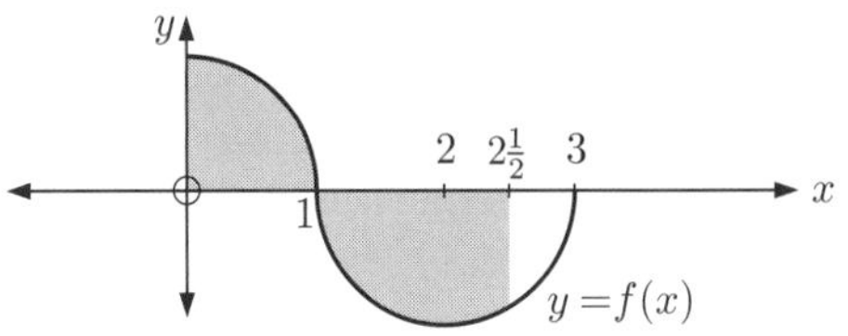


Find: **a** $\int_1^{2\frac{1}{2}} f(x)\,dx$ **b** $\int_0^{2\frac{1}{2}} f(x)\,dx$

**16** The function $f$ is defined by $f : x \mapsto 3 + 2x - x^2$.

**a** Find the axes intercepts of the graph $y = f(x)$.
**b** Write $f$ in the form $a(x - h)^2 + k$ and hence write down the coordinates of the vertex of the graph.
**c** Find the equation of the tangent to the curve $y = f(x)$ at the point where $x = 2$.
**d** Find the area of the region enclosed by $y = f(x)$, the $x$-axis, and the tangent found in **c**.

**17** Evaluate:

**a** $\int_0^1 (2x + 1)^3\,dx$ **b** $\int_0^7 \sqrt{3x + 4}\,dx$

**c** $\int_e^{2e} \dfrac{1}{2x + e}\,dx$ **d** $\int_{\frac{\pi}{6}}^{\frac{\pi}{3}} \sin 2x\,dx$

**18** Consider $f(x) = \sqrt{\ln x}$.

**a** State the domain and range of $f$.
**b** Find the gradient of the tangent to the curve at the point where $x = e$.
**c** Differentiate $x \ln x$ and hence find $\int \ln x\,dx$.
**d** Find the volume of the solid generated when the region bounded by the curve $y = \sqrt{\ln x}$, the $x$-axis, and the line $x = e$, is rotated through $360^o$ about the $x$-axis.

**19** The paddle wheel of a riverboat has a circular disc of radius 6 m. The wheel turns anti-clockwise at a constant rate of 3 revolutions every minute. The centre of the disc lies 3 m above the waterline. Sammy the freshwater snail is attached to the outer rim of the disc.

**a** In any given hour, how much time does Sammy spend under water?
**b** What is the area of the disc which is submerged at any given time?
**c** Sammy's height above the water at time $t$ seconds can be modelled by the function $h(t) = a + b\sin ct$ metres. Find the values of $a$, $b$ and $c$.

**20** Two spotlights are located at A(1, 0, 0) and B(3, 4, 0). Each unit of the grid represents 10 m.
The light from A shines in the direction $\mathbf{i} + 3\mathbf{j} + 5\mathbf{k}$.
The light from B is represented by

$$\mathbf{r}_\text{B} = \begin{pmatrix} 3 \\ 4 \\ 0 \end{pmatrix} + t\begin{pmatrix} 1 \\ 1 \\ -5 \end{pmatrix},\quad t \geqslant 0.$$

**a** Write a vector equation for the beam of light from A.
**b** Find the coordinates of the point where the beams meet.
**c** A bird flies through the intersection of the beams, and two seconds later is at the point (4, 7, 9). Find the speed of the bird.
**d** Find the cosine of the angle between the beams.

## EXAM PRACTICE SET 6 CALCULATORS

**1** An amphitheatre has 30 rows of seats. There are 20 seats in the first row, 23 seats in the second row, and each successive row of seats has 3 more seats than the previous row.

Calculate: **a** the number of seats in the 30th row

**b** the total number of seats in the amphitheatre.

**2** Let $p = \log_b 3$ and $q = \log_b 5$. In terms of $p$ and $q$, write expressions for:

**a** $\log_b 45$ **b** $\log_b 0.6$ **c** $\log_5 3$

**3**

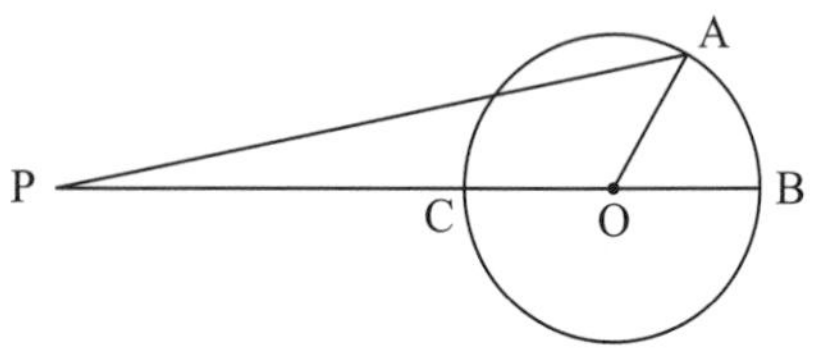


In the diagram above, O is the centre of the circle, and the radius of the circle is 9 cm.

If the size of $\text{A}\hat{\text{O}}\text{B}$ is $40^o$ and $\text{PC} = 12$ cm, find the length of [AP].

**4** **a** A ticket is randomly selected from a basket containing 5 green, 3 yellow, and 2 blue tickets. A second ticket is then chosen without replacing the first ticket.

**i** Draw a tree diagram to represent this experiment, including the probability of each event.

**ii** Find the probability distribution for the number of blue tickets that are chosen.

**iii** Find the probability of getting 2 different coloured tickets.

**b** A manufacturer finds that 7% of gadgets produced are faulty. During an inspection the manager randomly selects 25 gadgets from the production line. Find the probability that the manufacturer selects:

**i** three faulty gadgets **ii** at least three faulty gadgets.

**5** \$20 000 is invested for 8 years. The rate of interest is fixed at 6.7% per annum, compounding annually.

**a** How much will the investment be worth at maturity?

**b** Find the total interest earned in these 8 years.

**6** A school has 82 Year 12 students in classes A, B and C.

There are $x$ students in class A, $y$ students in class B, and $z$ students in class C.

One sixth of class A, one third of class B, and one half of class C study Physics.

One tenth of class A, three eighths of class B, and one quarter of class C study Chinese.

27 students study Physics and 19 study Chinese.

**a** Show carefully how the information given leads to the following system of equations:

$$\begin{cases} x + y + z = 82 \\ x + 2y + 3z = 162 \\ 4x + 15y + 10z = 760 \end{cases}$$

**b** Find the number of students in each of the three classes.

**7** The quadratic function $f$ is defined by $f(x) = 2x^2 - 12x + 25$.

**a** Write $f$ in the form $f(x) = 2(x - h)^2 + k$.

**b** The graph of $y = f(x)$ is translated 5 units in the positive $x$-direction and then reflected in the $x$-axis. Find the equation of the transformed graph $y = g(x)$, giving your answer in the form $g(x) = a(x - p)^2 + q$.

**8** The different types of ticket sold for this weekend's football match are summarised in the following table:

| | *Adult* | *Concession* |
|---|---|---|
| *Category A* | 345 | 138 |
| *Category B* | 1623 | 1215 |

**a** How many tickets for the match have been sold?

**b** A person in the crowd is randomly selected to toss the coin at the start of the match. Find the probability that the person selected is:

**i** an adult **ii** sitting in a Category B seat.

**c** A concession ticket holder is randomly selected to receive an autographed team shirt. Find the probability that the recipient is sitting in a Category A seat.

**9** In a large company the ages of employees are normally distributed with random variable $X$. Find the mean and standard deviation of $X$ if $\text{P}(X < 20) = 0.08$ and $\text{P}(X > 35) = 0.23$.

**10** Find the constant term in the expansion of $\left(\frac{2}{x} + x^2\right)^6$.

**11** Consider the function $f(x) = a\ln x + b$ where $a > 0$.

The normal to the curve at $x = 1$ and the tangent to the curve at $x = e^2$ both pass through the origin. Find $a$ and $b$.

**12** 60 people were randomly selected in the mall and asked about what television programs they were interested in. 35 said they were interested in sport and 28 said they liked watching movies. 16 said they never watched sport or a movie.

**a** Display the given information on a Venn diagram.

**b** Estimate the probability that a randomly selected person:

**i** watches movies **ii** is not interested in sport

**iii** likes both sport and movies

**iv** likes movies but is not interested in sport.

**13** Solve for $x$:

**a** $25^x + 5^{x+1} + 6 = 0$ **b** $\ln\sqrt{x} - \ln x^2 = (\ln x)^2$

**14** Given $\tan\theta = -2$ and $\frac{\pi}{2} < \theta < \frac{3\pi}{2}$, find:

**a** $\sin\theta$ **b** $\cos\theta$

**15** The price of a stockmarket share at time $t$ months, $t \geqslant 0$, is given by $P(t) = 15 + t + 2\sin t$ dollars.

The figure shows the graph of $P(t)$, $0 \leqslant t \leqslant 2\pi$.

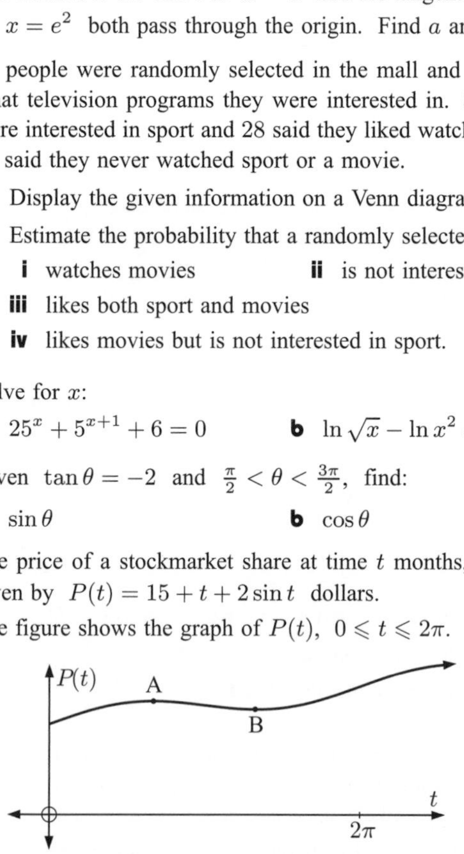


**a** Find the coordinates of point A, the first local maximum.

**b** Find the fall in price between point A and point B, the first local minimum.

**16** Let $\begin{pmatrix} 1 \\ 0 \end{pmatrix}$ represent a displacement of 1 km due east and $\begin{pmatrix} 0 \\ 1 \end{pmatrix}$ represent a displacement of 1 km due north.

The following diagram shows the position of buoys A, B and C in relation to a sailing club at the point O(0, 0).

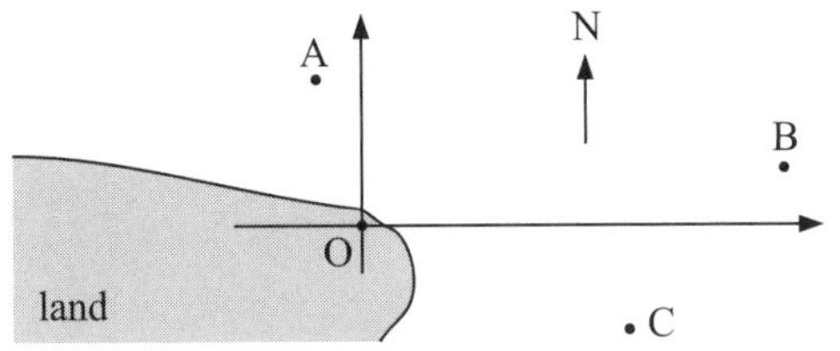


Buoy A is 2 km west and 24 km north of O.
Buoy B is 18 km east and 9 km north of O.
Buoy C is 8 km east and 15 km south of O.
At 9:00 am a yacht left A and sailed directly towards B at 10 $\text{km h}^{-1}$.
The position of the yacht $t$ hours after leaving A is given by the vector equation $\begin{pmatrix} x \\ y \end{pmatrix} = \begin{pmatrix} p \\ q \end{pmatrix} + t\begin{pmatrix} a \\ b \end{pmatrix}$.

**a** Find the values of $p$ and $q$. **b** Find $\overrightarrow{AB}$.

**c** Show that the velocity vector of the yacht is $\begin{pmatrix} 8 \\ -6 \end{pmatrix}$.

**d** Find the position of the yacht at 10:30 am.

**e** At what time did the yacht reach B?

After reaching the buoy at B, the yacht sailed directly to C at a constant speed of 13 km $\text{h}^{-1}$.

**f** At what time did the yacht reach C?

**g** Express, in terms of $t$, the coordinates of the yacht at any time when the yacht was between B and C.

**h** At what time after 11:30 am was the yacht closest to the sailing club?

**17** The population of a species of bird is given by

$$N(T) = b + cT + \frac{a}{T+1} \text{ thousands}$$

where $a$, $b$ and $c$ are constants, $T$ is time in years, and $T = 0$ is the beginning of the year 2000.
After 1 year there were 4000 birds and after 2 years there were 5000 birds. After 3 years there were 6500 birds.

**a** Show that the information above can be represented by the system of equations: $\begin{cases} a + 2b + 2c = 8 \\ a + 3b + 6c = 15 \\ a + 4b + 12c = 26. \end{cases}$

**b** Use matrix methods to find the values of $a$, $b$ and $c$.

**c** When did the population of birds reach 10 000?

**18** **a** Sketch the graph of $f(x) = \sqrt{2x+1}$ on $0 \leqslant x \leqslant 4$.

**b** If the graph in **a** is rotated about the $x$-axis to create a solid of revolution, what will be its volume?

**c** Suppose $f(x) = \sqrt{2x+1}$ is revolved about the $x$-axis on $k \leqslant x \leqslant 2k$ to create a solid of revolution. Find $k$ if the volume of the solid is 30 $\text{units}^3$.

**d**

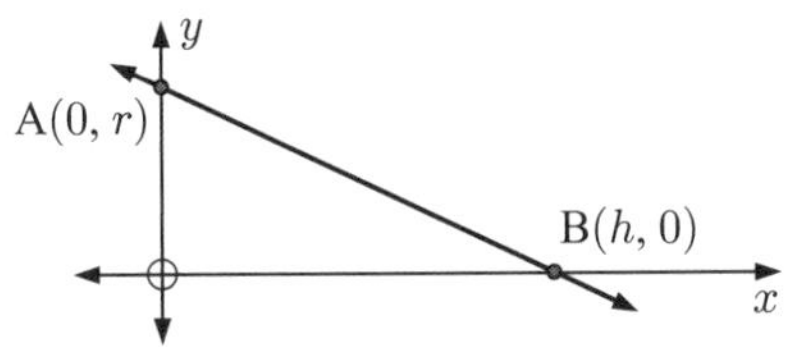


**i** Find the equation of the line (AB).

**ii** Illustrate what happens when the line segment [AB] is revolved about the $x$-axis.

**iii** Find a formula for the volume of the solid in **ii**.

**19** **a** Consider $y(t) = 8 - 4\cos(\frac{\pi}{4}t)$, $0 \leqslant t \leqslant 8$.

**i** State the period of $y(t)$.

**ii** Find the minimum value of $y(t)$ and when it occurs.

**iii** Find the maximum value of $y(t)$ and when it occurs.

**iv** Sketch the graph of $y(t)$.

**b** A simplified model for the depth of water at the entrance to a harbour is $y(t) = 8 - 4\cos(\frac{\pi}{4}t)$ metres, where $t$ is time measured in hours.

**i** What are the depths of water at low tide and high tide, when the water is at the lowest and highest levels?

**ii** On a certain day low tide occurs at 11.30 am. At what time is the next high tide?

**iii** A ship needs a depth of 9 metres of water to enter the harbour. Use the model $y(t) = 8 - 4\cos(\frac{\pi}{4}t)$ to find, to the nearest minute, the earliest time after low tide at 11.30 am when the ship can enter the harbour.

**20** In this question, distances are in kilometres and time is in hours.
An airport is situated at the point A(2, $-1$, 0).

The vectors $\begin{pmatrix} 1 \\ 0 \\ 0 \end{pmatrix}$ and $\begin{pmatrix} 0 \\ 1 \\ 0 \end{pmatrix}$ represent displacements of 1 km to the east and to the north of the airport respectively. $\begin{pmatrix} 0 \\ 0 \\ 1 \end{pmatrix}$ represents a vertical displacement of 1 km above the airport.
A small airplane is flying along a straight stretch of coast on beach patrol. It is moving at a constant height with a speed of 200 km $\text{h}^{-1}$ in the direction $\begin{pmatrix} 4 \\ -3 \\ 0 \end{pmatrix}$.

At 10:00 am, the airplane is at point B with coordinates ($-10$, 50, 1).

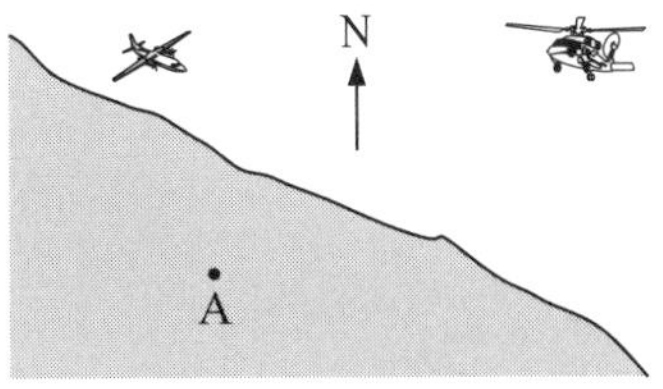


Meanwhile, an emergency medical helicopter is returning to the airport after completing a mission to a distant island. The position vector of the helicopter $t$ hours after 10:00 am is given by

$$\mathbf{h} = \begin{pmatrix} x \\ y \\ z \end{pmatrix} = \begin{pmatrix} 74 \\ 29 \\ 0.5 \end{pmatrix} + t\begin{pmatrix} -120 \\ -50 \\ 0.5 \end{pmatrix}.$$

**a** How far is the airplane from the airport at 10:00 am?

**b** Show that the position vector of the airplane $t$ hours after 10:00 am is

$$\mathbf{r} = \begin{pmatrix} x \\ y \\ z \end{pmatrix} = \begin{pmatrix} -10 \\ 50 \\ 1 \end{pmatrix} + t\begin{pmatrix} 160 \\ -120 \\ 0 \end{pmatrix}.$$

**c** Find the coordinates of the airplane at 10:30 am.

**d** At what height is the helicopter flying when $t = 0$?

**e** Find the speed of the helicopter.

**f** At the moment that the helicopter pilot notices that he is directly beneath the airplane, he begins his descent (in a straight line) to the airport.

**i** Find the time when the helicopter is directly beneath the airplane.

**ii** Find the coordinates of the helicopter at this time.

**iii** If the helicopter maintains an average speed equal to its present speed, find the time at which it will arrive at the airport.

# SOLUTIONS TO TOPIC 1 (ALGEBRA)

## NO CALCULATORS

**1** **a** 51, 45, 39, 33, .... is an arithmetic sequence with $u_1 = 51$ and $d = -6$.

$$\therefore \quad u_{20} = u_1 + 19d = 51 + 19 \times -6 = 51 - 114 = -63$$

**b** 0.125, 0.5, 2, 8, .... is a geometric sequence with $u_1 = \frac{1}{8}$ and $r = 4$.

$$\therefore \quad u_{20} = u_1 r^{19} = \tfrac{1}{8} \times 4^{19} = 2^{-3} \times 2^{38} = 2^{35}$$

**2** $u_1 = 27$ and $u_4 = 8$

$\therefore \; u_1 r^3 = 8$

$\therefore \; r^3 = \frac{8}{27}$

$\therefore \; r = \frac{2}{3}$

$\therefore$ the series has sum

$$S = \frac{u_1}{1-r} = \frac{27}{1 - \frac{2}{3}} = 81$$

**3** **a** $u_7 = 1$ and $u_{15} = -23$

$\therefore \; u_1 + 6d = 1$ and $u_1 + 14d = -23$

$\therefore \; u_{15} - u_7 = (u_1 + 14d) - (u_1 + 6d) = -23 - 1$

$\therefore \; 8d = -24$

$\therefore \; d = -3$

and $u_1 = 1 - 6d = 19$

So, $u_{27} = u_1 + 26d = 19 + 26(-3) = -59$

**b** $S_n = \frac{n}{2}(u_1 + u_n)$

$$\therefore \quad S_{27} = \tfrac{27}{2}(u_1 + u_{27}) = \tfrac{27}{2}(19 - 59) = -540$$

**4** **a** $x^2, 3x^2, 5x^2, ....$ is arithmetic with $u_1 = x^2$, $d = 2x^2$.

$$\therefore \quad u_{10} = u_1 + 9d = x^2 + 9(2x^2) = 19x^2$$

**b** $x^{-\frac{1}{2}}, x, x^{2\frac{1}{2}}, ....$ is geometric with $u_1 = x^{-\frac{1}{2}}$, $r = x^{1\frac{1}{2}}$.

$$\therefore \quad u_{10} = u_1 r^9 = x^{-\frac{1}{2}}\left(x^{\frac{3}{2}}\right)^9 = x^{-\frac{1}{2}+\frac{27}{2}} = x^{13}$$

**5** $u_1 = 18$ and $d = -3$.
If the series has $n$ terms, then

$$S_n = -210$$

$$\therefore \quad \frac{n}{2}(2u_1 + (n-1)d) = -210$$

$$\therefore \quad \frac{n}{2}(2 \times 18 + (n-1) \times (-3)) = -210$$

$$\therefore \quad \frac{n}{2}(36 - 3n + 3) = -210$$

$$n(39 - 3n) = -420$$

$$\therefore \quad 3n^2 - 39n - 420 = 0$$

$$\therefore \quad 3(n^2 - 13n - 140) = 0$$

$$\therefore \quad 3(n - 20)(n + 7) = 0$$

$$\therefore \quad n = 20 \;\; \{n > 0\}$$

So there are 20 terms in the series.

**6** **a** $(5x^2)^3 \times \left(\frac{x}{4}\right)^2 \times \frac{8}{25x^5}$

$= 5^3 x^6 \times \frac{x^2}{2^4} \times \frac{2^3}{5^2 x^5}$

$= 2^{3-4} 5^{3-2} x^{6+2-5}$

$= \frac{5}{2} x^3$

**b** $\frac{24a^3b^8}{15(a^2b)^3} \div \frac{5ab^3}{12a^6b}$

$= \frac{24a^3b^8}{15a^6b^3} \times \frac{12a^6b}{5ab^3}$

$= \frac{\overset{8}{\cancel{24}} \times 12}{\underset{5}{\cancel{15}} \times 5} a^{3-6+6-1} b^{8-3+1-3}$

$= \frac{96}{25} a^2 b^3$

**c** $\frac{8x^{-2}y^3}{3(xy^2)^0} \times \frac{9x^0y^{-1}}{4x^{-3}}$

$= \frac{8x^{-2}y^3}{3} \times \frac{9y^{-1}}{4x^{-3}}$

$= \frac{8 \times 9}{3 \times 4} x^{-2-(-3)} y^{3+(-1)}$

$= 6x^1y^2$

$= 6xy^2$

**d** $\frac{4x^{\frac{1}{2}} \times x^{-1\frac{1}{2}}}{8x^2}$

$= \frac{4}{8} x^{\frac{1}{2}-1\frac{1}{2}-2}$

$= \frac{1}{2} x^{-3}$

$= \frac{1}{2x^3}$

**e** $\sqrt[5]{a^3} \times \sqrt{a^5}$

$= a^{\frac{3}{5}} \times a^{\frac{5}{2}}$

$= a^{\frac{3}{5}+\frac{5}{2}}$

$= a^{\frac{31}{10}}$

$= a^{3.1}$

**7** **a** $16^{-\frac{1}{2}} = (4^2)^{-\frac{1}{2}} = 4^{-1} = \frac{1}{4}$

**b** $81^{\frac{1}{4}} = (3^4)^{\frac{1}{4}} = 3^1 = 3$

**c** $32^{\frac{2}{5}} = (2^5)^{\frac{2}{5}} = 2^2 = 4$

**d** $27^{-\frac{4}{3}} = (3^3)^{-\frac{4}{3}} = 3^{-4} = \frac{1}{3^4} = \frac{1}{81}$

**e** $\left(\frac{1}{9}\right)^{\frac{3}{2}} = (3^{-2})^{\frac{3}{2}} = 3^{-3} = \frac{1}{3^3} = \frac{1}{27}$

**f** $(0.008)^{-\frac{5}{3}} = \left(\frac{8}{1000}\right)^{-\frac{5}{3}} = \left(\frac{2}{10}\right)^{3\times-\frac{5}{3}} = \left(\frac{1}{5}\right)^{-5} = (5^{-1})^{-5} = 5^5$ or 3125

**8** **a** $9^x - 6(3^x) + 8 = (3^x)^2 - 6(3^x) + 8 = (3^x - 4)(3^x - 2)$

**b** $25^x + 5^{x+1} + 6 = (5^x)^2 + 5(5^x) + 6 = (5^x + 2)(5^x + 3)$

**9** **a** $\log 2 + \log 12 = \log(2 \times 12) = \log 24$

**b** $\log 36 - \log 12 = \log\left(\frac{36}{12}\right) = \log 3$

**c** $3\log 5 + 2\log 3 = \log 5^3 + \log 3^2 = \log(5^3 \times 3^2) = \log(125 \times 9) = \log 1125$

**d** $\frac{1}{4}\log 81 = \log 81^{\frac{1}{4}} = \log(3^4)^{\frac{1}{4}} = \log 3$

**10** $8^{2x-3} = 16^{2-x}$

$\therefore\ (2^3)^{2x-3} = (2^4)^{2-x}$

$\therefore\ 2^{6x-9} = 2^{8-4x}$

$\therefore\ 6x - 9 = 8 - 4x$

$\therefore\ 10x = 17$

$\therefore\ x = \frac{17}{10}$

**11** $\dfrac{3^{x+1} - 3^x}{2(3^x) - 3^{x-1}}$

$= \dfrac{3^{x-1}(3^2 - 3)}{3^{x-1}(2 \times 3 - 1)}$

$= \frac{6}{5}$

**12** $4^x + 4 = 17(2^{x-1})$

$\therefore\ 2^{2x} - 17(2^{x-1}) + 4 = 0$

$\therefore\ 2 \times 2^{2x} - 17(2^x) + 8 = 0$

$\therefore\ 2(2^x)^2 - 17(2^x) + 8 = 0$

$\therefore\ (2(2^x) - 1)(2^x - 8) = 0$

$\therefore\ 2^x = \frac{1}{2}$ or $8$

$\therefore\ 2^x = 2^{-1}$ or $2^3$

$\therefore\ x = -1$ or $3$

**13** **a** $\log_{10}(P^2 Q \sqrt{R})$

$= \log P^2 + \log Q + \log R^{\frac{1}{2}}$

$= 2\log P + \log Q + \frac{1}{2}\log R$

$= 2A + B + \frac{1}{2}C$

**b** $\log\left(\dfrac{R^3}{(PQ^2)^4}\right)$

$= \log R^3 - \log(PQ^2)^4$

$= 3\log R - 4\log(PQ^2)$

$= 3\log R - 4(\log P + \log Q^2)$

$= 3\log R - 4\log P - 8\log Q$

$= 3C - 4A - 8B$

**14** $\log_5(2x - 1) = -1$

$\therefore\ 5^{-1} = 2x - 1$

$\therefore\ \frac{1}{5} = 2x - 1$

$\therefore\ \frac{6}{5} = 2x$

$\therefore\ x = \frac{3}{5}$

**15** $\log_b a = \dfrac{\log_c a}{\log_c b}$

$\therefore\ \log_5 9 = \dfrac{\log_3 9}{\log_3 5}$

$\therefore\ \dfrac{8}{\log_5 9} = \dfrac{8}{\frac{\log_3 9}{\log_3 5}}$

$= \dfrac{8\log_3 5}{\log_3 9}$

$= \dfrac{8\log_3 5}{2}$

$= 4\log_3 5$

**16** $2\ln x + \ln(x - 1) - \ln(x - 2)$

$= \ln x^2 + \ln(x - 1) - \ln(x - 2)$

$= \ln\left(\dfrac{x^2(x - 1)}{(x - 2)}\right)$

**17** $\log_3 x + \log_3(x - 2) = 1$

$\therefore\ \log_3(x(x - 2)) = 1$

$\therefore\ 3^1 = x(x - 2)$

$\therefore\ 3 = x^2 - 2x$

$\therefore\ x^2 - 2x - 3 = 0$

$\therefore\ (x - 3)(x + 1) = 0$

$\therefore\ x = 3$ {since $x > 2$}

**18** **a** $\log_a(5a)$

$= \log_a 5 + \log_a a$

$= x + 1$

**b** $\log_a\left(\dfrac{a^2}{25}\right)$

$= \log_a a^2 - \log_a 25$

$= 2 - 2\log_a 5$

$= 2 - 2x$

**19** **a** $M = ab^3$

$\therefore\ \log_b M = \log_b(ab^3)$

$\therefore\ \log_b M = \log_b a + \log_b b^3$

$\therefore\ \log_b M = \log_b a + 3$

**b** $D = \dfrac{a}{b^2}$

$\therefore\ \log_b D = \log_b\left(\dfrac{a}{b^2}\right)$

$\therefore\ \log_b D = \log_b a - \log_b b^2$

$\therefore\ \log_b D = \log_b a - 2$

**20** **a** $\log_{10} M = 2x - 1$

$\therefore\ 10^{\log_{10} M} = 10^{2x-1}$

$\therefore\ M = 10^{2x-1}$

**b** $\log_a N = 2\log_a d - \log_a c$

$\therefore\ \log_a N = \log_a d^2 - \log_a c$

$\therefore\ \log_a N = \log_a\left(\dfrac{d^2}{c}\right)$

$\therefore\ N = \dfrac{d^2}{c}$

**21**

$$\begin{array}{ccccccccccc} & & & & & 1 & & & & & \\ & & & & 1 & & 1 & & & & \\ & & & 1 & & 2 & & 1 & & & \\ & & 1 & & 3 & & 3 & & 1 & & \\ & 1 & & 4 & & 6 & & 4 & & 1 & \\ 1 & & 5 & & 10 & & 10 & & 5 & & 1 \end{array} \quad \leftarrow \text{5th row, for } (a+b)^5$$

Using the 5th row of Pascal's triangle,

$(a + b)^5 = a^5 + 5a^4b + 10a^3b^2 + 10a^2b^3 + 5ab^4 + b^5$

$\therefore\ \left(x + \frac{1}{x}\right)^5 = x^5 + 5x^4\left(\frac{1}{x}\right) + 10x^3\left(\frac{1}{x}\right)^2 + 10x^2\left(\frac{1}{x}\right)^3 + 5x\left(\frac{1}{x}\right)^4 + \left(\frac{1}{x}\right)^5$

$= x^5 + 5x^3 + 10x + \dfrac{10}{x} + \dfrac{5}{x^3} + \dfrac{1}{x^5}$

## CALCULATORS

**1** $u_n = u_1 + (n - 1)d$

$= 100 + (n - 1)30$

So, we want to find $n$ where $100 + 30(n - 1) > 1200$

$\therefore\ 30(n - 1) > 1100$

$\therefore\ n - 1 > 36.667$

$\therefore\ n > 37.667$

$\therefore$ the first term is $u_{38}$ which is 1210.

**2** $u_5 = u_1 r^4 = 18$ and $u_8 = u_1 r^7 = 486$

$\therefore\ \dfrac{u_1 r^7}{u_1 r^4} = \dfrac{486}{18}$

$\therefore\ r^3 = 27$ and so $r = 3$

Since $u_1 r^4 = 18$, $u_1 \times 81 = 18$

$\therefore\ u_1 = \frac{2}{9}$

So, $u_{12} = u_1 r^{11}$

$= \frac{2}{9} \times 3^{11}$

$= \dfrac{2 \times 3^{11}}{3^2}$

$= 2 \times 3^9$ or $39\,366$

**3** **a** Her annual amount is geometric with $u_1 = 800$, $r = 107\% = 1.07$ and $n = 9$.

$u_9 = u_1 \times r^8 = 800 \times (1.07)^8$

$\approx 1374.55$ euro

**b** We need to solve $800 \times (1.07)^n = 4000$

$\therefore \quad (1.07)^n = 5$

$\therefore \quad \log(1.07)^n = \log 5$

$\therefore \quad n\log(1.07) = \log 5$

$\therefore \quad n = \dfrac{\log 5}{\log(1.07)}$

$\therefore \quad n \approx 23.79$

So, it will take 24 years.

**4** **a** $u_1 = 10$

$u_2 = 10 \times 110\% = 10 \times 1.1$

$u_3 = u_2 \times 1.1 = 10 \times (1.1)^2$

$\vdots$

$u_7 = 10 \times (1.1)^6 = 17.715\,61$

So, Ying ran 17.7 km on day 7.

**b** Total distance ran $= u_1 + u_2 + u_3 + .... + u_7$ which is geometric with $u_1 = 10,\ r = 1.1,\ n = 7$

$$\therefore\ S_7 = \frac{10\left((1.1)^7 - 1\right)}{1.1 - 1} = \frac{10\left((1.1)^7 - 1\right)}{0.1} \approx 94.8717$$

So, Ying ran a total of 94.9 km.

**5** **a** $10 + 14 + 18 + .... + 138$ is arithmetic with $u_1 = 10,\ d = 4.$

Now $u_1 + (n-1)d = 138$

$\therefore\ 10 + 4(n-1) = 138$

$\therefore\ 4(n-1) = 128$

$\therefore\ n - 1 = 32$

$\therefore\ n = 33$

So, the sum is

$$\frac{n}{2}(u_1 + u_{33}) = \tfrac{33}{2}(10 + 138) = \tfrac{33}{2}(148) = 2442$$

**b** $6 - 12 + 24 - 48 + 96 - .... + 1536$ is geometric with $u_1 = 6,\ r = -2.$

Now $u_1 r^{n-1} = 1536$

$\therefore\ 6 \times (-2)^{n-1} = 1536$

$\therefore\ (-2)^{n-1} = 256$

$\therefore\ (-2)^{n-1} = (-2)^8$

$\therefore\ n - 1 = 8$

$\therefore\ n = 9$

So, the sum is

$$\frac{u_1(1-r^n)}{1-r} = \frac{6(1-(-2)^9)}{1-(-2)} = \tfrac{6}{3}\left(1 - (-2)^9\right) = 2 \times 513 = 1026$$

**6** **a** $\dfrac{u_1}{1-r} = 1.5$

and $u_1 = 1$

$\therefore\ 1 - r = \frac{1}{1.5}$

$\therefore\ 1 - r = \frac{2}{3}$

$\therefore\ r = \frac{1}{3}$

**b** $S_n = \dfrac{u_1(1-r^n)}{1-r}$

$$\therefore\ S_7 = \frac{u_1(1-r^7)}{1-r} = \frac{1\left(1 - (\frac{1}{3})^7\right)}{1 - \frac{1}{3}} = \tfrac{3}{2}\left(1 - \tfrac{1}{2187}\right) = \tfrac{1093}{729}$$

**7** **a** $$\frac{u_{n+1}}{u_n} = \frac{12\left(\frac{2}{3}\right)^n}{12\left(\frac{2}{3}\right)^{n-1}} = \tfrac{2}{3} \text{ for all } n \in \mathbb{Z}^+$$

So, consecutive terms have a common ratio of $\frac{2}{3}$.

Thus, the sequence is geometric with $r = \frac{2}{3}$.

**b** $$u_5 = 12\left(\tfrac{2}{3}\right)^4 = 12\left(\tfrac{16}{81}\right) = \tfrac{64}{27}$$

**c** **i** $$\sum_{n=1}^{\infty} u_n = \frac{u_1}{1-r} = \frac{12\left(\frac{2}{3}\right)^0}{1 - \frac{2}{3}} = \frac{12}{\frac{1}{3}} = 36$$

**ii** $\displaystyle\sum_{n=1}^{20} u_n = S_{20}$

$$S_n = \frac{u_1(1-r^n)}{1-r}$$

$$\therefore\ S_{20} = \frac{12\left(1 - (\frac{2}{3})^{20}\right)}{1 - \frac{2}{3}} \approx 35.9892$$

**8** Time period $= 33$ months $= 11$ quarters

Interest rate $= 8\%$ p.a. $= 2\%$ per quarter

$\therefore\ r = 1.02$

$\therefore$ the amount after 11 quarters is

$$u_{12} = u_1 \times r^{11} = 3500 \times 1.02^{11} \approx 4351.8101$$

So, the maturing value is £4351.81.

**9** **a** $3^x = 243$

$\therefore\ 3^x = 3^5$

$\therefore\ x = 5$

**b** $5 \times 2^x = 160$

$\therefore\ 2^x = 32$

$\therefore\ 2^x = 2^5$

$\therefore\ x = 5$

**c** $e^x = 27$

$\therefore\ x = \ln 27$

$\therefore\ x \approx 3.30$

**d** $(1.25)^x = 10$

$\therefore\ \log(1.25)^x = \log 10$

$\therefore\ x\log(1.25) = 1$

$\therefore\ x = \dfrac{1}{\log(1.25)}$

$\therefore\ x \approx 10.3$

**e** $7e^x = 100$

$\therefore\ e^x = \frac{100}{7}$

$\therefore\ x = \ln\left(\frac{100}{7}\right) \approx 2.66$

**10** **a** $200e^{\frac{t}{4}} = 1500$

$\therefore\ e^{\frac{t}{4}} = 7.5$

$\therefore\ \dfrac{t}{4} = \ln(7.5)$

$\therefore\ t = 4 \times \ln(7.5)$

$t \approx 8.06$

**b** $0.15e^{0.012t} = 2.18$

$\therefore\ e^{0.012t} = \frac{2.18}{0.15}$

$\therefore\ 0.012t = \ln\left(\frac{218}{15}\right)$

$\therefore\ t = \ln\left(\frac{218}{15}\right) \div 0.012$

$\therefore\ t \approx 223$

**c** $20e^{0.2t} = 250$

$\therefore\ e^{0.2t} = \frac{250}{20} = \frac{25}{2}$

$\therefore\ 0.2t = \ln(12.5)$

$\therefore\ t = \ln(12.5) \div 0.2$

$\therefore\ t \approx 12.6$

**11** $x^2 > e^{-x} \Leftrightarrow x^2 - e^{-x} > 0$

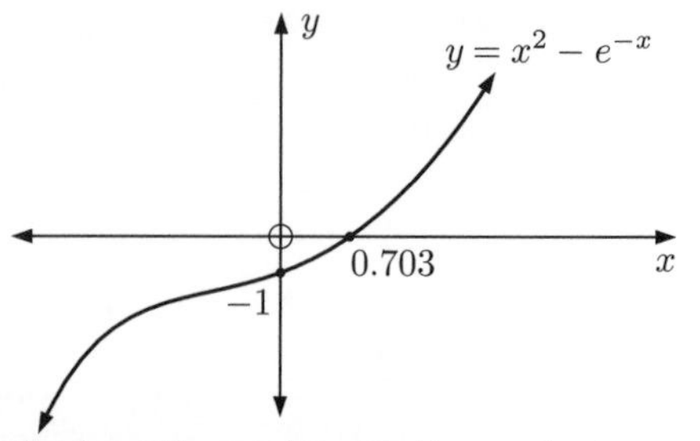


Using technology, the graph meets the $x$-axis at $x \approx 0.703$

Hence $x^2 > e^{-x}$ if $x > 0.703$.

**12** $\left(x+\dfrac{3}{x^2}\right)^9$ has general term

$$T_{r+1}=\binom{9}{r}x^{9-r}\left(\tfrac{3}{x^2}\right)^r,\quad r=0,1,2,....,9$$
$$=\binom{9}{r}x^{9-r}3^rx^{-2r}$$
$$=\binom{9}{r}x^{9-3r}3^r$$

The constant term occurs when $9-3r=0$

$\therefore\ r=3$

and $T_4=\binom{9}{3}3^3=2268$

**13** $(x+2y^3)^7$ has general term

$$T_{r+1}=\binom{7}{r}x^{7-r}(2y^3)^r,\quad r=0,1,2,....,7$$
$$=\binom{7}{r}x^{7-r}2^ry^{3r}$$

Now when $r=3$, $T_4=\binom{7}{3}2^3x^4y^9$

$\therefore$ the coefficient of $x^4y^9$ is $\binom{7}{3}2^3=280$

**14** $\left(2x-\dfrac{1}{x^2}\right)^{12}$ has general term

$$T_{r+1}=\binom{12}{r}(2x)^{12-r}\left(\frac{-1}{x^2}\right)^r$$
$$=\binom{12}{r}2^{12-r}x^{12-r}(-1)^rx^{-2r}$$
$$=\binom{12}{r}2^{12-r}(-1)^rx^{12-3r}$$

**a** $12-3r=3$

$\therefore\ r=3$

$\therefore\ T_4=\binom{12}{3}2^{12-3}(-1)^3x^3=-112\,640x^3$

The coefficient of $x^3$ is $-112\,640$.

**b** $12-3r=0$

$\therefore\ r=4$

$\therefore\ T_5=\binom{12}{4}2^{12-4}(-1)^4x^0=126\,720$

The constant term is 126 720.

**15** $\left(kx+\dfrac{1}{\sqrt{x}}\right)^9$ has general term

$$T_{r+1}=\binom{9}{r}(kx)^{9-r}\left(\frac{1}{\sqrt{x}}\right)^r$$
$$=\binom{9}{r}k^{9-r}x^{9-r}\frac{1}{x^{\frac{r}{2}}}$$
$$=\binom{9}{r}k^{9-r}x^{9-\frac{3r}{2}}$$

For the constant term, $9-\dfrac{3r}{2}=0$

$\therefore\ \dfrac{3r}{2}=9$

$\therefore\ r=6$

$T_7=\binom{9}{6}k^3x^0$

$\therefore\ 84k^3=-10\frac{1}{2}$

$\therefore\ k^3=-\frac{1}{8}$

$\therefore\ k=-\frac{1}{2}$

**16** $(x+2)(1-x)^{10}$

$$=(x+2)\left(\begin{array}{c}1^{10}+\binom{10}{1}1^9(-x)+....+\binom{10}{4}1^6(-x)^4\\ +\binom{10}{5}1^5(-x)^5+....\end{array}\right)$$
$$=(x+2)\left(1-10x+....+\binom{10}{4}x^4-\binom{10}{5}x^5+....\right)$$

So, the terms containing $x^5$ are $\binom{10}{4}x^5$ and $-2\binom{10}{5}x^5$.

$\therefore$ the coefficient of $x^5$ is $\binom{10}{4}-2\binom{10}{5}=-294$

**17** If $A=125\times e^{-kt}$

then $200=125e^{-3k}$

$\therefore\ e^{-3k}=\frac{200}{125}$

$\therefore\ e^{3k}=\frac{125}{200}$ {reciprocals}

$\therefore\ 3k=\ln\left(\frac{125}{200}\right)$

$\therefore\ k=\ln\left(\frac{125}{200}\right)\div3\approx-0.157$

**18** **a** Pierre added $\$10\times8=\$80$

Francesca added $\$(0.50+1+1.5+2+2.5+....+4)$
$=\$18$

**b** $u_{52}=u_1+51d$
$=0.50+51\times0.50$
$=26$ So, she added \$26.

**c** Pierre had $\$10\times52+\$100=\$620$

Francesca had $(0.50+1+1.50+....+26)+100$
$=\frac{52}{2}(0.5+26)+100$
$=26\times26.5+100$
$=\$789$

**19** **a** Hayley: $u_5=u_1+4d=60+4\times20$
$=140$ km in week 5

Patrick: $u_5=u_1r^4=60\times(1.2)^4$
$\approx124$ km in week 5

**b** For Hayley $u_8=60+7\times20=200$
and $u_9=60+8\times20=220$

For Patrick $u_7=60\times(1.2)^6\approx179$
and $u_8=60\times(1.2)^7\approx215$

So, Patrick is the first to cycle 210 km in a week.

**c** Hayley: $S_{12}=\frac{12}{2}(2\times60+11\times20)$
$=6\times(120+220)$
$=2040$ km

Patrick: $S_{12}=\dfrac{60\left([1.2]^{12}-1\right)}{1.2-1}\approx2370$ km

**20** **a** 2002: $u_1=2000$

2003: $u_2=2000+2000\times1.0825$

2004: $u_3=2000+[2000+2000\times1.0825]\times1.0825$
$=2000+2000r+2000r^2$ where $r=1.0825$
$=2000(1+r+r^2)$

2009: Total amount $=2000\left(1+r+r^2+r^3+....+r^7\right)$
$$=2000\left(\frac{r^8-1}{r-1}\right)$$
$$=\frac{2000\left(1.0825^8-1\right)}{0.0825}$$
$\approx21\,466.32$ rupees

**b** 2002: $u_1=2000$

2009: $2000\times8+7\left(\dfrac{2000\times9\times1}{100}\right)$

{8 deposits and 7 years simple interest}
$=16\,000+1260$
$=17\,260$ rupees

So, Kapil will be 4206.32 rupees better off with the compound interest option.

**21** **a** $K(t)=3200\times(0.85)^t$

$\therefore\ K(0)=3200\times1=3200$

So, initially there were 3200 kangaroos.

**b** $K(5) = 3200 \times (0.85)^5$
$\approx 1420$ kangaroos

**c** $N(5) = 2400 + 250 \times 5$
$= 2400 + 1250$
$= 3650$ koalas

**d** When $K(t) < 1000$

$$3200 \times (0.85)^t < 1000$$
$$\therefore \quad (0.85)^t < \tfrac{1000}{3200}$$
$$\therefore \quad \left(\tfrac{1}{0.85}\right)^t > 3.2 \quad \{\text{reciprocals}\}$$
$$\therefore \quad t\log\left(\tfrac{1}{0.85}\right) > \log(3.2)$$
$$\therefore \quad t > \frac{\log(3.2)}{\log\left(\frac{1}{0.85}\right)} \quad \left\{\log\left(\tfrac{1}{0.85}\right) > 0\right\}$$
$$\therefore \quad t > 7.1570$$

So, the kangaroo population falls below 1000 about 7 years 2 months after the start of 2000, which is the end of February 2007.

**e** We need to solve $2400 + 250t > 3200 \times (0.85)^t$.
Using technology, $t \approx 1.102$.
So, the number of koalas exceeds the number of kangaroos about 1 year 1 month after the start of 2000, which is at the start of February 2001.

## SOLUTIONS TO TOPIC 2 (FUNCTIONS AND EQUATIONS)

### NO CALCULATORS

**1** **a** No, as a vertical line can cut the graph more than once.
**b** Yes **c** Yes **d** No **e** No **f** Yes

**2** **a** $G(-1)$
$= 3 - (-1) - 2(-1)^2$
$= 3 + 1 - 2$
$= 2$

**b** $G(3)$
$= 3 - (3) - 2(3)^2$
$= 3 - 3 - 18$
$= -18$

**c** $G(a^3)$
$= 3 - (a^3) - 2(a^3)^2$
$= 3 - a^3 - 2a^6$

**d** $G(a-2)$
$= 3 - (a-2) - 2(a-2)^2$
$= 3 - a + 2 - 2[a^2 - 4a + 4]$
$= -3 + 7a - 2a^2$

**3** $f(x) = 5x - 2, \quad g(x) = 2x + 7$

**a** $(f \circ g)(x)$
$= f(g(x))$
$= f(2x+7)$
$= 5(2x+7) - 2$
$= 10x + 33$

**b** $(g \circ f)(x)$
$= g(f(x))$
$= g(5x-2)$
$= 2(5x-2) + 7$
$= 10x + 3$

**c** $g$ is $y = 2x + 7$ $\quad \therefore \quad g^{-1}$ is $x = 2y + 7$
or $x - 7 = 2y$
or $y = \dfrac{x-7}{2}$
So, $g^{-1}(x) = \dfrac{x-7}{2}$

**4** Domain $= \{x \mid x \geqslant -1, x \neq 1\}$

**5** Domain $= \{x \mid x > 2\}$, Range $= \{y \mid y \in \mathbb{R}\}$

**6** **a** $f(g(x)) = f(4-x)$
$= 3(4-x) + 1$
$= -3x + 13$

**b** $(g \circ f)(x) = g(3x+1)$
$= 4 - (3x+1)$
$= 3 - 3x$
$\therefore \quad (g \circ f)(-4) = 3 - 3(-4)$
$= 15$

**c** $f$ is $y = 3x + 1$, so $f^{-1}$ is $x = 3y + 1$
$\therefore \quad y = \dfrac{x-1}{3}$
$\therefore \quad f^{-1}(x) = \dfrac{x-1}{3}$
so $f^{-1}(\tfrac{1}{2}) = \dfrac{\frac{1}{2} - 1}{3} = -\tfrac{1}{6}$

**7** **a**

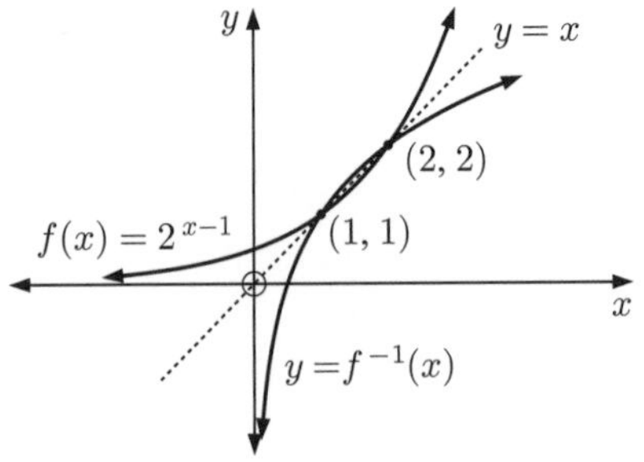


**b** $f(x)$ is $y = 2^{x-1}$
so $f^{-1}(x)$ is $x = 2^{y-1}$
$\therefore \quad \log x = (y-1)\log 2$
$\therefore \quad \dfrac{\log x}{\log 2} = y - 1$
$\therefore \quad y = \log_2 x + 1$
$\therefore \quad f^{-1}(x) = \log_2 x + 1$

**8** **a**

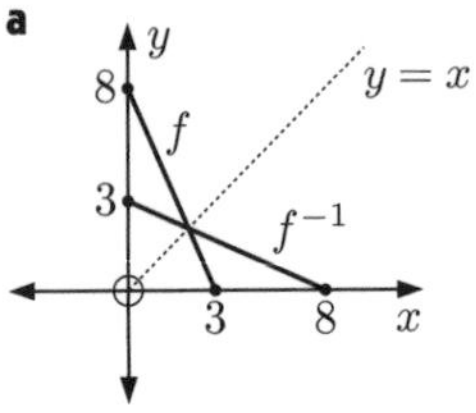


**b**

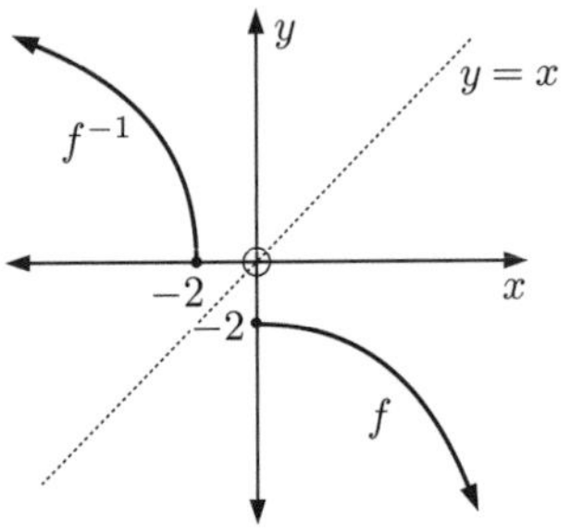


**9** **a**

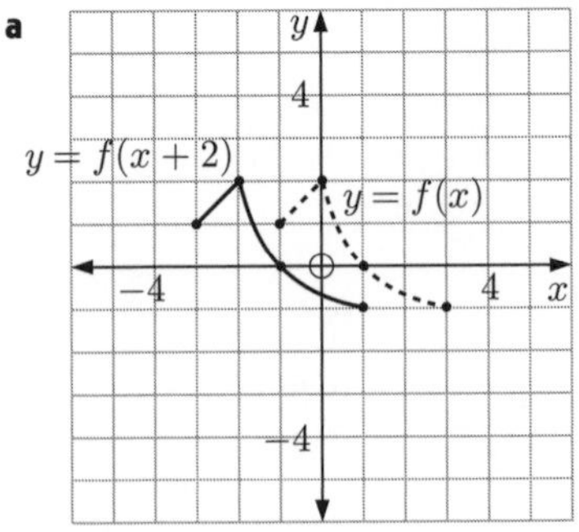


**b**

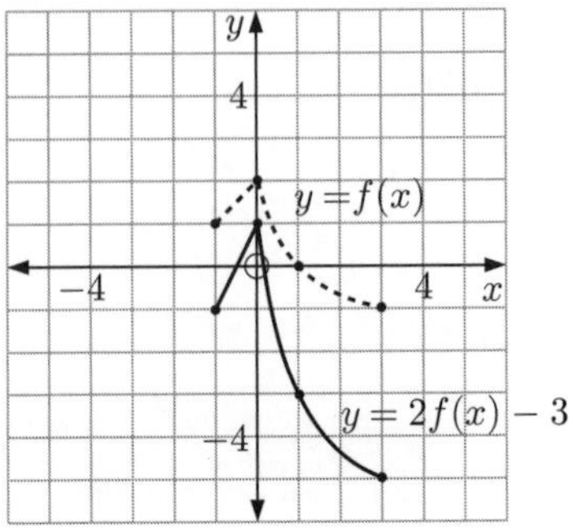

**c**

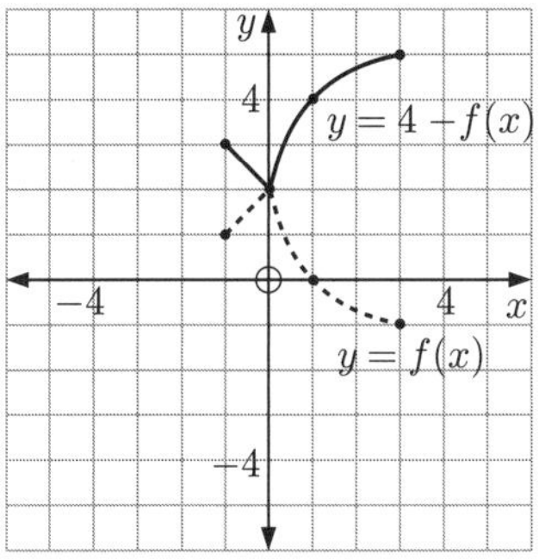


**10** **a**

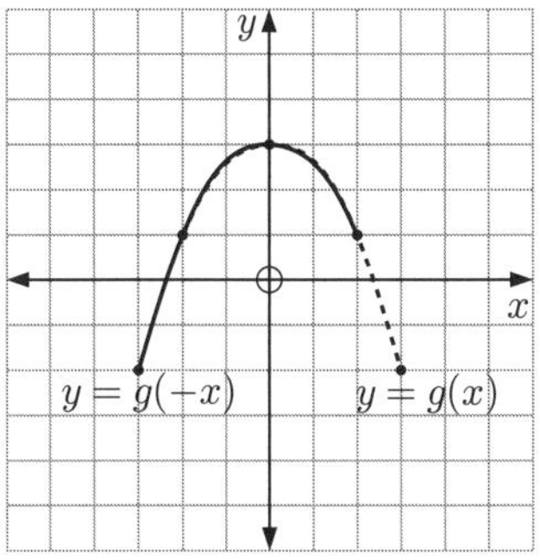


**b**

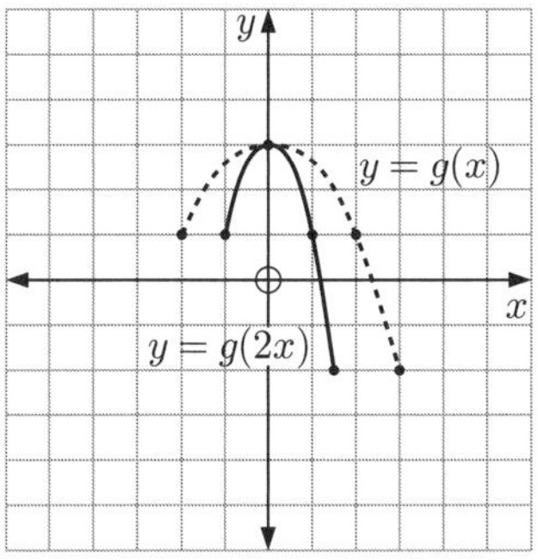


**11** **a** The gradient is $\dfrac{-3-2}{3--7} = \dfrac{-5}{10} = -\frac{1}{2}$

$\therefore$ its equation is $y--3 = -\frac{1}{2}(x-3)$

$\therefore\ 2(y+3) = -(x-3)$

$\therefore\ 2y+6 = -x+3$

$\therefore\ x+2y = -3$

**b** The equation is $y--1 = \frac{3}{5}(x-4)$

$\therefore\ 5(y+1) = 3(x-4)$

$\therefore\ 5y+5 = 3x-12$

$\therefore\ 3x-5y = 17$

**c** $8x+3y=10$ has gradient $-\frac{8}{3}$

$\therefore$ the required line has gradient $\frac{3}{8}$ and equation

$y-8 = \frac{3}{8}(x--2)$

$\therefore\ 8(y-8) = 3(x+2)$

$\therefore\ 8y-64 = 3x+6$

or $3x-8y = -70$

**d** Any line parallel to the $y$-axis has the form $x=k$.

$\therefore$ the equation is $x=4$.

**12** **a**

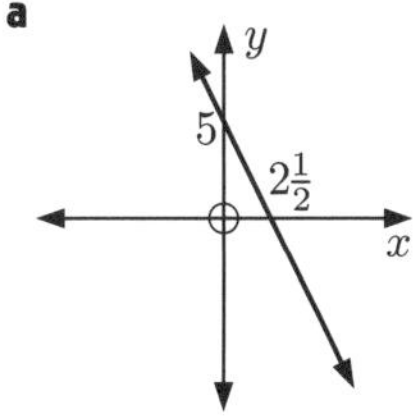


**b**

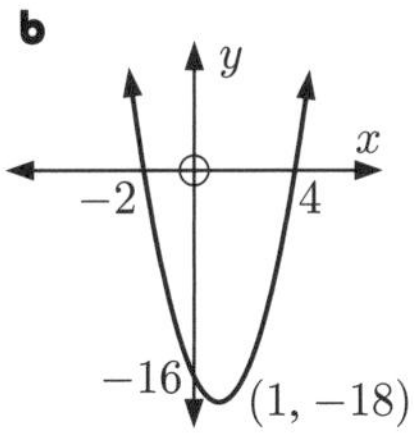


**c**

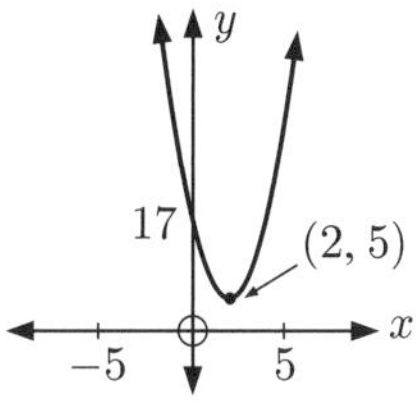


**d**

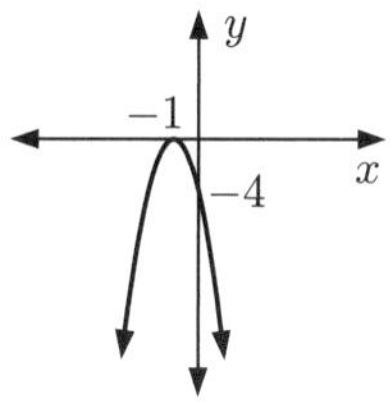


**13** **a** $y = -4x(x+3)$

**i** The graph cuts the $x$-axis when $y=0$

$\therefore\ -4x(x+3) = 0$

$\therefore\ x = 0$ or $-3$

**ii** The axis of symmetry is $x = -1\frac{1}{2}$

**iii** The vertex is at $(-1\frac{1}{2}, f(-\frac{3}{2}))$

which is $\left(-1\frac{1}{2},\ -4\left(-\frac{3}{2}\right)\left(\frac{3}{2}\right)\right)$ or $\left(-1\frac{1}{2}, 9\right)$.

**iv** When $x=0$, $y=0$, so the $y$-intercept is 0.

**v**

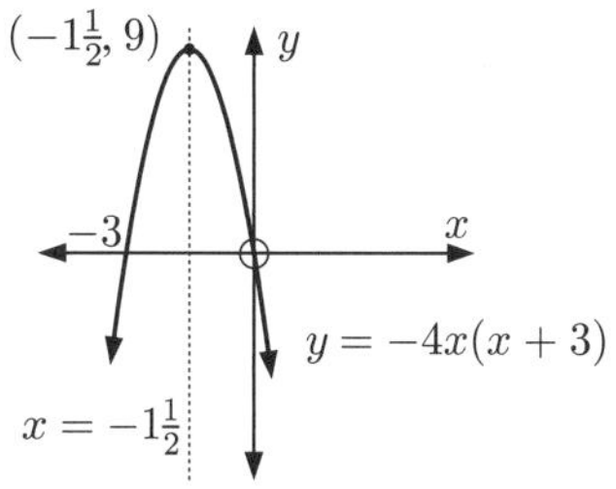


**b** $y = \frac{1}{2}(x+6)(x-4)$

**i** When $y=0$, $x=-6$ or $4$

$\therefore$ the $x$-intercepts are $-6$, $4$.

**ii** The axis of symmetry is $x=-1$.

**iii** The vertex is at $(-1,\ f(-1))$, which is $(-1, -12\frac{1}{2})$.

**iv** When $x=0$, $y = \frac{1}{2}(6)(-4) = -12$

$\therefore$ the $y$-intercept is $-12$.

**v**

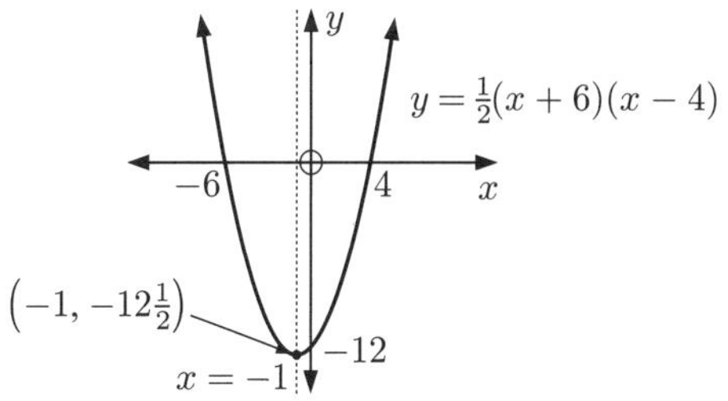


**c** $y = -3(x-2)^2$

**i** The graph cuts $x$-axis when $y=0$ $\therefore\ (x-2)^2 = 0$

$\therefore$ the graph touches the $x$-axis when $x=2$.

**ii** The axis of symmetry is $x=2$.

**iii** The vertex is at $(2, f(2))$, which is $(2, 0)$.

**iv** The $y$-intercept is $f(0) = -3(-2)^2 = -12$.

**v**

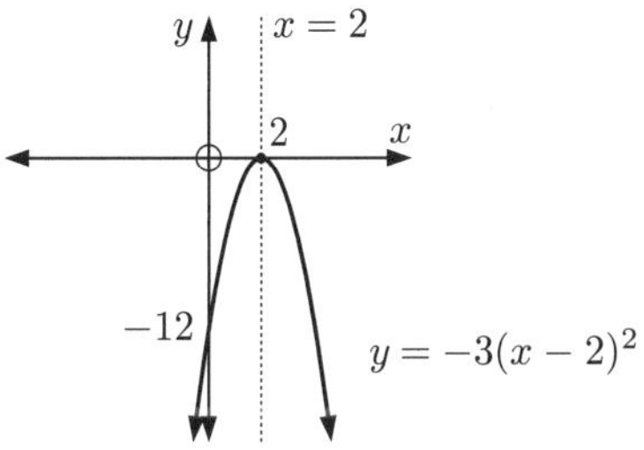


**d** $y = 2(x+5)^2 - 4$

**i** When $y=0$, $2(x+5)^2 - 4 = 0$

$\therefore\ (x+5)^2 = 2$

$\therefore\ x+5 = \pm\sqrt{2}$

$\therefore\ x = -5 \pm \sqrt{2}$

$\therefore$ the $x$-intercepts are $-5+\sqrt{2}$, $-5-\sqrt{2}$.

**ii** The axis of symmetry is $x = -5$.

**iii** The vertex is at $(-5, f(-5))$, which is $(-5, -4)$.

**iv** The $y$-intercept is $f(0) = 2(5)^2 - 4 = 46$.

**v**

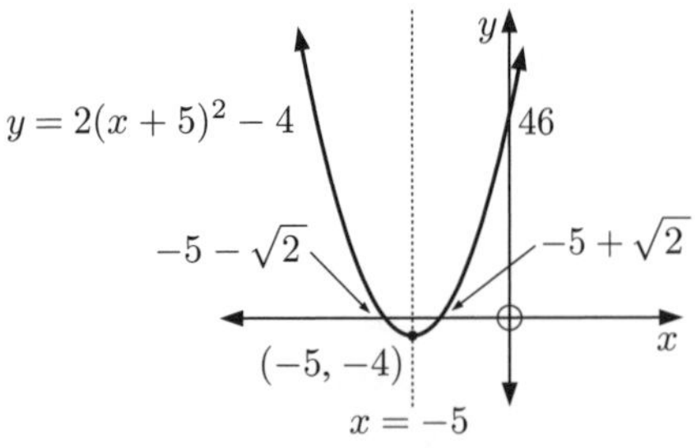


**14** **a** Since the $x$-intercepts are $-1$ and 5,

$f(x) = a(x+1)(x-5)$

But $f(0) = -20$, so $a(1)(-5) = -20$

$\therefore \quad a = 4$

So, $y = 4(x+1)(x-5)$

**b** The graph touches the $x$-axis at $-4$, so

$f(x) = a(x+4)^2$

But $f(0) = -8$, so $a(4)^2 = -8$

$\therefore \quad a = -\frac{1}{2}$

So, $y = -\frac{1}{2}(x+4)^2$

**c** Since the vertex is at $(5, -12)$, $f(x) = a(x-5)^2 - 12$

But $f(0) = 38$, so $a(-5)^2 - 12 = 38$

$\therefore \quad 25a = 50$

$\therefore \quad a = 2$

So, $y = 2(x-5)^2 - 12$

**15** **a** $y = x^2 - 4x + 9$

$= x^2 - 4x + 2^2 + 9 - 2^2$

$= (x-2)^2 + 5$

and the vertex is at $(2, 5)$.

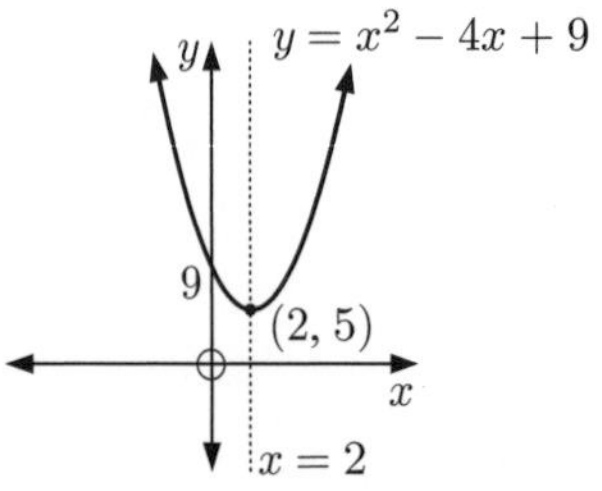


**b** $y = x^2 - 6x - 2$

$= x^2 - 6x + 3^2 - 2 - 3^2$

$= (x-3)^2 - 11$

and the vertex is at $(3, -11)$.

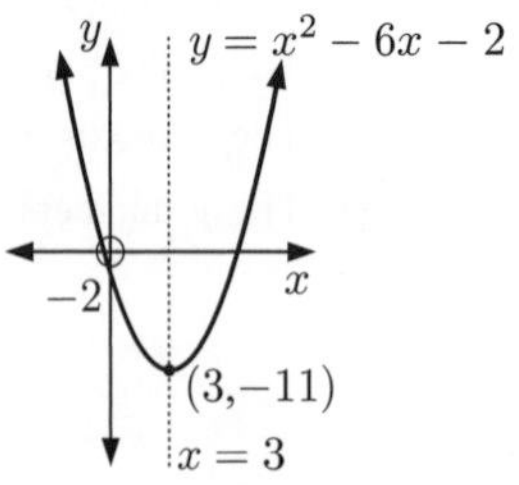


**c** $y = 4x^2 + 16x + 11$

$= 4(x^2 + 4x) + 11$

$= 4(x^2 + 4x + 2^2) + 11 - 4 \times 2^2$

$= 4(x+2)^2 - 5$

and the vertex is at $(-2, -5)$.

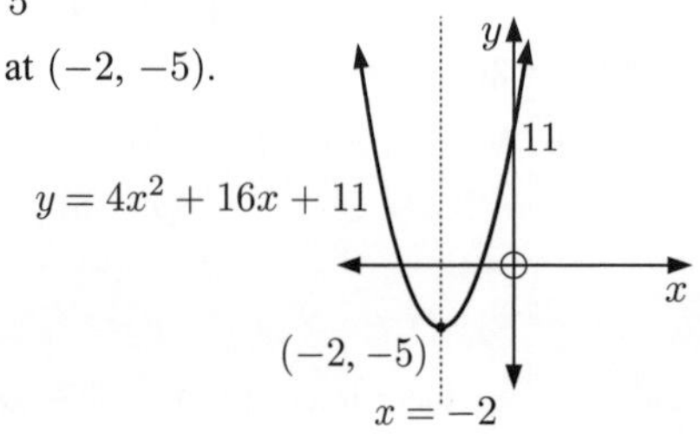


**d** $y = -3x^2 + 12x - 10$

$= -3(x^2 - 4x) - 10$

$= -3(x^2 - 4x + 2^2) - 10 + 3 \times 2^2$

$= -3(x-2)^2 + 2$

and the vertex is at $(2, 2)$.

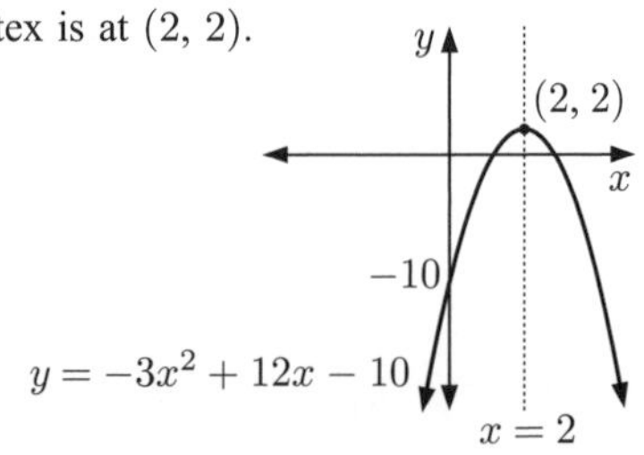


**16** **a** $x^2 + 12x + 8 = 0$

$$\therefore \quad x = \frac{-12 \pm \sqrt{144 - 4(1)(8)}}{2} = \frac{-12 \pm \sqrt{112}}{2} = \frac{-12 \pm 4\sqrt{7}}{2} = -6 \pm 2\sqrt{7}$$

**b** $3x^2 - 4x - 1 = 0$

$$\therefore \quad x = \frac{4 \pm \sqrt{16 - 4(3)(-1)}}{6} = \frac{4 \pm \sqrt{28}}{6} = \frac{4 \pm 2\sqrt{7}}{6} = \tfrac{2}{3} \pm \tfrac{1}{3}\sqrt{7}$$

**17** $x^2 + 8x + k = 0$ has $\Delta = b^2 - 4ac$

$= 8^2 - 4(1)(k)$

$= 64 - 4k$

**a** There are no real roots when $\Delta < 0$

$\therefore \quad 64 - 4k < 0$

$\therefore \quad 64 < 4k$

$\therefore \quad k > 16$

**b** There are two distinct real roots when $\Delta > 0$

$\therefore \quad k < 16$

**18** $y = mx^2 + 4x + 6$ lies entirely above the $x$-axis when $m > 0$ *and* $\Delta < 0$

So, $m > 0$ *and* $4^2 - 4(m)(6) < 0$

$\therefore \quad 16 - 24m < 0$

$\therefore \quad -24m < -16$

$\therefore \quad m > \frac{2}{3}$

So, $m > \frac{2}{3}$.

**19** Since $mx^2 + (m-2)x + m = 0$ has a repeated root, $\Delta = 0$.

$\therefore \quad (m-2)^2 - 4 \times m \times m = 0$

$\therefore \quad -3m^2 - 4m + 4 = 0$

$\therefore \quad -(3m-2)(m+2) = 0$

$\therefore \quad m = \frac{2}{3}$ or $-2$

**20** $(-2)^2 + b(-2) + (b-2) = 0$ {$-2$ is a solution}

$\therefore \quad 4 - 2b + b - 2 = 0$

$\therefore \quad b = 2$

$\therefore$ the equation is $x^2 + 2x = 0$

$\therefore \quad x(x+2) = 0$

$\therefore \quad x = 0$ is the other root

**21** $f(x) = 4 - \dfrac{1}{x-2}$

**a** $f(x)$ does not exist if $x - 2 = 0$
So, the domain is $\{x \mid x \neq 2\}$

**b** Since $\dfrac{1}{x-2} \neq 0$ for any $x$, $f(x) \neq 4$ for any $x$.
So, the range is $\{y \mid y \neq 4\}$

**c** When $x = 0$, $f(0) = 4 - (-\frac{1}{2}) = \frac{9}{2}$
$\therefore$ the $y$-intercept is $4\frac{1}{2}$.

When $y = 0$, $\dfrac{1}{x-2} = 4$
$\therefore$ $x - 2 = \frac{1}{4}$
$\therefore$ $x = 2\frac{1}{4}$
$\therefore$ the $x$-intercept is $2\frac{1}{4}$.

**d** The vertical asymptote is $x = 2$.
The horizontal asymptote is $y = 4$.

**22** **a**

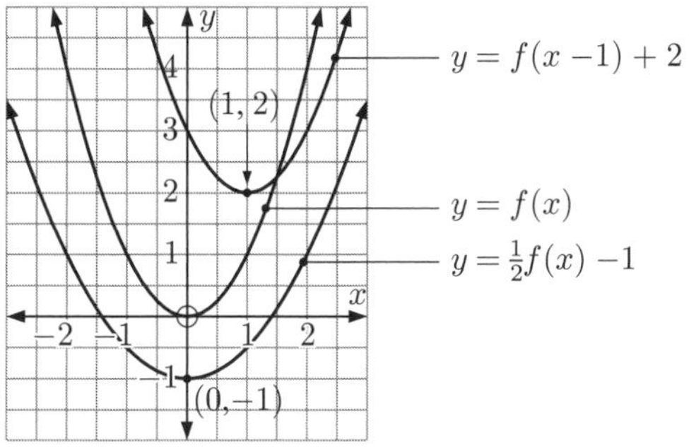


**b** $y = f(x-1) + 2$ is a translation of $y = f(x)$ through $\binom{1}{2}$.

$y = \frac{1}{2}f(x) - 1$ is a vertical stretch of $y = f(x)$ with dilation factor $\frac{1}{2}$, followed by a vertical translation of 1 unit downwards.

**23** **a**

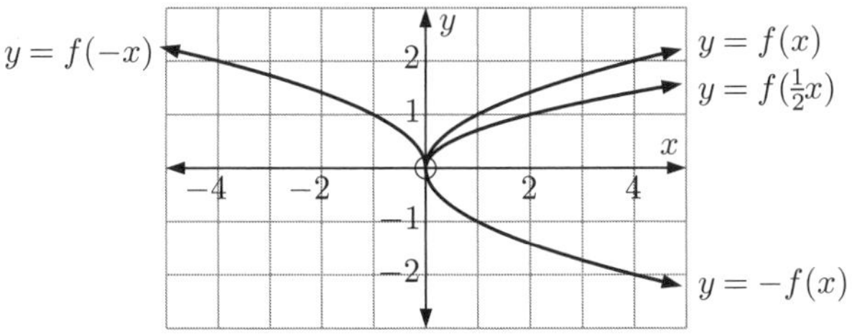


**b** $y = -f(x)$ is a reflection of $y = f(x)$ in the $x$-axis.
$y = f(-x)$ is a reflection of $y = f(x)$ in the $y$-axis.
$y = f\left(\frac{1}{2}x\right)$ is a horizontal stretch of $y = f(x)$ with dilation factor 2.

## CALCULATORS

**1** **a**

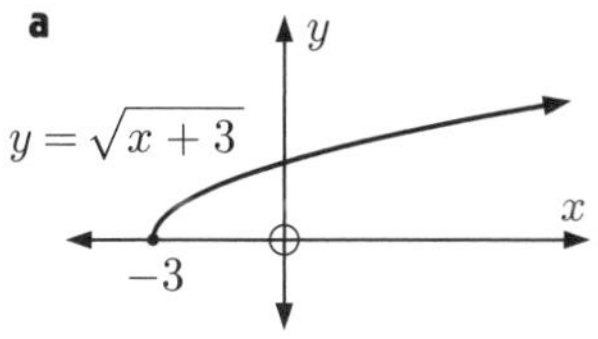


Domain is $\{x \mid x \geqslant -3\}$
Range is $\{y \mid y \geqslant 0\}$

**b**

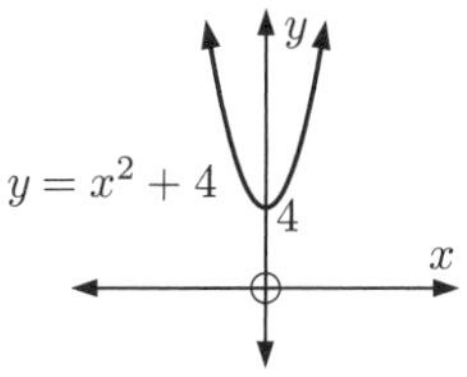


Domain is $\{x \mid x \in \mathbb{R}\}$
Range is $\{y \mid y \geqslant 4\}$

**c**

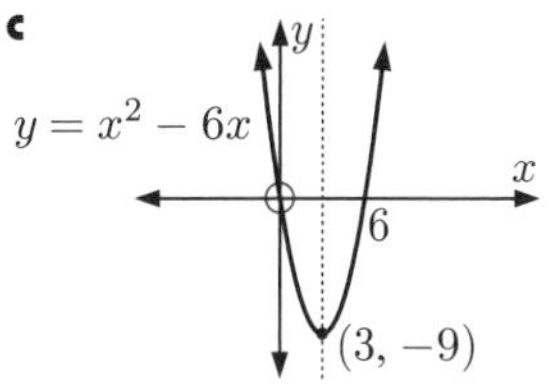


Domain is $\{x \mid x \in \mathbb{R}\}$
Range is $\{y \mid y \geqslant -9\}$

**d**

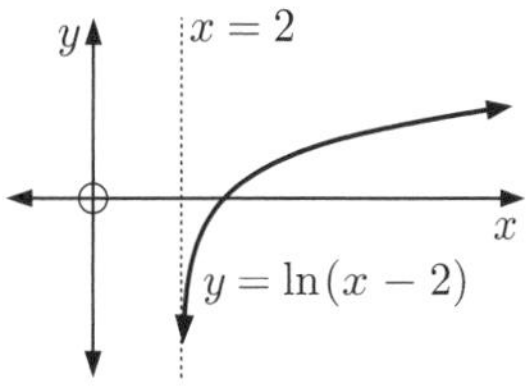


Domain is $\{x \mid x > 2\}$
Range is $\{y \mid y \in \mathbb{R}\}$

**e**

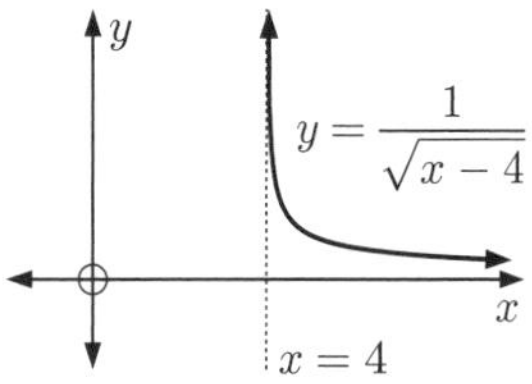


Domain is $\{x \mid x > 4\}$
Range is $\{y \mid y > 0\}$

**2** **a** Range is $\{y \mid y \leqslant 27.45\}$
**b** Range is $\{y \mid \frac{1}{e} \leqslant y \leqslant e\}$
**c** Range is $\{y \mid y \leqslant -4 \text{ or } y \geqslant 4\}$

**3** $f(x)$ is $y = e^{2x+1}$
so $f^{-1}(x)$ is $x = e^{2y+1}$
$\therefore$ $\ln x = \ln e^{2y+1}$
$\therefore$ $\ln x = 2y + 1$
$\therefore$ $y = \dfrac{\ln x - 1}{2}$

So, $f^{-1}(x) = \dfrac{\ln x - 1}{2}$
$\therefore$ $f^{-1}(7) = \dfrac{\ln 7 - 1}{2}$
$\approx 0.473$

**4**

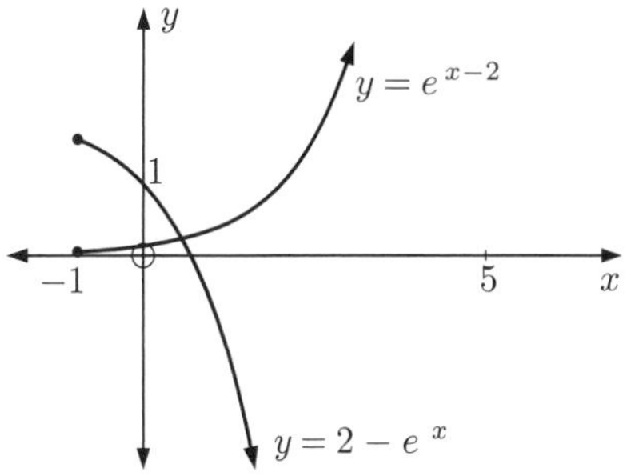


Using technology, the point of intersection is $\approx (0.566, 0.238)$.

**5** $f(x) = \ln x$, $g(x) = x^3$

**a** $(f \circ g)(2)$
$= f(g(2))$
$= f(8)$
$= \ln 8$
$\approx 2.08$

**b** $(g \circ f)(2)$
$= g(f(2))$
$= g(\ln 2)$
$= (\ln 2)^3$
$\approx 0.333$

**c** $f$ is $y = \ln x$,
$\therefore$ $f^{-1}$ is $x = \ln y$
or $y = e^x$
So, $f^{-1}(x) = e^x$
So, $(f^{-1} \circ g)(1.2) = f^{-1}(g(1.2))$
$= f^{-1}((1.2)^3)$
$= e^{1.2^3}$
$\approx 5.63$

**d** $$g \circ f \text{ is } y = g(f(x)) = g(\ln x) = (\ln x)^3$$

$\therefore \quad (g \circ f)^{-1}$ is $x = (\ln y)^3$

$\therefore \quad \ln y = \sqrt[3]{x}$

$\therefore \quad y = e^{\sqrt[3]{x}}$

$\therefore \quad (g \circ f)^{-1}(8) = e^{\sqrt[3]{8}} = e^2$

**6** **a** $f$ is $y = \ln(x+2) - 5, \ x > -2$

$\therefore \quad f^{-1}$ is $x = \ln(y+2) - 5, \quad y > -2$

$\therefore \quad \ln(y+2) = x + 5$

$\therefore \quad y + 2 = e^{x+5}$

So, $f^{-1}(x) = e^{x+5} - 2, \ x \in \mathbb{R}$

**b**

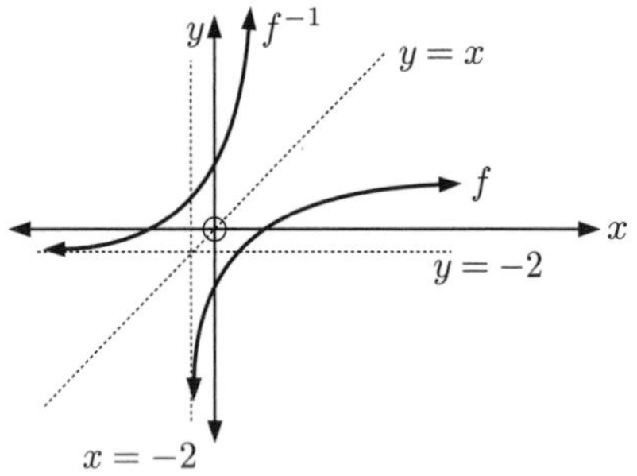


**c** $f$ has domain $\{x \mid x > -2\}$ and range $\{y \mid y \in \mathbb{R}\}$.
$f^{-1}$ has domain $\{x \mid x \in \mathbb{R}\}$ and range $\{y \mid y > -2\}$.

**7** **a** If $7x^2 - 10x + 2 = 0$ then $x \approx 0.240\,48$ or $1.188\,09$.

**b** If $2x^2 = 11x + 15$ then $x \approx -1.131\,04$ or $6.631\,04$.

**8** $y = 2x^2 - 9x + 3$

**a** The axis of symmetry is $x = -\dfrac{b}{2a}$ or $x = \frac{9}{4}$.

**b** The vertex is at $\left(\frac{9}{4}, f\left(\frac{9}{4}\right)\right)$

which is $\left(\frac{9}{4}, 2\left(\frac{9}{4}\right)^2 - 9\left(\frac{9}{4}\right) + 3\right)$ or $\left(2\frac{1}{4}, -7\frac{1}{8}\right)$.

**c** The graph cuts the $y$-axis at $f(0) = 3$
and the $x$-axis when $y = 0$

$\therefore \quad 2x^2 - 9x + 3 = 0$

$\therefore \quad x \approx 0.363$ or $4.137$

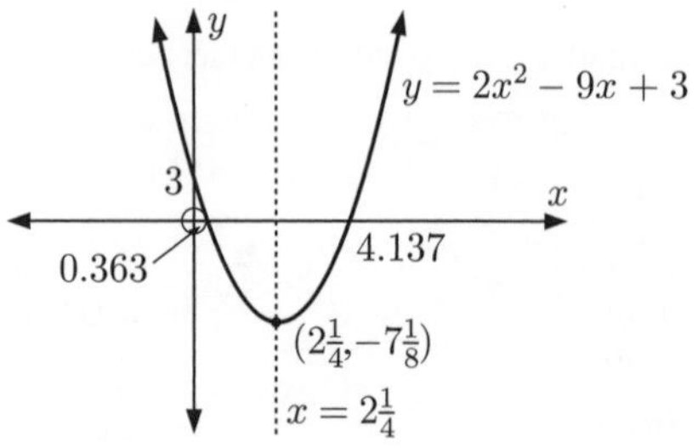


**9** $f(x) = \dfrac{6 - 2x}{x + 4}$ has V.A. $x = -4$ and H.A. $y = -2$

*Sketch:*

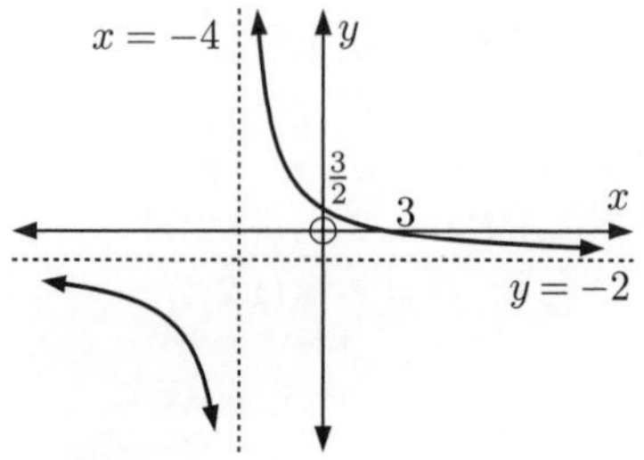


**10** **a** $f(x) = \dfrac{2x+9}{x^2 - 5x - 6} = \dfrac{2x+9}{(x-6)(x+1)}$

has V.A.s $x = 6$, $x = -1$ and H.A. $y = 0$.

*Sketch:*

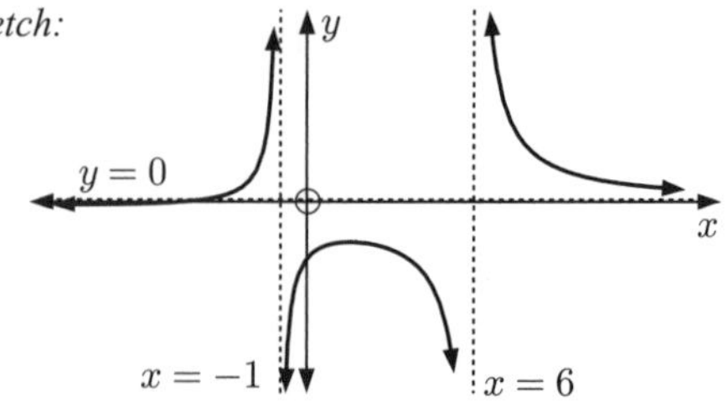


**b** $f(x) = \dfrac{2}{\sqrt{25 - x^2}}$ has V.A.s $x = 5$, $x = -5$
but no H.A.

*Sketch:*

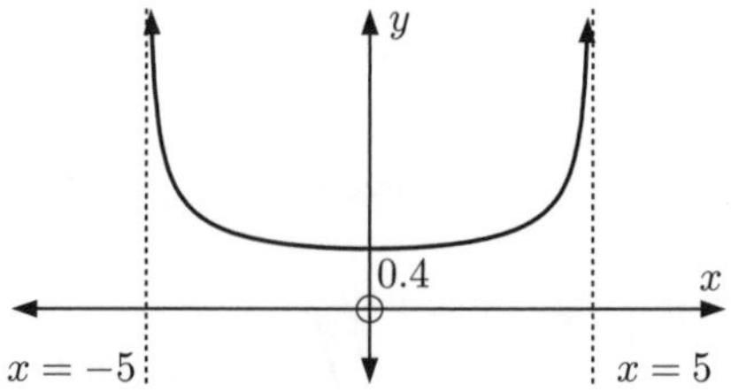


**11**

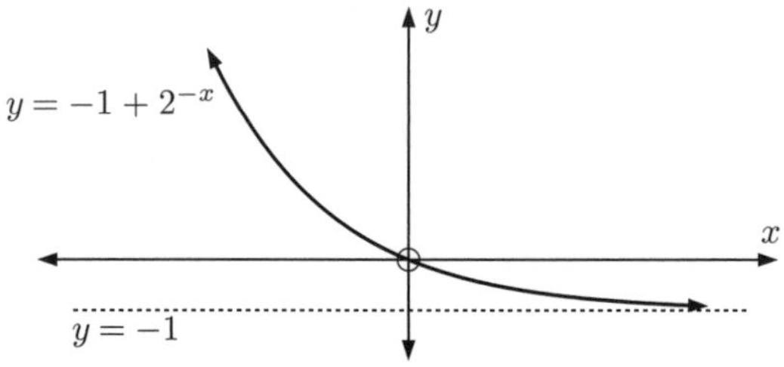


**12** **a**

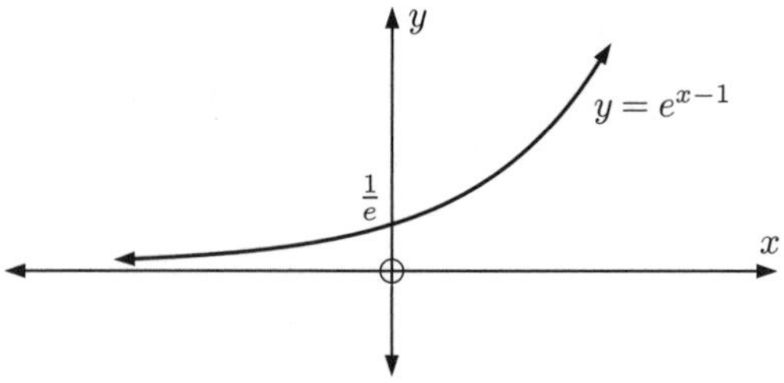


**b** Domain $= \{x \mid x \in \mathbb{R}\}$, Range $= \{y \mid y > 0\}$

**13** **a** $I(0) = 40e^{-0.1 \times 0} = 40$ amps

So, the initial current was 40 amps.

**b** $I(100) = 40e^{-0.1 \times 100} = 40e^{-10} \approx 0.001\,82$ amps

So, the current after 100 milliseconds is about 0.00182 amps.

**c**

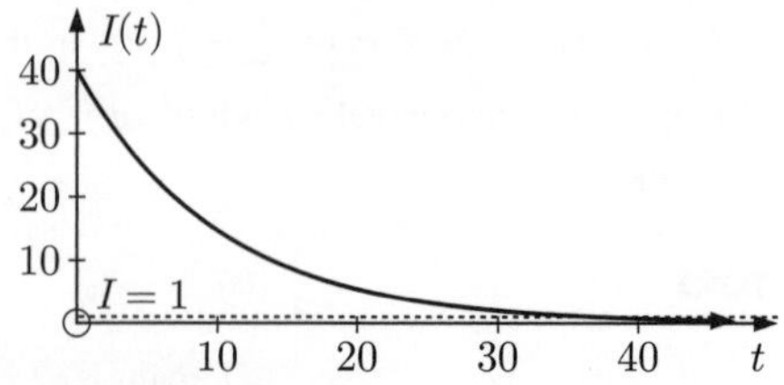


**d** Using technology, $40e^{-0.1t} = 1$ when
$t \approx 36.9$ milliseconds.

So, it will take about 36.9 milliseconds.

**14** Suppose the equilateral triangle ends have side length $x$ cm.

$\therefore$ each end has area

$$= \frac{x}{2} \times \sqrt{x^2 - \left(\frac{x}{2}\right)^2}$$

$$= \frac{x}{2} \times \sqrt{x^2\left(1 - \frac{1}{4}\right)}$$

$$= \frac{\sqrt{3}}{4}x^2 \text{ cm}^2$$

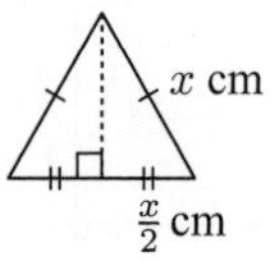

Suppose the prism has height $y$ cm.

$\therefore$ the sum of the side lengths of the prism is

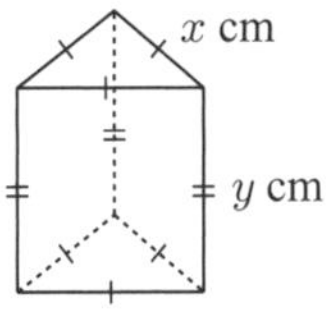


$$6x + 3y = 180$$
$$\therefore \quad 2x + y = 60$$
$$\therefore \quad y = 60 - 2x$$

So, each side has area

$$= xy$$
$$= x(60 - 2x)$$

$\therefore$ the total area $= 2 \times \frac{\sqrt{3}}{4}x^2 + 3x(60 - 2x)$

$$= \left(\tfrac{\sqrt{3}}{2} - 6\right)x^2 + 180x$$

Since $\frac{\sqrt{3}}{2} - 6 < 0$, the area is maximised when

$$x = -\frac{180}{2\left(\frac{\sqrt{3}}{2} - 6\right)} \approx 17.5$$

and $y = 60 - 2x \approx 24.9$

So, the aquarium should have the dimensions shown:

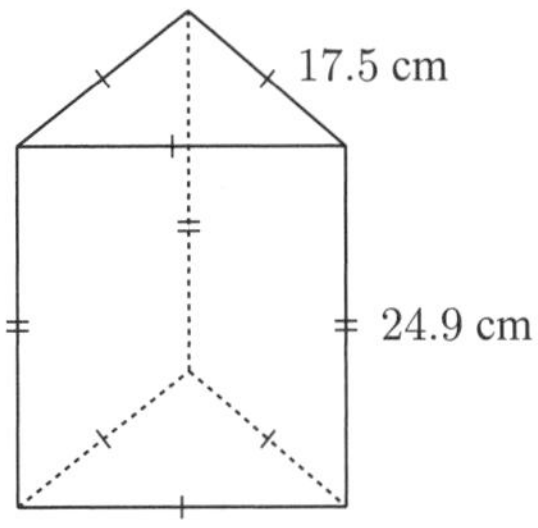


## SOLUTIONS TO TOPIC 3 (CIRCULAR FUNCTIONS AND TRIGONOMETRY)

### NO CALCULATORS

**1** **a** $60^o = \frac{180^o}{3} = \frac{\pi}{3}$ radians

**b** $210^o = 180^o \times \frac{7}{6} = \frac{7\pi}{6}$ radians

**c** $-135^o = -180^o \times \frac{3}{4} = -\frac{3\pi}{4}$ radians

**2** **a** $\frac{2\pi}{3} = \frac{2}{3} \times 180^o = 120^o$

**b** $\frac{5\pi}{4} = \frac{5}{4} \times 180^o = 225^o$

**c** $\frac{-11\pi}{6} = -\frac{11}{6} \times 180^o = -330^o$

**3** **a**

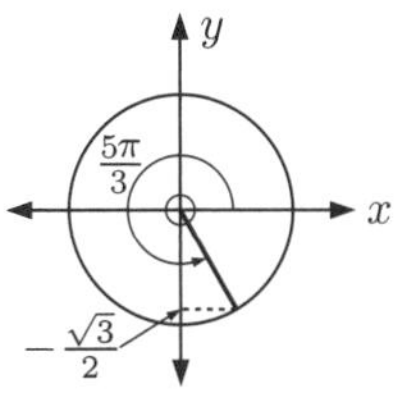


$\sin\left(\frac{5\pi}{3}\right) = -\frac{\sqrt{3}}{2}$

**b**

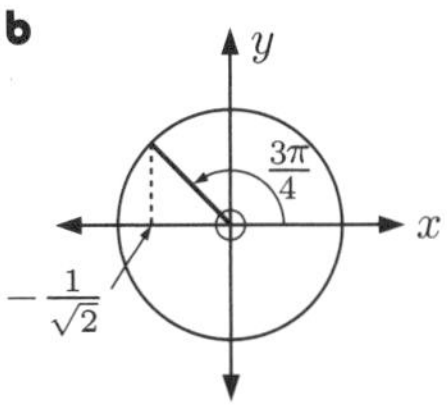


$\cos\left(\frac{3\pi}{4}\right) = -\frac{1}{\sqrt{2}}$

**c**

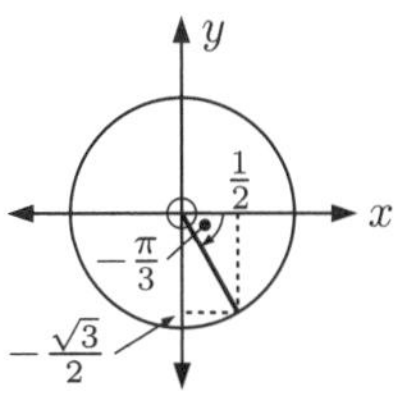


$$\tan\left(-\tfrac{\pi}{3}\right) = \frac{-\frac{\sqrt{3}}{2}}{\frac{1}{2}} = -\sqrt{3}$$

**4**

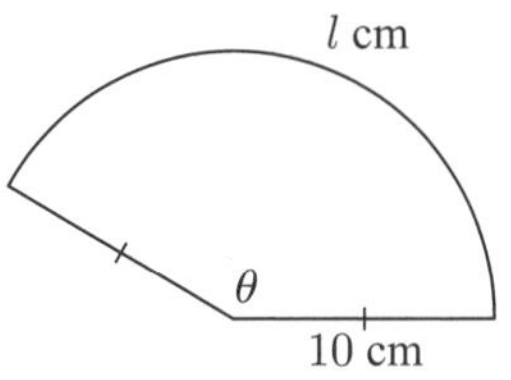


perimeter $= 40$ cm

$$\therefore \quad 10 + 10 + l = 40$$
$$\therefore \quad l = 20$$

$$\text{area} = \tfrac{1}{2}\theta r^2$$
$$= \tfrac{1}{2}lr \qquad \{l = \theta r\}$$
$$= \tfrac{1}{2} \times 20 \times 10$$
$$= 100 \text{ cm}^2$$

**5**

$$\text{area} = 20 \text{ cm}^2$$
$$\therefore \quad \tfrac{1}{2}\theta r^2 = 20$$
$$\therefore \quad \tfrac{1}{2}lr = 20 \qquad \{l = \theta r\}$$
$$\therefore \quad \tfrac{1}{2}(6)r = 20$$
$$\therefore \quad r = \tfrac{20}{3} \text{ cm}$$

So, $\theta = \frac{l}{r} = \frac{6}{\frac{20}{3}} = 0.9$

**6** **a**

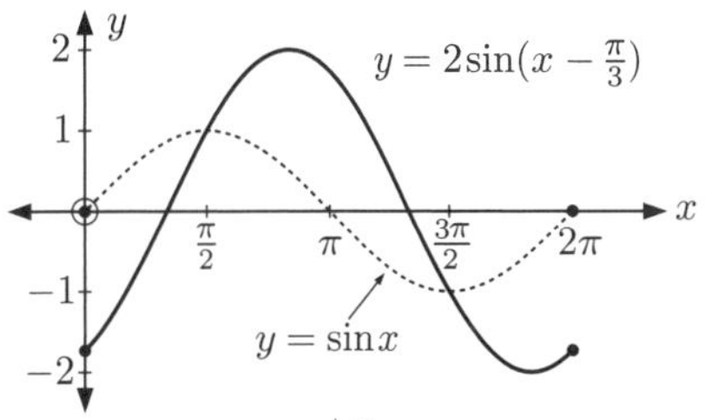


**b**

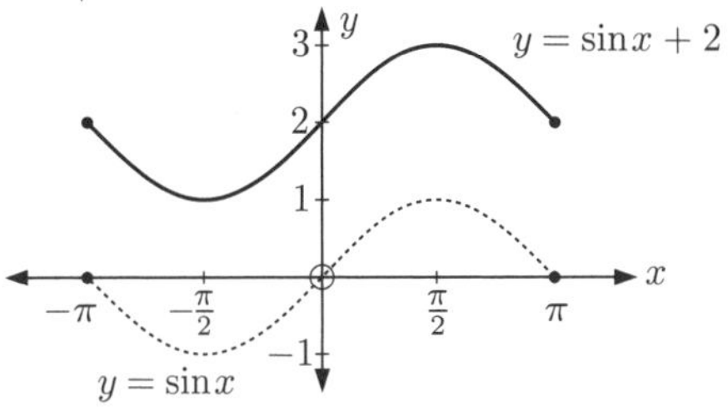


**c**

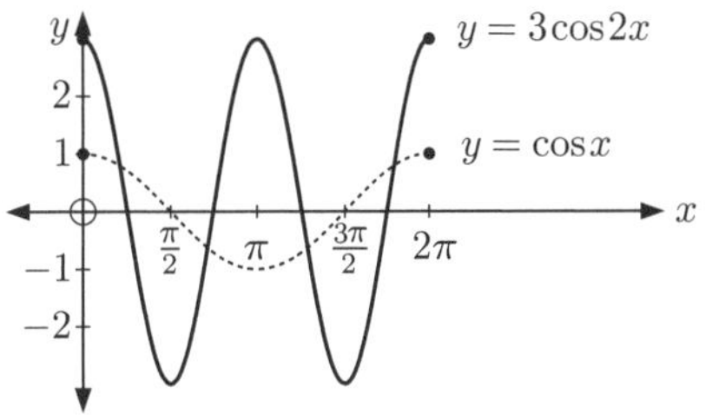


**d**

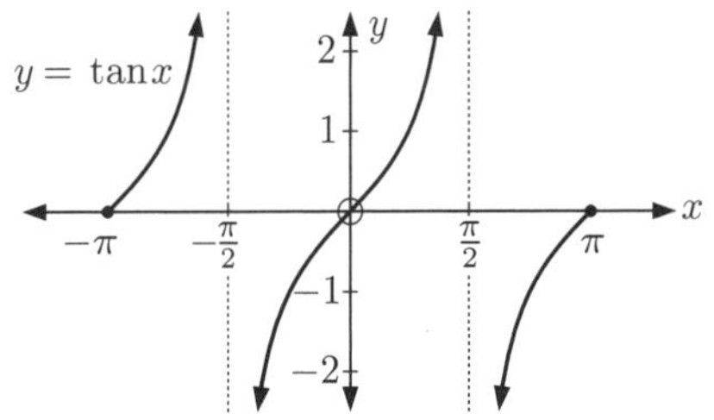


**e**

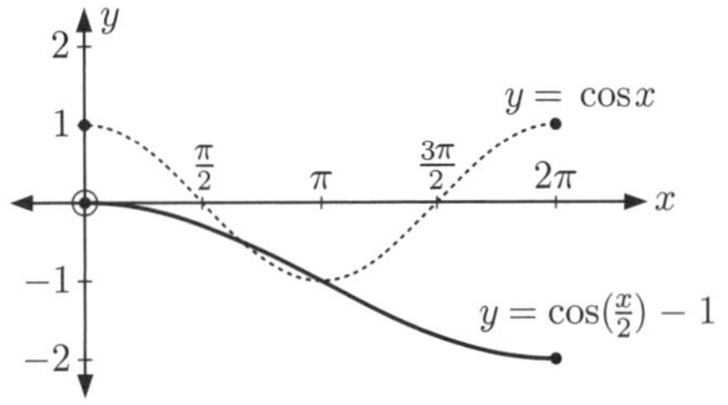


**7** **a** **i** period $= \frac{2\pi}{2} = \pi$ **ii** amplitude $= |1| = 1$

**b** **i** period $= \frac{2\pi}{1} = 2\pi$ **ii** amplitude $= |4| = 4$

**c** **i** period $= \frac{\pi}{3}$ **ii** amplitude not applicable

**d** **i** period $= \frac{2\pi}{3}$ **ii** amplitude $= |-6| = 6$

**8**

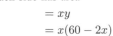

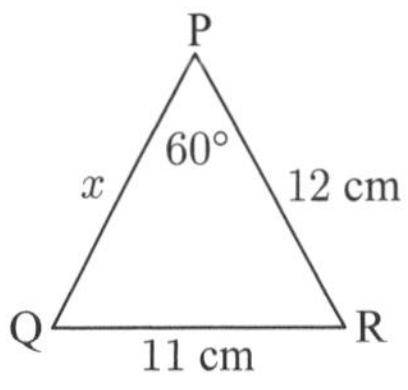


Using the cosine rule,

$$11^2 = x^2 + 12^2 - 2 \times x \times 12 \times \cos 60^o$$

$\therefore\ 121 = x^2 + 144 - 12x$

$\therefore\ x^2 - 12x + 23 = 0$

$\therefore\ x = \dfrac{12 \pm \sqrt{(-12)^2 - 4 \times 1 \times 23}}{2 \times 1}$

$\therefore\ x = 6 \pm \sqrt{13}$, so $\text{PQ} = 6 \pm \sqrt{13}$ cm

**9** **a** A vertical stretch with dilation factor 2, and a horizontal stretch with dilation factor 3.

**b** A translation of $\frac{\pi}{3}$ units to the left, and a translation of 4 units downwards.

**10** **a** period $= \frac{2\pi}{3}$ **b** period $= \frac{2\pi}{\frac{1}{2}} = 4\pi$

**c** $\sin^2 x + 5 = \left(\frac{1}{2} - \frac{1}{2}\cos 2x\right) + 5$

$= -\frac{1}{2}\cos 2x + \frac{11}{2}$

$\therefore$ period $= \frac{2\pi}{2} = \pi$

**11** **a** $\sqrt{2}\cos x + 1 = 0$

$\therefore\ \cos x = -\frac{1}{\sqrt{2}}$

$\therefore\ x = \frac{3\pi}{4}$ or $\frac{5\pi}{4}$

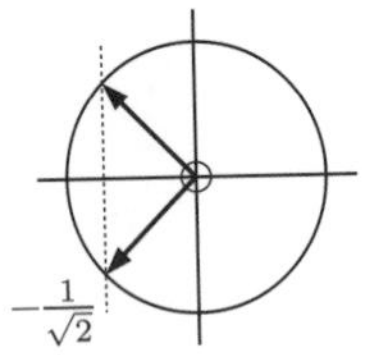


**b** $2\sin x = \sqrt{3}$

$\therefore\ \sin x = \frac{\sqrt{3}}{2}$

$\therefore\ x = \frac{\pi}{3}$ or $\frac{2\pi}{3}$

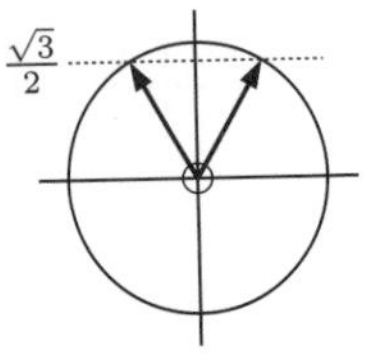


**c** $2\sin^2 x + 3\cos x = 3$

$2(1 - \cos^2 x) + 3\cos x - 3 = 0$

$\therefore\ 2 - 2\cos^2 x + 3\cos x - 3 = 0$

$\therefore\ -2\cos^2 x + 3\cos x - 1 = 0$

$\therefore\ 2\cos^2 x - 3\cos x + 1 = 0$

$\therefore\ (2\cos x - 1)(\cos x - 1) = 0$

$\therefore\ \cos x = \frac{1}{2}$ or 1

$\therefore\ x = 0, \frac{\pi}{3}, \frac{5\pi}{3}, 2\pi$

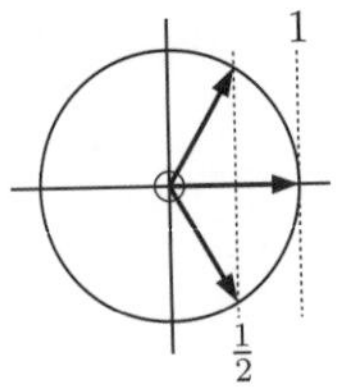


**d** $\sin 2x + \sin x = 0$

$\therefore\ 2\sin x\cos x + \sin x = 0$

$\therefore\ \sin x(2\cos x + 1) = 0$

$\therefore\ \sin x = 0$ or $\cos x = -\frac{1}{2}$

$\therefore\ x = 0, \frac{2\pi}{3}, \pi, \frac{4\pi}{3}, 2\pi$

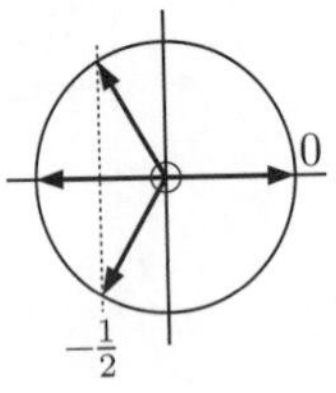


**12** Period $= \dfrac{2\pi}{b} = \pi$ $\therefore\ b = 2,\ a = 10$ {amplitude}
$c = 15$

$\therefore\ y = 10\sin 2x + 15$

*Check:* $y\left(\frac{\pi}{4}\right) = 10\sin(\frac{\pi}{2}) + 15$

$= 10(1) + 15$

$= 25$ ✓

**13** **a** $y = 2 - 3\cos x,\ -\pi \leqslant x \leqslant \pi$

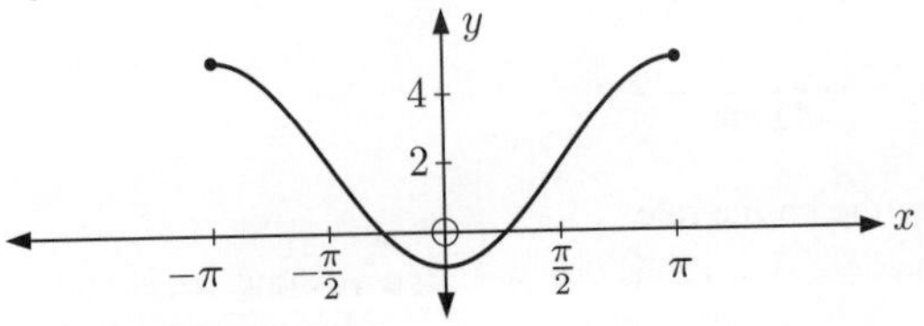


**b** $y = \cos 3x + 2\quad -\pi \leqslant x \leqslant \pi$

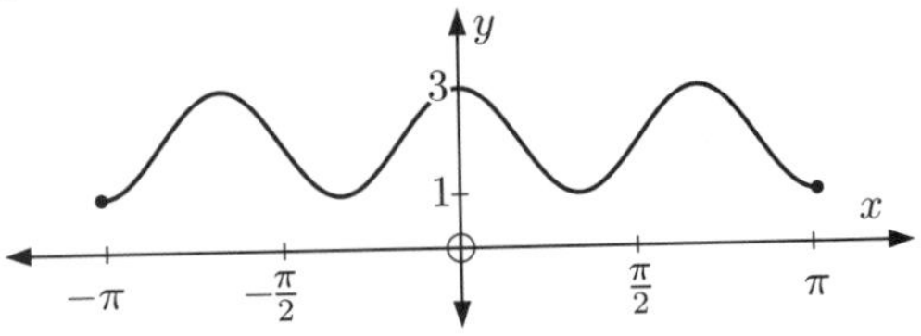


**14** **a** Amplitude $= 1$
The principal axis is
$y = 0$
Period $= \frac{2\pi}{4} = \frac{\pi}{2}$

**b** Amplitude $= 2$
The principal axis is
$y = -1$
Period $= \dfrac{2\pi}{\frac{1}{2}} = 4\pi$

**15** **a** $\sin^2\theta + \cos^2\theta = 1$

$\therefore\ \sin^2\theta + \frac{9}{64} = 1$

$\therefore\ \sin^2\theta = \frac{55}{64}$

$\therefore\ \sin\theta = \pm\frac{\sqrt{55}}{8}$

$\therefore\ \sin\theta = \frac{\sqrt{55}}{8}$ {$\theta$ is acute}

**b** $\sin 2\theta = 2\sin\theta\cos\theta$

$= 2\left(\frac{\sqrt{55}}{8}\right)\left(\frac{3}{8}\right)$

$= \frac{3}{32}\sqrt{55}$

**16** **a** $\cos^2\alpha + \sin^2\alpha = 1$

$\therefore\ \cos^2\alpha + \frac{4}{9} = 1$

$\therefore\ \cos^2\alpha = \frac{5}{9}$

$\therefore\ \cos\alpha = \pm\frac{\sqrt{5}}{3}$

$\therefore\ \cos\alpha = -\frac{\sqrt{5}}{3}$ {$\alpha$ is obtuse}

**b** $\cos 2\alpha = 1 - 2\sin^2\alpha$

$= 1 - 2\left(\frac{2}{3}\right)^2$

$= 1 - \frac{8}{9}$

$= \frac{1}{9}$

**17** $\cos 2\alpha = \frac{5}{13}$

$\therefore\ 1 - 2\sin^2\alpha = \frac{5}{13}$

$\therefore\ 2\sin^2\alpha = \frac{8}{13}$

$\therefore\ \sin^2\alpha = \frac{4}{13}$

$\therefore\ \sin\alpha = \pm\frac{2}{\sqrt{13}}$

But $\alpha$ is acute and so
$\sin\alpha > 0$

$\therefore\ \sin\alpha = \frac{2}{\sqrt{13}}$

**18** **a** $\theta = \frac{7\pi}{6}$

**b** $\tan\theta = \dfrac{\sin\theta}{\cos\theta}$

$= \frac{1}{\sqrt{3}}$

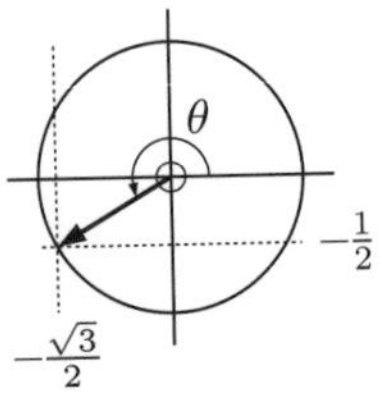


**19** **a** $y(0) = 4$ so $a + b\sin 0 = 4$

$\therefore\ a = 4$

**b** $y(\frac{\pi}{2}) = 1$

$\therefore\ 4 + b\sin(\frac{\pi}{2}) = 1$

$\therefore\ b(1) = -3$

$\therefore\ b = -3$

*Check:* $y = 4 - 3\sin x$

$y(\pi) = 4 - 3\sin\pi = 4 - 0 = 4$ ✓

**20** **a** $\tan 60^o = \sqrt{3}$

$\therefore$ the equation is $y = \sqrt{3}x$

**b** $\tan 120^o = -\sqrt{3}$

$\therefore$ the equation is

$y = -\sqrt{3}x + c$

But when $x = 4,\ y = 0$

$\therefore\ 0 = -4\sqrt{3} + c$

$\therefore\ c = 4\sqrt{3}$

So, $y = -\sqrt{3}x + 4\sqrt{3}$

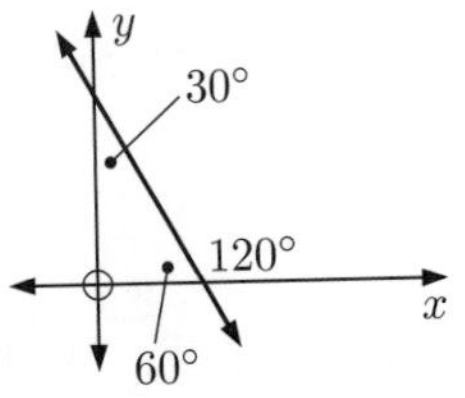

**21** **a** $f(x) = \dfrac{1}{\sin x}$ is defined when

$\sin x \neq 0$

$\therefore \quad x \neq 0 + k\pi$

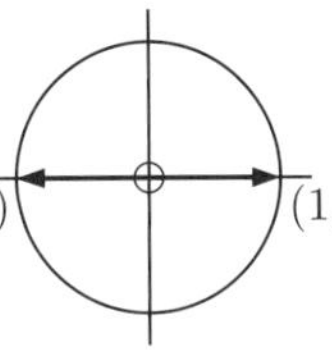


So, the domain is $\{x \mid x \neq k\pi,\ k \in \mathbb{Z}\}$

Since $\sin x$ values lie between $-1$ and 1,

$\dfrac{1}{\sin x}$ values are $\leqslant -1$ or $\geqslant 1$

So, the range is $\{y \mid y \leqslant -1 \text{ or } y \geqslant 1\}$.

**b** $f(x)$ is undefined when $x = k\pi,\ k \in \mathbb{Z}$

So, $x = 0,\ x = \pm\pi,\ x = \pm 2\pi,\ ....$

are all vertical asymptotes.

**22** $f(x) = 1 - 3\sin 2x$

**a** period $= \dfrac{2\pi}{2} = \pi$

**b** For $y = a\sin x$, the amplitude is $|a|$.

$\therefore$ the amplitude of $f(x)$ is $|-3| = 3$.

**c**

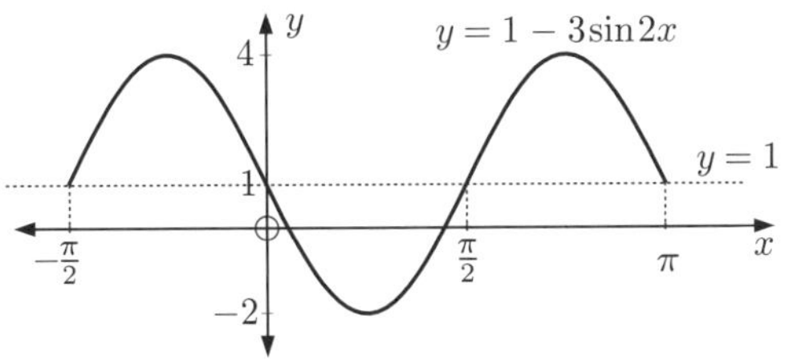


**23** **a**

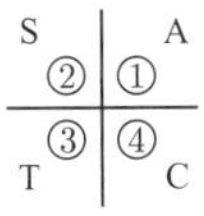


$\tan\theta > 0$ and $\cos\theta < 0$ in the third quadrant.

**b**

$$\frac{\sin\theta}{\cos\theta} = 2$$

$\therefore \quad \sin\theta = 2\cos\theta$

Now $\cos^2\theta + \sin^2\theta = 1$

$\therefore \quad \cos^2\theta + (2\cos\theta)^2 = 1$

$\therefore \quad 5\cos^2\theta = 1$

$\therefore \quad \cos\theta = \pm\frac{1}{\sqrt{5}}$

But $\cos\theta < 0$ in Q3

$\therefore \quad \cos\theta = -\frac{1}{\sqrt{5}}$

**24** **a** reflection in the $x$-axis

*or* $y = -\sin x = \sin(x + \pi)$

which is a horizontal translation $\pi$ units to the left.

**b** vertical stretch, factor 2

**c** horizontal stretch, factor $\frac{1}{2}$

**d** translation through $\begin{pmatrix} -\frac{\pi}{6} \\ 2 \end{pmatrix}$

**25** **a** For the sine function $y = a\sin b(x - c) + d$:

- the amplitude $= 2$, so $a = 2$
- the period $= \pi$, so $\frac{2\pi}{b} = \pi \quad \therefore b = 2$
- the principal axis is $y = 1$, so $d = 1$
- there is no horizontal translation, so $c = 0$.

$\therefore$ the function is $y = 2\sin 2x + 1$

**b** We need to solve $2\sin 2x + 1 = 0,\ 0 \leqslant x \leqslant \pi$

$\therefore \quad \sin 2x = -\frac{1}{2}$

$\therefore \quad 2x = \frac{7\pi}{6}$ or $\frac{11\pi}{6}$

$\therefore \quad x = \frac{7\pi}{12}$ or $\frac{11\pi}{12}$

So, P is $\left(\frac{7\pi}{12}, 0\right)$ and

Q is $\left(\frac{11\pi}{12}, 0\right)$.

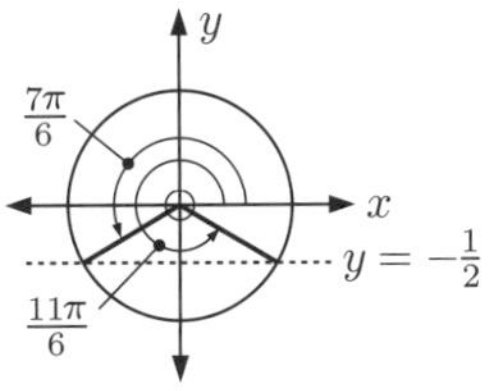


**26** $\tan\theta = \dfrac{\sin\theta}{\cos\theta} \quad \therefore \quad \cos\theta = \dfrac{\sin\theta}{\tan\theta} = \dfrac{-\frac{4}{5}}{-\frac{4}{3}} = \frac{3}{5}$

**27** We label points W, X, Y and Z as shown, and let $\widehat{YXZ} = \beta$ and $\widehat{WZX} = \alpha$.

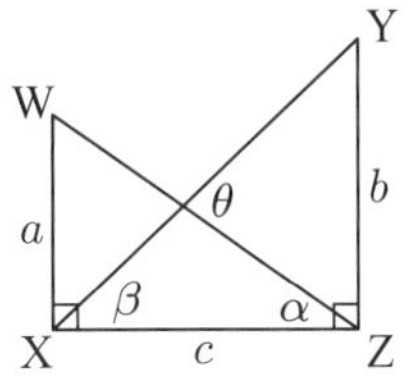


Now $\tan\beta = \dfrac{b}{c}$ {from $\Delta$XYZ}

$\therefore \quad \beta = \tan^{-1}\left(\dfrac{b}{c}\right)$

Likewise, $\tan\alpha = \dfrac{a}{c}$ {from $\Delta$XWZ}

$\therefore \quad \alpha = \tan^{-1}\left(\dfrac{a}{c}\right)$

Now $\theta = \alpha + \beta$ {external angle of a triangle}

$\therefore \quad \theta = \tan^{-1}\left(\dfrac{a}{c}\right) + \tan^{-1}\left(\dfrac{b}{c}\right)$ as required.

**28**

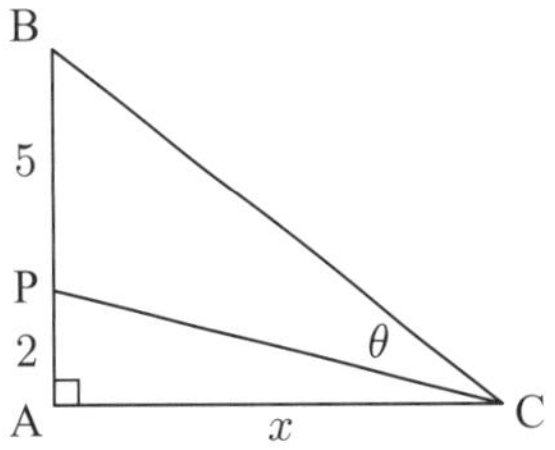


$\widehat{BCA} = \tan^{-1}\left(\dfrac{7}{x}\right)$ and $\widehat{PCA} = \tan^{-1}\left(\dfrac{2}{x}\right)$

Now $\theta = \widehat{BCA} - \widehat{PCA}$

$\therefore \quad \theta = \tan^{-1}\left(\dfrac{7}{x}\right) - \tan^{-1}\left(\dfrac{2}{x}\right)$

**29**

$$1 - \frac{\sin^2\theta}{1+\cos\theta} = \frac{1+\cos\theta}{1+\cos\theta} - \frac{\sin^2\theta}{1+\cos\theta}$$

$$= \frac{1+\cos\theta - (1-\cos^2\theta)}{1+\cos\theta}$$

$$= \frac{\cos\theta + \cos^2\theta}{1+\cos\theta}$$

$$= \frac{\cos\theta(1+\cos\theta)}{1+\cos\theta}$$

$$= \cos\theta$$

**30** $\cos 2x = \frac{5}{8}$

$\therefore \quad 1 - 2\sin^2 x = \frac{5}{8}$ {double angle formula}

$\therefore \quad 2\sin^2 x = \frac{3}{8}$

$\therefore \quad \sin x = \pm\frac{\sqrt{3}}{4}$

**31** $\sin^2\theta + \cos^2\theta = 1$

$\therefore \quad \left(\frac{2}{3}\right)^2 + \cos^2\theta = 1$

$\therefore \quad \cos^2\theta = \frac{5}{9}$

$\therefore \quad \cos\theta = -\frac{\sqrt{5}}{3}$ {$\theta$ is obtuse}

$\sin 2\theta = 2\sin\theta\cos\theta$

$= 2 \times \frac{2}{3} \times -\frac{\sqrt{5}}{3}$

$= -\frac{4\sqrt{5}}{9}$

**32** $(\sin x + \cos x)^2 = \sin^2 x + \cos^2 x$

$\therefore \quad \sin^2 x + 2\sin x\cos x + \cos^2 x = \sin^2 x + \cos^2 x$

$\therefore \quad 2\sin x\cos x = 0$

$\therefore \quad \sin x = 0$ or $\cos x = 0$

Since $0 \leqslant x \leqslant \pi$, $x = 0, \frac{\pi}{2}$, or $\pi$.

**33** **a** $\tan(-\frac{\pi}{6}) = \dfrac{\sin(-\frac{\pi}{6})}{\cos(-\frac{\pi}{6})}$

From the unit circle,

$\sin(-\frac{\pi}{6}) = -\frac{1}{2}$

$\cos(-\frac{\pi}{6}) = \frac{\sqrt{3}}{2}$

$\therefore \quad \tan(-\frac{\pi}{6}) = \dfrac{-\frac{1}{2}}{\frac{\sqrt{3}}{2}} = -\frac{1}{\sqrt{3}}$

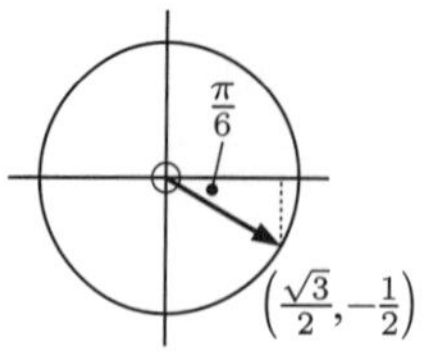


**b** $\dfrac{\sqrt{2}}{\sin\left(\frac{3\pi}{4}\right)} = \dfrac{\sqrt{2}}{\frac{1}{\sqrt{2}}}$

$= \sqrt{2} \times \frac{\sqrt{2}}{1}$

$= 2$

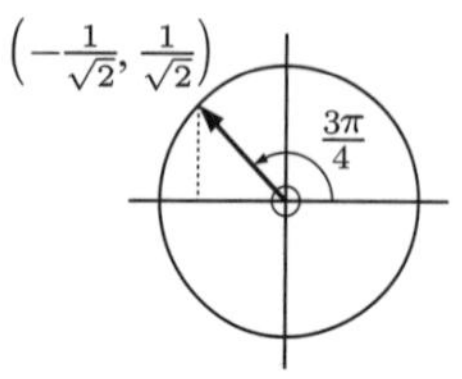


**34** **a**

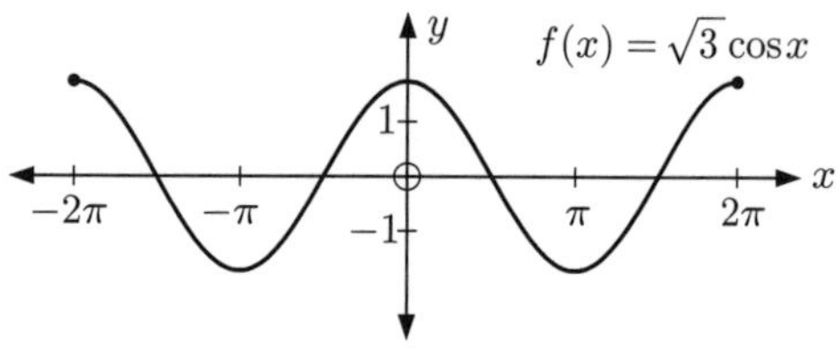


**b**

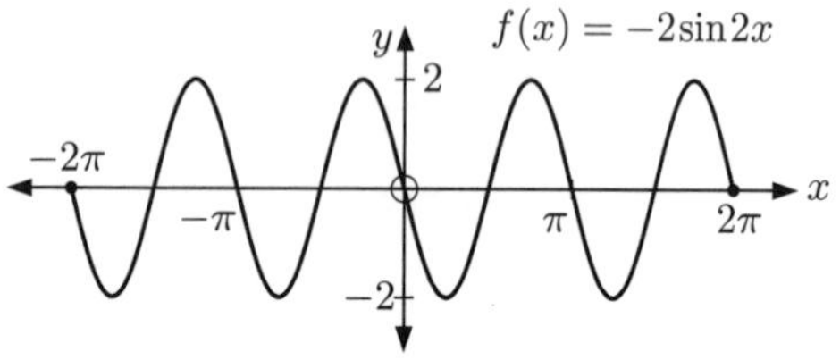


**35** $y = 2^{-x}\sin 2x$ cuts the $x$-axis when $y = 0$,

which is when $\dfrac{\sin 2x}{2^x} = 0$.

Now $2^x > 0$ for all $x$,

so $\sin 2x = 0$

$\therefore \quad 2x = k\pi$ for $k$ any integer

$\therefore \quad x = \dfrac{k\pi}{2}$

$\therefore$ for $0 \leqslant x \leqslant 3\pi$, the graph cuts the $x$-axis when $x = 0, \frac{\pi}{2}, \pi, \frac{3\pi}{2}, 2\pi, \frac{5\pi}{2}, 3\pi$

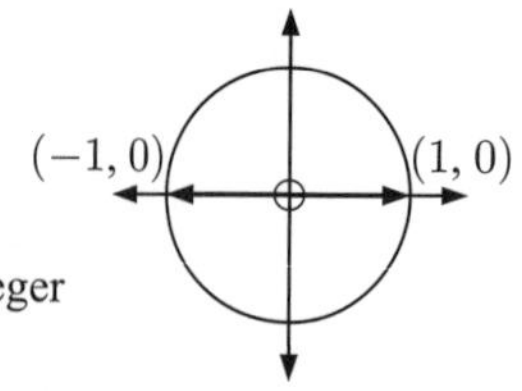


**36** $\sin^2 t + \cos^2 t = 1,$

$\therefore \quad \sin^2 t = 1 - \cos^2 t$

For $0 < t < \pi$, $\sin t > 0$

$\therefore \quad \sin t = \sqrt{1 - \cos^2 t}$

$\therefore \quad \tan t = \dfrac{\sin t}{\cos t} = \dfrac{\sqrt{1-\cos^2 t}}{\cos t}$ for $0 < t < \pi$

**37**

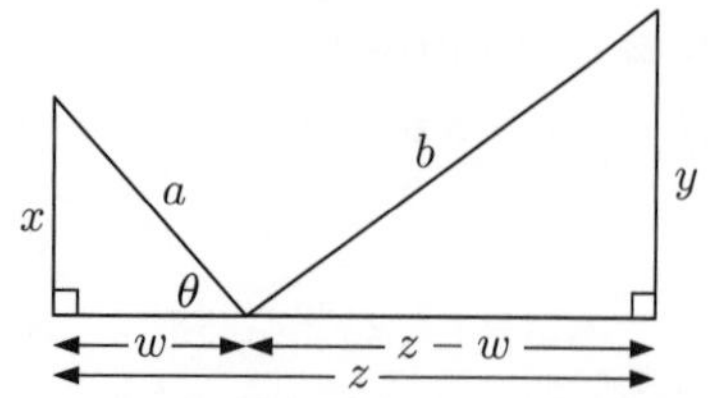


Divide the length $z$ into lengths $w$ and $z - w$ as shown above.

Then $a = \sqrt{x^2 + w^2}$ {Pythagoras}

and $b = \sqrt{y^2 + (z-w)^2}$ {Pythagoras}

$\therefore \quad a + b = \sqrt{x^2 + w^2} + \sqrt{y^2 + (z-w)^2}$

Now $\tan\theta = \dfrac{x}{w}$, so $w = \dfrac{x}{\tan\theta}$

$\therefore \quad a + b = \sqrt{x^2 + \left(\dfrac{x}{\tan\theta}\right)^2} + \sqrt{y^2 + \left(z - \dfrac{x}{\tan\theta}\right)^2}$

**38** $\sin^{-1}(3x^2 - 2x) = \frac{5\pi}{6}$

$\therefore \quad 3x^2 - 2x = \sin\left(\frac{5\pi}{6}\right) = \frac{1}{2}$

$\therefore \quad 6x^2 - 4x - 1 = 0$

$\therefore \quad x = \dfrac{4 \pm \sqrt{(-4)^2 - 4 \times 6(-1)}}{2 \times 6}$

$= \dfrac{4 \pm \sqrt{40}}{12} = \dfrac{2 \pm \sqrt{10}}{6}$

**39** $\dfrac{1 - \cos 2\theta}{\sin 2\theta} = \sqrt{3}$

$\therefore \quad \dfrac{1 - (1 - 2\sin^2\theta)}{2\sin\theta\cos\theta} = \sqrt{3}$ {double angle formulae}

$\therefore \quad \dfrac{2\sin^2\theta}{2\sin\theta\cos\theta} = \sqrt{3}$

$\therefore \quad \dfrac{\sin\theta}{\cos\theta} = \sqrt{3}$ provided $\sin\theta \neq 0$, $\cos\theta \neq 0$

$\therefore \quad \tan\theta = \sqrt{3}$

But $0 < \theta < \frac{\pi}{2}$, so $\theta = \frac{\pi}{3}$

**40** **a** $2\sin\theta \leqslant \sqrt{3}$, $-2\pi \leqslant \theta \leqslant 2\pi$

$\therefore \quad \sin\theta \leqslant \frac{\sqrt{3}}{2}$

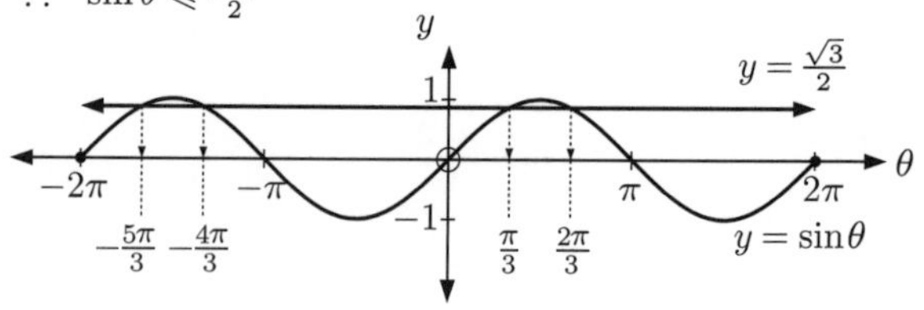


$\therefore \quad -2\pi \leqslant \theta \leqslant -\frac{5\pi}{3}$, $-\frac{4\pi}{3} \leqslant \theta \leqslant \frac{\pi}{3}$ or $\frac{2\pi}{3} \leqslant \theta \leqslant 2\pi$.

**b** $\sqrt{2}\cos\theta \leqslant -1$

$\therefore \quad \cos\theta \leqslant -\frac{1}{\sqrt{2}}$

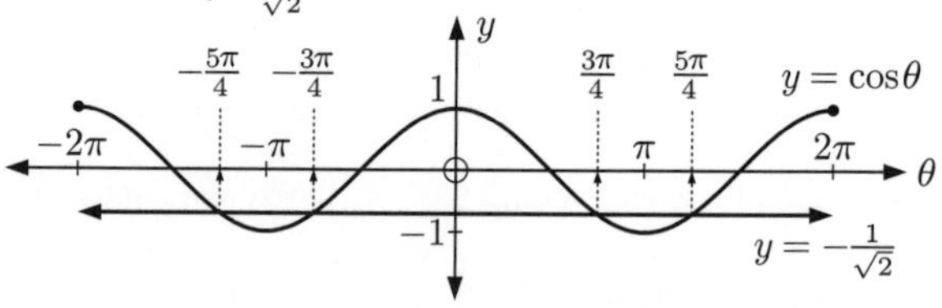


$\therefore \quad -\frac{5\pi}{4} \leqslant \theta \leqslant -\frac{3\pi}{4}$ or $\frac{3\pi}{4} \leqslant \theta \leqslant \frac{5\pi}{4}$.

**41** $\sin x + \sqrt{3}\cos x = 0$

$\therefore \quad \sin x = -\sqrt{3}\cos x$

$\therefore \quad \dfrac{\sin x}{\cos x} = -\sqrt{3}$

$\therefore \quad \tan x = -\sqrt{3}$

$\therefore$ for $0 \leqslant x \leqslant 2\pi$, $x = \frac{2\pi}{3}, \frac{5\pi}{3}$

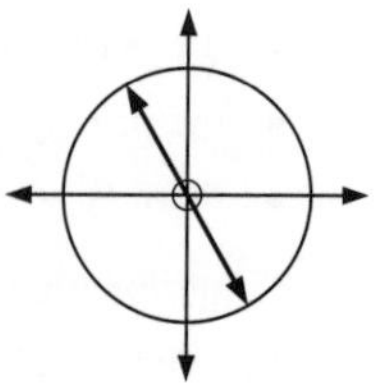

**42** $\dfrac{\sin^2\theta}{1 + \cos\theta} = \dfrac{1 - \cos^2\theta}{1 + \cos\theta}$

$= \dfrac{(1 + \cos\theta)(1 - \cos\theta)}{(1 + \cos\theta)}$

$= (1 - \cos\theta)$ provided $\cos\theta \neq -1$

**43**

$$\tan 2A = \sin A$$
$$\therefore \quad \frac{\sin 2A}{\cos 2A} = \sin A$$
$$\therefore \quad \frac{2\sin A\cos A}{2\cos^2 A - 1} = \sin A \qquad \{\text{double angle formula}\}$$
$$\therefore \quad \frac{2\cos A}{2\cos^2 A - 1} = 1 \qquad \{\sin A \neq 0\}$$
$$2\cos A = 2\cos^2 A - 1$$
$$\therefore \quad 2\cos^2 A - 2\cos A - 1 = 0$$
$$\therefore \quad \cos A = \frac{2 \pm \sqrt{(-2)^2 - 4\times 2\times(-1)}}{2\times 2}$$
$$= \frac{1\pm\sqrt{3}}{2}$$

But $-1 \leqslant \cos A \leqslant 1$, so $\cos A = \dfrac{1-\sqrt{3}}{2}$

## CALCULATORS

**1** **a** 0.815 radians
$= 0.815 \times \frac{180}{\pi}$ degrees
$\approx 46.7$ degrees

**b** 2.7 radians
$= 2.7 \times \frac{180}{\pi}$ degrees
$\approx 154.7$ degrees

**2** **a** $48^o$
$= 48 \times \frac{\pi}{180}$ radians
$\approx 0.838$ radians

**b** $203^o$
$= 203 \times \frac{\pi}{180}$ radians
$\approx 3.543$ radians

**3** **a**

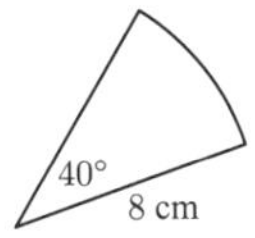


perimeter
$= 2\times 8 + \frac{40}{360}\times 2\pi\times 8$
$\approx 21.6$ cm

area
$= \frac{40}{360}\times\pi\times 8^2$
$\approx 22.3\ \text{cm}^2$

**b**

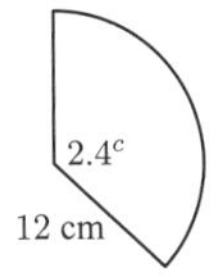


perimeter
$= 2\times 12 + \theta r$
$= 24 + 2.4\times 12$
$= 52.8$ cm

area
$= \frac{1}{2}\theta r^2$
$= \frac{1}{2}\times 2.4\times 12^2$
$= 172.8\ \text{cm}^2$

**4**

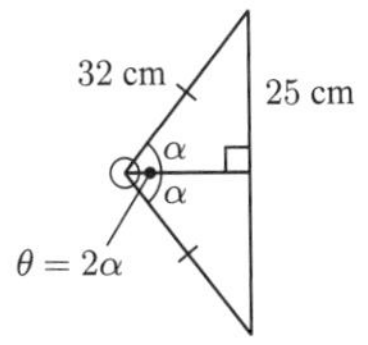


$\sin\alpha = \frac{25}{32}$
$\therefore \quad \alpha = \sin^{-1}\left(\frac{25}{32}\right)$
$\therefore \quad \alpha \approx 51.3752^o$
$\therefore \quad \theta = 2\alpha \approx 102.750^o$
$\approx 1.793$ radians

Area of segment = area of sector − area of triangle
$= \frac{1}{2}\theta r^2 - \frac{1}{2}r^2\sin\theta \quad \{\text{where } \theta \text{ is in radians}\}$
$= \frac{1}{2}\times 1.793\times 32^2$
$\quad - \frac{1}{2}\times 32^2\times\sin(1.793)$
$\approx 419\ \text{cm}^2$

**5** **a** area $= \frac{1}{2}\times 12\times 18\times\sin 27^o \approx 49.0\ \text{cm}^2$

**b** area $= \frac{1}{2}\times 5.4\times 7.8\times\sin 125^o \approx 17.3\ \text{cm}^2$

**6** **a** The third angle $= 180^o - 37^o - 29^o = 114^o$

By the sine rule, $\dfrac{a}{\sin 114^o} = \dfrac{16}{\sin 29^o}$

$$a = \frac{16\times\sin 114^o}{\sin 29^o} \approx 30.1$$

**b** By the cosine rule,
$a^2 = 100^2 + 120^2 - 2\times 100\times 120\times\cos 31^o$
$\therefore \quad a = \sqrt{100^2 + 120^2 - 200\times 120\times\cos 31^o}$
$\therefore \quad a \approx 61.9$

**7**

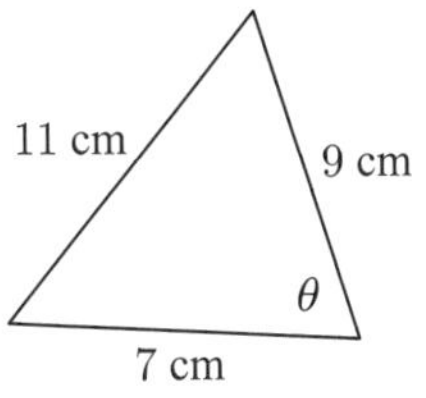


The largest angle is opposite the longest side.

$\cos\theta = \dfrac{9^2 + 7^2 - 11^2}{2\times 9\times 7}$ {cosine rule}

$\therefore \quad \cos\theta = \frac{9}{126}$
$\therefore \quad \theta \approx 85.9^o$

**8**

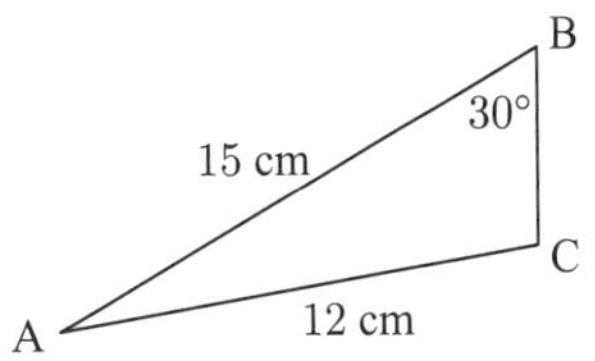


$\dfrac{\sin C}{15} = \dfrac{\sin 30^o}{12}$ {sine rule}
$\therefore \quad C = \sin^{-1}\left(\dfrac{15\sin 30^o}{12}\right)$
$\therefore \quad C \approx 38.7^o$ or $141.3^o$

**9** **a**

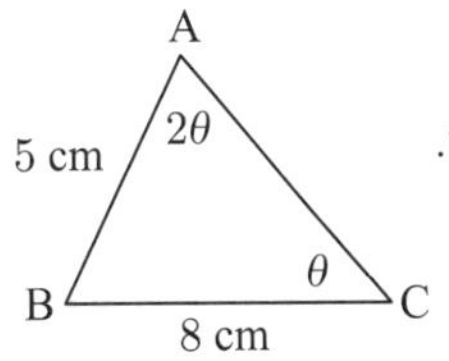


$\dfrac{\sin 2\theta}{8} = \dfrac{\sin\theta}{5}$ {sine rule}
$\therefore \quad \dfrac{2\sin\theta\cos\theta}{8} = \dfrac{\sin\theta}{5}$
$\therefore \quad \cos\theta = \frac{4}{5}$

**b** $\widehat{ABC} = \pi - 3\theta$
$= \pi - 3\cos^{-1}\left(\frac{4}{5}\right)$
$\approx 1.211$

Area of triangle
$\approx \frac{1}{2}\times 5\times 8\times\sin(1.211)$
$\approx 18.7\ \text{cm}^2$

**10** **a** $\sin x = 0.785$
$\therefore \quad x \approx 0.9027$ or $\pi - 0.9027$
$\therefore \quad x \approx 0.903$ or $2.24$

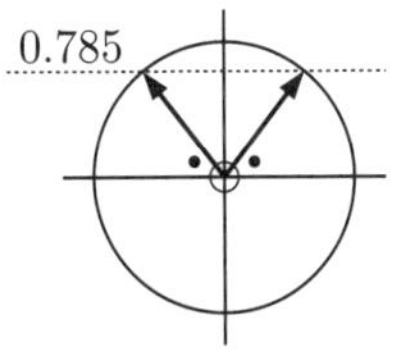


**b** $2\cos x = 5\sin x$
$\therefore \quad \frac{2}{5} = \dfrac{\sin x}{\cos x}$
$\therefore \quad \tan x = \frac{2}{5}$
$\therefore \quad x \approx 0.380\,51$ or $\pi + 0.38051$
$\therefore \quad x \approx 0.381$ or $3.52$

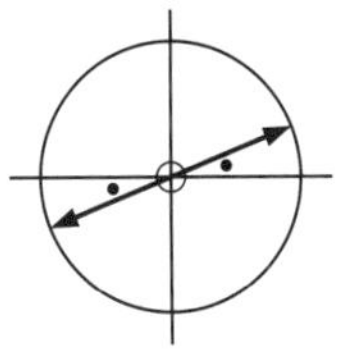

**c** $\tan 3x = 0.9$
$\therefore \quad 3x \approx 0.732\,82 + k\pi$
$\therefore \quad x \approx 0.24427 + k\frac{\pi}{3}$
$\therefore \quad x \approx 0.244, 1.29, 2.34,$
$3.39, 4.43, 5.48$

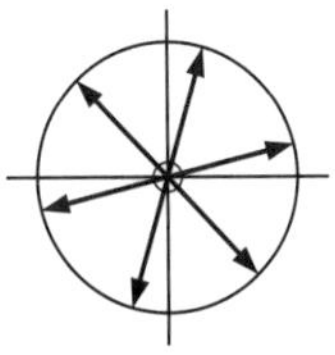

**11** **a** $5\sin(2t-3) = 2, \quad 0 \leqslant t \leqslant 12$
$\therefore \quad \sin(2t-3) = \frac{2}{5}$
$\therefore \quad 2t - 3 = \sin^{-1}\left(\frac{2}{5}\right)$
$\therefore \quad 2t - 3 \approx \begin{cases} 0.411\,52 \\ \pi - 0.41152 \end{cases} + k2\pi$
$\therefore \quad 2t \approx \begin{cases} 3.411\,52 \\ 5.73008 \end{cases} + k2\pi$
$\therefore \quad t \approx \begin{cases} 1.705\,76 \\ 2.865\,04 \end{cases} + k\pi$
$\therefore \quad t \approx 1.71, 2.87, 4.85, 6.01, 7.99, 9.15, 11.1$

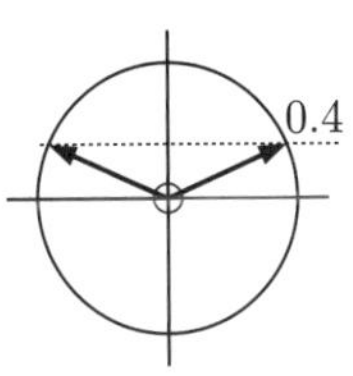

**b** $15+3\cos\left(\frac{t}{2}+1\right)=14.5$

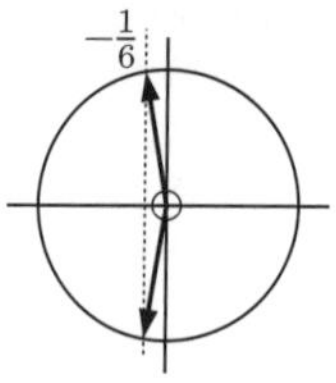


$\therefore\ 3\cos\left(\frac{t}{2}+1\right)=-0.5$

$\therefore\ \cos\left(\frac{t}{2}+1\right)=-\frac{1}{6}$

$\therefore\ \frac{t}{2}+1\approx\left\{\begin{matrix}1.738\,24\\2\pi-1.738\,24\end{matrix}\right.+k2\pi$

$\therefore\ \frac{t}{2}+1\approx\left\{\begin{matrix}1.738\,24\\4.544\,94\end{matrix}\right.+k2\pi$

$\therefore\ \frac{t}{2}\approx\left\{\begin{matrix}0.738\,24\\3.544\,94\end{matrix}\right.+k2\pi$

$\therefore\ t\approx\left\{\begin{matrix}1.4765\\7.0899\end{matrix}\right.+k4\pi$

$\therefore\ t\approx 1.48,\ 7.09$

**12** $d=a+b\sin\left(\frac{2\pi t}{k}\right)$

When $t=3$ and $15$, $d_{\max}=22.5$

At this time, $\sin\left(\frac{2\pi t}{k}\right)=1$

$\therefore\ 22.5=a+b$ .... (1)

When $t=9$, and $21$, $d_{\min}=8.7$

At this time, $\sin\left(\frac{2\pi t}{k}\right)=-1$

$\therefore\ 8.7=a-b$ .... (2)

Adding (1) and (2), we get $2a=31.2$

$\therefore\ a=15.6$ and $b=6.9$

The period $=\frac{2\pi}{\frac{2\pi}{k}}=12$, so $k=12$

Thus $a=15.6$, $b=6.9$, $k=12$.

*Check:* $d=15.6+6.9\sin\left(\frac{\pi t}{6}\right)$ has max. value

$15.6+6.9=22.5$ when $\sin\left(\frac{\pi t}{6}\right)=1$

$\therefore\ \frac{\pi t}{6}=\frac{\pi}{2}+k2\pi$

$\therefore\ \frac{t}{6}=\frac{1}{2}+2k$

$\therefore\ t=3+12k$ ✓

**13**

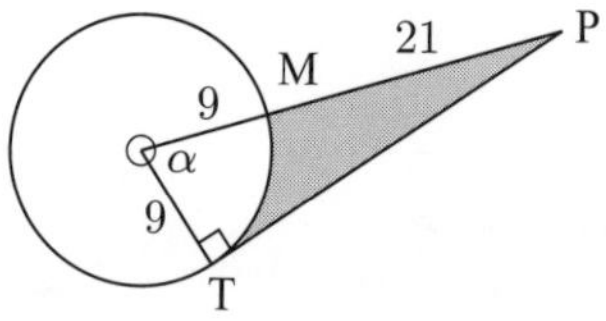


In $\Delta$OTP, $\cos\alpha=\frac{9}{30}=0.3$

$\therefore\ \alpha=\cos^{-1}(0.3)$

$\therefore\ \alpha\approx 72.542^o$

Area of $\Delta$OTP $\approx\frac{1}{2}\times 9\times 30\times\sin 72.542^o$

$\approx 128.78\ \text{cm}^2$

Area of sector OTM $=\left(\frac{\alpha}{360}\right)\times\pi\times 9^2$

$\approx\frac{72.542}{360}\times\pi\times 81$

$\approx 51.28\ \text{cm}^2$

$\therefore$ Area of shaded region $\approx 128.78-51.28$

$\approx 77.5\ \text{cm}^2$

**14** **a** $4\cos^2\theta=1,\ \ 0^o\leqslant\theta\leqslant 360^o$

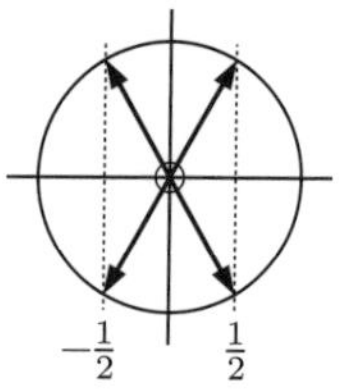


$\therefore\ \cos^2\theta=\frac{1}{4}$

$\therefore\ \cos\theta=\pm\frac{1}{2}$

$\therefore\ \theta=60^o,\ 120^o,\ 240^o,\ 300^o$

**b** $4\sin^2\theta=\cos^2\theta$

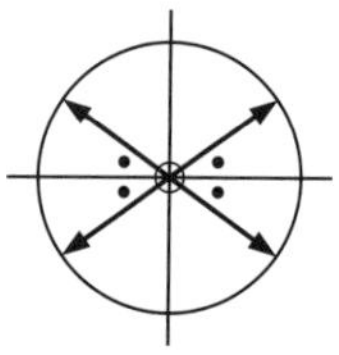

$\therefore\ \frac{\sin^2\theta}{\cos^2\theta}=\frac{1}{4}$

$\therefore\ \tan^2\theta=\frac{1}{4}$

$\therefore\ \tan\theta=\pm\frac{1}{2}$

So $\theta\approx 27^o,\ 153^o,\ 207^o,\ 333^o$

**15**

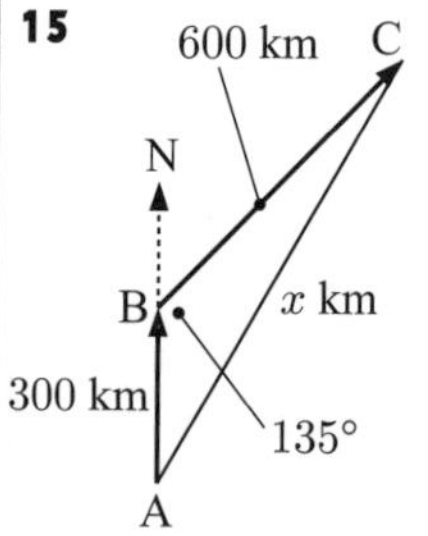


$\text{AB}=400\times\frac{3}{4}=300$ km

$\text{BC}=400\times 1\frac{1}{2}=600$ km

Using the cosine rule,

$x^2=300^2+600^2-2\times 300\times 600\cos 135^o$

$\therefore\ x=\sqrt{300^2+600^2-600^2\times\cos 135^o}$

$\therefore\ x\approx 839.38$

$\therefore$ the distance is about 839 km.

**16**

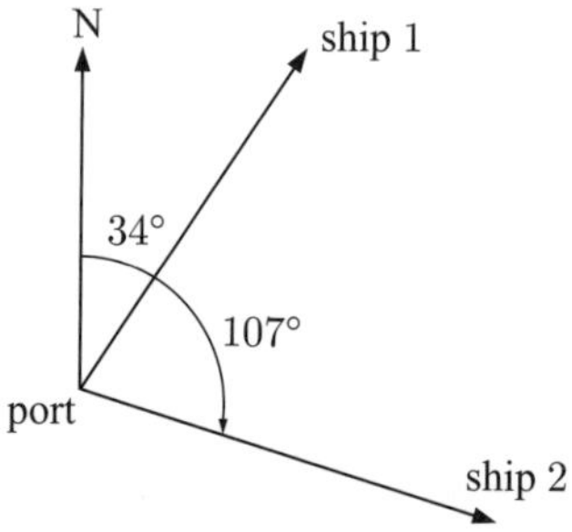


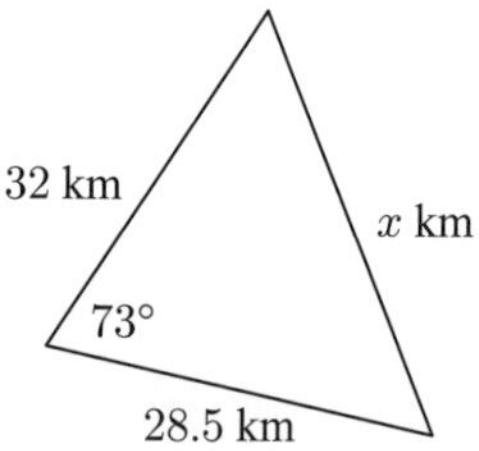


At 4:00 pm, ship 1 has travelled at 16 km h$^{-1}$ for 2 hours, so is 32 km from port.

Ship 2 has travelled at 19 km h$^{-1}$ for 1.5 hours, so is 28.5 km from port.

Using the cosine rule,

$x^2=32^2+28.5^2-2\times 32\times 28.5\times\cos 73^o$

$\therefore\ x^2\approx 1302.96$

$\therefore\ x\approx 36.1$

$\therefore$ the two ships are about 36.1 km apart at 4:00 pm.

**17** Consider the graphs of $y=\frac{\sin x}{x^2+1}$ and $y=0.3$.

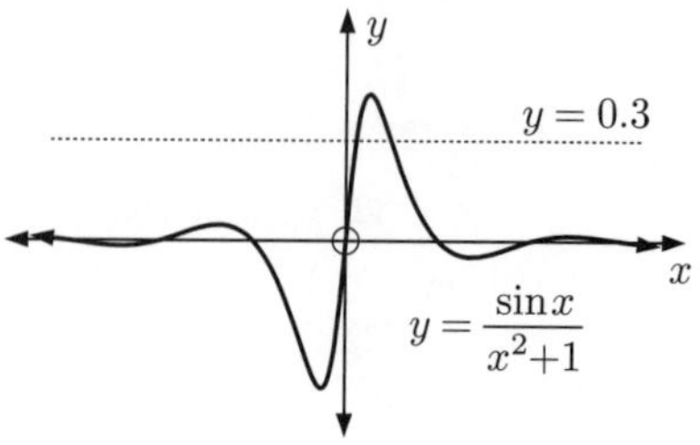


Using technology, the $x$-coordinates of the points of intersection are about $0.342$ and $1.526$.

$\therefore$ the solutions of $\frac{\sin x}{x^2+1}=0.3$

are $x\approx 0.342$ and $x\approx 1.526$

**18** **a** $2\cos 2x + 1 = 0$

$\therefore \quad \cos 2x = -\frac{1}{2}$

$\therefore \quad 2x = \begin{cases} \frac{2\pi}{3} \\ \frac{4\pi}{3} \end{cases} + k2\pi$

$\therefore \quad x = \begin{cases} \frac{\pi}{3} \\ \frac{2\pi}{3} \end{cases} + k\pi$

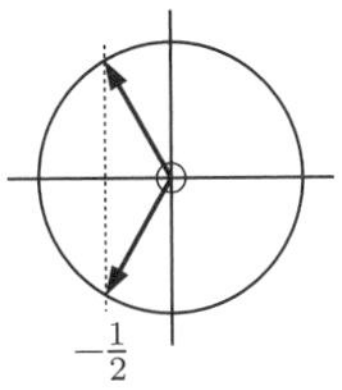


$\therefore \quad x = \frac{\pi}{3}, \frac{2\pi}{3}, \frac{4\pi}{3}, \frac{5\pi}{3} \quad \{\text{on } 0 \leqslant x \leqslant 2\pi\}$

**b** $\cos 2x = 2\cos x, \quad 0 \leqslant x \leqslant 3\pi$

$\therefore \quad 2\cos^2 x - 1 = 2\cos x$

$\therefore \quad 2\cos^2 x - 2\cos x - 1 = 0$

$\therefore \quad \cos x = \dfrac{2 \pm \sqrt{(-2)^2 - 4 \times 2(-1)}}{2 \times 2}$

{quadratic formula}

$= \dfrac{2 \pm \sqrt{12}}{4} = \dfrac{1 \pm \sqrt{3}}{2}$

But $\dfrac{1+\sqrt{3}}{2} > 1$, so $\cos x = \dfrac{1-\sqrt{3}}{2} \approx -0.366\,025$

$\therefore \quad x \approx \begin{cases} 1.9455 \\ 2\pi - 1.9455 \end{cases} + k2\pi$

$\therefore \quad x \approx 1.95, 4.34, 8.23$

$\{\text{on } 0 \leqslant x \leqslant 3\pi\}$

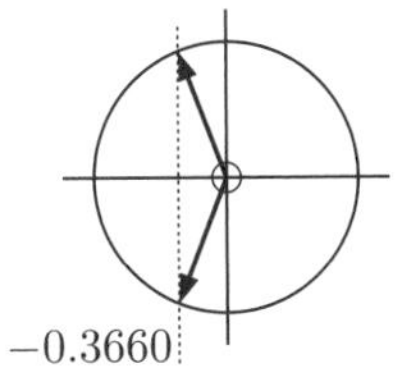


**19** The solutions to $2^{-x}\sin x = \frac{1}{2}x - 1$ are the $x$-coordinates of the points of intersection of the curves.

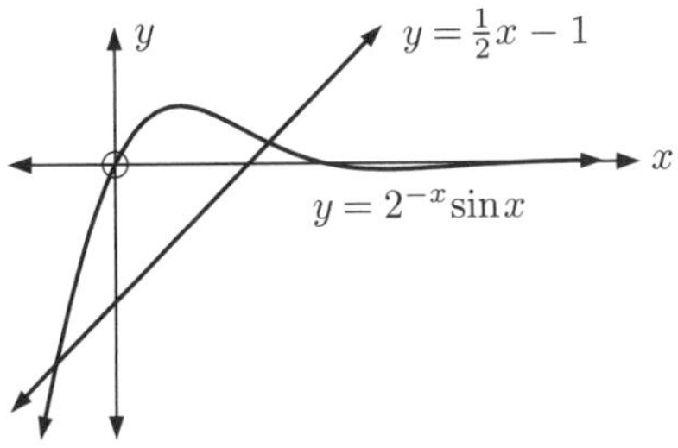


Using technology, the only solution for $x > 0$ is $x \approx 2.30$.

**20** $\tan\theta = 2\cos\theta$

$\therefore \quad \dfrac{\sin\theta}{\cos\theta} = 2\cos\theta$

$\therefore \quad \sin\theta = 2\cos^2\theta \qquad \{\text{as } 0 < \theta < \frac{\pi}{2}, \ \cos\theta \neq 0\}$

$\therefore \quad \sin\theta = 2(1 - \sin^2\theta)$

$\therefore \quad \sin\theta = 2 - 2\sin^2\theta$

$\therefore \quad 2\sin^2\theta + \sin\theta - 2 = 0$

$\therefore \quad \sin\theta = \dfrac{-1 \pm \sqrt{1^2 - 4 \times 2(-2)}}{2 \times 2} = \dfrac{-1 \pm \sqrt{17}}{4}$

But $-1 \leqslant \sin\theta \leqslant 1$,

so $\sin\theta = \dfrac{-1+\sqrt{17}}{4} \approx 0.7808$

$\therefore \quad \theta \approx 0.896$ or $2.25$

$\therefore \quad \theta \approx 0.896 \quad \{\text{as } 0 < \theta < \frac{\pi}{2}\}$

**21** $y = \sin x + x - 1,$
$0 \leqslant x \leqslant 6$

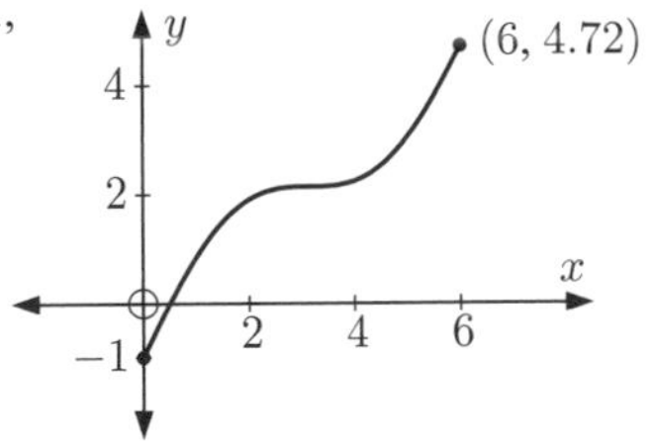


# SOLUTIONS TO TOPIC 4 (MATRICES)

## NO CALCULATORS

**1** $\mathbf{A} = \begin{pmatrix} 2 & -1 \\ 3 & 4 \end{pmatrix}, \quad \mathbf{B} = \begin{pmatrix} -3 & 2 \\ 6 & -5 \end{pmatrix}$

**a** $\mathbf{A} + 2\mathbf{B} = \begin{pmatrix} 2 & -1 \\ 3 & 4 \end{pmatrix} + \begin{pmatrix} -6 & 4 \\ 12 & -10 \end{pmatrix} = \begin{pmatrix} -4 & 3 \\ 15 & -6 \end{pmatrix}$

**b** $3\mathbf{A} - 6\mathbf{I} = \begin{pmatrix} 6 & -3 \\ 9 & 12 \end{pmatrix} - \begin{pmatrix} 6 & 0 \\ 0 & 6 \end{pmatrix} = \begin{pmatrix} 0 & -3 \\ 9 & 6 \end{pmatrix}$

**c** $\mathbf{AB} = \begin{pmatrix} 2 & -1 \\ 3 & 4 \end{pmatrix}\begin{pmatrix} -3 & 2 \\ 6 & -5 \end{pmatrix} = \begin{pmatrix} -12 & 9 \\ 15 & -14 \end{pmatrix}$

**d** $\det \mathbf{B} = (-3) \times (-5) - 2 \times 6 = 15 - 12 = 3$

**e** $\mathbf{A}^{-1} = \dfrac{1}{8 - -3}\begin{pmatrix} 4 & 1 \\ -3 & 2 \end{pmatrix} = \begin{pmatrix} \frac{4}{11} & \frac{1}{11} \\ -\frac{3}{11} & \frac{2}{11} \end{pmatrix}$

**f** $\mathbf{A}^2 = \begin{pmatrix} 2 & -1 \\ 3 & 4 \end{pmatrix}\begin{pmatrix} 2 & -1 \\ 3 & 4 \end{pmatrix} = \begin{pmatrix} 1 & -6 \\ 18 & 13 \end{pmatrix}$

**2** $\mathbf{M} = \begin{pmatrix} 7 & 2 & 1 \\ -3 & 4 & 4 \\ 2 & 1 & 6 \end{pmatrix}, \quad \mathbf{N} = \begin{pmatrix} 2 & 8 & -3 \\ 1 & 2 & 1 \\ 4 & -2 & 5 \end{pmatrix}$

**a** $3\mathbf{M} - 2\mathbf{N} = \begin{pmatrix} 21 & 6 & 3 \\ -9 & 12 & 12 \\ 6 & 3 & 18 \end{pmatrix} - \begin{pmatrix} 4 & 16 & -6 \\ 2 & 4 & 2 \\ 8 & -4 & 10 \end{pmatrix}$

$= \begin{pmatrix} 17 & -10 & 9 \\ -11 & 8 & 10 \\ -2 & 7 & 8 \end{pmatrix}$

**b** $\mathbf{MN} = \begin{pmatrix} 7 & 2 & 1 \\ -3 & 4 & 4 \\ 2 & 1 & 6 \end{pmatrix}\begin{pmatrix} 2 & 8 & -3 \\ 1 & 2 & 1 \\ 4 & -2 & 5 \end{pmatrix}$

$= \begin{pmatrix} 20 & 58 & -14 \\ 14 & -24 & 33 \\ 29 & 6 & 25 \end{pmatrix}$

**3** $\begin{pmatrix} 3 & 2 \\ 5 & 4 \end{pmatrix}^{-1} = \frac{1}{12-10}\begin{pmatrix} 4 & -2 \\ -5 & 3 \end{pmatrix} = \frac{1}{2}\begin{pmatrix} 4 & -2 \\ -5 & 3 \end{pmatrix}$

The system has matrix equation

$\begin{pmatrix} 3 & 2 \\ 5 & 4 \end{pmatrix}\begin{pmatrix} x \\ y \end{pmatrix} = \begin{pmatrix} 14 \\ 22 \end{pmatrix} \quad \{\mathbf{AX} = \mathbf{B}\}$

$\therefore \quad \begin{pmatrix} x \\ y \end{pmatrix} = \begin{pmatrix} 3 & 2 \\ 5 & 4 \end{pmatrix}^{-1}\begin{pmatrix} 14 \\ 22 \end{pmatrix}$

$= \frac{1}{2}\begin{pmatrix} 4 & -2 \\ -5 & 3 \end{pmatrix}\begin{pmatrix} 14 \\ 22 \end{pmatrix}$

$= \frac{1}{2}\begin{pmatrix} 12 \\ -4 \end{pmatrix}$

$= \begin{pmatrix} 6 \\ -2 \end{pmatrix}$ So, $x = 6$, $y = -2$.

**4** $\mathbf{S} = \underset{2 \times 3}{\begin{pmatrix} 7 & 1 & 5 \\ 2 & -3 & 3 \end{pmatrix}}$ and $\mathbf{T} = \underset{3 \times 2}{\begin{pmatrix} 8 & -2 \\ 4 & -1 \\ 3 & 2 \end{pmatrix}}$

$\mathbf{ST} = \begin{pmatrix} 7 & 1 & 5 \\ 2 & -3 & 3 \end{pmatrix}\begin{pmatrix} 8 & -2 \\ 4 & -1 \\ 3 & 2 \end{pmatrix} = \begin{pmatrix} 75 & -5 \\ 13 & 5 \end{pmatrix}$

**5** $2\mathbf{A} + \mathbf{X} = 3\mathbf{B}$

$\therefore \quad \mathbf{X} = 3\mathbf{B} - 2\mathbf{A}$

$\therefore \quad \begin{pmatrix} a & 2 \\ 1 & -a \end{pmatrix} = \begin{pmatrix} 24 & 6 \\ 9 & -12 \end{pmatrix} - \begin{pmatrix} 14 & 4 \\ 8 & -2 \end{pmatrix}$

$\therefore \begin{pmatrix} a & 2 \\ 1 & -a \end{pmatrix} = \begin{pmatrix} 10 & 2 \\ 1 & -10 \end{pmatrix}$

$\therefore \quad a = 10$

**6** To evaluate $2\mathbf{A} - 3\mathbf{B}$, $\mathbf{A}$ and $\mathbf{B}$ must have the same order. Since $\mathbf{A}$ has order $m \times n$, $\mathbf{B}$ must have order $m \times n$. So, $p = m$ and $q = n$.

**7** $\mathbf{A} = \mathbf{B}$ if: (1) $\mathbf{A}$ and $\mathbf{B}$ have the same order
(2) each element of $\mathbf{A}$ is equal to the corresponding element of $\mathbf{B}$.

**8** **a** $\mathbf{C}$ exists provided $n = p$.
**b** If $\mathbf{C}$ exists then it has order $m \times q$.

**9** If $\mathbf{O}$ is the matrix with all entries 0 and with the same order as $\mathbf{A}$, then $\mathbf{A} + \mathbf{O} = \mathbf{O} + \mathbf{A} = \mathbf{A}$.

**10** $\mathbf{A}$ and $\mathbf{I}$ must be square matrices of the same order $n \times n$. $\mathbf{I}$ is the identity matrix. It has 1s along the leading diagonal and 0s everywhere else.

**11** **a** $\mathbf{A} = \begin{pmatrix} 2 & 4 \\ 3 & 2 \end{pmatrix} \quad \therefore |\mathbf{A}| = 4 - 12 = -8$

$\therefore \mathbf{A}^{-1} = \begin{pmatrix} \frac{2}{-8} & \frac{-4}{-8} \\ \frac{-3}{-8} & \frac{2}{-8} \end{pmatrix} = \begin{pmatrix} -\frac{1}{4} & \frac{1}{2} \\ \frac{3}{8} & -\frac{1}{4} \end{pmatrix}$

Now $\mathbf{A}\begin{pmatrix} x \\ y \end{pmatrix} = \begin{pmatrix} 15 \\ -5 \end{pmatrix}$

$\therefore \begin{pmatrix} x \\ y \end{pmatrix} = \mathbf{A}^{-1}\begin{pmatrix} 15 \\ -5 \end{pmatrix}$

$= \begin{pmatrix} -\frac{2}{8} & \frac{4}{8} \\ \frac{3}{8} & -\frac{2}{8} \end{pmatrix}\begin{pmatrix} 15 \\ -5 \end{pmatrix}$

$= \begin{pmatrix} -\frac{50}{8} \\ \frac{55}{8} \end{pmatrix} \quad \therefore x = -\frac{25}{4}, \quad y = \frac{55}{8}$

**b** $\mathbf{N} = \begin{pmatrix} a & b \\ a^2 & b^2 \end{pmatrix}$ where $a \neq 0, \ b \neq 0$

If $\mathbf{N}$ does not have an inverse, then $|\mathbf{N}| = 0$

$\therefore \quad ab^2 - a^2b = 0$

$\therefore \quad ab(b-a) = 0$

$\therefore \quad a = b \qquad \{\text{as } a \neq 0, b \neq 0\}$

**12** $\mathbf{A}^{-1}$ exists if $|\mathbf{A}| \neq 0$. So, $a(a+2) - 8 \neq 0$

$\therefore \quad a^2 + 2a - 8 \neq 0$

$\therefore \quad (a-2)(a+4) \neq 0$

$\therefore \quad a \neq 2, \ a \neq -4$

**13** $3\begin{pmatrix} a & 4 \\ 1 & b \end{pmatrix} = \begin{pmatrix} a & 1 \\ 0 & b \end{pmatrix}\begin{pmatrix} 1 & 2 \\ -1 & 1 \end{pmatrix} + \begin{pmatrix} 3 & 9 \\ 2 & -2 \end{pmatrix}$

$\therefore \begin{pmatrix} 3a & 12 \\ 3 & 3b \end{pmatrix} = \begin{pmatrix} a-1 & 2a+1 \\ -b & b \end{pmatrix} + \begin{pmatrix} 3 & 9 \\ 2 & -2 \end{pmatrix}$

$\therefore \begin{pmatrix} 3a & 12 \\ 3 & 3b \end{pmatrix} = \begin{pmatrix} a+2 & 2a+10 \\ 2-b & b-2 \end{pmatrix}$

$\therefore \begin{cases} 3a = a+2 \\ 12 = 2a+10 \\ 3 = 2-b \\ 3b = b-2 \end{cases} \quad \therefore a = 1, \ b = -1$

**14** $\mathbf{A} = \begin{pmatrix} 2 & -1 \\ -4 & 3 \end{pmatrix}$ and $|\mathbf{A}| = 6 - 4 = 2$

$\therefore \mathbf{A}^{-1} = \begin{pmatrix} \frac{3}{2} & \frac{1}{2} \\ \frac{4}{2} & \frac{2}{2} \end{pmatrix} = \begin{pmatrix} \frac{3}{2} & \frac{1}{2} \\ 2 & 1 \end{pmatrix}$

If $\begin{pmatrix} 2 & -1 \\ -4 & 3 \end{pmatrix}\begin{pmatrix} x \\ y \end{pmatrix} = \begin{pmatrix} 6 \\ -2 \end{pmatrix}$ then

$\begin{pmatrix} x \\ y \end{pmatrix} = \begin{pmatrix} 2 & -1 \\ -4 & 3 \end{pmatrix}^{-1}\begin{pmatrix} 6 \\ -2 \end{pmatrix}$

$= \begin{pmatrix} \frac{3}{2} & \frac{1}{2} \\ 2 & 1 \end{pmatrix}\begin{pmatrix} 6 \\ -2 \end{pmatrix}$

$= \begin{pmatrix} 8 \\ 10 \end{pmatrix}$ So, $x = 8, \ y = 10$.

**15** $\begin{vmatrix} 8 & -1 \\ n & 4 \end{vmatrix} = \begin{vmatrix} 1 & n & 0 \\ 3 & -1 & n \\ 2 & 1 & 4 \end{vmatrix}$

$\therefore \ 32 - (-n) = 1\begin{vmatrix} -1 & n \\ 1 & 4 \end{vmatrix} - n\begin{vmatrix} 3 & n \\ 2 & 4 \end{vmatrix}$

$\therefore \ 32 + n = (-4-n) - n(12-2n)$

$\therefore \ 32 + n = 2n^2 - 13n - 4$

$\therefore \ 2n^2 - 14n - 36 = 0$

$\therefore \ 2(n^2 - 7n - 18) = 0$

$\therefore \ 2(n-9)(n+2) = 0$

$\therefore \ n = 9 \text{ or } -2$

**16** $\mathbf{P}$ is non-singular if $|\mathbf{P}| \neq 0$.

Now $|\mathbf{P}| = \begin{vmatrix} 2 & x & -1 \\ -1 & 0 & 4 \\ 2 & 3 & -1 \end{vmatrix}$

$= 2\begin{vmatrix} 0 & 4 \\ 3 & -1 \end{vmatrix} - x\begin{vmatrix} -1 & 4 \\ 2 & -1 \end{vmatrix} + (-1)\begin{vmatrix} -1 & 0 \\ 2 & 3 \end{vmatrix}$

$= 2(-12) - x(-7) - (-3)$

$= 7x - 21$

So, $|\mathbf{P}| = 0$ when $x = 3$

$\therefore$ $\mathbf{P}$ is non-singular if $x \neq 3$.

**17** $\mathbf{A} = \begin{pmatrix} 0 & -2 \\ -1 & 1 \end{pmatrix}$

$\mathbf{A}^2 = \begin{pmatrix} 0 & -2 \\ -1 & 1 \end{pmatrix}\begin{pmatrix} 0 & -2 \\ -1 & 1 \end{pmatrix} = \begin{pmatrix} 2 & -2 \\ -1 & 3 \end{pmatrix}$

$\mathbf{A} + 2\mathbf{I} = \begin{pmatrix} 0 & -2 \\ -1 & 1 \end{pmatrix} + \begin{pmatrix} 2 & 0 \\ 0 & 2 \end{pmatrix} = \begin{pmatrix} 2 & -2 \\ -1 & 3 \end{pmatrix}$

Thus $\mathbf{A}^2 = \mathbf{A} + 2\mathbf{I}$ is verified.

Now $\mathbf{A}^4 = \mathbf{A}^2\mathbf{A}^2$

$= (\mathbf{A} + 2\mathbf{I})(\mathbf{A} + 2\mathbf{I})$

$= \mathbf{A}^2 + 2\mathbf{AI} + 2\mathbf{IA} + 4\mathbf{I}^2$

$= \mathbf{A}^2 + 4\mathbf{A} + 4\mathbf{I} \qquad \{\mathbf{AI} = \mathbf{IA} = \mathbf{A}, \ \mathbf{I}^2 = \mathbf{I}\}$

$= (\mathbf{A} + 2\mathbf{I}) + 4\mathbf{A} + 4\mathbf{I}$

$= 5\mathbf{A} + 6\mathbf{I}$

**18** **a** $\mathbf{A} = \begin{pmatrix} 1 & 5 \\ 1 & 4 \end{pmatrix}$ and $\mathbf{B} = \begin{pmatrix} 1 & -2 \\ 0 & 1 \end{pmatrix}$

$\therefore \mathbf{A}^{-1} = \begin{pmatrix} \frac{4}{-1} & \frac{-5}{-1} \\ \frac{-1}{-1} & \frac{1}{-1} \end{pmatrix} = \begin{pmatrix} -4 & 5 \\ 1 & -1 \end{pmatrix}$

and $\mathbf{B}^{-1} = \begin{pmatrix} \frac{1}{1} & \frac{2}{1} \\ \frac{0}{1} & \frac{1}{1} \end{pmatrix} = \begin{pmatrix} 1 & 2 \\ 0 & 1 \end{pmatrix}$

$\therefore \mathbf{B}^{-1}\mathbf{A}^{-1} = \begin{pmatrix} 1 & 2 \\ 0 & 1 \end{pmatrix}\begin{pmatrix} -4 & 5 \\ 1 & -1 \end{pmatrix} = \begin{pmatrix} -2 & 3 \\ 1 & -1 \end{pmatrix}$

Also $\mathbf{AB} = \begin{pmatrix} 1 & 5 \\ 1 & 4 \end{pmatrix}\begin{pmatrix} 1 & -2 \\ 0 & 1 \end{pmatrix} = \begin{pmatrix} 1 & 3 \\ 1 & 2 \end{pmatrix}$

$\therefore (\mathbf{AB})^{-1} = \begin{pmatrix} \frac{2}{-1} & \frac{-3}{-1} \\ \frac{-1}{-1} & \frac{1}{-1} \end{pmatrix} = \begin{pmatrix} -2 & 3 \\ 1 & -1 \end{pmatrix}$

Thus $(\mathbf{AB})^{-1} = \mathbf{B}^{-1}\mathbf{A}^{-1}$ is verified.

**b** $\mathbf{C}^2 - 4\mathbf{C} = \begin{pmatrix} 3 & 2 \\ -1 & 1 \end{pmatrix}\begin{pmatrix} 3 & 2 \\ -1 & 1 \end{pmatrix} - 4\begin{pmatrix} 3 & 2 \\ -1 & 1 \end{pmatrix}$

$= \begin{pmatrix} 7 & 8 \\ -4 & -1 \end{pmatrix} - \begin{pmatrix} 12 & 8 \\ -4 & 4 \end{pmatrix}$

$= \begin{pmatrix} -5 & 0 \\ 0 & -5 \end{pmatrix}$

$= -5\begin{pmatrix} 1 & 0 \\ 0 & 1 \end{pmatrix} = -5\mathbf{I}$

**c** From **b**, $\mathbf{C}^2 - 4\mathbf{C} + 5\mathbf{I} = \mathbf{O}$.

When premultiplied by $\mathbf{C}^{-1}$, we get

$\mathbf{C}^{-1}(\mathbf{C}^2 - 4\mathbf{C} + 5\mathbf{I}) = \mathbf{C}^{-1}\mathbf{O}$

$\therefore \quad \mathbf{C} - 4\mathbf{I} + 5\mathbf{C}^{-1} = \mathbf{O}$

$\therefore \quad 5\mathbf{C}^{-1} = 4\mathbf{I} - \mathbf{C}$

$\therefore \quad \mathbf{C}^{-1} = \frac{1}{5}(4\mathbf{I} - \mathbf{C})$

**19** Given $\begin{cases} x - y = 3 \\ 2x + cy = 6 \end{cases}$

we can write $\begin{pmatrix} 1 & -1 \\ 2 & c \end{pmatrix}\begin{pmatrix} x \\ y \end{pmatrix} = \begin{pmatrix} 3 \\ 6 \end{pmatrix}$

which has the form $\mathbf{AX} = \mathbf{B}$.

$\mathbf{A}^{-1}$ exists provided $|\mathbf{A}| \neq 0$, so $\begin{vmatrix} 1 & -1 \\ 2 & c \end{vmatrix} \neq 0$

$\therefore \quad c + 2 \neq 0$

$\therefore \quad c \neq -2$

For $c \neq -2$, $\mathbf{X} = \mathbf{A}^{-1}\mathbf{B} = \frac{1}{c+2}\begin{pmatrix} c & 1 \\ -2 & 1 \end{pmatrix}\begin{pmatrix} 3 \\ 6 \end{pmatrix}$

$= \frac{1}{c+2}\begin{pmatrix} 3c+6 \\ 0 \end{pmatrix}$

$= \begin{pmatrix} 3 \\ 0 \end{pmatrix}$

$\therefore$ $x = 3$, $y = 0$ is a unique solution provided $c \neq -2$.

**20** $\mathbf{A} = \begin{pmatrix} -8 & -6 & -6 \\ 2 & 0 & 2 \\ 8 & 8 & 6 \end{pmatrix}$

$\therefore \quad \mathbf{A}^2 = \begin{pmatrix} -8 & -6 & -6 \\ 2 & 0 & 2 \\ 8 & 8 & 6 \end{pmatrix}^2 = \begin{pmatrix} 4 & 0 & 0 \\ 0 & 4 & 0 \\ 0 & 0 & 4 \end{pmatrix} = 4\mathbf{I}$

Since $4\mathbf{I} = \mathbf{A}^2$, $4\mathbf{IA}^{-1} = \mathbf{A}^2\mathbf{A}^{-1}$

$\therefore \quad 4\mathbf{A}^{-1} = \mathbf{A}$

$\therefore \quad \mathbf{A}^{-1} = \frac{1}{4}\mathbf{A} = \begin{pmatrix} -2 & -\frac{3}{2} & -\frac{3}{2} \\ \frac{1}{2} & 0 & \frac{1}{2} \\ 2 & 2 & \frac{3}{2} \end{pmatrix}$

**21** **a** $\mathbf{M} = \begin{pmatrix} n-1 & 4 \\ 3 & n-2 \end{pmatrix}$

$\therefore \quad \det \mathbf{M} = (n-1)(n-2) - 12$

$= n^2 - 3n + 2 - 12$

$= n^2 - 3n - 10$

$= (n-5)(n+2)$

$\therefore \quad \det \mathbf{M} = 0$ when $n = 5$ or $-2$.

$\therefore \quad \mathbf{M}^{-1}$ exists when $n \neq 5$ or $-2$.

**b** $\mathbf{PQ} = \begin{pmatrix} -4 & 2 \\ 1 & -3 \\ -2 & 6 \end{pmatrix}\begin{pmatrix} 3 & -2 \\ 1 & -4 \end{pmatrix} = \begin{pmatrix} -10 & 0 \\ 0 & 10 \\ 0 & -20 \end{pmatrix}$

$3 \times 2 \qquad 2 \times 2 \qquad 3 \times 2$

**QP** cannot be found as $(2 \times 2)$ by $(3 \times 2)$
↑ ↑ not equal.

**22** If $\mathbf{A} = \begin{pmatrix} 2 & 0 & 0 \\ 0 & 3 & 1 \\ 0 & 1 & 3 \end{pmatrix}$ then

$\mathbf{A}^2 = \begin{pmatrix} 2 & 0 & 0 \\ 0 & 3 & 1 \\ 0 & 1 & 3 \end{pmatrix}\begin{pmatrix} 2 & 0 & 0 \\ 0 & 3 & 1 \\ 0 & 1 & 3 \end{pmatrix} = \begin{pmatrix} 4 & 0 & 0 \\ 0 & 10 & 6 \\ 0 & 6 & 10 \end{pmatrix}$

and $\mathbf{A}^2 - 6\mathbf{A} = \begin{pmatrix} 4 & 0 & 0 \\ 0 & 10 & 6 \\ 0 & 6 & 10 \end{pmatrix} - 6\begin{pmatrix} 2 & 0 & 0 \\ 0 & 3 & 1 \\ 0 & 1 & 3 \end{pmatrix}$

$= \begin{pmatrix} -8 & 0 & 0 \\ 0 & -8 & 0 \\ 0 & 0 & -8 \end{pmatrix}$

$= -8\begin{pmatrix} 1 & 0 & 0 \\ 0 & 1 & 0 \\ 0 & 0 & 1 \end{pmatrix} = -8\mathbf{I}$

Now since $\mathbf{A}^2 - 6\mathbf{A} = -8\mathbf{I}$,

$\mathbf{A}^{-1}(\mathbf{A}^2 - 6\mathbf{A}) = \mathbf{A}^{-1}(-8\mathbf{I})$

$\therefore \quad \mathbf{A} - 6\mathbf{I} = -8\mathbf{A}^{-1}$

$\therefore \quad 6\mathbf{I} - \mathbf{A} = 8\mathbf{A}^{-1}$

$\therefore \quad \frac{1}{8}(6\mathbf{I} - \mathbf{A}) = \mathbf{A}^{-1}$

**23** $\mathbf{A} = \begin{pmatrix} 1 & 2 & k \\ 2 & -1 & 1 \\ k & -1 & 2 \end{pmatrix}$

Now $\det \mathbf{A} = 0$

$\therefore \quad \begin{vmatrix} 1 & 2 & k \\ 2 & -1 & 1 \\ k & -1 & 2 \end{vmatrix} = 0$

$\therefore \quad 1\begin{vmatrix} -1 & 1 \\ -1 & 2 \end{vmatrix} - 2\begin{vmatrix} 2 & 1 \\ k & 2 \end{vmatrix} + k\begin{vmatrix} 2 & -1 \\ k & -1 \end{vmatrix} = 0$

$\therefore \quad 1(-1) - 2(4-k) + k(-2+k) = 0$

$\therefore \quad -1 - 8 + 2k - 2k + k^2 = 0$

$\therefore \quad k^2 - 9 = 0$

$\therefore \quad (k+3)(k-3) = 0$

$\therefore \quad k = \pm 3$

**24** $\mathbf{A} = \begin{pmatrix} 1 & 1 & 1 \\ x & 2 & 3 \\ x^2 & 4 & 9 \end{pmatrix}$

Now $\det \mathbf{A} = 0$

$\therefore \quad 1\begin{vmatrix} 2 & 3 \\ 4 & 9 \end{vmatrix} - 1\begin{vmatrix} x & 3 \\ x^2 & 9 \end{vmatrix} + 1\begin{vmatrix} x & 2 \\ x^2 & 4 \end{vmatrix} = 0$

$\therefore \quad 1(6) - 1(9x - 3x^2) + 1(4x - 2x^2) = 0$

$\therefore \quad 6 - 9x + 3x^2 + 4x - 2x^2 = 0$

$\therefore \quad x^2 - 5x + 6 = 0$

$\therefore \quad (x-3)(x-2) = 0$

$\therefore \quad x = 3$ or $2$

**25** $\mathbf{A} = \begin{pmatrix} 2 & 4 \\ -1 & -3 \end{pmatrix} \quad \therefore \quad |\mathbf{A}| = -6 - (-4) = -2$

and $\mathbf{A}^{-1} = \begin{pmatrix} \frac{-3}{-2} & \frac{-4}{-2} \\ \frac{1}{-2} & \frac{2}{-2} \end{pmatrix} = \begin{pmatrix} \frac{3}{2} & 2 \\ -\frac{1}{2} & -1 \end{pmatrix}$

Given $\begin{cases} 2x + 4y = 2 \\ -x - 3y = 1 \end{cases}$ we can write

$\begin{pmatrix} 2 & 4 \\ -1 & -3 \end{pmatrix}\begin{pmatrix} x \\ y \end{pmatrix} = \begin{pmatrix} 2 \\ 1 \end{pmatrix}$ which has the form $\mathbf{AX} = \mathbf{B}$

$\therefore \quad \mathbf{A}\begin{pmatrix} x \\ y \end{pmatrix} = \begin{pmatrix} 2 \\ 1 \end{pmatrix}$

$\therefore \quad \begin{pmatrix} x \\ y \end{pmatrix} = \mathbf{A}^{-1}\begin{pmatrix} 2 \\ 1 \end{pmatrix}$

$$\therefore \quad \begin{pmatrix} x \\ y \end{pmatrix} = \begin{pmatrix} \frac{3}{2} & 2 \\ -\frac{1}{2} & -1 \end{pmatrix}\begin{pmatrix} 2 \\ 1 \end{pmatrix} = \begin{pmatrix} 5 \\ -2 \end{pmatrix}$$

So, $x = 5$, $y = -2$.

*Check:* $2(5) + 4(-2) = 2$ ✓ and $-(5) - 3(-2) = 1$ ✓

**26** **a** $\mathbf{A} = \begin{pmatrix} 3 & 4 \\ -2 & -3 \end{pmatrix} \quad \therefore \quad |\mathbf{A}| = -9 - (-8) = -1$

$$\therefore \quad \mathbf{A}^{-1} = \begin{pmatrix} \frac{-3}{-1} & \frac{-4}{-1} \\ \frac{2}{-1} & \frac{3}{-1} \end{pmatrix} = \begin{pmatrix} 3 & 4 \\ -2 & -3 \end{pmatrix}$$

$$\mathbf{A}^2 = \begin{pmatrix} 3 & 4 \\ -2 & -3 \end{pmatrix}\begin{pmatrix} 3 & 4 \\ -2 & -3 \end{pmatrix} = \begin{pmatrix} 1 & 0 \\ 0 & 1 \end{pmatrix} = \mathbf{I}$$

**b** $\mathbf{A}^3 = \mathbf{A}^2\mathbf{A} = \mathbf{IA} = \mathbf{A}$

$$\therefore \quad \mathbf{A}^3 + 4\mathbf{A}^2 - 2\mathbf{A} - 3\mathbf{I} = \mathbf{A} + 4\mathbf{I} - 2\mathbf{A} - 3\mathbf{I} = -\mathbf{A} + \mathbf{I} = \begin{pmatrix} -3 & -4 \\ 2 & 3 \end{pmatrix} + \begin{pmatrix} 1 & 0 \\ 0 & 1 \end{pmatrix} = \begin{pmatrix} -2 & -4 \\ 2 & 4 \end{pmatrix}$$

which has determinant $= -8 - (-8) = 0$

$\therefore$ this matrix has no inverse.

**27** **a** $\mathbf{A} = \begin{pmatrix} 3 & 0 \\ 0 & 4 \end{pmatrix} \quad \therefore \quad |\mathbf{A}| = 12$

$$\therefore \quad \mathbf{A}^{-1} = \begin{pmatrix} \frac{4}{12} & \frac{0}{12} \\ \frac{0}{12} & \frac{3}{12} \end{pmatrix} = \begin{pmatrix} \frac{1}{3} & 0 \\ 0 & \frac{1}{4} \end{pmatrix}$$

$\mathbf{B} = \begin{pmatrix} 1 & -2 \\ -1 & 1 \end{pmatrix} \quad \therefore \quad |\mathbf{B}| = 1 - 2 = -1$

$$\therefore \quad \mathbf{B}^{-1} = \begin{pmatrix} \frac{1}{-1} & \frac{2}{-1} \\ \frac{1}{-1} & \frac{1}{-1} \end{pmatrix} = \begin{pmatrix} -1 & -2 \\ -1 & -1 \end{pmatrix}$$

**b** If $\mathbf{AXB} = \mathbf{C}$ then $\mathbf{A}^{-1}(\mathbf{AXB})\mathbf{B}^{-1} = \mathbf{A}^{-1}\mathbf{CB}^{-1}$

$\therefore \quad \mathbf{IXI} = \mathbf{A}^{-1}\mathbf{CB}^{-1}$

$\therefore \quad \mathbf{X} = \mathbf{A}^{-1}\mathbf{CB}^{-1}$

$$\therefore \quad \mathbf{X} = \begin{pmatrix} \frac{1}{3} & 0 \\ 0 & \frac{1}{4} \end{pmatrix}\begin{pmatrix} 2 & -2 \\ 3 & 1 \end{pmatrix}\begin{pmatrix} -1 & -2 \\ -1 & -1 \end{pmatrix} = \begin{pmatrix} \frac{1}{3} & 0 \\ 0 & \frac{1}{4} \end{pmatrix}\begin{pmatrix} 0 & -2 \\ -4 & -7 \end{pmatrix} = \begin{pmatrix} 0 & -\frac{2}{3} \\ -1 & -\frac{7}{4} \end{pmatrix}$$

**28** $$\mathbf{AB} = \begin{pmatrix} x & 0 & 2 \\ 1 & -1 & 0 \end{pmatrix}\begin{pmatrix} 0 & 1 \\ 2 & x \\ 0 & -1 \end{pmatrix} = \begin{pmatrix} 0 & x-2 \\ -2 & 1-x \end{pmatrix}$$

$2 \times 3 \qquad 3 \times 2 \qquad 2 \times 2$

$$\mathbf{BA} = \begin{pmatrix} 0 & 1 \\ 2 & x \\ 0 & -1 \end{pmatrix}\begin{pmatrix} x & 0 & 2 \\ 1 & -1 & 0 \end{pmatrix} = \begin{pmatrix} 1 & -1 & 0 \\ 3x & -x & 4 \\ -1 & 1 & 0 \end{pmatrix}$$

Now $\det(\mathbf{AB}) = \det(\mathbf{BA})$

$$\therefore \quad \begin{vmatrix} 0 & x-2 \\ -2 & 1-x \end{vmatrix} = \begin{vmatrix} 1 & -1 & 0 \\ 3x & -x & 4 \\ -1 & 1 & 0 \end{vmatrix}$$

$$\therefore \quad 2(x-2) = 1\begin{vmatrix} -x & 4 \\ 1 & 0 \end{vmatrix} - (-1)\begin{vmatrix} 3x & 4 \\ -1 & 0 \end{vmatrix} + 0$$

$\therefore \quad 2x - 4 = 1(-4) + (4) + 0$

$\therefore \quad 2x - 4 = 0$

$\therefore \quad x = 2$

**29** $$\begin{vmatrix} a & -a & a \\ -a & a & -a \\ a & -a & a \end{vmatrix} = a\begin{vmatrix} a & -a \\ -a & a \end{vmatrix} - (-a)\begin{vmatrix} -a & -a \\ a & a \end{vmatrix} + a\begin{vmatrix} -a & a \\ a & -a \end{vmatrix}$$

$= a(0) + a(0) + a(0)$

$= 0$

**30** **a** $\mathbf{ABC} = 2\mathbf{I}$

$\therefore \quad \mathbf{A}^{-1}(\mathbf{ABC}) = 2\mathbf{A}^{-1}\mathbf{I}$ {premultiply by $\mathbf{A}^{-1}$}

$\therefore \quad \mathbf{IBC} = 2\mathbf{A}^{-1}$

$\therefore \quad \frac{1}{2}\mathbf{BC} = \mathbf{A}^{-1}$ So, $\mathbf{A}^{-1} = \frac{1}{2}\mathbf{BC}$

**b** $\mathbf{ABC} = 2\mathbf{I}$

$\therefore \quad \mathbf{A}^{-1}(\mathbf{ABC})\mathbf{C}^{-1} = 2\mathbf{A}^{-1}\mathbf{IC}^{-1}$

$\therefore \quad \mathbf{IBI} = 2\mathbf{A}^{-1}\mathbf{C}^{-1}$

$\therefore \quad \mathbf{B} = 2\mathbf{A}^{-1}\mathbf{C}^{-1}$

$\therefore \quad \mathbf{B}^{-1} = (2\mathbf{A}^{-1}\mathbf{C}^{-1})^{-1}$

$\therefore \quad \mathbf{B}^{-1} = \frac{1}{2}(\mathbf{A}^{-1}\mathbf{C}^{-1})^{-1} = \frac{1}{2}\mathbf{CA}$

**c** $\mathbf{ABC} = 2\mathbf{I}$

$\therefore \quad (\mathbf{ABC})\mathbf{C}^{-1} = 2\mathbf{IC}^{-1}$ {postmultiply by $\mathbf{C}^{-1}$}

$\therefore \quad \mathbf{AB} = 2\mathbf{C}^{-1}$

$\therefore \quad \frac{1}{2}\mathbf{AB} = \mathbf{C}^{-1}$ So, $\mathbf{C}^{-1} = \frac{1}{2}\mathbf{AB}$

## CALCULATORS

**1** $\mathbf{P} = \begin{pmatrix} -3 & 2 \\ 6 & 8 \end{pmatrix}$, $\mathbf{Q} = \begin{pmatrix} 7 & -2 & 3 \\ 4 & 2 & 1 \\ 0 & -3 & 5 \end{pmatrix}$

**a** $\det \mathbf{P} = -24 - 12 = -36$

**b** $$\det \mathbf{Q} = 7\begin{vmatrix} 2 & 1 \\ -3 & 5 \end{vmatrix} - (-2)\begin{vmatrix} 4 & 1 \\ 0 & 5 \end{vmatrix} + 3\begin{vmatrix} 4 & 2 \\ 0 & -3 \end{vmatrix}$$

$= 7(13) + 2(20) + 3(-12)$

$= 91 + 40 - 36$

$= 95$

**c** $$\mathbf{P}^{-1} = -\frac{1}{36}\begin{pmatrix} 8 & -2 \\ -6 & -3 \end{pmatrix} = \begin{pmatrix} -\frac{2}{9} & \frac{1}{18} \\ \frac{1}{6} & \frac{1}{12} \end{pmatrix}$$

**d** $$\mathbf{Q}^{-1} = \begin{pmatrix} \frac{13}{95} & \frac{1}{95} & -\frac{8}{95} \\ -\frac{4}{19} & \frac{7}{19} & \frac{1}{19} \\ -\frac{12}{95} & \frac{21}{95} & \frac{22}{95} \end{pmatrix}$$ {using technology}

**2** $$\begin{pmatrix} 3 & 1 & 2 \\ 2 & 4 & 1 \\ 1 & -2 & 1 \end{pmatrix}^{-1} = \begin{pmatrix} 6 & -5 & -7 \\ -1 & 1 & 1 \\ -8 & 7 & 10 \end{pmatrix}$$ {using technology}

This system in matrix form is:

$$\begin{pmatrix} 3 & 1 & 2 \\ 2 & 4 & 1 \\ 1 & -2 & 1 \end{pmatrix}\begin{pmatrix} x \\ y \\ z \end{pmatrix} = \begin{pmatrix} 18 \\ 8 \\ 9 \end{pmatrix} \quad \{\mathbf{AX} = \mathbf{B}\}$$

$$\therefore \quad \begin{pmatrix} x \\ y \\ z \end{pmatrix} = \begin{pmatrix} 3 & 1 & 2 \\ 2 & 4 & 1 \\ 1 & -2 & 1 \end{pmatrix}^{-1}\begin{pmatrix} 18 \\ 8 \\ 9 \end{pmatrix} = \begin{pmatrix} 6 & -5 & -7 \\ -1 & 1 & 1 \\ -8 & 7 & 10 \end{pmatrix}\begin{pmatrix} 18 \\ 8 \\ 9 \end{pmatrix} = \begin{pmatrix} 5 \\ -1 \\ 2 \end{pmatrix}$$

$\therefore \quad x = 5, \quad y = -1, \quad z = 2$

**3** Let the cost of 1 soccer ball be $\$x$, the cost of 1 softball be $\$y$ and the cost of 1 basketball be $\$z$.

School A paid $2x + 1y + 3z = 90$.

School B paid $3x + 2y + 1z = 81$.

School C paid $5x + 0y + 2z = 104$.

In matrix form, $\begin{pmatrix} 2 & 1 & 3 \\ 3 & 2 & 1 \\ 5 & 0 & 2 \end{pmatrix}\begin{pmatrix} x \\ y \\ z \end{pmatrix} = \begin{pmatrix} 90 \\ 81 \\ 104 \end{pmatrix}$.

This system has solution $x = 14,\ y = 11,\ z = 17$.

So, a soccer ball costs \$14, a softball costs \$11 and a basketball costs \$17.

**4**

| E | W | Y |
|---|---|---|
| 10 | 5 | 12 |
| 8 | 12 | 6 |
| 4 | 1 | 2 |
| €17.20 | €9.80 | €13.60 |

Let the cost of a bread roll be €$x$, an apple be €$y$, and a bag of chips be €$z$.

$$\therefore\ \begin{aligned} 10x + 8y + 4z &= 17.2 \\ 5x + 12y + z &= 9.8 \\ 12x + 6y + 2z &= 13.6 \end{aligned}$$

So, $\begin{pmatrix} 10 & 8 & 4 \\ 5 & 12 & 1 \\ 12 & 6 & 2 \end{pmatrix}\begin{pmatrix} x \\ y \\ z \end{pmatrix} = \begin{pmatrix} 17.2 \\ 9.8 \\ 13.6 \end{pmatrix}$

$$\therefore\ \begin{pmatrix} x \\ y \\ z \end{pmatrix} = \begin{pmatrix} 10 & 8 & 4 \\ 5 & 12 & 1 \\ 12 & 6 & 2 \end{pmatrix}^{-1}\begin{pmatrix} 17.2 \\ 9.8 \\ 13.6 \end{pmatrix} = \begin{pmatrix} 0.6 \\ 0.4 \\ 2 \end{pmatrix}$$

$\therefore\ x = 0.6,\ \ y = 0.4,\ \ z = 2$

$\therefore$ a bread roll costs 60 cents, an apple costs 40 cents, and a bag of chips costs €2.

**5 a** $\mathbf{AB} = \begin{pmatrix} 1 & 2 & 1 \\ 3 & -2 & 0 \end{pmatrix}\begin{pmatrix} 1 & 2 \\ -1 & 1 \\ 0 & 2 \end{pmatrix} = \begin{pmatrix} -1 & 6 \\ 5 & 4 \end{pmatrix}$

But $\mathbf{AB} - 2\mathbf{C} = \begin{pmatrix} -1 & -4 \\ 3 & 8 \end{pmatrix}$

$$\therefore -2\mathbf{C} = \begin{pmatrix} -1 & -4 \\ 3 & 8 \end{pmatrix} - \begin{pmatrix} -1 & 6 \\ 5 & 4 \end{pmatrix}$$

$$\therefore\ -2\mathbf{C} = \begin{pmatrix} 0 & -10 \\ -2 & 4 \end{pmatrix}$$

$$\therefore\ \mathbf{C} = \begin{pmatrix} 0 & 5 \\ 1 & -2 \end{pmatrix}$$

**b** $\mathbf{D} = \begin{pmatrix} 0 & 2 \\ -2 & 0 \end{pmatrix}$

$\therefore\ \mathbf{D}^2 = \begin{pmatrix} -4 & 0 \\ 0 & -4 \end{pmatrix}$ {using technology}

$\therefore\ \mathbf{D}^2 = -4\begin{pmatrix} 1 & 0 \\ 0 & 1 \end{pmatrix}$

$\therefore\ \mathbf{D}^2 = -4\mathbf{I}$

$\therefore\ -\frac{1}{4}\mathbf{D}^2 = \mathbf{I}$

$\therefore\ (-\frac{1}{4}\mathbf{D})\mathbf{D} = \mathbf{I}$

Now $|\mathbf{D}| = 0 - (-4) = 4 \neq 0$ so $\mathbf{D}^{-1}$ exists.

Thus $(-\frac{1}{4}\mathbf{D})\mathbf{D}\mathbf{D}^{-1} = \mathbf{I}\mathbf{D}^{-1}$ {postmultiply by $\mathbf{D}^{-1}$}

$\therefore\ (-\frac{1}{4}\mathbf{D})\mathbf{I} = \mathbf{D}^{-1}$

$\therefore\ \mathbf{D}^{-1} = -\frac{1}{4}\mathbf{D}$

**6** $\mathbf{A} = \begin{pmatrix} 2 & 1 & -1 \\ 0 & 1 & 0 \\ 0 & 0 & 1 \end{pmatrix}$ and $\mathbf{B} = \begin{pmatrix} 0 & 1 & 1 \\ 1 & 1 & 0 \\ 1 & 2 & 1 \end{pmatrix}$.

$\mathbf{AB} = \begin{pmatrix} 2 & 1 & -1 \\ 0 & 1 & 0 \\ 0 & 0 & 1 \end{pmatrix}\begin{pmatrix} 0 & 1 & 1 \\ 1 & 1 & 0 \\ 1 & 2 & 1 \end{pmatrix} = \begin{pmatrix} 0 & 1 & 1 \\ 1 & 1 & 0 \\ 1 & 2 & 1 \end{pmatrix}$ {using technology}

$\therefore\ \mathbf{AB} = \mathbf{B}$

$$\begin{aligned} \therefore\ \mathbf{A}^{10}\mathbf{B} &= \mathbf{A}^9(\mathbf{AB}) \\ &= \mathbf{A}^9\mathbf{B} \\ &= \mathbf{A}^8(\mathbf{AB}) \\ &= \mathbf{A}^8\mathbf{B} \\ &\ \ \vdots \\ &= \mathbf{AB} \\ &= \mathbf{B} \end{aligned}$$

So, $\mathbf{A}^{10}\mathbf{B} = \begin{pmatrix} 0 & 1 & 1 \\ 1 & 1 & 0 \\ 1 & 2 & 1 \end{pmatrix}$

**7 a** $\mathbf{A} = \begin{pmatrix} 4 & 1 \\ 3 & 2 \end{pmatrix}$ $\quad\therefore\ |\mathbf{A}| = 8 - 3 = 5$

$\therefore\ \mathbf{A}^{-1} = \frac{1}{5}\begin{pmatrix} 2 & -1 \\ -3 & 4 \end{pmatrix} = \begin{pmatrix} \frac{2}{5} & -\frac{1}{5} \\ -\frac{3}{5} & \frac{4}{5} \end{pmatrix}$

**b** $\det(\mathbf{AB})^{-1} = \frac{1}{10}$ {using technology}

**8 a i** $\mathbf{B} = \begin{pmatrix} 1 & 2 & 4 \\ 4 & 3 & 8 \\ -4 & -4 & -9 \end{pmatrix} + 4\begin{pmatrix} 1 & 0 & 0 \\ 0 & 1 & 0 \\ 0 & 0 & 1 \end{pmatrix}$

$= \begin{pmatrix} 5 & 2 & 4 \\ 4 & 7 & 8 \\ -4 & -4 & -5 \end{pmatrix}$

**ii** $\mathbf{AB} = \begin{pmatrix} -3 & 0 & 0 \\ 0 & -3 & 0 \\ 0 & 0 & -3 \end{pmatrix} = -3\mathbf{I}$

**iii** $\mathbf{A}^{-1}(\mathbf{AB}) = -3\mathbf{A}^{-1}\mathbf{I}$ {using **ii**}

$\therefore\ \mathbf{IB} = -3\mathbf{A}^{-1}$

$\therefore\ -3\mathbf{A}^{-1} = \mathbf{IB}$

$\therefore\ \mathbf{A}^{-1} = -\frac{1}{3}\mathbf{B}$

$\therefore\ \mathbf{A}^{-1} = \begin{pmatrix} -\frac{5}{3} & -\frac{2}{3} & -\frac{4}{3} \\ -\frac{4}{3} & -\frac{7}{3} & -\frac{8}{3} \\ \frac{4}{3} & \frac{4}{3} & \frac{5}{3} \end{pmatrix}$

**b** $\begin{vmatrix} k & 2 \\ 2 & k-3 \end{vmatrix} = k(k-3) - 4$

$= k^2 - 3k - 4$

$= (k-4)(k+1)$

which is 0 for $k = 4$ or $-1$.

**9** Using technology, $x = -\frac{1}{2},\ y = 2,\ z = \frac{5}{2}$.

**10** $\mathbf{B} - 6\mathbf{A} = \begin{pmatrix} 15 & -1 & -4 \\ -1 & 15 & 4 \\ -4 & 4 & 16 \end{pmatrix} - 6\begin{pmatrix} 2 & 0 & -1 \\ 0 & 2 & 1 \\ -1 & 1 & 2 \end{pmatrix}$

$= \begin{pmatrix} 3 & -1 & 2 \\ -1 & 3 & -2 \\ 2 & -2 & 4 \end{pmatrix}$ {using technology}

and $\mathbf{A}(\mathbf{B} - 6\mathbf{A})$

$= \begin{pmatrix} 2 & 0 & -1 \\ 0 & 2 & 1 \\ -1 & 1 & 2 \end{pmatrix}\begin{pmatrix} 3 & -1 & 2 \\ -1 & 3 & -2 \\ 2 & -2 & 4 \end{pmatrix} = \begin{pmatrix} 4 & 0 & 0 \\ 0 & 4 & 0 \\ 0 & 0 & 4 \end{pmatrix}$

$= 4\mathbf{I}$

So, $k = 4$

Since $\mathbf{A}(\mathbf{B} - 6\mathbf{A}) = 4\mathbf{I}$,

$\mathbf{A}\frac{1}{4}(\mathbf{B} - 6\mathbf{A}) = \mathbf{I}$

$\therefore\ \mathbf{A}^{-1} = \frac{1}{4}(\mathbf{B} - 6\mathbf{A})$

$= \frac{1}{4}\begin{pmatrix} 3 & -1 & 2 \\ -1 & 3 & -2 \\ 2 & -2 & 4 \end{pmatrix} = \begin{pmatrix} \frac{3}{4} & -\frac{1}{4} & \frac{1}{2} \\ -\frac{1}{4} & \frac{3}{4} & -\frac{1}{2} \\ \frac{1}{2} & -\frac{1}{2} & 1 \end{pmatrix}$

**11** **a** Using technology, $x=-1,\ y=-1,\ z=-1$.

**b**
$$\begin{aligned} f(t) &= at^3+bt^2+ct+d \\ \therefore\ f(0) &= d=0 \\ \therefore\ f(-1) &= -a+b-c=1 \quad \text{.... (1)} \\ f'(t) &= 3at^2+2bt+c \\ \therefore\ f'(-1) &= 3a-2b+c=-2 \quad \text{.... (2)} \\ f''(t) &= 6at+2b \\ \therefore\ f''(1) &= 6a+2b=-8 \\ \therefore\ 3a+b &= -4 \quad \text{.... (3)} \end{aligned}$$

The three equations (1), (2) and (3) form the system in **a**, so $a=b=c=-1$

$\therefore\ f(t)=-t^3-t^2-t$

**12** **a** $P(t)=a+bt+ct^2$

For $P(1)=23$, $a+b+c=23$ .... (1)

For $P(2)=21$, $a+2b+4c=21$ .... (2)

For $P(3)=17$, $a+3b+9c=17$ .... (3)

**b** Using technology to solve (1), (2) and (3) simultaneously, $a=23,\ b=1,\ c=-1$.

**c** So, $P(t)=23+t-t^2$ thousand whales.

$\therefore\ P(4)=23+4-16=11$ thousand whales

$\therefore$ the model overestimates by 8000 whales.

**13** $\mathbf{A}=\begin{pmatrix} 3 & -2 & 10 \\ 0 & 1 & -3 \\ -1 & 1 & -4 \end{pmatrix}$ and using technology,

**a** $\mathbf{A}^2=\begin{pmatrix} 3 & -2 & 10 \\ 0 & 1 & -3 \\ -1 & 1 & -4 \end{pmatrix}^2=\begin{pmatrix} -1 & 2 & -4 \\ 3 & -2 & 9 \\ 1 & -1 & 3 \end{pmatrix}$

**b** $\mathbf{A}^3=\begin{pmatrix} 3 & -2 & 10 \\ 0 & 1 & -3 \\ -1 & 1 & -4 \end{pmatrix}^3=\begin{pmatrix} 1 & 0 & 0 \\ 0 & 1 & 0 \\ 0 & 0 & 1 \end{pmatrix}=\mathbf{I}$ ✓

Thus $\mathbf{A}^3(\mathbf{A}^{-1})=\mathbf{I}\mathbf{A}^{-1}$ and so $\mathbf{A}^2=\mathbf{A}^{-1}$.

**14** To find the required quantities of each nut, we calculate

$$\begin{pmatrix} 3000 & 4000 & 7000 \end{pmatrix}\begin{pmatrix} 0.4 & 0.3 & 0.3 \\ 0.3 & 0.2 & 0.5 \\ 0.3 & 0.1 & 0.6 \end{pmatrix}$$
(columns: hazelnuts, cashews, peanuts)

$=\begin{pmatrix} 4500 & 2400 & 7100 \end{pmatrix}$

So, 4500 kg of hazelnuts, 2400 kg of cashews, and 7100 kg of peanuts are required to fill the order.

**15** **a** (2, 4), (2, −6) and (−1, 3) lie on a circle with equation $x^2+y^2+ax+by+c=0$

$$\therefore \begin{cases} 2^2+4^2+a(2)+b(4)+c=0 \\ 2^2+(-6)^2+a(2)+b(-6)+c=0 \\ (-1)^2+3^2+a(-1)+b(3)+c=0 \end{cases}$$

$$\therefore \begin{cases} 2a+4b+c=-20 \\ 2a-6b+c=-40 \\ -a+3b+c=-10 \end{cases}$$

**b** Using technology to solve the matrix equation

$$\begin{pmatrix} 2 & 4 & 1 \\ 2 & -6 & 1 \\ -1 & 3 & 1 \end{pmatrix}\begin{pmatrix} a \\ b \\ c \end{pmatrix}=\begin{pmatrix} -20 \\ -40 \\ -10 \end{pmatrix}$$

we get $a=-4,\ b=2,\ c=-20$.

So, the equation of the circle is

$$x^2+y^2-4x+2y-20=0$$
$$\therefore\ (x-2)^2-4+(y+1)^2-1=20$$
$$\therefore\ (x-2)^2+(y+1)^2=25$$

## SOLUTIONS TO TOPIC 5 (VECTORS)

### NO CALCULATORS

**1** **a**

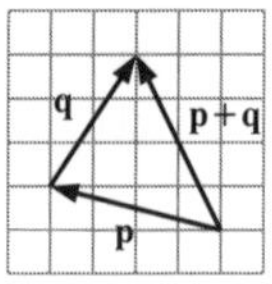


$\mathbf{p}+\mathbf{q}=\begin{pmatrix} -2 \\ 4 \end{pmatrix}$

**b**

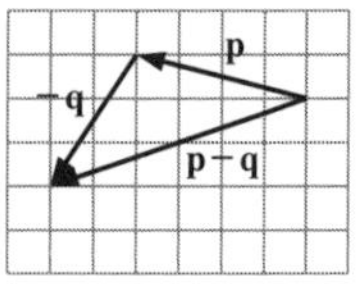


$\mathbf{p}-\mathbf{q}=\begin{pmatrix} -6 \\ -2 \end{pmatrix}$

**2** $\mathbf{a}=\begin{pmatrix} 3 \\ -1 \end{pmatrix},\quad \mathbf{b}=\begin{pmatrix} -1 \\ 2 \end{pmatrix}$

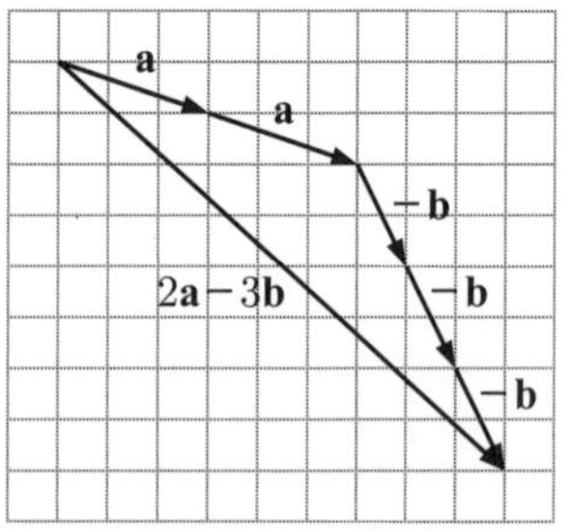


$2\mathbf{a}-3\mathbf{b}=\begin{pmatrix} 9 \\ -8 \end{pmatrix}$

*Check:* $2\mathbf{a}-3\mathbf{b}=\begin{pmatrix} 6 \\ -2 \end{pmatrix}-\begin{pmatrix} -3 \\ 6 \end{pmatrix}=\begin{pmatrix} 9 \\ -8 \end{pmatrix}$

**3** **a** $\mathbf{d}+\mathbf{c}+\mathbf{b}-\mathbf{a}=\mathbf{0}$

$\therefore\ \mathbf{a}=\mathbf{b}+\mathbf{c}+\mathbf{d}$

**b** $\mathbf{p}-\mathbf{q}+\mathbf{r}-\mathbf{s}+\mathbf{t}=\mathbf{0}$

$\therefore\ \mathbf{p}+\mathbf{r}+\mathbf{t}=\mathbf{q}+\mathbf{s}$

**4** **a** $\mathbf{a}=\mathbf{i}-2\mathbf{j}+3\mathbf{k}$

**b** magnitude $=\sqrt{1^2+(-2)^2+3^2}=\sqrt{14}$ units

**c** The unit vector in the opposite direction is $\dfrac{-1}{\sqrt{14}}\begin{pmatrix} 1 \\ -2 \\ 3 \end{pmatrix}$.

**5**

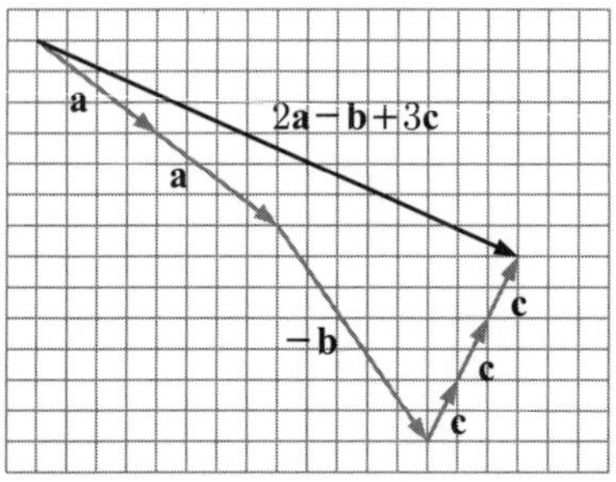


$$\begin{aligned} 2\mathbf{a}-\mathbf{b}+3\mathbf{c} &= 2\begin{pmatrix} 4 \\ -3 \end{pmatrix}-\begin{pmatrix} -5 \\ 7 \end{pmatrix}+3\begin{pmatrix} 1 \\ 2 \end{pmatrix} \\ &= \begin{pmatrix} 8+5+3 \\ -6-7+6 \end{pmatrix} \\ &= \begin{pmatrix} 16 \\ -7 \end{pmatrix} \end{aligned}$$
which checks with the diagram.

**6** **a** $\begin{pmatrix} k \\ 1 \\ 3 \end{pmatrix}$ and $\begin{pmatrix} 4 \\ k \\ 3k \end{pmatrix}$ are parallel if $\begin{pmatrix} 4 \\ k \\ 3k \end{pmatrix}=a\begin{pmatrix} k \\ 1 \\ 3 \end{pmatrix}$

for some $a$.

Thus, $4=ak$ .... (1)

$k=a$ .... (2)

$3k=3a$ .... (3)

From (1) and (2), $k^2=4$ and so $k=\pm 2$.

Hence the vectors are parallel if $k=\pm 2$.

- If $k = 2$, the vectors are $\begin{pmatrix} 2 \\ 1 \\ 3 \end{pmatrix}$ and $\begin{pmatrix} 4 \\ 2 \\ 6 \end{pmatrix}$.
- If $k = -2$, the vectors are $\begin{pmatrix} -2 \\ 1 \\ 3 \end{pmatrix}$ and $\begin{pmatrix} 4 \\ -2 \\ -6 \end{pmatrix}$.

**b** The vectors are perpendicular if $\begin{pmatrix} k \\ 1 \\ 3 \end{pmatrix} \bullet \begin{pmatrix} 4 \\ k \\ 3k \end{pmatrix} = 0$

$\therefore\ 4k + k + 9k = 0$ and so $k = 0$.

So, the vectors $\begin{pmatrix} 0 \\ 1 \\ 3 \end{pmatrix}$ and $\begin{pmatrix} 4 \\ 0 \\ 0 \end{pmatrix}$ are perpendicular.

**7** $\overrightarrow{AD} = \overrightarrow{BC}$. Let D be $(a, b)$

$\therefore\ \begin{pmatrix} a-1 \\ b-7 \end{pmatrix} = \begin{pmatrix} 8 - -1 \\ 4-2 \end{pmatrix} = \begin{pmatrix} 9 \\ 2 \end{pmatrix}$

$\therefore\ a - 1 = 9$ and $b - 7 = 2$

$\therefore\ a = 10$ and $b = 9$. So, D is $(10, 9)$.

**8 a**

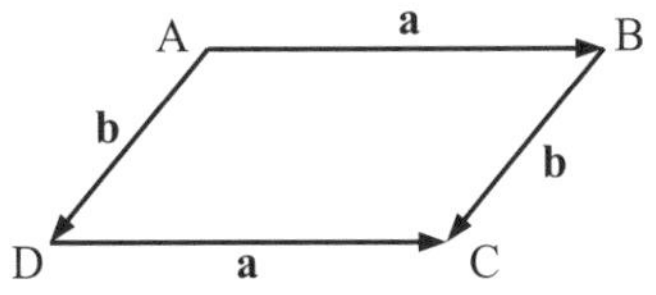


**b** $\overrightarrow{BC} = \overrightarrow{AD} = \mathbf{b}$ and $\overrightarrow{CD} = -\overrightarrow{AB} = -\mathbf{a}$

$\overrightarrow{AC} = \overrightarrow{AB} + \overrightarrow{BC} = \mathbf{a} + \mathbf{b}$ and $\overrightarrow{BD} = \overrightarrow{BC} + \overrightarrow{CD} = \mathbf{b} - \mathbf{a}$

**c** $\overrightarrow{AC} \bullet \overrightarrow{BD} = (\mathbf{a} + \mathbf{b}) \bullet (\mathbf{b} - \mathbf{a})$

$= \mathbf{a} \bullet \mathbf{b} - \mathbf{a} \bullet \mathbf{a} + \mathbf{b} \bullet \mathbf{b} - \mathbf{b} \bullet \mathbf{a}$

$= \mathbf{b} \bullet \mathbf{b} - \mathbf{a} \bullet \mathbf{a}$ {as $\mathbf{a} \bullet \mathbf{b} = \mathbf{b} \bullet \mathbf{a}$}

$= |\mathbf{b}|^2 - |\mathbf{a}|^2$

**d** If the parallelogram is a rhombus, then $|\mathbf{b}| = |\mathbf{a}|$

and so $\overrightarrow{AC} \bullet \overrightarrow{BD} = |\mathbf{b}|^2 - |\mathbf{b}|^2 = 0$

$\therefore\ \overrightarrow{AC}$ and $\overrightarrow{BD}$ are perpendicular.

**9** $r\begin{pmatrix} 3 \\ -6 \end{pmatrix} + s\begin{pmatrix} 7 \\ 2 \end{pmatrix} = \begin{pmatrix} 5 \\ 22 \end{pmatrix}$

$\therefore\ 3r + 7s = 5$ .... (1)

$-6r + 2s = 22$ .... (2)

$\therefore\ 6r + 14s = 10$ {2 × (1)}

$-6r + 2s = 22$

adding, $16s = 32$ and so $s = 2$

Substituting into (1), $3r + 7(2) = 5$

$\therefore\ 3r = 5 - 14 = -9$

$\therefore\ r = -3$

So, $r = -3$, $s = 2$

**10** $\begin{pmatrix} t \\ 1 \end{pmatrix} \bullet \begin{pmatrix} t-4 \\ -5 \end{pmatrix} = 0$

$\therefore\ t(t-4) + -5 = 0$

$\therefore\ t^2 - 4t - 5 = 0$

$\therefore\ (t-5)(t+1) = 0$

$\therefore\ t = 5$ or $-1$

**11 a** $\begin{pmatrix} x \\ y \end{pmatrix} = \begin{pmatrix} 1 \\ 6 \end{pmatrix} + t\begin{pmatrix} 4 \\ 2 \end{pmatrix}$, $t \in \mathbb{R}$

**b** The line has direction vector $= \begin{pmatrix} 5 - -3 \\ -2 - 2 \end{pmatrix} = \begin{pmatrix} 8 \\ -4 \end{pmatrix}$

$\therefore$ its equation is $\begin{pmatrix} x \\ y \end{pmatrix} = \begin{pmatrix} -3 \\ 2 \end{pmatrix} + t\begin{pmatrix} 8 \\ -4 \end{pmatrix}$, $t \in \mathbb{R}$

**12 a** $\begin{pmatrix} x \\ y \end{pmatrix} = \begin{pmatrix} -5 \\ -2 \end{pmatrix} + t\begin{pmatrix} 2 \\ 3 \end{pmatrix}$, $t \in \mathbb{R}$

**b** $x = -5 + 2t$, $y = -2 + 3t$, $t \in \mathbb{R}$

**13** $r(\mathbf{v} - \mathbf{w}) = (r+s)\mathbf{i} - 20\mathbf{j}$

$\therefore\ r(5\mathbf{i} - 2\mathbf{j} - \mathbf{i} - 3\mathbf{j}) = (r+s)\mathbf{i} - 20\mathbf{j}$

$\therefore\ r(4\mathbf{i} - 5\mathbf{j}) = (r+s)\mathbf{i} - 20\mathbf{j}$

$\therefore\ 4r\mathbf{i} - 5r\mathbf{j} = (r+s)\mathbf{i} - 20\mathbf{j}$

$\therefore\ 4r = r + s$ and $-5r = -20$

$\therefore\ r = 4$

$\therefore\ 16 = 4 + s$

So, $r = 4$, $s = 12$.

**14** The line has direction vector $= \begin{pmatrix} -3-6 \\ 5 - -2 \end{pmatrix} = \begin{pmatrix} -9 \\ 7 \end{pmatrix}$

$\therefore$ its vector equation is $\begin{pmatrix} x \\ y \end{pmatrix} = \begin{pmatrix} 6 \\ -2 \end{pmatrix} + t\begin{pmatrix} -9 \\ 7 \end{pmatrix}$, $t \in \mathbb{R}$

**15** The line has direction vector $= \begin{pmatrix} 3 \\ 1 \end{pmatrix}$

$\therefore$ its vector equation is $\begin{pmatrix} x \\ y \end{pmatrix} = \begin{pmatrix} 0 \\ 4 \end{pmatrix} + t\begin{pmatrix} 3 \\ 1 \end{pmatrix}$, $t \in \mathbb{R}$

**16 a**

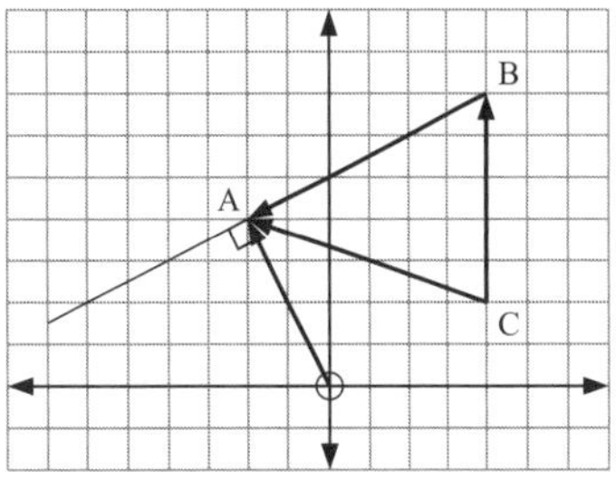


**b** $\overrightarrow{OB} = \begin{pmatrix} 4 \\ 7 \end{pmatrix}$

**17** $L_1$ meets $L_2$ where $\mathbf{r}_1 = \mathbf{r}_2$

$\therefore\ \begin{pmatrix} 4 \\ -2 \end{pmatrix} + t\begin{pmatrix} 3 \\ 2 \end{pmatrix} = \begin{pmatrix} -1 \\ -1 \end{pmatrix} + s\begin{pmatrix} 5 \\ -1 \end{pmatrix}$

$\therefore\ t\begin{pmatrix} 3 \\ 2 \end{pmatrix} - s\begin{pmatrix} 5 \\ -1 \end{pmatrix} = \begin{pmatrix} -1 \\ -1 \end{pmatrix} - \begin{pmatrix} 4 \\ -2 \end{pmatrix}$

So, $3t - 5s = -5$ .... (1)

$2t + s = 1$ .... (2)

$\therefore\ 3t - 5s = -5$

$10t + 5s = 5$ {5 × (2)}

adding, $13t = 0$

$\therefore\ t = 0$

So, $\mathbf{r}_1 = \begin{pmatrix} 4 \\ -2 \end{pmatrix} + 0\begin{pmatrix} 3 \\ 2 \end{pmatrix} = \begin{pmatrix} 4 \\ -2 \end{pmatrix}$. They meet at $(4, -2)$.

**18** $\mathbf{r} - 3\mathbf{x} = \mathbf{q}$

$\therefore\ 3\mathbf{x} + \mathbf{q} = \mathbf{r}$

$\therefore\ 3\mathbf{x} = \mathbf{r} - \mathbf{q}$

$\therefore\ \mathbf{x} = \frac{1}{3}(\mathbf{r} - \mathbf{q})$

**19 a** $3\mathbf{m} - \mathbf{n}$

$= 3(3\mathbf{i} + \mathbf{j} + 2\mathbf{k}) - (-2\mathbf{i} + 5\mathbf{j} - 4\mathbf{k})$

$= 9\mathbf{i} + 3\mathbf{j} + 6\mathbf{k} + 2\mathbf{i} - 5\mathbf{j} + 4\mathbf{k}$

$= 11\mathbf{i} - 2\mathbf{j} + 10\mathbf{k}$

**b** $\mathbf{m} \bullet \mathbf{n} = (3 \times -2) + (1 \times 5) + (2 \times -4)$

$= -6 + 5 - 8$

$= -9$

**c** $\quad \mathbf{m}+\mathbf{n} = \mathbf{i}+6\mathbf{j}-2\mathbf{k}$

$\therefore \quad |\mathbf{m}+\mathbf{n}| = \sqrt{1+36+4}$

$= \sqrt{41}$ units

**d** $\quad \mathbf{m} \bullet (2\mathbf{i}+\mathbf{k})$

$= (3\mathbf{i}+\mathbf{j}+2\mathbf{k}) \bullet (2\mathbf{i}+\mathbf{k})$

$= 6+0+2$

$= 8$

**20** $\quad \mathbf{a} - 4\mathbf{x} = 2\mathbf{b}$

$\therefore \quad -4\mathbf{x} = 2\mathbf{b} - \mathbf{a}$

$\therefore \quad \mathbf{x} = \frac{1}{4}(\mathbf{a} - 2\mathbf{b})$

$$= \frac{1}{4}\left(\begin{pmatrix} 4 \\ -2 \\ 1 \end{pmatrix} - \begin{pmatrix} 6 \\ 4 \\ -8 \end{pmatrix}\right)$$

$$= \frac{1}{4}\begin{pmatrix} -2 \\ -6 \\ 9 \end{pmatrix}$$

$$= \begin{pmatrix} -\frac{1}{2} \\ -1\frac{1}{2} \\ 2\frac{1}{4} \end{pmatrix}$$

**21** As the vectors are parallel, there exists a scalar $k$ such that

$$\begin{pmatrix} a \\ b \\ -15 \end{pmatrix} = k\begin{pmatrix} 4 \\ -1 \\ 5 \end{pmatrix}, \quad k \neq 0$$

$$\therefore \quad \begin{pmatrix} a \\ b \\ -15 \end{pmatrix} = \begin{pmatrix} 4k \\ -k \\ 5k \end{pmatrix}$$

$\therefore \quad 5k = -15, \quad b = -k, \quad a = 4k$

$\therefore \quad k = -3, \quad b = 3, \quad a = -12$

**22** **a** $3\mathbf{i}+\mathbf{j}-\mathbf{k}$ has length $\sqrt{9+1+1} = \sqrt{11}$ units

$\therefore$ a unit vector parallel to it is

$\frac{1}{\sqrt{11}}(3\mathbf{i}+\mathbf{j}-\mathbf{k})$ or $-\frac{1}{\sqrt{11}}(3\mathbf{i}+\mathbf{j}-\mathbf{k})$.

**b** A parallel vector of length 4 would be

$\frac{4}{\sqrt{11}}(3\mathbf{i}+\mathbf{j}-\mathbf{k})$ or $-\frac{4}{\sqrt{11}}(3\mathbf{i}+\mathbf{j}-\mathbf{k})$.

**23** The vectors are perpendicular, so $\begin{pmatrix} 2t \\ -4 \\ 7 \end{pmatrix} \bullet \begin{pmatrix} 3 \\ t \\ -8 \end{pmatrix} = 0$

$\therefore \quad 6t - 4t - 56 = 0$

$\therefore \quad 2t = 56$

$\therefore \quad t = 28$

**24** **a** $\overrightarrow{AB} = \begin{pmatrix} 5-1 \\ -1--1 \\ -1-2 \end{pmatrix} = \begin{pmatrix} 4 \\ 0 \\ -3 \end{pmatrix}$

So, $L$ has equation $\begin{pmatrix} x \\ y \\ z \end{pmatrix} = \begin{pmatrix} 1 \\ -1 \\ 2 \end{pmatrix} + t\begin{pmatrix} 4 \\ 0 \\ -3 \end{pmatrix}, \ t \in \mathbb{R}$.

**b** Any point P on $L$ has coordinates $(1+4t, -1, 2-3t)$.

$$\therefore \quad \overrightarrow{AP} = \begin{pmatrix} 4t \\ 0 \\ -3t \end{pmatrix}$$

Now $|\overrightarrow{AP}| = 20$, so $\sqrt{(4t)^2 + (-3t)^2} = 20$

$\therefore \quad 16t^2 + 9t^2 = 400$

$\therefore \quad t^2 = 16$

$\therefore \quad t = \pm 4$

So, letting $t = 4$, a point on $L$ which is 20 units from A is $(1+4(4), -1, 2-3(4)) = (17, -1, -10)$.

**25** **a** $\overrightarrow{PQ} = \begin{pmatrix} 13-4 \\ -8--2 \\ 14-11 \end{pmatrix} = \begin{pmatrix} 9 \\ -6 \\ 3 \end{pmatrix}$

$\overrightarrow{QR} = \begin{pmatrix} 19-13 \\ -12--8 \\ 16-14 \end{pmatrix} = \begin{pmatrix} 6 \\ -4 \\ 2 \end{pmatrix} = \frac{2}{3}\overrightarrow{PQ}$

$\therefore \quad \overrightarrow{PQ} \parallel \overrightarrow{QR}$, and Q is common.

$\therefore$ P, Q and R are collinear.

**b** The ratio in which Q divides [PR] is

$\overrightarrow{PQ} : \overrightarrow{QR} = 3\begin{pmatrix} 3 \\ -2 \\ 1 \end{pmatrix} : 2\begin{pmatrix} 3 \\ -2 \\ 1 \end{pmatrix} = 3 : 2$

$\therefore$ Q divides [PR] in the ratio $3 : 2$.

**26** **a** $\begin{pmatrix} x \\ y \\ z \end{pmatrix} = \begin{pmatrix} 5 \\ 0 \\ -2 \end{pmatrix} + t\begin{pmatrix} 1 \\ 2 \\ 3 \end{pmatrix}, \quad t \in \mathbb{R}$

**b** $\begin{pmatrix} x \\ y \\ z \end{pmatrix} = \begin{pmatrix} -2 \\ 5 \\ 4 \end{pmatrix} + t\begin{pmatrix} 2 \\ -3 \\ 4 \end{pmatrix}, \quad t \in \mathbb{R}$

**c** $\mathbf{j} = \begin{pmatrix} 0 \\ 1 \\ 0 \end{pmatrix}$ is perpendicular to the $XOZ$ plane.

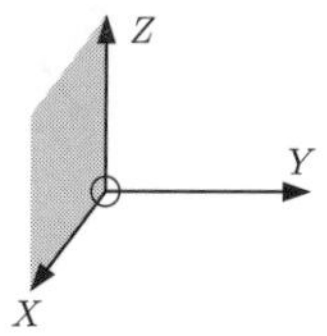


$\therefore \quad \begin{pmatrix} x \\ y \\ z \end{pmatrix} = \begin{pmatrix} 2 \\ -4 \\ 1 \end{pmatrix} + t\begin{pmatrix} 0 \\ 1 \\ 0 \end{pmatrix}, \quad t \in \mathbb{R}$

**27** **a** $x = 5+7t, \ y = -1+2t, \ z = 2-3t, \ t \in \mathbb{R}$

**b** $x = 2t, \ y = 2-3t, \ z = -6+t, \ t \in \mathbb{R}$

**c** The direction vector $= \begin{pmatrix} 8-2 \\ 6-5 \\ 2-1 \end{pmatrix} = \begin{pmatrix} 6 \\ 1 \\ 1 \end{pmatrix}$

$\therefore \quad x = 2+6t, \ y = 5+t, \ z = 1+t, \ t \in \mathbb{R}$

**28** The line meets the $YOZ$ plane when $x = 0$

$\therefore \quad -1+3t = 0$

$\therefore \quad t = \frac{1}{3}$

$$\therefore \quad \begin{pmatrix} x \\ y \\ z \end{pmatrix} = \begin{pmatrix} -1 \\ 4 \\ 3 \end{pmatrix} + \frac{1}{3}\begin{pmatrix} 3 \\ 2 \\ -1 \end{pmatrix} = \begin{pmatrix} 0 \\ 4\frac{2}{3} \\ 2\frac{2}{3} \end{pmatrix}$$

So, the point is $\left(0, 4\frac{2}{3}, 2\frac{2}{3}\right)$.

**29** **a**

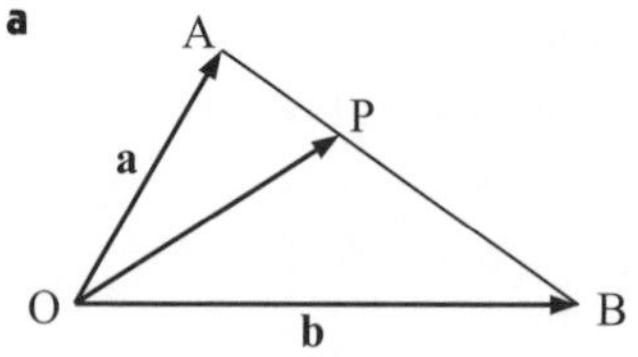


$\overrightarrow{AB} = -\mathbf{a}+\mathbf{b} = \mathbf{b}-\mathbf{a}$

$\therefore \quad \overrightarrow{OP} = \overrightarrow{OA} + \overrightarrow{AP}$

$= \overrightarrow{OA} + t\overrightarrow{AB}$

$= \mathbf{a} + t(\mathbf{b}-\mathbf{a})$

$= (1-t)\mathbf{a} + t\mathbf{b}$

**b** $\overrightarrow{AP} : \overrightarrow{PB} = 2 : 5$

$\therefore \quad \overrightarrow{AP} = \frac{2}{7}\overrightarrow{AB}$

$\therefore \quad \mathbf{p} = \frac{5}{7}\mathbf{a} + \frac{2}{7}\mathbf{b}$ {from **a**}

$$= \frac{5}{7}\begin{pmatrix} 2 \\ -1 \\ 4 \end{pmatrix} + \frac{2}{7}\begin{pmatrix} -3 \\ 1 \\ -1 \end{pmatrix}$$

$$= \begin{pmatrix} \frac{4}{7} \\ -\frac{3}{7} \\ \frac{18}{7} \end{pmatrix}$$

So, P is $\left(\frac{4}{7}, -\frac{3}{7}, \frac{18}{7}\right)$.

**30** **a** $\overrightarrow{AB} = \begin{pmatrix} 0 - -1 \\ 1-2 \\ 3-1 \end{pmatrix} = \begin{pmatrix} 1 \\ -1 \\ 2 \end{pmatrix}$

$\therefore$ line (AB) has equation $\mathbf{r} = \begin{pmatrix} -1 \\ 2 \\ 1 \end{pmatrix} + t \begin{pmatrix} 1 \\ -1 \\ 2 \end{pmatrix}$, $t \in \mathbb{R}$

**b** The line $L$ has direction vector $\begin{pmatrix} 2 \\ 0 \\ -1 \end{pmatrix}$

and (AB) has direction vector $\begin{pmatrix} 1 \\ -1 \\ 2 \end{pmatrix}$.

If $\theta$ is the angle between the lines, then

$$\cos\theta = \frac{|\,2+0-2\,|}{\sqrt{2^2+(-1)^2}\sqrt{1^2+(-1)^2+2^2}}$$
$$= 0$$
$$\therefore \theta = 90^o$$

So, the angle between (AB) and $L$ is $90^o$.

**31** $\mathbf{b} = \begin{pmatrix} 2 \\ 0 \\ -1 \end{pmatrix}$, $\mathbf{c} - 2\mathbf{a} = \begin{pmatrix} -1 \\ 2 \\ 3 \end{pmatrix} - 2\begin{pmatrix} 1 \\ 3 \\ k \end{pmatrix}$

$= \begin{pmatrix} -3 \\ -4 \\ 3-2k \end{pmatrix}$

Now $\mathbf{b}$ is perpendicular to $\mathbf{c} - 2\mathbf{a}$

$$\therefore \begin{pmatrix} 2 \\ 0 \\ -1 \end{pmatrix} \bullet \begin{pmatrix} -3 \\ -4 \\ 3-2k \end{pmatrix} = 0$$
$$\therefore -6 - 3 + 2k = 0$$
$$\therefore 2k = 9$$
$$\therefore k = \tfrac{9}{2}$$

## CALCULATORS

**1** **a** $|\,\mathbf{v}\,| = \sqrt{(-4)^2+3^2} = \sqrt{25} = 5$ units

**b** $\mathbf{v} + \mathbf{w} = \begin{pmatrix} -4 \\ 3 \end{pmatrix} + \begin{pmatrix} 2 \\ 6 \end{pmatrix} = \begin{pmatrix} -2 \\ 9 \end{pmatrix}$

$\therefore |\,\mathbf{v}+\mathbf{w}\,| = \sqrt{4+81} = \sqrt{85}$ units

**c** $3\mathbf{w} - 2\mathbf{v} = \begin{pmatrix} 6 \\ 18 \end{pmatrix} - \begin{pmatrix} -8 \\ 6 \end{pmatrix} = \begin{pmatrix} 14 \\ 12 \end{pmatrix}$

**d** $\mathbf{v} \bullet \mathbf{w} = \begin{pmatrix} -4 \\ 3 \end{pmatrix} \bullet \begin{pmatrix} 2 \\ 6 \end{pmatrix} = -8 + 18 = 10$

**e** $\mathbf{w} \bullet \mathbf{w} = \begin{pmatrix} 2 \\ 6 \end{pmatrix} \bullet \begin{pmatrix} 2 \\ 6 \end{pmatrix} = 4 + 36 = 40$

**2** **a** $\overrightarrow{AC}$

$= \begin{pmatrix} 16-2 \\ 6-10 \end{pmatrix}$

$= \begin{pmatrix} 14 \\ -4 \end{pmatrix}$

**b** M is $\left(\dfrac{-2+16}{2}, \dfrac{2+6}{2}\right)$

or (7, 4)

$\therefore \overrightarrow{AM} = \begin{pmatrix} 7-2 \\ 4-10 \end{pmatrix} = \begin{pmatrix} 5 \\ -6 \end{pmatrix}$

**c**

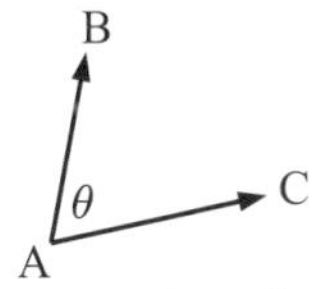


$\overrightarrow{AB} = \begin{pmatrix} -2-2 \\ 2-10 \end{pmatrix} = \begin{pmatrix} -4 \\ -8 \end{pmatrix}$

and $\overrightarrow{AC} = \begin{pmatrix} 14 \\ -4 \end{pmatrix}$

$$\overrightarrow{AB} \bullet \overrightarrow{AC} = |\,\overrightarrow{AB}\,|\,|\,\overrightarrow{AC}\,| \cos\theta$$
$$\therefore -56 + 32 = \sqrt{16+64}\sqrt{196+16}\cos\theta$$
$$\therefore -24 = \sqrt{80}\sqrt{212}\cos\theta$$
$$\therefore \cos\theta = \frac{-24}{\sqrt{80 \times 212}}$$
$$\theta = \cos^{-1}\left(\frac{-24}{\sqrt{80 \times 212}}\right) \approx 101^o$$

**3** $\mathbf{p} = 4\mathbf{i} - 9\mathbf{j}$, $\mathbf{q} = -12\mathbf{i} + 5\mathbf{j}$

**a** $|\,\mathbf{q}\,| = \sqrt{144+25}$
$= \sqrt{169}$
$= 13$ units

**b** $\mathbf{p} \bullet \mathbf{q}$
$= \begin{pmatrix} 4 \\ -9 \end{pmatrix} \bullet \begin{pmatrix} -12 \\ 5 \end{pmatrix}$
$= -48 + -45$
$= -93$

**c** The angle $\theta$ between $\mathbf{p}$ and $\mathbf{q}$ has

$$\cos\theta = \frac{\mathbf{p} \bullet \mathbf{q}}{|\,\mathbf{p}\,|\,|\,\mathbf{q}\,|}$$
$$\therefore \cos\theta = \frac{-93}{\sqrt{16+81} \times 13}$$
$$\therefore \cos\theta = \frac{-93}{13\sqrt{97}}$$
$$\therefore \theta \approx 137^o$$

**d** A unit vector parallel to $\mathbf{p} = \dfrac{1}{|\,\mathbf{p}\,|}\mathbf{p} = \frac{1}{\sqrt{97}}(4\mathbf{i} - 9\mathbf{j})$

$= \frac{4}{\sqrt{97}}\mathbf{i} - \frac{9}{\sqrt{97}}\mathbf{j}$

**4**

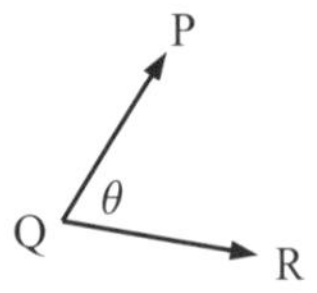


$\overrightarrow{QR} = \begin{pmatrix} 2-4 \\ 1-11 \end{pmatrix} = \begin{pmatrix} -2 \\ -10 \end{pmatrix}$

$\overrightarrow{QP} = \begin{pmatrix} 6-4 \\ -4-11 \end{pmatrix} = \begin{pmatrix} 2 \\ -15 \end{pmatrix}$

Now $\overrightarrow{QR} \bullet \overrightarrow{QP} = |\,\overrightarrow{QR}\,|\,|\,\overrightarrow{QP}\,| \cos\theta$

$$\therefore -4 + 150 = \sqrt{4+100}\sqrt{4+225}\cos\theta$$
$$\therefore 146 = \sqrt{104 \times 229}\cos\theta$$
$$\therefore \cos\theta = \frac{146}{\sqrt{104 \times 229}}$$
$$\therefore \theta = \cos^{-1}\left(\frac{146}{\sqrt{104 \times 229}}\right) \approx 18.9^o$$

**5** $y = 2x + 5$ has gradient $2 = \frac{2}{1}$ $\therefore \mathbf{l}_1 = \begin{pmatrix} 1 \\ 2 \end{pmatrix}$

$3x + 4y = 20$ has gradient $-\frac{3}{4}$ $\therefore \mathbf{l}_2 = \begin{pmatrix} 4 \\ -3 \end{pmatrix}$

$\therefore$ the acute angle $\theta$ between $L_1$ and $L_2$ has

$$\cos\theta = \frac{|\,\mathbf{l}_1 \bullet \mathbf{l}_2\,|}{|\,\mathbf{l}_1\,|\,|\,\mathbf{l}_2\,|}$$
$$\therefore \cos\theta = \frac{|\,4-6\,|}{\sqrt{1+4}\sqrt{16+9}}$$
$$\therefore \cos\theta = \tfrac{2}{5\sqrt{5}}$$
$$\therefore \theta \approx 79.7^o$$

**6** $\mathbf{a} = \begin{pmatrix} 3 \\ -3 \end{pmatrix}$ and $\mathbf{b} = \begin{pmatrix} 5 \\ -1 \end{pmatrix}$

$\therefore \mathbf{a} \bullet \mathbf{b} = 15 + 3 = 18$,

$|\,\mathbf{a}\,| = \sqrt{9+9} = \sqrt{18}$ and $|\,\mathbf{b}\,| = \sqrt{25+1} = \sqrt{26}$

$$\cos\theta = \frac{\mathbf{a} \bullet \mathbf{b}}{|\,\mathbf{a}\,|\,|\,\mathbf{b}\,|} = \frac{18}{\sqrt{18}\sqrt{26}}$$
$$= \tfrac{\sqrt{18}}{\sqrt{26}}$$
$$\therefore \theta \approx 34^o$$

**7** **a** $\mathbf{a} \bullet \mathbf{b} = |\,\mathbf{a}\,|\,|\,\mathbf{b}\,| \cos\theta$ where $\theta$ is the angle between **a** and **b**.
If $\mathbf{a} \bullet \mathbf{b} < 0$, then $\cos\theta < 0$ and so $90^o < \theta < 180^o$.

**b** $\mathbf{a} \bullet \mathbf{b} = \begin{pmatrix} -2 \\ 1 \\ 3 \end{pmatrix} \bullet \begin{pmatrix} 3 \\ -1 \\ 1 \end{pmatrix} = -6 - 1 + 3 = -4$

$|\,\mathbf{a}\,| = \sqrt{(-2)^2 + 1^2 + 3^2} = \sqrt{14}$ and

$|\,\mathbf{b}\,| = \sqrt{3^2 + (-1)^2 + 1^2} = \sqrt{11}$

and $\cos\theta = \dfrac{-4}{\sqrt{14}\sqrt{11}} \approx -0.3223$ and so $\theta \approx 108.8^o$.

**8** $\overrightarrow{AC} = \begin{pmatrix} 11 - 2 \\ 5 - 10 \end{pmatrix} = \begin{pmatrix} 9 \\ -5 \end{pmatrix}$, $\overrightarrow{BD} = \begin{pmatrix} -1 - 12 \\ 2 - 8 \end{pmatrix} = \begin{pmatrix} -13 \\ -6 \end{pmatrix}$

So, the acute angle $\theta$ has $\cos\theta = \dfrac{|\,\overrightarrow{AC} \bullet \overrightarrow{BD}\,|}{|\,\overrightarrow{AC}\,|\,|\,\overrightarrow{BD}\,|}$

$= \dfrac{|\,-117 + 30\,|}{\sqrt{81 + 25}\sqrt{169 + 36}}$

$= \dfrac{87}{\sqrt{106 \times 205}}$

$\therefore\ \theta \approx 53.8^o$

**9** $x = 3 + t,\ y = 4t - 3,\ t \geqslant 0$

**a** When $t = 0$, $x = 3$, $y = -3$
$\therefore$ the boat's initial position is (3, −3).

**b** The velocity vector is $\begin{pmatrix} 1 \\ 4 \end{pmatrix}$.

**c** The boat's speed is $\sqrt{1 + 16} = \sqrt{17}\ \text{m s}^{-1}$.

**10** **a** $x = 3 - 2t$, $y = 3t + 1$ $\therefore$ $x(0) = 3$, $y(0) = 1$
So, the ship is initially at (3, 1).

**b** **i** The ship's velocity vector is $\begin{pmatrix} -2 \\ 3 \end{pmatrix}$.

**ii** The ship's speed is $\sqrt{4 + 9} = \sqrt{13}\ \text{km h}^{-1}$.

**c** At 10.30 am, $t = 2$
So, the ship is at $(3 - 2(2), 3(2) + 1)$ or $(-1, 7)$
and the distance to (0, 10)

$= \sqrt{(0 - -1)^2 + (10 - 7)^2}$

$= \sqrt{1 + 9} = \sqrt{10}$ km.

**d** When the ship is directly west of the light house,

$3t + 1 = 10$

$\therefore\ 3t = 9$

$\therefore\ t = 3$ $\quad\therefore$ the time is 11:30 am.

**e**

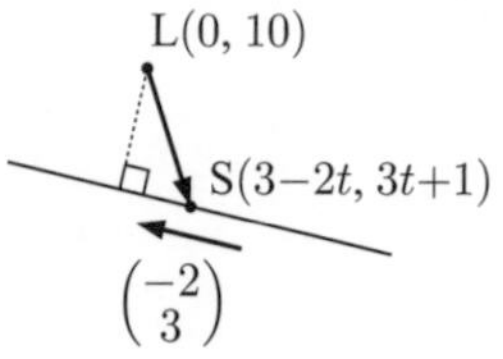


$\overrightarrow{LS} = \begin{pmatrix} 3 - 2t - 0 \\ 3t + 1 - 10 \end{pmatrix}$

$= \begin{pmatrix} 3 - 2t \\ 3t - 9 \end{pmatrix}$

The ship is nearest when

$\overrightarrow{LS} \perp \begin{pmatrix} -2 \\ 3 \end{pmatrix}$.

$\therefore\ \overrightarrow{LS} \bullet \begin{pmatrix} -2 \\ 3 \end{pmatrix} = 0$

$\therefore\ -2(3 - 2t) + 3(3t - 9) = 0$

$\therefore\ -6 + 4t + 9t - 27 = 0$

$\therefore\ 13t = 33$

$\therefore\ t = \frac{33}{13} \approx 2.538\,46$ h

$\therefore\ t \approx 2$ h 32 mins

So, the time is about 11:02 am.

**11** **a** The direction vector is $\begin{pmatrix} 5 \\ 12 \end{pmatrix}$ which has length

$\sqrt{25 + 144} = \sqrt{169} = 13$ units

$\therefore$ the velocity vector is $\begin{pmatrix} 5 \\ 12 \end{pmatrix}$

$\therefore\ \begin{pmatrix} x \\ y \end{pmatrix} = \begin{pmatrix} 10 \\ 6 \end{pmatrix} + t\begin{pmatrix} 5 \\ 12 \end{pmatrix}$

**b** The direction vector is $\begin{pmatrix} 4 \\ -3 \end{pmatrix}$ which has length

$\sqrt{16 + 9} = \sqrt{25} = 5$ units

$\therefore$ the velocity vector is $3\begin{pmatrix} 4 \\ -3 \end{pmatrix}$ or $\begin{pmatrix} 12 \\ -9 \end{pmatrix}$

$\therefore\ \begin{pmatrix} x \\ y \end{pmatrix} = \begin{pmatrix} -5 \\ 3 \end{pmatrix} + t\begin{pmatrix} 12 \\ -9 \end{pmatrix}$

**c** The direction vector is $\begin{pmatrix} 5 - -1 \\ 7 - 4 \end{pmatrix} = \begin{pmatrix} 6 \\ 3 \end{pmatrix}$

which has length $\sqrt{36 + 9} = \sqrt{45} = 3\sqrt{5}$ units

The car's speed $= \dfrac{3\sqrt{5}\ \text{m}}{3\ \text{s}} = \sqrt{5}\ \text{m s}^{-1}$

$\therefore$ its velocity vector is $\frac{1}{3}\begin{pmatrix} 6 \\ 3 \end{pmatrix} = \begin{pmatrix} 2 \\ 1 \end{pmatrix}$

$\therefore\ \begin{pmatrix} x \\ y \end{pmatrix} = \begin{pmatrix} -1 \\ 4 \end{pmatrix} + t\begin{pmatrix} 2 \\ 1 \end{pmatrix}$

**12** **a**

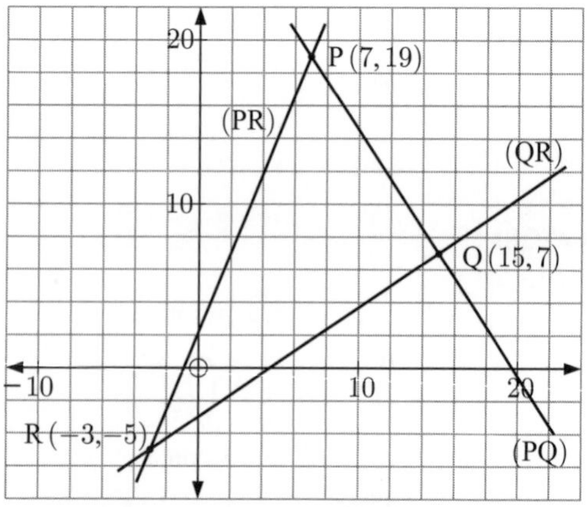


**b** $\overrightarrow{RQ} = \begin{pmatrix} 3 \\ 2 \end{pmatrix}$ and $\overrightarrow{PQ} = \begin{pmatrix} 4 \\ -6 \end{pmatrix}$

and $\overrightarrow{RQ} \bullet \overrightarrow{PQ} = 12 + (-12) = 0$ $\quad\therefore$ RQ $\perp$ PQ

$\therefore$ $\widehat{PQR}$ is a right angle and so $\Delta$PQR is right angled.

**c** Area $\Delta\text{PQR} = \frac{1}{2}\text{base} \times \text{altitude}$

$= \frac{1}{2}\,|\,\overrightarrow{QR}\,|\,|\,\overrightarrow{PQ}\,|$

$= \frac{1}{2}\left|\begin{pmatrix} -3 - 15 \\ -5 - 7 \end{pmatrix}\right|\left|\begin{pmatrix} 15 - 7 \\ 7 - 19 \end{pmatrix}\right|$

$= \frac{1}{2}\left|\begin{pmatrix} -18 \\ -12 \end{pmatrix}\right|\left|\begin{pmatrix} 8 \\ -12 \end{pmatrix}\right|$

$= \frac{1}{2}\sqrt{324 + 144}\sqrt{64 + 144}$

$= \frac{1}{2}\sqrt{468}\sqrt{208}$

$= 156\ \text{units}^2$

**13** **a** $\text{AB} = \sqrt{(-3 - 2)^2 + (1 - 0)^2 + (7 - 5)^2}$

$= \sqrt{25 + 1 + 4}$

$= \sqrt{30}$ units

**b** $BC = \sqrt{(4 - -3)^2 + (-2-1)^2 + (9-7)^2}$
$= \sqrt{49+9+4}$
$= \sqrt{62}$ units

**c** $\overrightarrow{AC} = \begin{pmatrix} 4-2 \\ -2-0 \\ 9-5 \end{pmatrix} = \begin{pmatrix} 2 \\ -2 \\ 4 \end{pmatrix}$

**d** $\overrightarrow{AB} = \begin{pmatrix} -3-2 \\ 1-0 \\ 7-5 \end{pmatrix} = \begin{pmatrix} -5 \\ 1 \\ 2 \end{pmatrix}$

**e**

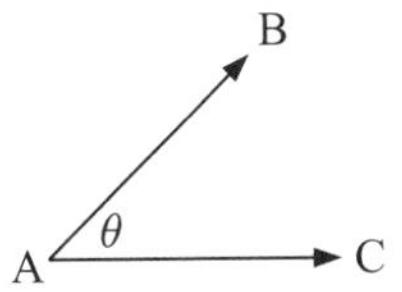


$\overrightarrow{AB} \bullet \overrightarrow{AC} = |\overrightarrow{AB}||\overrightarrow{AC}|\cos\theta$

$\therefore \quad -10 - 2 + 8 = \sqrt{25+1+4}\,\sqrt{4+4+16}\,\cos\theta$

$\therefore \quad -4 = \sqrt{30}\sqrt{24}\cos\theta$

$\therefore \quad \cos\theta = \dfrac{-4}{\sqrt{30\times 24}}$

$\therefore \quad \theta = \cos^{-1}\left(\dfrac{-4}{\sqrt{30\times 24}}\right)$

$\therefore \quad \theta \approx 98.6^o$

**14** **a** $\mathbf{p} + 2\mathbf{q} - \mathbf{r} = \begin{pmatrix} 3 \\ 1 \\ 3 \end{pmatrix} + \begin{pmatrix} -8 \\ 4 \\ 8 \end{pmatrix} - \begin{pmatrix} -4 \\ -3 \\ 2 \end{pmatrix} = \begin{pmatrix} -1 \\ 8 \\ 9 \end{pmatrix}$

**b** $\mathbf{r} + \mathbf{q} = \begin{pmatrix} -4 \\ -3 \\ 2 \end{pmatrix} + \begin{pmatrix} -4 \\ 2 \\ 4 \end{pmatrix} = \begin{pmatrix} -8 \\ -1 \\ 6 \end{pmatrix}$

$\therefore \quad |\mathbf{r} + \mathbf{q}| = \sqrt{64+1+36} = \sqrt{101}$ units

**c** $|\mathbf{q}| = \sqrt{16+4+16} = \sqrt{36} = 6$

$\therefore$ a unit vector parallel to $\mathbf{q}$ is $\frac{1}{6}\begin{pmatrix} -4 \\ 2 \\ 4 \end{pmatrix} = \begin{pmatrix} -\frac{2}{3} \\ \frac{1}{3} \\ \frac{2}{3} \end{pmatrix}$.

**d** $\mathbf{p} \bullet \mathbf{q} = \begin{pmatrix} 3 \\ 1 \\ 3 \end{pmatrix} \bullet \begin{pmatrix} -4 \\ 2 \\ 4 \end{pmatrix} = -12 + 2 + 12 = 2$

**e** $(\mathbf{p} + \mathbf{q}) \bullet \mathbf{q} = \begin{pmatrix} -1 \\ 3 \\ 7 \end{pmatrix} \bullet \begin{pmatrix} -4 \\ 2 \\ 4 \end{pmatrix}$
$= 4 + 6 + 28$
$= 38$

**15** **a** $\overrightarrow{AB} = \begin{pmatrix} 7-2 \\ -3 - -5 \\ -1-3 \end{pmatrix} = \begin{pmatrix} 5 \\ 2 \\ -4 \end{pmatrix}$

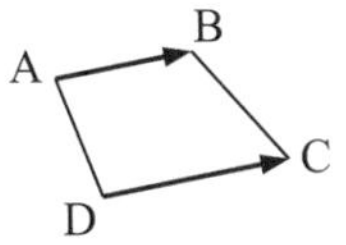


$\overrightarrow{DC} = \begin{pmatrix} 1 - -4 \\ 3-1 \\ 0-4 \end{pmatrix} = \begin{pmatrix} 5 \\ 2 \\ -4 \end{pmatrix}$

$\therefore \quad \overrightarrow{AB} = \overrightarrow{DC}$

Thus AB $\parallel$ DC and $|\overrightarrow{AB}| = |\overrightarrow{DC}|$
which is sufficient to deduce that ABCD is a parallelogram.

**b** $\overrightarrow{AD} = \begin{pmatrix} -4-2 \\ 1 - -5 \\ 4-3 \end{pmatrix} = \begin{pmatrix} -6 \\ 6 \\ 1 \end{pmatrix}$

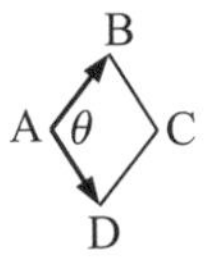


$\overrightarrow{AB} \bullet \overrightarrow{AD} = |\overrightarrow{AB}||\overrightarrow{AD}|\cos\theta$

$\therefore \quad -30 + 12 - 4 = \sqrt{25+4+16}\,\sqrt{36+36+1}\cos\theta$

$\therefore \quad -22 = \sqrt{45}\sqrt{73}\cos\theta$

$\therefore \quad \cos\theta = \dfrac{-22}{\sqrt{45\times 73}}$

$\therefore \quad \theta = \cos^{-1}\left(\dfrac{-22}{\sqrt{45\times 73}}\right) \approx 112.6^o$

$\therefore$ the smaller angles are $180^o - 112.6^o \approx 67.4^o$.

**16** The direction vector of the $Z$-axis is $\mathbf{k} = \begin{pmatrix} 0 \\ 0 \\ 1 \end{pmatrix}$

$\begin{pmatrix} 0 \\ 0 \\ 1 \end{pmatrix} \bullet \begin{pmatrix} 4 \\ -1 \\ 3 \end{pmatrix} = \sqrt{0+0+1}\sqrt{16+1+9}\cos\theta$

$\therefore \quad 3 = \sqrt{26}\cos\theta$

$\cos\theta = \frac{3}{\sqrt{26}}$

$\therefore \quad \theta = \cos^{-1}\left(\frac{3}{\sqrt{26}}\right) \approx 54.0^o$

**17** $\overrightarrow{LK} = \begin{pmatrix} 4-6 \\ -2-1 \\ 7 - -1 \end{pmatrix} = \begin{pmatrix} -2 \\ -3 \\ 8 \end{pmatrix}$

$\overrightarrow{LM} = \begin{pmatrix} 3-6 \\ -2-1 \\ 5 - -1 \end{pmatrix} = \begin{pmatrix} -3 \\ -3 \\ 6 \end{pmatrix}$

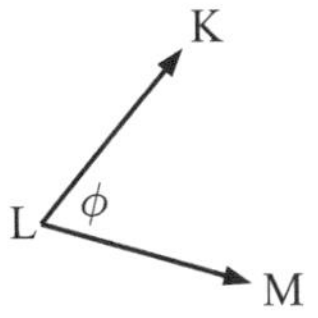


$\overrightarrow{LK} \bullet \overrightarrow{LM} = |\overrightarrow{LK}||\overrightarrow{LM}|\cos\phi$

$\therefore \quad 6 + 9 + 48 = \sqrt{4+9+64}\sqrt{9+9+36}\cos\phi$

$\therefore \quad 63 = \sqrt{77}\sqrt{54}\cos\phi$

$\therefore \quad \cos\phi = \dfrac{63}{\sqrt{77\times 54}}$

$\therefore \quad \phi = \cos^{-1}\left(\dfrac{63}{\sqrt{77\times 54}}\right) \approx 12.3^o$

**18** **a** $\overrightarrow{BC} = \overrightarrow{BA} + \overrightarrow{AC} = \begin{pmatrix} -4 \\ 6 \\ -2 \end{pmatrix} + \begin{pmatrix} -2 \\ 7 \\ -3 \end{pmatrix} = \begin{pmatrix} -6 \\ 13 \\ -5 \end{pmatrix}$

**b**

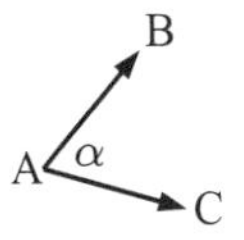


$\overrightarrow{AB} \bullet \overrightarrow{AC} = |\overrightarrow{AB}||\overrightarrow{AC}|\cos\alpha$

$\therefore \quad -8 - 42 - 6 = \sqrt{16+36+4}\sqrt{4+49+9}\cos\alpha$

$\therefore \quad -56 = \sqrt{56}\times\sqrt{62}\cos\alpha$

$\therefore \quad \cos\alpha = \dfrac{-56}{\sqrt{56}\sqrt{62}} = -\sqrt{\frac{56}{62}}$

$\therefore \quad \alpha = \cos^{-1}\left(-\sqrt{\frac{56}{62}}\right)$

$\therefore \quad \alpha \approx 162^o$

**19**

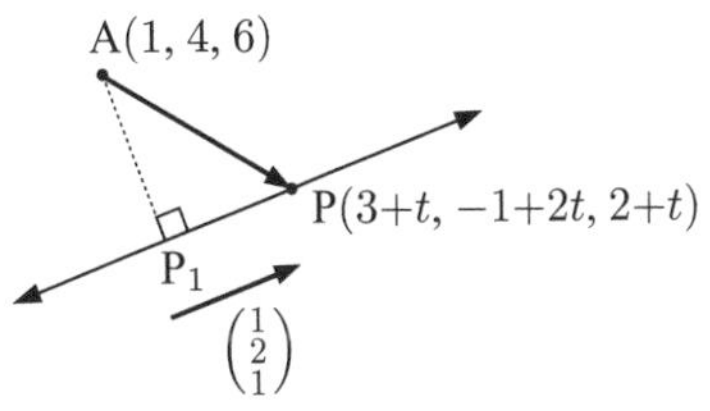


$\overrightarrow{AP} = \begin{pmatrix} 3+t-1 \\ -1+2t-4 \\ 2+t-6 \end{pmatrix} = \begin{pmatrix} t+2 \\ 2t-5 \\ t-4 \end{pmatrix}$

When P is nearest to A, $\overrightarrow{AP} \perp \begin{pmatrix} 1 \\ 2 \\ 1 \end{pmatrix}$

$$\therefore \quad \overrightarrow{AP} \bullet \begin{pmatrix} 1 \\ 2 \\ 1 \end{pmatrix} = 0$$

$$\therefore \quad 1(t+2) + 2(2t-5) + 1(t-4) = 0$$

$$\therefore \quad t + 2 + 4t - 10 + t - 4 = 0$$

$$\therefore \quad 6t = 12$$

$$\therefore \quad t = 2$$

$$\therefore \quad \overrightarrow{AP_1} = \begin{pmatrix} 4 \\ -1 \\ -2 \end{pmatrix} \quad \text{where } |\overrightarrow{AP_1}| = \sqrt{16+1+4} = \sqrt{21}$$

$\therefore$ the shortest distance is $\sqrt{21}$ units.

**20** **a** $L_1$ and $L_2$ have direction vectors $\begin{pmatrix} 3 \\ -6 \\ -3 \end{pmatrix}$ and $\begin{pmatrix} -1 \\ 2 \\ 1 \end{pmatrix}$ respectively.

Since $\begin{pmatrix} 3 \\ -6 \\ -3 \end{pmatrix} = -3 \begin{pmatrix} -1 \\ 2 \\ 1 \end{pmatrix}$, $L_1$ is parallel to $L_2$.

**b** $L_1$ and $L_3$ meet if $\begin{cases} 2 + 3t = 5 - 3s \\ 1 - 6t = 5 + 4s \\ -1 - 3t = 1 + 2s \end{cases}$

$$\therefore \begin{cases} 3s + 3t = 3 \\ 4s + 6t = -4 \\ 2s + 3t = -2 \end{cases}$$

Solving this system using technology, $s = 5$ and $t = -4$.

$\therefore$ the lines meet at $(-10, 25, 11)$.

$L_3$ has direction vector $\begin{pmatrix} -3 \\ 4 \\ 2 \end{pmatrix}$.

$$\text{So, } \begin{pmatrix} 3 \\ -6 \\ -3 \end{pmatrix} \bullet \begin{pmatrix} -3 \\ 4 \\ 2 \end{pmatrix} = \sqrt{9+36+9}\sqrt{9+16+4}\cos\phi$$

$$\therefore \quad -9 - 24 - 6 = \sqrt{54}\sqrt{29}\cos\phi$$

$$\therefore \quad -39 = \sqrt{54}\sqrt{29}\cos\phi$$

$$\therefore \quad \cos\phi = \frac{-39}{\sqrt{54}\sqrt{29}}$$

$$\therefore \quad \phi = \cos^{-1}\left(\frac{-39}{\sqrt{54}\sqrt{29}}\right) \approx 170^o$$

## SOLUTIONS TO TOPIC 6 (STATISTICS AND PROBABILITY)

### NO CALCULATORS

**1** **a**

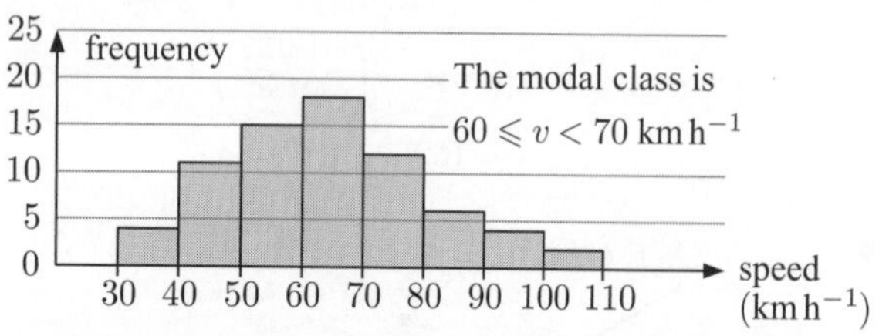


**b**

| *Speed* ($km\,h^{-1}$) | *Frequency* | *Cumul. Frequency* |
|---|---|---|
| $v < 30$ | 0 | 0 |
| $30 \leqslant v < 40$ | 4 | 4 |
| $40 \leqslant v < 50$ | 11 | 15 |
| $50 \leqslant v < 60$ | 15 | 30 |
| $60 \leqslant v < 70$ | 18 | 48 |
| $70 \leqslant v < 80$ | 12 | 60 |
| $80 \leqslant v < 90$ | 6 | 66 |
| $90 \leqslant v < 100$ | 4 | 70 |
| $100 \leqslant v < 110$ | 2 | 72 |

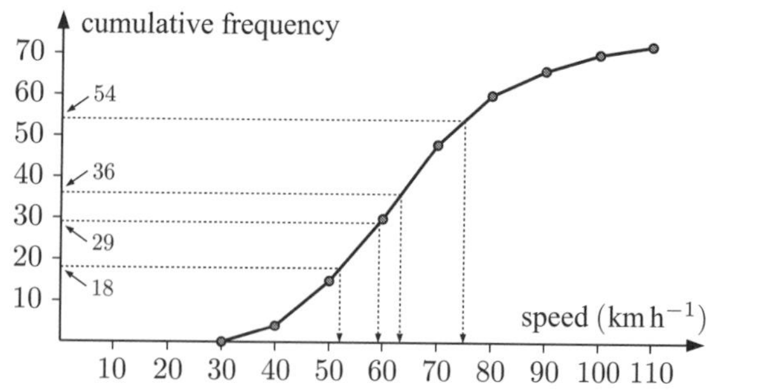


**i** median $= Q_2 \approx 63$ km h$^{-1}$

**ii** $Q_1 \approx 52$, $Q_3 \approx 75$ $\quad \therefore$ IQR $= Q_3 - Q_1$ $\approx 75 - 52 \approx 23$ km h$^{-1}$

**iii** 40% of $72 \approx 29$, so the 40th percentile $\approx 59$ km h$^{-1}$.

**2** mean $= \dfrac{\text{total}}{7}$, so $11 = \dfrac{\text{total}}{7}$ $\quad \therefore$ total $= 77$

If she scores $x$ goals next game, then $12 = \dfrac{77 + x}{8}$

$$\therefore \quad 96 = 77 + x$$

$$\therefore \quad x = 19$$

So, she must score 19 goals next time.

**3**

85 96 98 100 105 $\underbrace{106\ 108}_{Q_1}$ 108 112 112 118 $\underbrace{120\ 123}_{Q_2}$
125 126 128 133 $\underbrace{135\ 140}_{Q_3}$ 144 144 148 148 156

**a** **i** $Q_1 = 107$ **ii** median $= Q_2 = 121.5$
**iii** $Q_3 = 137.5$ **iv** 30.5 **v** $156 - 85 = 71$

**b**

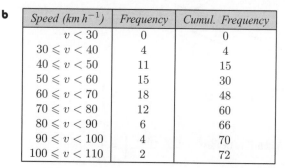

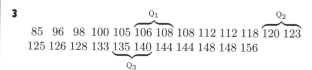

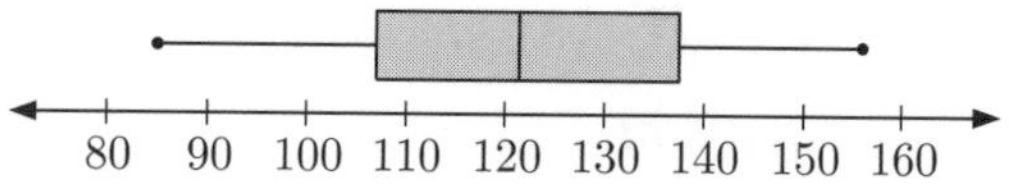


**4** **a** **i** 22 cm **ii** 4 cm **iii** 19 cm **iv** 17 cm

**b** **i** range $= 22 - 4$ $= 18$ cm **ii** IQR $= 19 - 11$ $= 8$ cm

**c** 75% of them

**d** No. It is negatively skewed (skewed to the left).

**5** **a** From the graph, 100 units were sold for $<$ \$200 000.

**b** When $N = \frac{1}{2}$ of $800 = 400$,
the value $= 300$ thousand

$\therefore$ the median $=$ \$300 000

**c** IQR $= Q_3 - Q_1$
$=$ \$375 000 $-$ \$250 000
$=$ \$125 000

**d** 60% of $800 = 480$
So, when $N = 480$, the value $\approx 325\,000$
$\therefore$ the 60% percentile $\approx$ \$325 000

**6**

| *die 2* | | | | | | |
|---|---|---|---|---|---|---|
| 6 | 5 | 4 | (3) | 2 | 1 | 0 |
| 5 | 4 | (3) | 2 | 1 | 0 | 1 |
| 4 | (3) | 2 | 1 | 0 | 1 | 2 |
| 3 | 2 | 1 | 0 | 1 | 2 | (3) |
| 2 | 1 | 0 | 1 | 2 | (3) | 4 |
| 1 | 0 | 1 | 2 | (3) | 4 | 5 |
| | 1 | 2 | 3 | 4 | 5 | 6 *die 1* |

There are 6 outcomes where the difference is 3.
As all outcomes are equally possible, the probability of the difference being 3 is $\frac{6}{36} = \frac{1}{6}$.

**7** Let $R$ be the right-handed people and $B$ be the people with blonde hair.

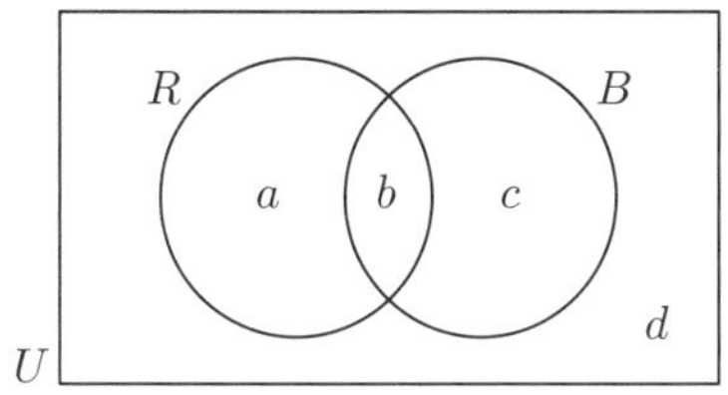


$a+b=71 \quad \therefore \quad b=71-a$

$a+c=44 \quad \therefore \quad c=44-a$

$a+d=21 \quad \therefore \quad d=21-a$

Now $a+b+c+d=100$

$\therefore \quad a+(71-a)+(44-a)+(21-a)=100$

$\therefore \quad 136-2a=100$

$\therefore \quad a=18$

So, $b=53,\ c=26,\ d=3$

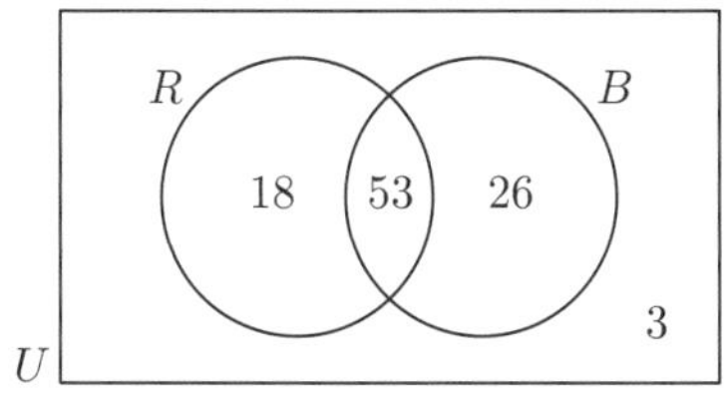


**a** $\mathrm{P}(R\cap B')=\frac{18}{100}=0.18$ **b** $\mathrm{P}(R\cap B)=\frac{53}{100}=0.53$

**c** $\mathrm{P}(R\cup B)=\frac{18+53+26}{100}=0.97$

**8** **a** $f(x)\geqslant 0$ on a given interval $a\leqslant x\leqslant b$, and $\int_a^b f(x)\,dx=1$.

**b** $\mathrm{P}(x_1\leqslant X\leqslant x_2)=\int_{x_1}^{x_2} f(x)\,dx$

**9** **a** The random variable is discrete.

**b** $\frac{1}{3}+\frac{1}{6}+k+\frac{1}{12}=1$

$\therefore \quad k+\frac{7}{12}=1$

$\therefore \quad k=\frac{5}{12}$

**c** $\mathrm{E}(X)=-2(\frac{1}{3})+0(\frac{1}{6})+3(\frac{5}{12})+5(\frac{1}{12})=1$

**10**

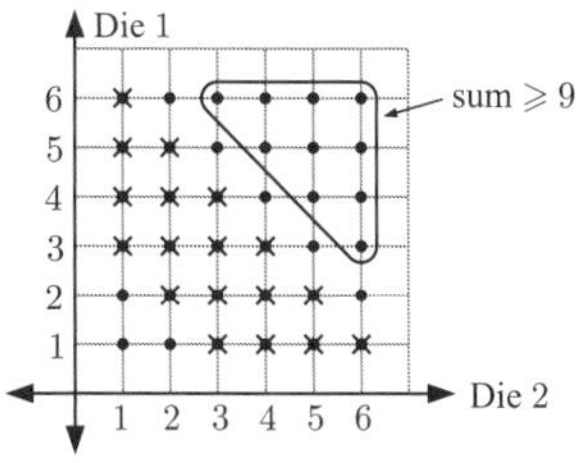


There are 36 possible outcomes each shown by a dot point.

**a** $\mathrm{P}(\text{sum}>8)$
$=\mathrm{P}(\text{sum}\geqslant 9)$
$=\frac{10}{36}$
$=\frac{5}{18}$

**b** $\mathrm{P}(\text{more than 3, but less than 8})$
$=\mathrm{P}(4\leqslant \text{sum}\leqslant 7)$
$=\frac{18}{36}$ {marked ×}
$=\frac{1}{2}$

**c** $\mathrm{P}(\text{sum}=6)=\frac{5}{36}$ $\{1+5,\ 2+4,\ 3+3,\ 4+2,\ 5+1\}$

**11** **a**

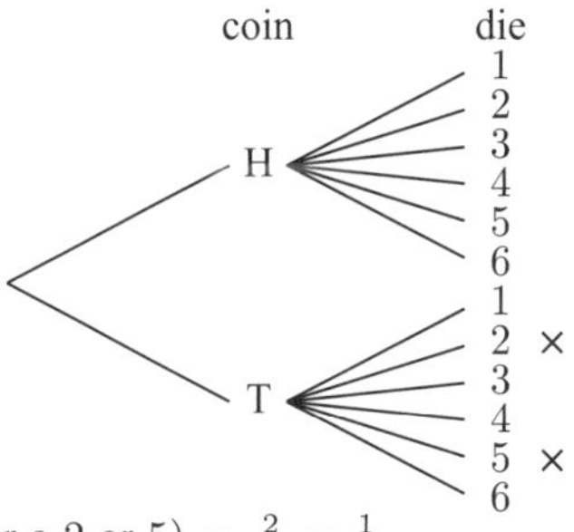


$\mathrm{P}(\text{T and either a 2 or 5})=\frac{2}{12}=\frac{1}{6}$

**b**

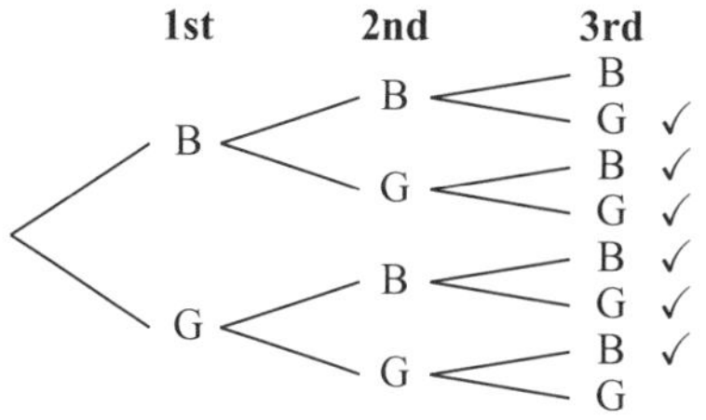


$\mathrm{P}(\text{at least one of each sex})=\frac{6}{8}=\frac{3}{4}$

**12**

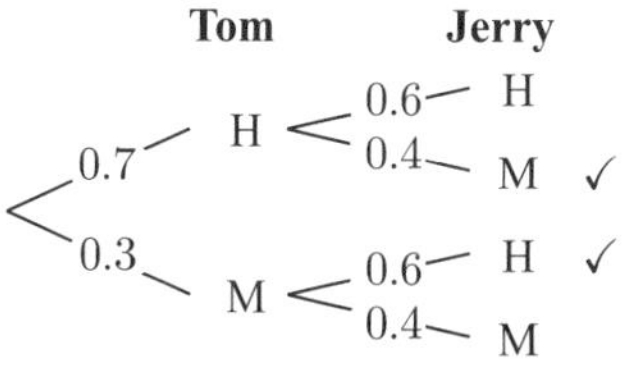


**a** $\mathrm{P}(\text{only one of them is successful})$
$=(0.7)(0.4)+(0.3)(0.6)$
$=0.46$

**b** $\mathrm{P}(\text{at least one is successful})$
$=1-\mathrm{P}(\text{both miss})$
$=1-(0.3)(0.4)$
$=1-0.12$
$=0.88$

**13** **a**

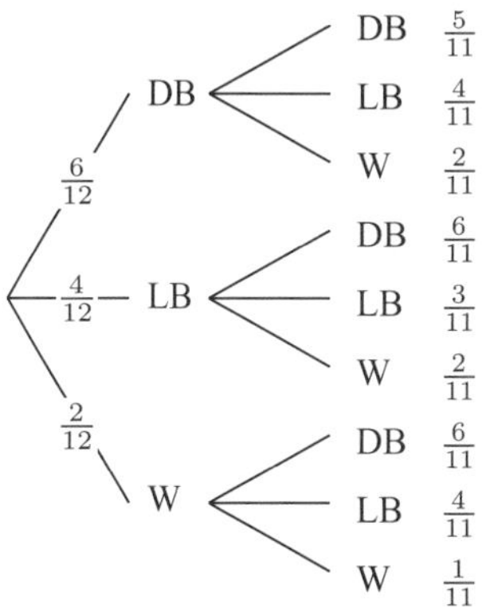


**b** **i** $\mathrm{P}(\text{2 whites})=\frac{2}{12}\times\frac{1}{11}=\frac{1}{66}$

**ii** $\mathrm{P}(\text{2 different colours})$
$=1-\mathrm{P}(\text{2 the same colour})$
$=1-\left[(\frac{6}{12})(\frac{5}{11})+(\frac{4}{12})(\frac{3}{11})+(\frac{2}{12})(\frac{1}{11})\right]$
$=1-\frac{44}{12\times 11}=\frac{2}{3}$

**14** There are $11+8+4+2=25$ students.

**a** $\mathrm{P}(H)$
$=\dfrac{11+8}{25}$
$=\frac{19}{25}$

**b** $\mathrm{P}(T')$
$=\dfrac{11+2}{25}$
$=\frac{13}{25}$

**c** $\mathrm{P}(\text{plays at least one sport})$
$=\dfrac{11+8+4}{25}$
$=\frac{23}{25}$

**d** $\mathrm{P}(T\,|\,H)$
$=\dfrac{8}{11+8}$
$=\frac{8}{19}$

**15**

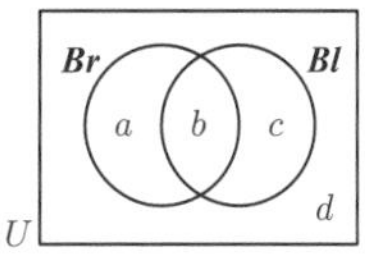


$a+b+c+d=30$

$a+b=17$

$b+c=12$

$d=4$

$\therefore \quad a+b+c=26$

Since $a+b=17,\quad 17+c=26$

$\therefore \quad c=9$

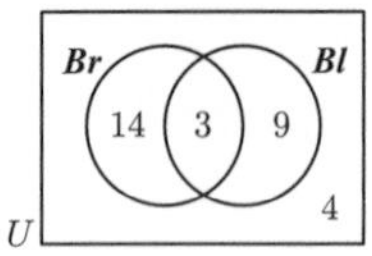


Since $b + c = 12$, $\quad b + 9 = 12$

$\therefore \quad b = 3$

$a + 3 + 9 = 26$

$\therefore \quad a + 12 = 26$

$\therefore \quad a = 14$

**a** 3 students have both brown hair and blue eyes.

**b** **i** $\text{P}(Bl \text{ but not } Br) = \frac{9}{30} = 0.3$

**ii** $\text{P}(Br \mid Bl) = \frac{3}{12} = 0.25$

## CALCULATORS

**1** Using technology, $\overline{x} = 7.52$

**2** **a** 37, 43, 50, 50, 51, 55, 58, 59, 60

**i** mean $\approx 51.4$ **ii** median $= 51$ **iii** mode $= 50$

**b** 18, 21, 21, 21, 23, 23, 26, 27, 28, 30

**i** mean $= 23.8$ **ii** median $= 23$ **iii** mode $= 21$

**c** **i** mean $\approx 8.94$ **ii** median $= 9$ **iii** mode $= 8$

**3** $\overline{x} = \dfrac{\sum fx}{\sum f} \quad \therefore \quad \dfrac{0 + 4 + 6 + 3a + 8}{6 + 4 + 3 + a + 2} = 1.65$

$\therefore \quad \dfrac{3a + 18}{a + 15} = 1.65$

$\therefore \quad 3a + 18 = 1.65a + 24.75$

$\therefore \quad 1.35a = 6.75$

$\therefore \quad a = \dfrac{6.75}{1.35}$

$\therefore \quad a = 5$

**4** Using technology

**a** $\mu \approx 3.56, \ \sigma \approx 0.512$ **b** $\mu \approx 16.3, \ \sigma \approx 3.21$

**c** $\mu \approx 184, \ \sigma \approx 2.64$ **d** $\mu \approx 67.9, \ \sigma \approx 12.2$

**5** **a** The sum of the frequencies is 30, so 30 drives were chosen.

**b**

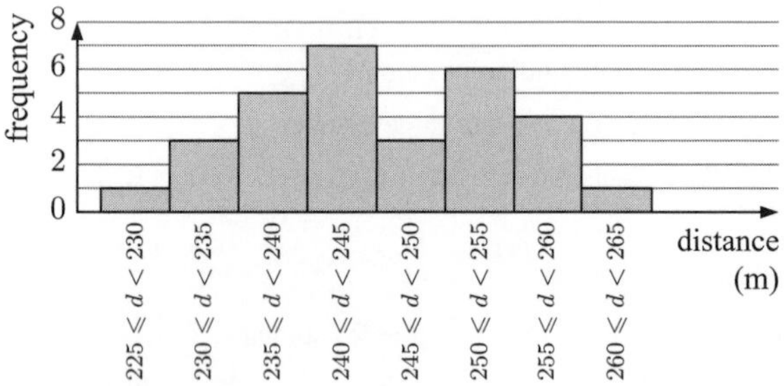


**c** An estimate of the mean is 245.
An estimate of the median is 243.
The modal class is $240 \leqslant d < 245$.
Since the mean, median and mode are about equal, the data appears to be symmetric.

**d**

| *Distance (m)* | *Frequency* | *Cumul. Frequency* |
|---|---|---|
| $225 \leqslant d < 230$ | 1 | 1 |
| $230 \leqslant d < 235$ | 3 | 4 |
| $235 \leqslant d < 240$ | 5 | 9 |
| $240 \leqslant d < 245$ | 7 | 16 |
| $245 \leqslant d < 250$ | 3 | 19 |
| $250 \leqslant d < 255$ | 6 | 25 |
| $255 \leqslant d < 260$ | 4 | 29 |
| $260 \leqslant d < 265$ | 1 | 30 |

**e** $30 - 4 = 26$ **f** $\frac{19}{30} \approx 63.3\%$

**6**

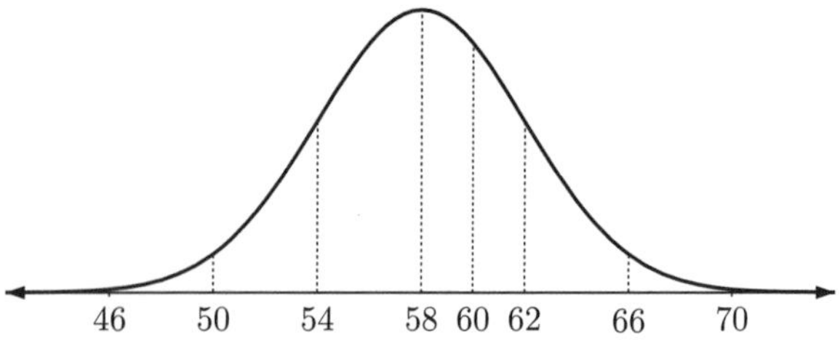


**a** $\text{P}(X > 60)$

$\approx 0.309$

So, over a 100 year period we would expect this to occur 31 times.

**b** $\text{P}(50 < X < 60)$

$\approx 0.669$

So, over a 100 year period we would expect this to occur 67 times.

**7** The tree diagram uses: $F$ for female $\quad L$ for left-handed
$M$ for male $\quad R$ for right-handed

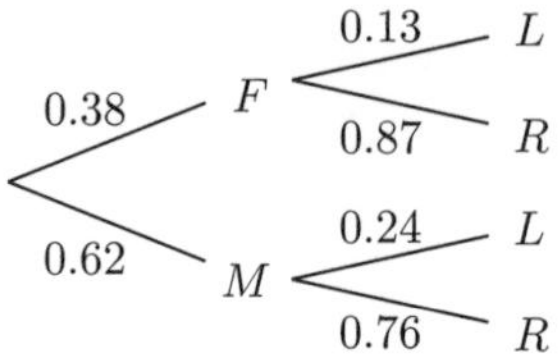


**a** $\text{P}(L) = (0.38)(0.13) + (0.62)(0.24) \approx 0.198$

**b** $\text{P}(F \mid L) = \dfrac{\text{P}(F \cap L)}{\text{P}(L)} = \dfrac{(0.38)(0.13)}{0.1982} \approx 0.249$

**8** $\text{P}(A \cup B) = \text{P}(A) + \text{P}(B) - \text{P}(A \cap B)$

But $A$ and $B$ are independent, so $\text{P}(A \cap B) = \text{P}(A)\,\text{P}(B)$.

Hence, $\text{P}(A \cup B) = \text{P}(A) + \text{P}(B) - \text{P}(A)\,\text{P}(B)$

Let $\text{P}(A) = x$.

$\therefore \quad 0.63 = x + 0.36 - 0.36x$

$\therefore \quad 0.27 = 0.64x$

$\therefore \quad x = \text{P}(A) \approx 0.422$

**9** $\text{P}(A \cup B) = 1 - \text{P}(A \cup B)' = 1 - \frac{1}{12} = \frac{11}{12}$

$\text{P}(A \cup B) = \text{P}(A) + \text{P}(B) - \text{P}(A \cap B)$

$\therefore \quad \frac{11}{12} = 0.46 + \frac{5}{7} - \text{P}(A \cap B)$

$\therefore \quad \text{P}(A \cap B) = 0.46 + \frac{5}{7} - \frac{11}{12}$

$\therefore \quad \text{P}(A \cap B) \approx 0.258$

**10** $\mu = 310$ mL, $\sigma = 5$ mL

**a** $\text{P}(300 < X < 310) \approx 0.477$

$\therefore$ 47.7% lie between 300 mL and 310 mL.

**b** $\text{P}(X \geqslant 304) \approx 0.885$

$\therefore$ 88.5% are at least 304 mL.

**c** $\text{P}(X < 300) \approx 0.0228$

**11** Ashleigh's $z$-score $= \dfrac{44 - 40}{8} = 0.5$

Bart's $z$-score $= \dfrac{32 - 40}{8} = -1$

Carissa's $z$-score $= \dfrac{37 - 40}{8} = -0.375$

David's $z$-score $= \dfrac{47 - 40}{8} = 0.875$

Ethan's $z$-score $= \dfrac{53 - 40}{8} = 1.625$

**12** $z$-score for English $\dfrac{80-75}{8} = 0.625$

$z$-score for History $\dfrac{72-60}{15} = 0.800$

$\therefore$ the student achieved a higher standard in History.

For English, $P(X > 80) \approx 0.266$

$\therefore$ 26.6% scored above 80

For History, $P(X > 72) \approx 0.212$

$\therefore$ 21.2% scored above 72

**13** $X \sim N(\mu, \sigma^2)$

$$\begin{aligned}
\text{Now} \quad & P(X > 90) = 0.12 \\
\therefore \quad & P(X \leqslant 90) = 0.88 \\
\therefore \quad & P\left(\frac{X-\mu}{\sigma} \leqslant \frac{90-\mu}{\sigma}\right) = 0.88 \\
\therefore \quad & P\left(Z \leqslant \frac{90-\mu}{\sigma}\right) = 0.88 \\
\therefore \quad & \frac{90-\mu}{\sigma} \approx 1.1750 \\
& 90-\mu \approx 1.1750\sigma \quad .... \ (1)
\end{aligned}$$

$$\begin{aligned}
\text{Also,} \quad & P(X < 60) = 0.20 \\
\therefore \quad & P\left(\frac{X-\mu}{\sigma} < \frac{60-\mu}{\sigma}\right) = 0.20 \\
\therefore \quad & P\left(Z < \frac{60-\mu}{\sigma}\right) = 0.20 \\
\therefore \quad & \frac{60-\mu}{\sigma} \approx -0.8416 \\
\therefore \quad & 60-\mu \approx -0.8416\sigma \quad .... \ (2)
\end{aligned}$$

Solving (1) and (2):

$$\begin{aligned}
90-\mu &\approx 1.1750\sigma \\
-60+\mu &\approx 0.8416\sigma \\
\hline
\text{adding,} \quad 30 &\approx 2.0166\sigma \\
\therefore \quad \sigma &\approx \frac{30}{2.0166} \approx 14.88 \\
\text{and} \quad 90-\mu &\approx 1.1750 \times 14.88 \\
\therefore \quad \mu &\approx 72.5
\end{aligned}$$

Thus $\mu \approx 72.5$ and $\sigma \approx 14.9$

**14** $C \sim N(70, 12^2)$, $M \sim N(65, 11^2)$

**a** $P(C \geqslant 74)$
$\approx 0.369$
$\therefore$ 36.9% of the students scored 74 or greater.

**b** $P(M \geqslant 70)$
$\approx 0.325$
$\therefore$ 32.5% of the students scored 70 or greater.

**c** Ben's $z$-score for Chemistry is
$\dfrac{74-70}{12} = \frac{4}{12} \approx 0.333$
Alice's $z$-score for Maths is
$\dfrac{70-65}{11} = \frac{5}{11} \approx 0.455$
Since Alice's $z$-score is higher, she can claim to have performed better.

**d** Let $m$ be the Mathematics mark comparable to a 74 in Chemistry.
The $z$-scores have to be equal.

$$\begin{aligned}
\therefore \quad \frac{m-65}{11} &= \frac{74-70}{12} = \tfrac{1}{3} \\
\therefore \quad m-65 &= \tfrac{11}{3} = 3\tfrac{2}{3} \\
\therefore \quad m &= 68\tfrac{2}{3}
\end{aligned}$$

and if whole number marks only are given, then $m = 69$.

**15** $p = \frac{4}{5} = 0.8$

Let $X$ be the number of people sampled who oppose the traffic lights.

$X \sim B(20, 0.8)$

**a** $P(X = 16)$
$\approx 0.218$

**b** $P(X \geqslant 16)$
$= 1 - P(X \leqslant 15)$
$\approx 1 - 0.370$
$\approx 0.630$

**16** If Robert gets the 5 known correct then there are 10 answers he guesses.

Let $X$ be the number he correctly guesses, so

$X \sim B(10, 0.25)$

**a** P(Robert fails)
$= P(X \leqslant 2)$
$\approx 0.526$

**b** P(gets exactly 8 correct)
$= P(X = 3)$
$\approx 0.250$

**c** P(gets an A)
$= P(X \geqslant 5)$
$= 1 - P(X \leqslant 4)$
$\approx 1 - 0.9219$
$\approx 0.0781$

**17** $\mu = 0$, $\sigma = 1$, and $X \sim N(0, 1^2)$.

**a** $P(X \leqslant 1) \approx 0.841$

**b** $P(-0.5 \leqslant X \leqslant 0.5) \approx 0.383$

**c** $P(X > 2) \approx 0.0228$

$\therefore$ we can expect that $0.0228 \times 850 \approx 19$ speeds measured will exceed the actual speed by more than 2 $\text{km h}^{-1}$.

**18** $\mu = 40$, $\sigma = 5$, and $X \sim N(40, 5^2)$.

**a** $P(X > 45) \approx 0.159$

**b** $P(35 < X < 50) \approx 0.819$

**c** We need to find $k$ such that $P(X > k) = 0.1$

Now $P(X > k) = 0.1$ means that

$$\begin{aligned}
& P\left(Z > \frac{k-40}{5}\right) = 0.1 \\
\therefore \quad & P\left(Z \leqslant \frac{k-40}{5}\right) = 0.9 \\
\therefore \quad & \frac{k-40}{5} \approx 1.281 \\
\therefore \quad & k \approx 5 \times 1.281 + 40 \\
\therefore \quad & k \approx 46.4
\end{aligned}$$

So, the minimum length of the longest 10% of fish is 46.4 cm.

**19** $\mu = 500$, $\sigma = 2.5$

**a** $P(X < 495) \approx 0.0228$

**b** **i** $0.0228 \times 1000 \approx 23$ bottles will require extra sauce.

**ii** This will cost $23 \times 4 = 92$ cents.

**20** $\mu = 38.4$, $\sigma = 4.6$

**a** $P(X > 43.5) \approx 0.134$

**b** $P(X \leqslant 36.4) \approx 0.332$

**c** $P(30 \leqslant X \leqslant 40) \approx 0.602$

**d** We need to find $k$ such that $P(X > k) = 0.9$

Now $P(X > k) = 0.9$ means that

$$\begin{aligned}
& P\left(Z > \frac{k-38.4}{4.6}\right) = 0.9 \\
\therefore \quad & P\left(Z \leqslant \frac{k-38.4}{4.6}\right) = 0.1 \\
\therefore \quad & \frac{k-38.4}{4.6} \approx -1.281
\end{aligned}$$

$\therefore \quad k \approx 4.6 \times (-1.281) + 38.4$

$\therefore \quad k \approx 32.5$

So, 90% will reduce their oxygen consumption by in excess of 32.5 mL.

**21** **a** $\text{P}(X < 56) = 0.8$ means that $\text{P}\left(Z < \dfrac{56 - \mu}{\sigma}\right) = 0.8$

$\therefore \quad \dfrac{56-\mu}{\sigma} \approx 0.8416$

$\therefore \quad 56 - \mu \approx 0.8416\sigma$

So, a score of 56 is 0.842 standard deviations from the mean.

**b** If $\sigma = 4$ then from **a**, $56 - \mu \approx 0.8416(4)$

$\therefore \quad 56 - \mu \approx 3.366$

$\therefore \quad \mu \approx 52.6$

**22** $\mu = 1020, \ \sigma = 15$

**a** $\text{P}(X < 1000) \approx 0.0912$

**b** Containers that overflow have more than 1050 mL added to them.

Now $\text{P}(X > 1050) \approx 0.0228$

$\therefore$ 2.28% of the containers overflow

**c** $\text{P}(1000 \leqslant X \leqslant 1030) \approx 0.6563$

So, in a sample of 1500, we expect $0.6563 \times 1500 \approx 984$ containers will hold between 1 litre and 1.03 litres.

**23** $X \sim \text{B}(10, 0.88)$ so $n = 10, \ p = 0.88$.

**a** $\text{P}(X = 8) \approx 0.233$

**b** A student passes if they pass 8 or more of the tests.

$\text{P}(X \geqslant 8) = 1 - \text{P}(X \leqslant 7)$

$\approx 1 - 0.109$

$\approx 0.891$

**24** $X \sim \text{B}(6, 0.05)$ so $n = 6, \ p = 0.05$.

The manufacturer must pay double money back if more than two items are defective.

P(more than 2)

$\approx 1 - \text{P}(X \leqslant 2)$

$\approx 1 - 0.99777$

$\approx 0.00223$

So, the manufacturer will have to pay double money back on 0.223% of boxes.

**25**

| | *Defective* | *Not defective* | *Total* |
|---|---|---|---|
| *Corn* | 37 | 581 | 618 |
| *Pineapple* | 24 | 617 | 641 |
| *Total* | 61 | 1198 | 1259 |

**a** 1259 tins

**b** **i** 641 out of the 1259 tins are pineapple.

$\therefore$ P(pineapple) $\approx \frac{641}{1259} \approx 0.509$

**ii** 61 out of the 1259 tins are defective.

$\therefore$ P(defective) $\approx \frac{61}{1259} \approx 0.0485$

**iii** 37 of the 61 defective tins are corn.

$\therefore$ P(corn | defective) $\approx \frac{37}{61} \approx 0.607$

**iv** 37 out of 618 corn tins are defective.

$\therefore$ P(defective | corn) $\approx \frac{37}{618} \approx 0.0599$

**26**

| | $< 50$ | $\geqslant 50$ | *Total* |
|---|---|---|---|
| *Male* | 136 | 469 | 605 |
| *Female* | 155 | 310 | 465 |
| *Total* | 291 | 779 | 1070 |

**a** 1070 patients

**b** **i** 605 of the 1070 patients were male.

$\therefore$ P(male) $= \frac{605}{1070} \approx 0.565$

**ii** 291 of the 1070 patients were younger than 50.

$\therefore$ P(younger than 50) $= \frac{291}{1070} \approx 0.272$

**iii** Of the 779 patients who were 50 or older, 469 were male.

$\therefore$ P(male | 50 or older) $= \frac{469}{779} \approx 0.602$

**iv** Of the 465 female patients, 310 were 50 or older.

$\therefore$ P(50 or older | female) $= \frac{310}{465} \approx 0.667$

**27** $X$ = number of allergic reactions

$X \sim \text{B}(5000, 0.1)$

$\text{P}(X < 470) = \text{P}(X \leqslant 469)$

$\approx 0.0743$

**28** The length $X$ cm of a chopstick is normally distributed with mean $\mu$ cm and standard deviation 0.5 cm.

Now $\text{P}(X < 24) = 0.01$

$\therefore \quad \text{P}\left(\dfrac{X-\mu}{0.5} < \dfrac{24-\mu}{0.5}\right) = 0.01$

$\therefore \quad \text{P}\left(Z < \dfrac{24-\mu}{0.5}\right) = 0.01$

$\therefore \quad \dfrac{24-\mu}{0.5} \approx -2.326$

$\therefore \quad 24 - \mu \approx -1.163$

$\therefore \quad \mu \approx 25.2$ cm

**29** If $X$ cm is the length of a steel rod then $X$ is normally distributed with mean 13.8 cm.

Now $\text{P}(X < 13.2) = 0.015$

$\therefore \quad \text{P}\left(\dfrac{X - 13.8}{\sigma} < \dfrac{13.2 - 13.8}{\sigma}\right) = 0.015$

$\therefore \quad \text{P}\left(Z < \dfrac{-0.6}{\sigma}\right) = 0.015$

$\therefore \quad \dfrac{-0.6}{\sigma} \approx -2.17009$

$\therefore \quad \sigma \approx 0.276$ cm

**30** $\text{P}(X = x) = \frac{1}{24}(x + 6), \quad x \in \{1, 2, 3\}$

**a** $\text{P}(1) = \frac{1}{24}(7) = \frac{7}{24}$

$\text{P}(2) = \frac{1}{24}(8) = \frac{8}{24}$

$\text{P}(3) = \frac{1}{24}(9) = \frac{9}{24}$

**b** $\text{E}(X) = \sum_{i=1}^{3} x_i \, \text{P}(X = x_i)$

$= 1(\frac{7}{24}) + 2(\frac{8}{24}) + 3(\frac{9}{24})$

$= \frac{50}{24}$

$= 2\frac{1}{12}$

**31** **a** $0.05 + k + 0.5 + 0.3 = 1$

$\therefore \quad k + 0.85 = 1$

$\therefore \quad k = 0.15$

**b** $\text{E}(X) = \sum x_i p_i$

$= 0(0.05) + 1(0.15) + 2(0.5) + 3(0.3)$

$= 0.15 + 1 + 0.9$

$= 2.05$

**32** $\text{E}(X) = \sum x_i p_i$

$= 0(0.3) + 1(0.2) + 2(0.15) + 3(0.35)$

$= 0.2 + 0.3 + 1.05$

$= 1.55$

**33** **a** The random variable $X$ is the number of sales.

**b** The possible outcomes are:

0 sales, 8 non-sales
1 sale, 7 non-sales
2 sales, 6 non-sales
3 sales, 5 non-sales
4 sales, 4 non-sales
5 sales, 3 non-sales
6 sales, 2 non-sales
7 sales, 1 non-sale
8 sales, 0 non-sales

So, $X$ can be 0, 1, 2, 3, 4, 5, 6, 7 or 8.

**c** $X \sim B(8, 0.4)$

$P(X = 0) \approx 0.017$
$P(X = 1) \approx 0.090$
$P(X = 2) \approx 0.209$
$P(X = 3) \approx 0.279$
$P(X = 4) \approx 0.232$
$P(X = 5) \approx 0.124$
$P(X = 6) \approx 0.041$
$P(X = 7) \approx 0.008$
$P(X = 8) \approx 0.001$

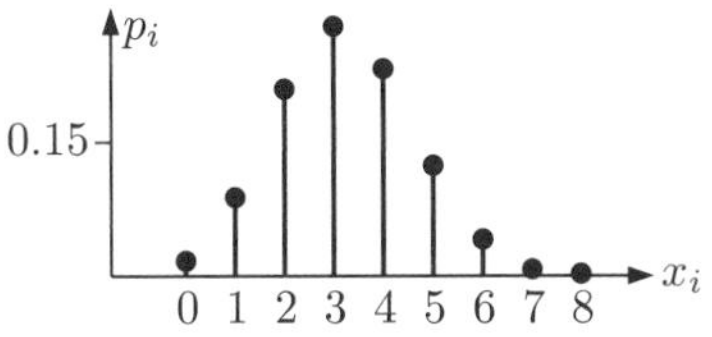


The distribution is slightly positively skewed (skewed right). As the number of people increases, the distribution will approximate a normal distribution.

**d** Using **c**, **i** $P(X = 5) \approx 0.124$

**ii** $P(X \geqslant 2) = 1 - P(X \leqslant 1)$
$= 1 - P(X = 0 \text{ or } X = 1)$
$\approx 1 - (0.0168 + 0.0896)$
$\approx 0.894$

**e** The commission is \$100 per sale plus \$30 for every sale after the second. Costs are \$200.

$\therefore$ if the number of sales is $X$ and $X > 2$, the profit is
$\$[100X + 30(X - 2) - 200]$
$= \$(130X - 260)$.

$\therefore$ the profit $= \$450$ when $X \approx 5.46$
When $X = 5$, the profit $= 650 - 260 = \$390$.
When $X = 6$, the profit $= 780 - 260 = \$520$.
$\therefore$ the salesman makes a profit of \$450 or greater when he makes at least six sales.
$\therefore$ we need $P(X \geqslant 6)$
$= P(X = 6 \text{ or } X = 7 \text{ or } X = 8)$
$\approx 0.041\,29 + 0.007\,86 + 0.000\,66$
$\approx 0.0498$

**34** $P(X) = 0.8$, $P(Y) = 0.6$

**a** $P(\text{both } X \text{ and } Y)$
$= P(X \cap Y)$
$= P(X)P(Y)$ {$X$ and $Y$ are independent}
$= 0.8 \times 0.6$
$= 0.48$

$0.8 - 0.48 = 0.32$

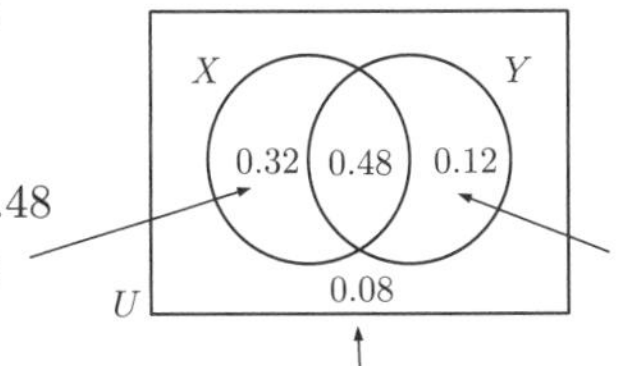


$0.6 - 0.48 = 0.12$

$1 - 0.32 - 0.48 - 0.12 = 0.08$

**b** $P(X \text{ or } Y, \text{ both not both})$
$= 0.32 + 0.12$
$= 0.44$

**c** $P(X \mid Y')$
$= \dfrac{0.32}{0.32 + 0.08}$
$= \dfrac{0.32}{0.40}$
$= 0.8$

**d** $P(\text{neither } X \text{ nor } Y) = 0.08$

**35**

$$P(X \leqslant 15) = 0.613$$
$$\therefore P\left(\frac{X-\mu}{\sigma} \leqslant \frac{15-\mu}{\sigma}\right) = 0.613$$
$$\therefore P\left(Z \leqslant \frac{15-13}{\sigma}\right) = 0.613$$
$$\therefore \frac{2}{\sigma} \approx 0.287$$
$$\therefore \sigma \approx 6.97$$

**36**

$$P(X \leqslant 24) = 0.035$$
$$\therefore P\left(Z \leqslant \frac{24-\mu}{\sigma}\right) = 0.035$$
$$\therefore \frac{24-\mu}{\sigma} \approx -1.812$$
$$\therefore 24 - \mu \approx -1.812\sigma \quad .... (1)$$

Also, $P(X \geqslant 33) = 0.262$
$$\therefore P(X < 33) = 0.738$$
$$\therefore P\left(Z < \frac{33-\mu}{\sigma}\right) = 0.738$$
$$\therefore \frac{33-\mu}{\sigma} \approx 0.6372$$
$$\therefore 33 - \mu \approx 0.6372\sigma \quad .... (2)$$

(1) $-$ (2) gives
$$(24-\mu) - (33-\mu) \approx -1.812\sigma - 0.6372\sigma$$
$$\therefore -9 \approx -2.449\sigma$$
$$\therefore \sigma \approx 3.67$$
$$\therefore \mu \approx 24 + 1.812(3.67) \approx 30.7$$

# SOLUTIONS TO TOPIC 7 (CALCULUS)

## NO CALCULATORS

**1**

$$f(x) = 7x - x^2$$
$$\therefore f(x+h) = 7(x+h) - (x+h)^2$$
$$= 7x + 7h - (x^2 + 2xh + h^2)$$
$$= 7x + 7h - x^2 - 2xh - h^2$$

Now
$$f'(x) = \lim_{h\to 0} \frac{f(x+h) - f(x)}{h}$$
$$= \lim_{h\to 0} \frac{7x + 7h - x^2 - 2xh - h^2 - 7x + x^2}{h}$$
$$= \lim_{h\to 0} \frac{7h - 2xh - h^2}{h}$$
$$= \lim_{h\to 0} \frac{h(7 - 2x - h)}{1h} \quad \{\text{as } h \neq 0\}$$
$$= \lim_{h\to 0} (7 - 2x - h)$$
$$= 7 - 2x$$

**2** **a**
$$y = \frac{3x+1}{\sqrt{x}} = 3x^{\frac{1}{2}} + x^{-\frac{1}{2}}$$
$$\therefore \frac{dy}{dx} = \tfrac{3}{2}x^{-\frac{1}{2}} - \tfrac{1}{2}x^{-\frac{3}{2}} = \frac{3}{2\sqrt{x}} - \frac{1}{2x\sqrt{x}}$$

**b**
$$y = (x^4 + 9)^{-1}$$
$$\therefore \frac{dy}{dx} = -(x^4+9)^{-2} \times (4x^3)$$

**c**
$$y = x^2(1-x^2)^{\frac{1}{2}}$$
$$\therefore \frac{dy}{dx} = 2x(1-x^2)^{\frac{1}{2}} + x^2 \times \tfrac{1}{2}(1-x^2)^{-\frac{1}{2}} \times (-2x)$$
$$= 2x\sqrt{1-x^2} - \frac{x^3}{\sqrt{1-x^2}}$$

**3** **a**
$$y = (2x+3)^5$$
$$\therefore \frac{dy}{dx} = 5(2x+3)^4 \times 2 = 10(2x+3)^4$$

**b**
$$y = (x^2 + x + 1)^{\frac{1}{2}}$$
$$\therefore \frac{dy}{dx} = \tfrac{1}{2}(x^2+x+1)^{-\frac{1}{2}} \times (2x+1)$$

**4** $v = t^3 - 9t^2 + 24t \text{ m s}^{-1}$ where $t \geqslant 0$

$\therefore \quad \dfrac{dv}{dt} = 3t^2 - 18t + 24 = 3(t^2 - 6t + 8)$

$= 3(t-4)(t-2)$

Sign diagram for $\dfrac{dv}{dt}$:

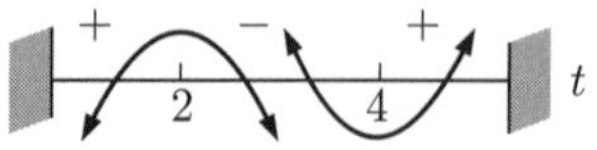


$v_{\max}$ is the larger of $v(2)$ or $v(6)$

Now $v(2) = 8 - 36 + 48 = 20 \text{ m s}^{-1}$

$v(6) = 216 - 324 + 144 = 36 \text{ m s}^{-1}$

$\therefore \quad v_{\max} = 36 \text{ m s}^{-1}$ when $t = 6$ s.

**5** $h(t) = 100 + 32t - 4t^2$

$\therefore \quad h'(t) = 32 - 8t$

$\therefore \quad h'(t) = 0$ when $32 = 8t$ or $t = 4$

Sign diagram for $h'(t)$:

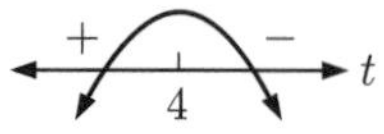


So, the height is maximum when $t = 4$ s.

Now $h(4) = 100 + 32(4) - 4(4)^2 = 164$ m

$\therefore$ the maximum height is 164 m.

**6** $f(x) = x^3 - 2x^2$

$\therefore \quad f'(x) = 3x^2 - 4x$

$= x(3x - 4)$

$\therefore \quad f'(x) = 0$ when $x = 0$ or $\frac{4}{3}$

Sign diagram for $f'(x)$ on $-1 \leqslant x \leqslant 1$:

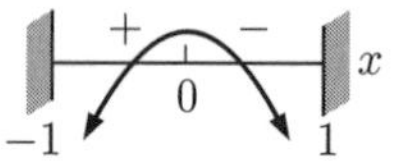


Now $f(0) = 0$, so the greatest value is 0 when $x = 0$.

Also, $f(-1) = (-1)^3 - 2(-1)^2 = -3$

and $f(1) = 1^3 - 2(1)^2 = -1$

$\therefore$ the least value is $-3$ when $x = -1$.

**7** The curves meet where $\sqrt{3x+1} = \sqrt{5x - x^2}$

$\therefore \quad 3x + 1 = 5x - x^2$

$\therefore \quad x^2 - 2x + 1 = 0$

$\therefore \quad (x-1)^2 = 0$

$\therefore \quad x = 1$

$\therefore$ they meet at (1, 2).

For $y = (3x+1)^{\frac{1}{2}}$, $\dfrac{dy}{dx} = \frac{1}{2}(3x+1)^{-\frac{1}{2}}(3) = \dfrac{3}{2\sqrt{3x+1}}$

$\therefore$ when $x = 1$, $\dfrac{dy}{dx} = \frac{3}{4}$.

For $y = (5x - x^2)^{\frac{1}{2}}$, $\dfrac{dy}{dx} = \frac{1}{2}(5x - x^2)^{-\frac{1}{2}}(5 - 2x)$

$\therefore$ when $x = 1$, $\dfrac{dy}{dx} = \frac{1}{2}(4^{-\frac{1}{2}})3 = \frac{3}{4}$.

Both curves have the same gradient $\frac{3}{4}$ at their point of intersection, so the equation of the common tangent is

$\dfrac{y-2}{x-1} = \frac{3}{4}$ which is $4y - 8 = 3x - 3$

or $3x - 4y = -5$

**8** $y = x^3 - 5 \quad \therefore \quad \dfrac{dy}{dx} = 3x^2$

$\therefore$ at (1, −4), $\dfrac{dy}{dx} = 3$

$\therefore$ the equation of the tangent at (1, −4) is

$\dfrac{y - -4}{x - 1} = 3$ which is $y + 4 = 3x - 3$

or $3x - y = 7$

When $y = 0$, $3x = 7$

So, the tangent cuts the $x$-axis at $(\frac{7}{3}, 0)$.

**9** Profit per article = sale price per article − cost per article

$= 50 - (N^2 - 6N + 35)$

$= -N^2 + 6N + 15$ cents

$\therefore$ profit, $P = (-N^2 + 6N + 15)N$ cents

$= -N^3 + 6N^2 + 15N$

$\therefore \quad \dfrac{dP}{dN} = -3N^2 + 12N + 15$

$= -3(N^2 - 4N - 5)$

$= -3(N-5)(N+1)$

Sign diagram for $\dfrac{dP}{dN}$:

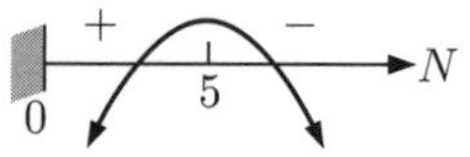


$\therefore$ $P$ is maximised when $N = 5$ articles.

If the cost per article is $C = N^2 - 6N + 35$

then $\dfrac{dC}{dN} = 2N - 6$

$\therefore \quad \dfrac{dC}{dN} = 0$ when $N = 3$.

Sign diagram for $\dfrac{dC}{dN}$:

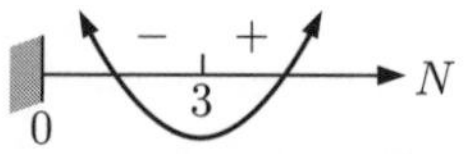


$\therefore$ $C$ is minimised when $N = 3$, and this is not when the profit is maximised.

**10** $y = -2x^3 + 3x^2 - 1$

$\therefore \quad \dfrac{dy}{dx}$

$= \lim\limits_{h \to 0} \dfrac{(-2(x+h)^3 + 3(x+h)^2 - 1) - (-2x^3 + 3x^2 - 1)}{h}$

$= \lim\limits_{h \to 0} \dfrac{\left(\begin{array}{r} -2(x^3 + 3x^2h + 3xh^2 + h^3) + 3(x^2 + 2xh + h^2) \\ -1 - (-2x^3 + 3x^2 - 1) \end{array}\right)}{h}$

$= \lim\limits_{h \to 0} \dfrac{\left(\begin{array}{r} -2x^3 - 6x^2h - 6xh^2 - 2h^3 + 3x^2 + 6xh + 3h^2 \\ -1 + 2x^3 - 3x^2 + 1 \end{array}\right)}{h}$

$= \lim\limits_{h \to 0} \dfrac{-6x^2h + 6xh - 6xh^2 + 3h^2 - 2h^3}{h}$

$= \lim\limits_{h \to 0} \dfrac{h(-6x^2 + 6x - 6xh + 3h - 2h^2)}{h_1}$

$= \lim\limits_{h \to 0} (-6x^2 + 6x - 6xh + 3h - 2h^2) \quad$ {as $h \neq 0$}

$= -6x^2 + 6x$

**11** **a** $y = \dfrac{1 - 2x}{\sqrt[3]{x}} = \dfrac{1 - 2x}{x^{\frac{1}{3}}} = x^{-\frac{1}{3}} - 2x^{\frac{2}{3}}$

$\therefore \quad \dfrac{dy}{dx} = -\frac{1}{3}x^{-\frac{4}{3}} - \frac{4}{3}x^{-\frac{1}{3}}$

**b** $y = 2x(1 + 2x)^4$

$\therefore \quad \dfrac{dy}{dx} = 2(1 + 2x)^4 + 2x(4)(1 + 2x)^3(2)$

$= 2(1 + 2x)^4 + 16x(1 + 2x)^3$

**12** **a** $y = \dfrac{3}{x^2} = 3x^{-2}$

$\therefore \quad \dfrac{dy}{dx} = -6x^{-3}$

$\therefore \quad \dfrac{d^2y}{dx^2} = 18x^{-4} = \dfrac{18}{x^4}$

**b** $y = x^2 \sin 3x$

$\therefore \quad \dfrac{dy}{dx} = 2x \sin 3x + x^2(3 \cos 3x) \quad$ {product rule}

$= 2x \sin 3x + 3x^2 \cos 3x$

$$\therefore \quad \frac{d^2y}{dx^2} = 2\sin 3x + 2x(3\cos 3x) + 6x\cos 3x + 3x^2(-3\sin 3x)$$
$$= 12x\cos 3x + (2 - 9x^2)\sin 3x$$

**13** $f(x) = \dfrac{x-4}{x+2}$

Since $f(3) = \frac{-1}{5}$, the point of contact is $\left(3, -\frac{1}{5}\right)$.

Now $f'(x) = \dfrac{1(x+2) - (x-4)1}{(x+2)^2}$ {quotient rule}

$= \dfrac{6}{(x+2)^2}$

$\therefore \ f'(3) = \frac{6}{25}$

$\therefore$ the tangent has equation $6x - 25y = 6(3) - 25(-\frac{1}{5})$
or $6x - 25y = 23$

**14** $y = x^2 - 2x - 4$

$\therefore \ \dfrac{dy}{dx} = 2x - 2$

When $x = -1$, $y = (-1)^2 - 2(-1) - 4 = -1$

and $\dfrac{dy}{dx} = 2(-1) - 2 = -4$

So, the normal has gradient $\frac{1}{4}$.

Thus, the equation of the normal is

$x - 4y = (-1) - 4(-1)$

or $x - 4y = 3$

**15** Let $f(x) = x^3 + 2x + 1$

$\therefore \ f(-1) = (-1)^3 + 2(-1) + 1 = -2$

Now $f'(x) = 3x^2 + 2$

$\therefore \ f'(-1) = 3(-1)^2 + 2 = 5$

$\therefore$ the tangent at $(-1, -2)$ has gradient 5, and its equation is

$5x - y = 5(-1) - (-2)$

which is $5x - y = -3$

or $y = 5x + 3$

Now $y = 5x + 3$ meets $y = x^3 + 2x + 1$ where

$x^3 + 2x + 1 = 5x + 3$

$\therefore \ x^3 - 3x - 2 = 0$

The tangent touches the curve at $x = -1$, so $(x+1)^2$ is a factor of this function.

$\therefore \ (x+1)^2(x-2) = 0$

$\therefore \ x = -1$ or $2$

When $x = 2$, $y = 2^3 + 2(2) + 1 = 13$

So, the tangent meets the curve again at (2, 13).

**16** **a** $s(t) = 12t - 3t^3 + 1$

$\therefore \ v(t) = s'(t) = 12 - 9t^2$

$\therefore \ a(t) = v'(t) = -18t$

**b** $v(t) = 12 - 9t^2$

$= 3(4 - 3t^2)$

$= 3(2 + t\sqrt{3})(2 - t\sqrt{3})$

which has sign diagram:

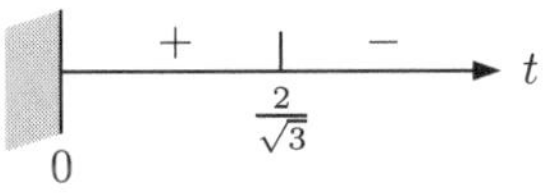


$a(t) = -18t$

which has sign diagram:

**i** Speed is decreasing when $v(t)$ and $a(t)$ have the opposite sign.

$\therefore$ the speed is decreasing for $0 \leqslant t \leqslant \frac{2}{\sqrt{3}}$.

**ii** Velocity is decreasing when $v'(t) \leqslant 0$.

Since $v'(t) = a(t) \leqslant 0$ for all $t \geqslant 0$, the velocity is decreasing for $t \geqslant 0$.

**17** **a** $\dfrac{d}{dx}(2+x)(3-x)^{\frac{1}{2}}$

$= 1(3-x)^{\frac{1}{2}} + (2+x)(\frac{1}{2})(3-x)^{-\frac{1}{2}}(-1)$ {product rule}

$= \sqrt{3-x} - \dfrac{(2+x)}{2\sqrt{3-x}}$

**b** $\dfrac{d}{dx}(x + x^{-1})^4 = 4(x + x^{-1})^3(1 - x^{-2})$

$= 4\left(x + \dfrac{1}{x}\right)^3\left(1 - \dfrac{1}{x^2}\right)$

**18** **a** $y = x(x^2 - 12x + 45) = x^3 - 12x^2 + 45x$

$\therefore \ \dfrac{dy}{dx} = 3x^2 - 24x + 45$

$= 3(x^2 - 8x + 15)$

$= 3(x-3)(x-5)$

Sign diagram for $\dfrac{dy}{dx}$:

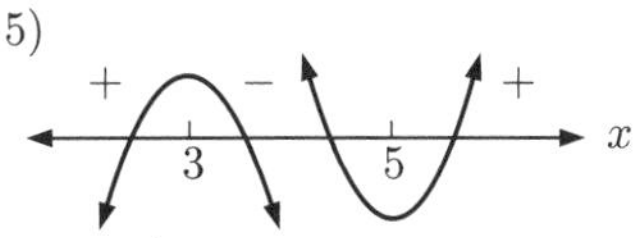


When $x = 3$, $y = (3)^3 - 12(3)^2 + 45(3)$

$= 27 - 108 + 135$

$= 54$

and when $x = 5$, $y = (5)^3 - 12(5)^2 + 45(5)$

$= 125 - 300 + 225$

$= 50$

$\therefore$ there is a local maximum at $(3, 54)$ and a local minimum at $(5, 50)$.

The graph cuts the $x$ and $y$-axes at 0.

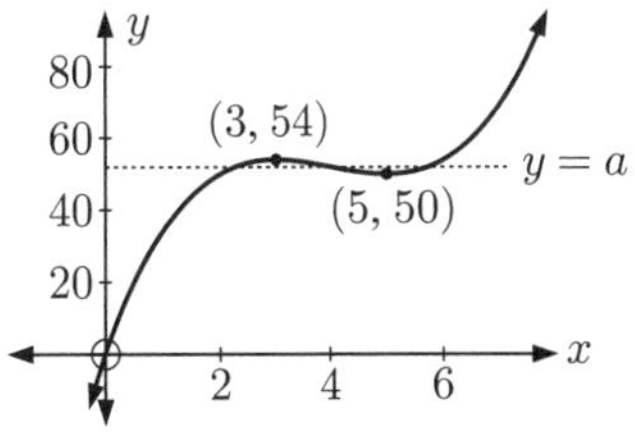


**b** The equation $x^3 - 12x^2 + 45x - a = 0$ has 3 real roots if $x(x^2 - 12x + 45) = a$ has 3 real roots.

This occurs provided $y = x(x^2 - 12x + 45)$ meets $y = a$ in 3 places, and this occurs when $50 < a < 54$.

**19** **a** $f(x) = x^3 - 3x^2 - 9x + 5$

$\therefore \ f'(x) = 3x^2 - 6x - 9$

$= 3(x+1)(x-3)$

which has sign diagram:

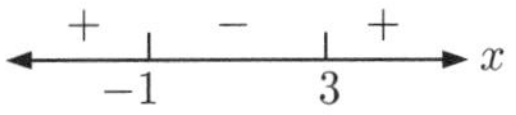

So, $f(x)$ is increasing for $x \leqslant -1$ and $x \geqslant 3$.

**b** $f'(x) = 3x^2 - 6x - 9$

$\therefore \ f''(x) = 6x - 6$

$= 6(x-1)$

which has sign diagram:

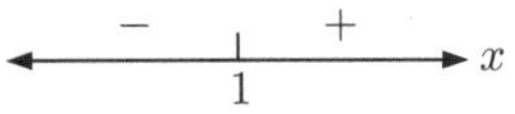


So, $f(x)$ is concave up for $x \geqslant 1$.

**20** **a** **i** $y = \dfrac{x}{e^x}$

$\therefore \ \dfrac{dy}{dx} = \dfrac{1(e^x) - xe^x}{e^{2x}} = \dfrac{e^x(1-x)}{e^{2x}} = \dfrac{1-x}{e^x}$

**ii** $y = x^2 e^{-(x+2)}$

$\therefore \quad \dfrac{dy}{dx} = 2xe^{-(x+2)} + x^2 e^{-(x+2)}(-1)$

$= xe^{-(x+2)}(2-x)$

**iii** $y = \dfrac{e^{2x}+1}{e^{2x}-1}$

$\therefore \quad \dfrac{dy}{dx} = \dfrac{(e^{2x})(2)(e^{2x}-1)-(e^{2x}+1)(e^{2x})(2)}{(e^{2x}-1)^2}$

**b** $\int (x^2 + e^{2x+1})\,dx = \dfrac{x^3}{3} + \frac{1}{2}e^{2x+1} + c$

**21 a** $p(x) = x^3 + ax^2 + b$

$\therefore \quad p'(x) = 3x^2 + 2ax$

$= x(3x+2a)$

$\therefore \quad p'(x) = 0$ when $x = 0$ or $x = \dfrac{-2a}{3}$

Thus $p(x)$ has a stationary point at $x = 0$ for all $a$ and $b$.

**b** If $(-2, 6)$ is a second stationary point, then $\dfrac{-2a}{3} = -2$

$\therefore \quad -2a = -6$

$\therefore \quad a = 3$

Also, $p(-2) = 6$, so $(-2)^3 + 3(-2)^2 + b = 6$

$\therefore \quad -8 + 12 + b = 6$

$\therefore \quad b = 2$

$\therefore \quad p'(x) = 3x(x+2)$

Sign diagram for $p'(x)$:

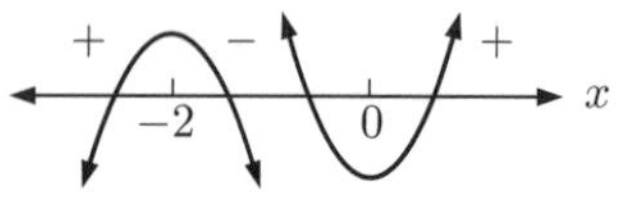


$\therefore$ there is a local maximum at $(-2, 6)$ and a local minimum at $(0, 2)$.

**c** If $(h, k)$ is the second stationary point, then $\dfrac{-2a}{3} = h$

$\therefore \quad a = \dfrac{-3h}{2}$

Also, $p(h) = k$, so $h^3 + ah^2 + b = k$

$\therefore \quad h^3 + \left(\dfrac{-3h}{2}\right)h^2 + b = k$

$\therefore \quad h^3 - \dfrac{3h^3}{2} + b = k$

$\therefore \quad -\dfrac{h^3}{2} + b = k$

$\therefore \quad b = k + \dfrac{h^3}{2}$

**22** $y = x^2 \quad \therefore \quad \dfrac{dy}{dx} = 2x$

$\therefore$ at P(2, 4), $\dfrac{dy}{dx} = 4$

$\therefore$ the gradient of the normal at P(2, 4) is $-\frac{1}{4}$.

$\therefore$ the equation of the normal is $x + 4y = (2) + 4(4)$

or $x + 4y = 18$

The normal meets $y = x^2$ when $x + 4x^2 = 18$

$\therefore \quad 4x^2 + x - 18 = 0$

$\therefore \quad (x-2)(4x+9) = 0$

$\therefore \quad x = 2$ or $-\frac{9}{4}$.

When $x = -\frac{9}{4}$, $y = \frac{81}{16}$

$\therefore$ the normal intersects the curve again at $(-\frac{9}{4}, \frac{81}{16})$.

**23** Area $A = xy + (0.6)x^2$

Perimeter $P = 48 = 3.6x + 2y$

$\therefore \quad y = \dfrac{48 - 3.6x}{2}$

$\therefore \quad A = x\left(\dfrac{48-3.6x}{2}\right) + 0.6x^2$

$= 24x - 1.8x^2 + 0.6x^2$

$= 24x - 1.2x^2$

$\therefore \quad \dfrac{dA}{dx} = 24 - 2.4x = 2.4(10 - x)$

$\therefore \quad \dfrac{dA}{dx} = 0$ when $x = 10$

Sign diagram for $\dfrac{dA}{dx}$:

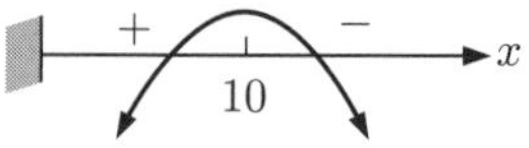


The maximum area occurs when $x = 10$.

$\therefore$ the maximum area $= 24(10) - 1.2(10)^2 = 120$ units$^2$.

**24** $f(x) = 8x^{-2}$

$\therefore \quad f'(x) = -16x^{-3} = \dfrac{-16}{x^3}$

$\therefore \quad f'(2) = \dfrac{-16}{8} = -2$

$\therefore$ the gradient of the normal at (2, 2) is $\frac{1}{2}$

$\therefore$ the equation of normal is $\dfrac{y-2}{x-2} = \frac{1}{2}$

which is $2y - 4 = x - 2$

or $x - 2y = -2$

**25 a** Total surface area

$= 2(\frac{1}{2}xx) + 2xy$ {area of $\Delta = \frac{1}{2}$ base $\times$ height}

$= x^2 + 2xy$

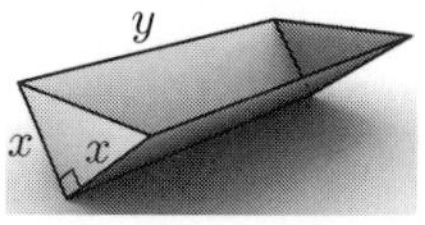


Thus $x^2 + 2xy = 27$.

**b** $V =$ area of end $\times$ length

$= \frac{1}{2}xx \times y = \frac{1}{2}x^2 y$

From **a**, $x^2 + 2xy = 27 \quad \therefore \quad y = \dfrac{27 - x^2}{2x}$

$\therefore \quad V = \frac{1}{2}x^2\left(\dfrac{27-x^2}{2x}\right)$

$= \frac{27}{4}x - \dfrac{x^3}{4}$

**c** $\dfrac{dV}{dx} = \frac{27}{4} - \dfrac{3x^2}{4}$

$= \frac{3}{4}(9 - x^2)$

$= \frac{3}{4}(3+x)(3-x)$

Sign diagram for $\dfrac{dV}{dx}$:

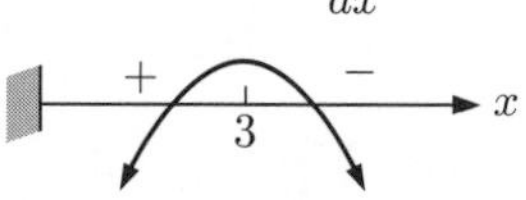


$\therefore \quad V$ is maximised when $x = 3$ and $y = \dfrac{27 - 3^2}{2(3)} = 3$

So, $x = y = 3$ metres

**26** $y = (1+x)^{\frac{1}{2}}$

$\therefore \quad \dfrac{dy}{dx} = \frac{1}{2}(1+x)^{-\frac{1}{2}}(1)$

$= \dfrac{1}{2\sqrt{1+x}}$

**27**

| *point* | $f'(x)$ | $f''(x)$ |
|---|---|---|
| A | 0 | $>0$ |
| B | 0 | 0 |
| C | $>0$ | 0 |
| D | $>0$ | $<0$ |

**28 a** $f(x) = x + 5 + \dfrac{4}{x}$

$\therefore \quad f(x) = 0$ when $x + 5 + \dfrac{4}{x} = 0$

$\therefore \quad x^2 + 5x + 4 = 0$

$\therefore \quad (x+1)(x+4) = 0$

$\therefore \quad x = -1$ or $-4$

**b** $f(x) = x + 5 + 4x^{-1}$

$\therefore\ f'(x) = 1 - 4x^{-2}$

$= 1 - \dfrac{4}{x^2}$

$= \dfrac{x^2 - 4}{x^2}$

$= \dfrac{(x+2)(x-2)}{x^2}$

$\therefore\ f'(x) = 0$ when $x = \pm 2$

Sign diagram for $f'(x)$:

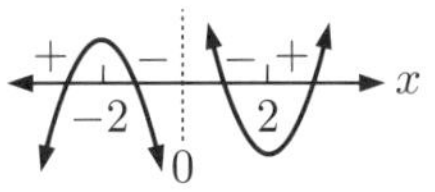


Now $f(-2) = -2+5+\frac{4}{-2} = 1$ and $f(2) = 2+5+\frac{4}{2} = 9$

So, there is a local maximum at $(-2, 1)$ and a local minimum at $(2, 9)$.

**c**

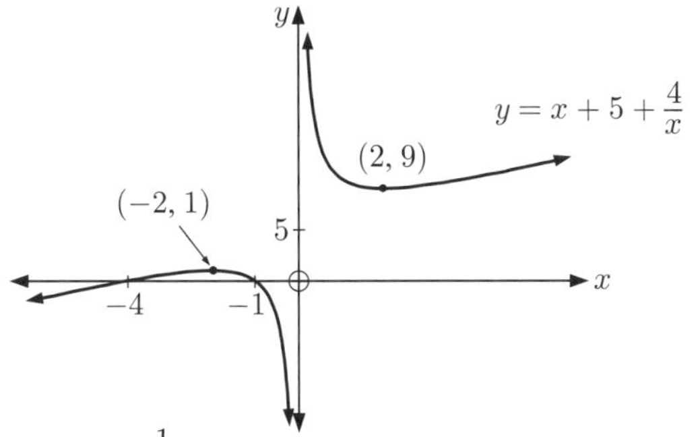


**29** **a** **i** $f'(x) = \dfrac{1}{x}$

**ii** $F'(x) = (1)\ln x + x\left(\dfrac{1}{x}\right) - 1$ provided $x > 0$

$= \ln x$ provided $x > 0$

From **ii**, $\int \ln x\, dx = x\ln x - x + c$

$\therefore\ \int f(x)\, dx = F(x) + c$

$F(x)$ is the antiderivative of $f(x)$.

**b** **i** The shaded area, $A$

$= \text{area } \Delta\text{OPQ} - \int_1^t \ln x\, dx,$

$1 < t \leqslant e$

$= \frac{1}{2}t\ln t - \int_1^t \ln x\, dx$

$= \frac{1}{2}t\ln t - [x\ln x - x]_1^t$

$= \frac{1}{2}t\ln t - t\ln t + t - 1$

$= t - \frac{1}{2}t\ln t - 1$ units$^2$

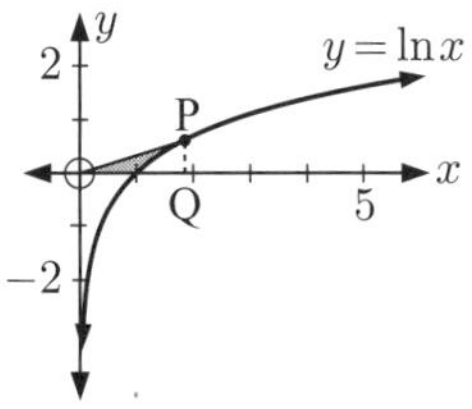


$\dfrac{dA}{dt} = 1 - \left(\frac{1}{2}\ln t + \frac{1}{2}t\left(\dfrac{1}{t}\right)\right) = \frac{1}{2}(1 - \ln t)$

$\therefore\ \dfrac{dA}{dt} = 0$ when $t = e$

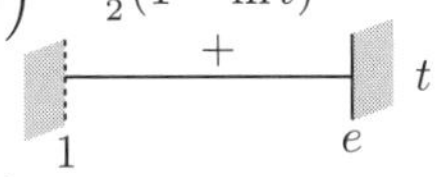


$\therefore$ the area is a maximum when $t = e$.

**ii** $y = \ln x$ $\quad\therefore\ \dfrac{dy}{dx} = \dfrac{1}{x}$

$\therefore$ at $(t, \ln t)$, $\dfrac{dy}{dx} = \dfrac{1}{t}$

$\therefore$ the tangent has equation $\dfrac{y - \ln t}{x - t} = \dfrac{1}{t}$

which is $ty - t\ln t = x - t$

or $x - ty = t - t\ln t$.

The tangent passes through $(0, 0)$ if

$t - t\ln t = 0$

$\therefore\ t(1 - \ln t) = 0$

$\therefore\ \ln t = 1$ $\{$as $t > 1\}$

$\therefore\ t = e$

*Conclusion:* The shaded region is maximised in area when [OP] is a tangent to C.

**30** $\text{RQ} = \sqrt{x^2 + 64}$ km

{Pythagoras}

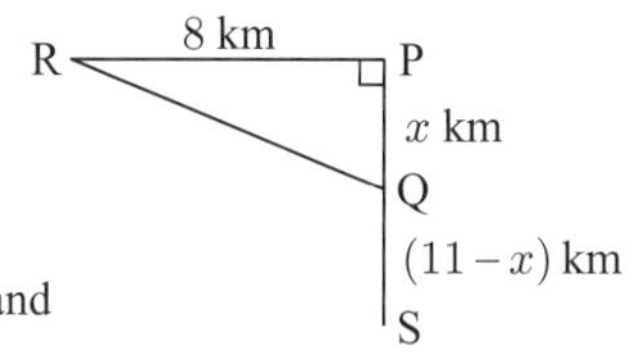


$\therefore$ the total cost $C(x)$

= cost under sea + cost on land

$= 5\sqrt{x^2 + 64} + 3(11 - x)$

$= 5\sqrt{x^2 + 64} + 33 - 3x$

millions of dollars.

So, $C(x) = 5(x^2 + 64)^{\frac{1}{2}} + 33 - 3x$

$\therefore\ C'(x) = \frac{5}{2}(x^2 + 64)^{-\frac{1}{2}}(2x) - 3$

$= \dfrac{5x}{\sqrt{x^2 + 64}} - 3$

$\therefore\ C'(x) = 0$ when $\dfrac{5x}{\sqrt{x^2 + 64}} = 3$

$\therefore\ 5x = 3\sqrt{x^2 + 64}$

$\therefore\ 25x^2 = 9(x^2 + 64)$

$\therefore\ 25x^2 = 9x^2 + 9 \times 64$

$\therefore\ 16x^2 = 9 \times 64$

$\therefore\ x^2 = 9 \times 4 = 36$

$\therefore\ x = 6$ $\{$as $x > 0\}$

Sign diagram for $C'(x)$:

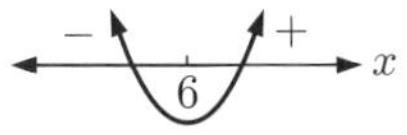


$\therefore$ $C(x)$ is minimised when $x = 6$

$\therefore$ $C_{\min} = C(6)$

$= 5\sqrt{36 + 64} + 33 - 3 \times 6$

$= 5\sqrt{100} + 33 - 18$

$= 50 + 15$

$= 65$ million dollars.

**31**

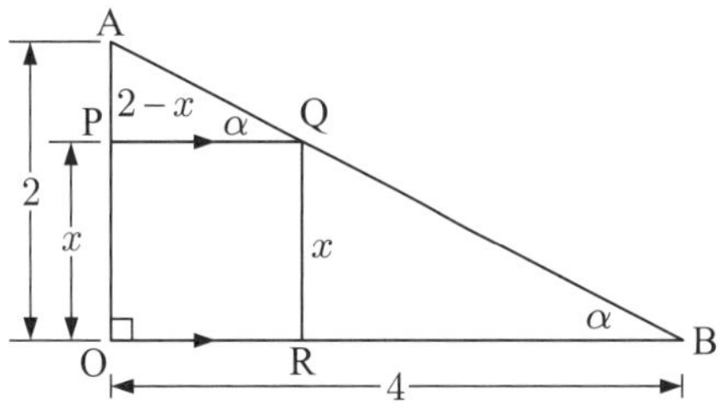


$\Delta$s APQ and AOB are similar, so $\dfrac{\text{AP}}{\text{PQ}} = \dfrac{\text{AO}}{\text{OB}}$

$\therefore\ \dfrac{2 - x}{\text{PQ}} = \frac{2}{4} = \frac{1}{2}$

$\therefore\ \text{PQ} = 2(2 - x)$

$\therefore\ \text{PQ} = 4 - 2x$

So, the area of rectangle OPQR = length × breadth

$= x(4 - 2x)$

$= 4x - 2x^2$ cm$^2$

This is a quadratic with "$a$" $= -2 < 0$

$\therefore$ its shape is

$\therefore$ the area is a maximum when $x = -\dfrac{b}{2a} = \dfrac{-4}{2(-2)} = 1.$

**32** C follows the curve $y = x^2$, so C is $(x, x^2)$

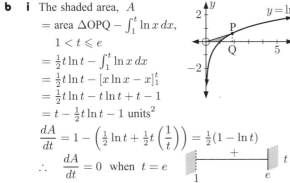

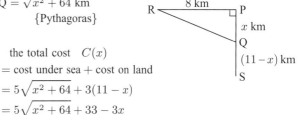

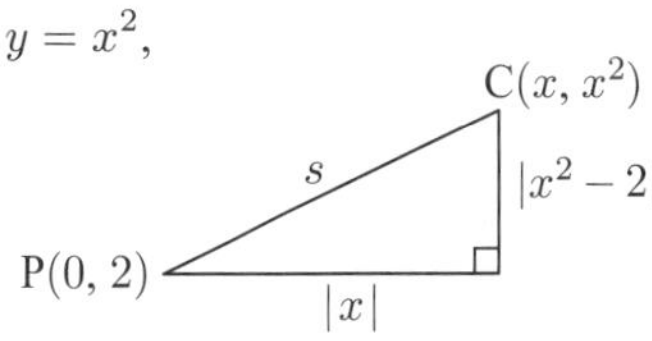

**a** $s^2 = x^2 + (x^2 - 2)^2$ {Pythagoras}

$\therefore\ s^2 = x^2 + x^4 - 4x^2 + 4$

$\therefore\ s^2 = x^4 - 3x^2 + 4$

$\therefore\ s = \sqrt{x^4 - 3x^2 + 4}$ {as $s > 0$}

**b** Since $s > 0$, $s$ is minimised when $s^2$ is minimised.

Now $s^2 = x^4 - 3x^2 + 4$

$$\therefore\ \frac{d[s^2]}{dx} = 4x^3 - 6x$$
$$= 2x(2x^2 - 3)$$
$$= 2x(\sqrt{2}x + \sqrt{3})(\sqrt{2}x - \sqrt{3})$$

Sign diagram for $\frac{d[s^2]}{dx}$:

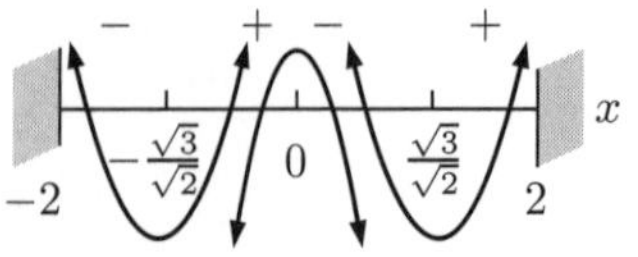


Now by symmetry,

$$s\left(-\tfrac{\sqrt{3}}{\sqrt{2}}\right) = s\left(\tfrac{\sqrt{3}}{\sqrt{2}}\right) = \sqrt{\tfrac{9}{4} - 3(\tfrac{3}{2}) + 4}$$
$$= \sqrt{\tfrac{9}{4} - \tfrac{9}{2} + 4}$$
$$= \tfrac{\sqrt{7}}{2} \text{ units}$$

$\therefore$ the minimum distance is $\frac{\sqrt{7}}{2}$ units when $x = \pm\frac{\sqrt{3}}{\sqrt{2}}$.

The maximum distance occurs either when $x = 0$ or at one of the endpoints of the domain.

$s(-2) = s(2) = \sqrt{16 - 12 + 4} = \sqrt{8}$

and $s(0) = \sqrt{4} = 2$

$\therefore$ the maximum distance is $\sqrt{8}$ units when $x = \pm 2$.

**33** $y = 3x^4 + 16x^3 + 24x^2 + 1$

$$\therefore\ \frac{dy}{dx} = 12x^3 + 48x^2 + 48x$$
$$= 12x(x^2 + 4x + 4)$$
$$= 12x(x + 2)^2$$

which has sign diagram:

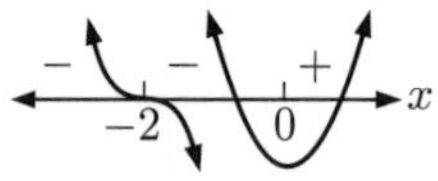


Now $f(-2) = 3(16) + 16(-8) + 24(4) + 1 = 17$

and $f(0) = 1$.

$\therefore$ there is a stationary inflection at $(-2, 17)$ and local minimum at $(0, 1)$.

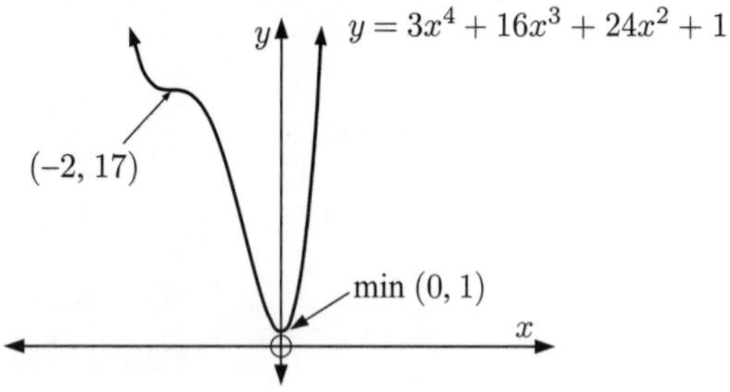


**34** **a** The manufacturer makes $x$ chairs per week, where $0 < x \leqslant 150$.

Cost, $C = 26x + x^{\frac{3}{2}} + 500$ dollars.

Sales, $S = x\left(44 + \dfrac{600}{x}\right) = 44x + 600$ dollars.

Profit $P(x) = S - C$

$$= 44x + 600 - 26x - x^{\frac{3}{2}} - 500$$
$$= -x^{\frac{3}{2}} + 18x + 100 \text{ dollars}$$

**b** $P'(x) = -\frac{3}{2}x^{\frac{1}{2}} + 18 = -\frac{3}{2}\sqrt{x} + 18$

$\therefore\ P'(x) = 0$ when $\frac{3}{2}\sqrt{x} = 18$

$\therefore\ \sqrt{x} = 12$

$\therefore\ x = 144$

$P'(x)$ has sign diagram:

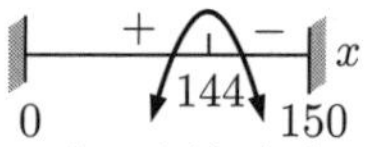


$\therefore$ the maximum profit occurs when 144 chairs are made.

**c** $P(144) = -144^{\frac{3}{2}} + 18(144) + 100$

$$= -12^3 + 18(144) + 100$$
$$= 144(18 - 12) + 100$$
$$= 964$$

$\therefore$ the maximum profit is \$964.

**35** **a** Let sides be $x$ m and $y$ m long.

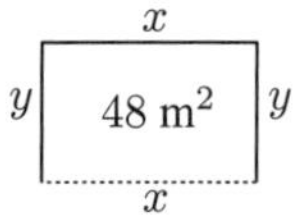


Now $xy = 48$, so $y = \dfrac{48}{x}$

$\therefore$ the total cost $C = 18(2y + x) + 30x$

$$= 36y + 48x$$
$$= 36\left(\frac{48}{x}\right) + 48x$$
$$= 48\left(\frac{36}{x} + x\right)$$

**b** Since $C = 48(36x^{-1} + x)$, $\dfrac{dC}{dx} = 48(-36x^{-2} + 1)$

$$= 48\left(1 - \frac{36}{x^2}\right)$$
$$= 48\left(\frac{x^2 - 36}{x^2}\right)$$
$$= \frac{48(x + 6)(x - 6)}{x^2}$$

$\therefore\ \dfrac{dC}{dx}$ has sign diagram:

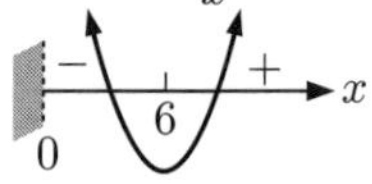


$\therefore$ $C$ is a minimum when $x = 6$ and $y = 8$.

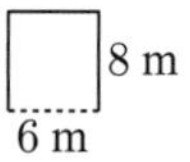


**36** **a** **i** $y = 4x^3 - 3x^4$ cuts the $x$-axis when $y = 0$

$\therefore\ 4x^3 - 3x^4 = 0$

$\therefore\ x^3(4 - 3x) = 0$

$\therefore\ x = 0$ or $\frac{4}{3}$

$\therefore$ the $x$-intercepts are 0 and $\frac{4}{3}$, the $y$-intercept is 0.

**ii** $\dfrac{dy}{dx} = 12x^2 - 12x^3 = 12x^2(1 - x)$

which has sign diagram:

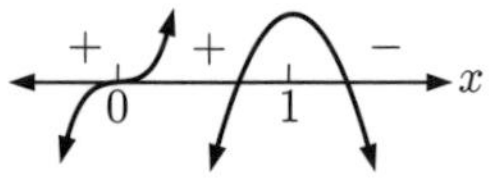


When $x = 0$, $y = 0$ and when $x = 1$, $y = 4 - 3 = 1$

$\therefore$ there is a stationary inflection at $(0, 0)$ and a local maximum at $(1, 1)$.

**iii** $\dfrac{d^2y}{dx^2} = 24x - 36x^2 = 12x(2 - 3x)$

which has sign diagram:

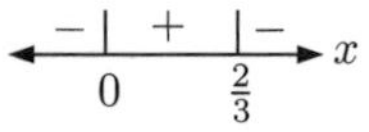


When $x = \frac{2}{3}$, $y = 4\left(\frac{2}{3}\right)^3 - 3\left(\frac{2}{3}\right)^4$

$$= \tfrac{32}{27} - \tfrac{16}{27}$$
$$= \tfrac{16}{27}$$

$\therefore$ there is a non-stationary inflection at $(\frac{2}{3}, \frac{16}{27})$.

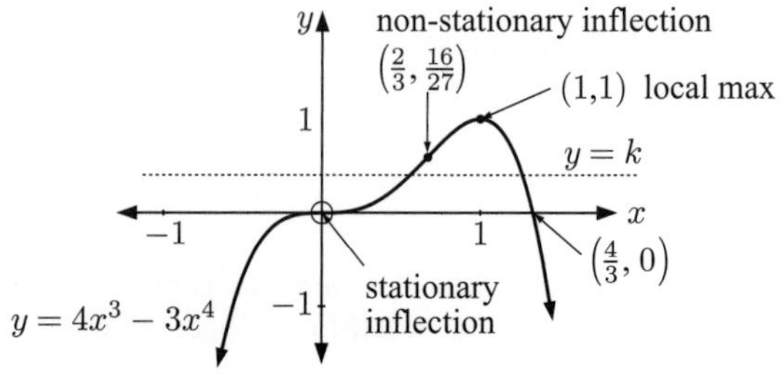

**b** If $4x^3 - 3x^4 = k$ has exactly 2 distinct positive solutions then the horizontal line $y = k$ meets the graph of $y = 4x^3 - 3x^4$ in 2 different points with $x$-coordinate $> 0$. Thus $0 < k < 1$.

**37** **a** $y = x\ln(x+1),\ x > -1$

$$\therefore \frac{dy}{dx} = (1)\ln(x+1) + x\left(\frac{1}{x+1}\right),\quad x > -1$$
$$= \ln(x+1) + \frac{x}{x+1}$$

**b** $y = x\ln x^2 = 2x\ln x$ as $x > 0$

$$\therefore \frac{dy}{dx} = (2)\ln x + 2x\left(\frac{1}{x}\right) = 2\ln x + 2,\quad x > 0$$

**c** $y = \dfrac{e^{2x}}{2x+1}$ $\quad\therefore\quad$ $\dfrac{dy}{dx} = \dfrac{e^{2x}(2)(2x+1) - e^{2x}(2)}{(2x+1)^2}$

$$= \frac{e^{2x}[4x+2-2]}{(2x+1)^2}$$
$$= \frac{4xe^{2x}}{(2x+1)^2},\quad x \neq -\frac{1}{2}$$

**38** $f(x) = \ln\left(\dfrac{1-2x}{x^2+2}\right)$

$$= \ln(1-2x) - \ln(x^2+2) \qquad \left\{\ln\left(\frac{a}{b}\right) = \ln a - \ln b\right\}$$

$$\therefore\quad f'(x) = \frac{-2}{1-2x} - \frac{2x}{x^2+2}$$
$$= \frac{-2x^2 - 4 - 2x(1-2x)}{(1-2x)(x^2+2)}$$
$$= \frac{2x^2 - 2x - 4}{(1-2x)(x^2+2)}$$
$$= \frac{2(x-2)(x+1)}{(1-2x)(x^2+2)}$$

Now $x^2 + 2 > 0$ always, so $f(x)$ is defined when $1 - 2x > 0$ or in other words $x < \frac{1}{2}$.

So, $f'(x)$ has sign diagram:

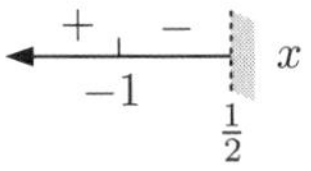


$f(x)$ is decreasing on the interval where $f'(x) \leqslant 0$.

$\therefore\quad f(x)$ is decreasing for $-1 \leqslant x < \frac{1}{2}$.

**39** **a** $y = xe^{4x}$ $\quad\therefore\quad$ $\dfrac{dy}{dx} = (1)e^{4x} + xe^{4x}(4)$

$$= e^{4x}(1+4x)$$

**b** $y = \dfrac{x^3+2}{(x-3)^{\frac{1}{2}}},\quad x > 3$

$$\therefore\quad \frac{dy}{dx} = \frac{3x^2(x-3)^{\frac{1}{2}} - (x^3+2)(\frac{1}{2})(x-3)^{-\frac{1}{2}}(1)}{x-3}$$

**c** $y = \dfrac{e^{5x}}{x^2+1}$ $\quad\therefore\quad$ $\dfrac{dy}{dx} = \dfrac{e^{5x}(5)(x^2+1) - e^{5x}(2x)}{(x^2+1)^2}$

$$= \frac{e^{5x}(5x^2+5-2x)}{(x^2+1)^2}$$
$$= \frac{e^{5x}(5x^2-2x+5)}{(x^2+1)^2}$$

**d** $y = \ln\left(\dfrac{x-4}{x^2+4}\right) = \ln(x-4) - \ln(x^2+4),\quad x > 4$

$$\therefore\quad \frac{dy}{dx} = \frac{1}{x-4} - \frac{2x}{x^2+4},\quad x > 4$$

**40** **a** $f(x) = 1 - \dfrac{4x}{x^2+4}$

$f(0) = 1$, so the $y$-intercept $= 1$

$f(x) = 0$ when $\quad 1 - \dfrac{4x}{x^2+4} = 0$

$$\therefore\quad \frac{4x}{x^2+4} = 1$$
$$\therefore\quad 4x = x^2 + 4$$
$$\therefore\quad x^2 - 4x + 4 = 0$$
$$\therefore\quad (x-2)^2 = 0$$
$$\therefore\quad x = 2$$

So, the $x$-intercept is 2.

**b** $f'(x) = 0 - \left(\dfrac{4(x^2+4) - 4x(2x)}{(x^2+4)^2}\right)$

$$= \frac{8x^2 - 4x^2 - 16}{(x^2+4)^2}$$
$$= \frac{4x^2 - 16}{(x^2+4)^2}$$
$$= \frac{4(x+2)(x-2)}{(x^2+4)^2}$$

$f'(x)$ has sign diagram:

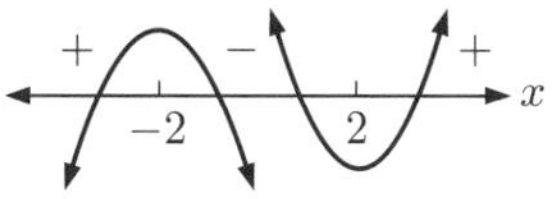


$f(-2) = 1 - (\frac{-8}{8}) = 2$

$f(2) = 1 - (\frac{8}{8}) = 0$

$\therefore$ there is a local maximum at $(-2, 2)$ and a local minimum at $(2, 0)$.

**c**

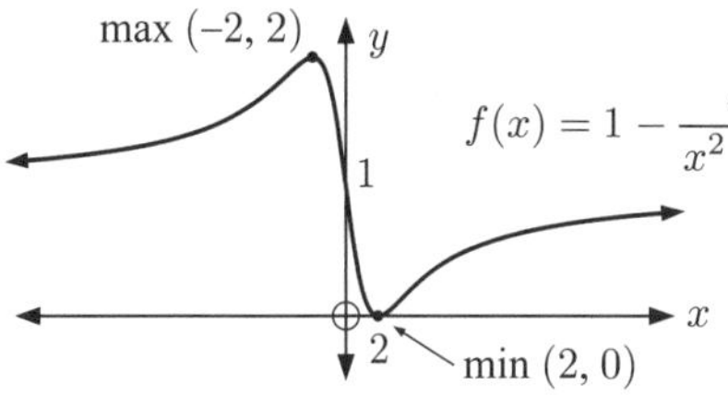


**41**

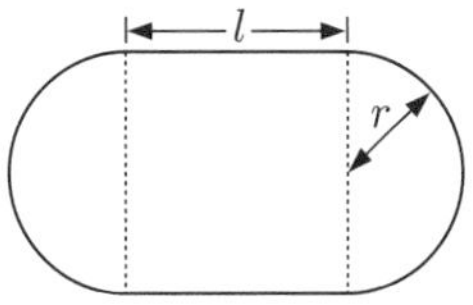


Let $l$ be the length of the straight section.

Let $r$ be the radius of the semi-circular sections.

The area $A = \pi r^2 + 2rl$ which is a constant

$$\therefore\quad l = \frac{A - \pi r^2}{2r} \quad \text{....(1)}$$

Let $p$ be the cost per unit length of straight wall.

$\therefore$ the total cost is

$$C = (2l + 2\pi r(\tfrac{5}{4}))p$$
$$= \left(\frac{A}{r} - \pi r + \frac{5\pi r}{2}\right)p \quad \{\text{using (1)}\}$$
$$= \left(\frac{A}{r} + \frac{3\pi}{2}r\right)p$$
$$= \left(Ar^{-1} + \frac{3\pi}{2}r\right)p$$

$$\therefore\quad \frac{dC}{dr} = \left(-\frac{A}{r^2} + \frac{3\pi}{2}\right)p$$

$$\therefore\quad \frac{dC}{dr} = 0 \text{ when } r^2 = \frac{2A}{3\pi}$$

$\dfrac{dC}{dr}$ has sign diagram:

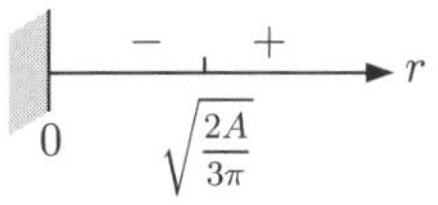


So, the minimum cost is when $r = \sqrt{\dfrac{2A}{3\pi}}$

$\therefore$ the area of the shaded portion $= \pi r^2 = \pi\left(\dfrac{2A}{3\pi}\right) = \frac{2}{3}A$

**42** **a** $\int_2^5 f(x)\,dx = 6$ **b** $\int_5^8 f(x)\,dx = -4$

**c** $\int_2^8 f(x)\,dx = \int_2^5 f(x)\,dx + \int_5^8 f(x)\,dx$
$= 6 + (-4)$
$= 2$

**43** Since $\int_0^a f(x)\,dx = 4$, the shaded area $= 4$
$\therefore\ \frac{1}{4}\pi a^2 = 4$
$\therefore\ a^2 = \frac{16}{\pi}$
$\therefore\ a = \frac{4}{\sqrt{\pi}}$ $\{a > 0\}$

**44** **a** $\int (2x^2 + x - 3)\,dx = \dfrac{2x^3}{3} + \dfrac{x^2}{2} - 3x + c$

**b** $\int_0^1 (5x+4)^{\frac{1}{2}}\,dx = \left[\frac{1}{5} \times \dfrac{(5x+4)^{\frac{3}{2}}}{\frac{3}{2}}\right]_0^1$
$= \frac{2}{15}\left[(5x+4)^{\frac{3}{2}}\right]_0^1$
$= \frac{2}{15}\left(9^{\frac{3}{2}} - 4^{\frac{3}{2}}\right)$
$= \frac{2}{15}(27 - 8)$
$= \frac{38}{15}$

**c** $\int \left(x + \dfrac{1}{x}\right)^2 dx$
$= \int \left[x^2 + 2x\left(\dfrac{1}{x}\right) + \left(\dfrac{1}{x}\right)^2\right] dx$
$= \int (x^2 + 2 + x^{-2})\,dx$ provided $x \neq 0$
$= \dfrac{x^3}{3} + 2x + \dfrac{x^{-1}}{-1} + c$
$= \frac{1}{3}x^3 + 2x - \dfrac{1}{x} + c$

**45** **a** Now $v = \dfrac{10}{\sqrt{5t+4}} = 10(5t+4)^{-\frac{1}{2}}$

$\therefore\ s = \int v\,dt = 10\left(\frac{1}{5} \times \dfrac{(5t+4)^{\frac{1}{2}}}{\frac{1}{2}}\right) + c$
$= 4(5t+4)^{\frac{1}{2}} + c$

When $t = 0$, $s = 0$, so $0 = 4\sqrt{4} + c$
$\therefore\ c = -8$
$\therefore\ s = 4\sqrt{5t+4} - 8$ m

**b** $a = \dfrac{dv}{dt} = 10(-\frac{1}{2})(5t+4)^{-\frac{3}{2}}(5)$
$= \dfrac{-25}{(5t+4)^{\frac{3}{2}}}\ \text{m s}^{-2}$

**46** $f(x) = x(3-2x)^{\frac{1}{2}}$

$f'(x) = (1)(3-2x)^{\frac{1}{2}} + x(\frac{1}{2})(3-2x)^{-\frac{1}{2}}(-2)$
$= \dfrac{\sqrt{3-2x}}{1} - \dfrac{x}{\sqrt{3-2x}}$
$= \dfrac{3-2x-x}{\sqrt{3-2x}}$
$= \dfrac{3(1-x)}{(3-2x)^{\frac{1}{2}}}$

Thus $3\int \dfrac{1-x}{(3-2x)^{\frac{1}{2}}}\,dx = x(3-2x)^{\frac{1}{2}} + c_1$

$\therefore\ \int \dfrac{x-1}{(3-2x)^{\frac{1}{2}}}\,dx = -\frac{1}{3}x(3-2x)^{\frac{1}{2}} + c$

**47** **a** $\int \dfrac{2x^2 - x - 3}{x^2}\,dx$
$= \int \left(2 - \dfrac{1}{x} - 3x^{-2}\right) dx$
$= 2x - \ln x - \dfrac{3x^{-1}}{-1} + c$ provided $x > 0$
$= 2x - \ln x + \dfrac{3}{x} + c$

**b** $\int_1^5 \dfrac{2x^3+1}{x^2}\,dx$
$= \int_1^5 (2x + x^{-2})\,dx$
$= \left[x^2 - \dfrac{1}{x}\right]_1^5$
$= \left(5^2 - \frac{1}{5}\right) - \left(1^2 - 1\right)$
$= 24\frac{4}{5}$

**c** $\int \sin^2 3x\,dx$
$= \int \left(\frac{1}{2} - \frac{1}{2}\cos 6x\right) dx$
$= \frac{1}{2}x - \frac{1}{2}(\frac{1}{6})\sin 6x + c$
$= \frac{1}{2}x - \frac{1}{12}\sin 6x + c$

**48** $y = 1 - x^2$ meets $y = -3$
where $1 - x^2 = -3$
$\therefore\ 4 = x^2$
$\therefore\ x = \pm 2$

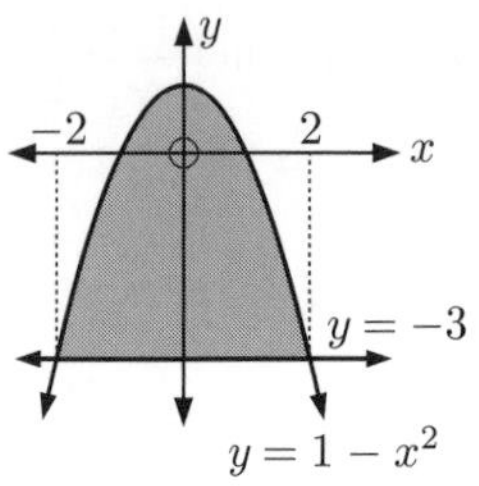


Using the symmetry about the $y$-axis,
Area $= 2\int_0^2 \left((1-x^2) - (-3)\right) dx$
$= 2\int_0^2 \left(4 - x^2\right) dx$
$= 2\left[4x - \frac{1}{3}x^3\right]_0^2$
$= 2\left(8 - \frac{8}{3} - 0 + 0\right)$
$= 2 \times \frac{16}{3}$
$= 10\frac{2}{3}$ units$^2$

**49** $y = x\sqrt{4-x} = x(4-x)^{\frac{1}{2}}$
$\dfrac{dy}{dx} = 1(4-x)^{\frac{1}{2}} + x(\frac{1}{2})(4-x)^{-\frac{1}{2}}(-1)$ {product rule}
$= \sqrt{4-x} - \dfrac{x}{2\sqrt{4-x}}$
$= \dfrac{2(4-x) - x}{2\sqrt{4-x}} = \dfrac{8-3x}{2\sqrt{4-x}}$

Hence $\int_0^2 \dfrac{8-3x}{\sqrt{4-x}}dx = 2\int_0^2 \dfrac{8-3x}{2\sqrt{4-x}}\,dx$
$= 2\left[x\sqrt{4-x}\right]_0^2$
$= 2(2\sqrt{2} - 0\sqrt{4})$
$= 4\sqrt{2}$

**50** **a** $\int_{-2}^2 f(x)\,dx = \int_{-2}^2 (x^3 - x^2 - 4x + 4)\,dx$
$= \left[\dfrac{x^4}{4} - \dfrac{x^3}{3} - \dfrac{4x^2}{2} + 4x\right]_{-2}^2$
$= \left(4 - \frac{8}{3} - 8 + 8\right) - \left(4 + \frac{8}{3} - 8 - 8\right)$
$= \frac{32}{3}$

**b** No, the shaded portion has area
$= \int_{-2}^1 f(x)\,dx - \int_1^2 f(x)\,dx$
whereas $\int_{-2}^2 f(x)\,dx = \int_{-2}^1 f(x)\,dx + \int_1^2 f(x)\,dx$

**51** $\displaystyle\int_0^4 \frac{1}{\sqrt{x+4}}\,dx = \int_0^4 (x+4)^{-\frac{1}{2}}\,dx = \left[\frac{(x+4)^{\frac{1}{2}}}{\frac{1}{2}}\right]_0^4$

$$= \left[2\sqrt{x+4}\right]_0^4$$
$$= 2\sqrt{8} - 2\sqrt{4}$$
$$= 4\sqrt{2} - 4$$

**52**
$$\frac{d}{dx}\left(x^2 \ln x\right) = 2x\ln x + x^2\left(\frac{1}{x}\right)$$
$$= 2x\ln x + x$$
$$\therefore\ \int (2x\ln x + x)\,dx = x^2 \ln x + c_1$$
$$\therefore\ \int 2x\ln x\,dx + \int x\,dx = x^2\ln x + c_1$$
$$\therefore\ 2\int x\ln x\,dx + \tfrac{1}{2}x^2 + c_2 = x^2\ln x + c_1$$
$$\therefore\ 2\int x\ln x\,dx = x^2\ln x - \tfrac{1}{2}x^2 + c_3$$
$$\therefore\ \int x\ln x\,dx = \tfrac{1}{2}x^2\ln x - \tfrac{1}{4}x^2 + c$$

**53** **a** $a = \dfrac{dv}{dt} = 2 - 3t$

$\therefore\ v = \int (2-3t)\,dt = 2t - \dfrac{3t^2}{2} + c$

Now when $t = 1$, $v = 0$ $\quad\therefore\ 0 = 2 - \frac{3}{2} + c$

$\therefore\ 0 = \frac{1}{2} + c$

$\therefore\ c = -\frac{1}{2}$

$\therefore\ v = 2t - \dfrac{3t^2}{2} - \frac{1}{2}$

$\therefore\ s = \int v\,dt = \displaystyle\int \left(2t - \frac{3t^2}{2} - \frac{1}{2}\right) dt$

$= \dfrac{2t^2}{2} - \dfrac{3t^3}{2(3)} - \frac{1}{2}t + d$

$= t^2 - \frac{1}{2}t^3 - \frac{1}{2}t + d$

But when $t = 0$, $s = 3$ $\quad\therefore\ d = 3$

$\therefore\ s = t^2 - \frac{1}{2}t^3 - \frac{1}{2}t + 3$

**b** Now $v = 0$ when $\quad 2t - \dfrac{3t^2}{2} - \frac{1}{2} = 0$

$\therefore\ 4t - 3t^2 - 1 = 0$

$\therefore\ 3t^2 - 4t + 1 = 0$

$\therefore\ (3t-1)(t-1) = 0$

$\therefore\ t = \frac{1}{3}$ or $t = 1$

$\therefore\ t = \frac{1}{3}$ s is the other time.

**54** $y = 4 - x^2$ meets $y = -2x - 4$ where

$-2x - 4 = 4 - x^2$

$\therefore\ x^2 - 2x - 8 = 0$

$\therefore\ (x+2)(x-4) = 0$

$\therefore\ x = -2$ or $4$

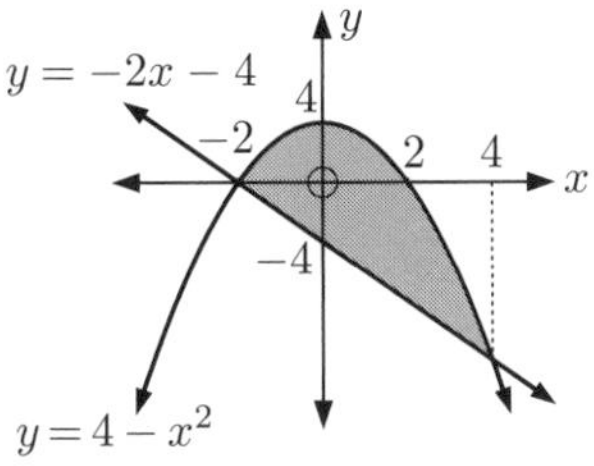


Area $= \int_{-2}^{4} [(4 - x^2) - (-2x - 4)]\,dx$

$= \int_{-2}^{4} (-x^2 + 2x + 8)\,dx$

$= \left[\dfrac{-x^3}{3} + x^2 + 8x\right]_{-2}^{4}$

$= (-\frac{64}{3} + 16 + 32) - (\frac{8}{3} + 4 - 16)$

$= 36$ units$^2$

**55** $v = 2t - 3t^2 = t(2 - 3t)$

Sign diagram of $v$: $\quad -\ \ |_{0}\ \ +\ \ |_{\frac{2}{3}}\ \ -\ \ \rightarrow t$

$\therefore$ a change in direction occurs at $t = \frac{2}{3}$ s (and at $t = 0$ s).

Now $\quad s = \int v\,dt = \int (2t - 3t^2)\,dt$

$= \dfrac{2t^2}{2} - \dfrac{3t^3}{3} + c$

$= t^2 - t^3 + c$

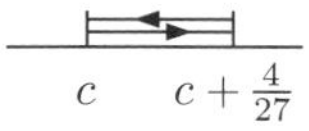


$\therefore\ s(0) = c,\ s(\frac{2}{3}) = \frac{4}{27} + c,\ s(1) = c$

The total distance travelled $= \frac{4}{27} + \frac{4}{27} = \frac{8}{27}$ m.

**56** **a** $y = x - 2$ meets $y = x^3 - 2x$

where $x^3 - 2x = x - 2$

$\therefore\ x^3 - 3x + 2 = 0$

If the point of tangency is to occur when $x = 1$ then $(x-1)^2$ must be a factor of the LHS.

Factorising, we find that $(x-1)^2(x+2) = 0$

$\therefore\ x = 1$ or $x = -2$

So, $y = x - 2$ is a tangent to $y = x^3 - 2x$

When $x = 1$, $y = -1$,

and when $x = -2$, $y = -2 - 2 = -4$

$\therefore$ T is $(1, -1)$ and P is $(-2, -4)$.

**b** Consider $y = x^3 - 2x$.

When $x = 0$, $y = 0$, so the $y$-intercept is 0.

When $y = 0$, $x^3 - 2x = 0$

$\therefore\ x(x^2 - 2) = 0$

$\therefore\ x(x + \sqrt{2})(x - \sqrt{2}) = 0$

$\therefore$ the $x$-intercepts are $\pm\sqrt{2}$ and 0.

**c**

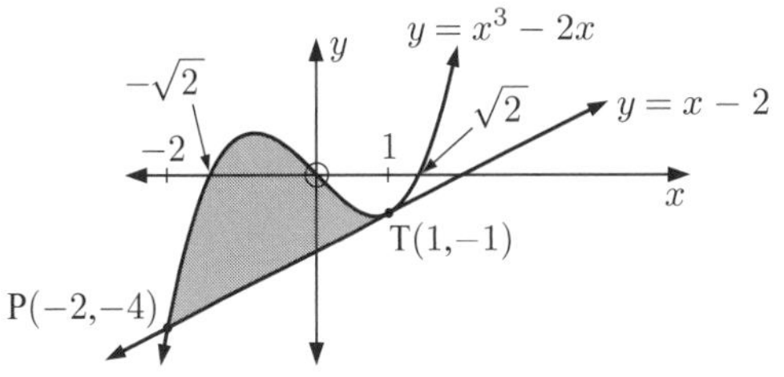


**d** Area $= \int_{-2}^{1} (x^3 - 2x) - (x - 2)\,dx$

$= \int_{-2}^{1} x^3 - 3x + 2\,dx$

$= \left[\dfrac{x^4}{4} - \dfrac{3x^2}{2} + 2x\right]_{-2}^{1}$

$= (\frac{1}{4} - \frac{3}{2} + 2) - (4 - 6 - 4)$

$= 6\frac{3}{4}$ units$^2$

**57**

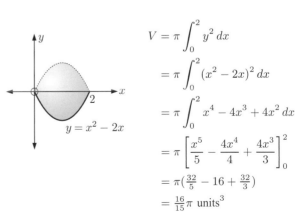

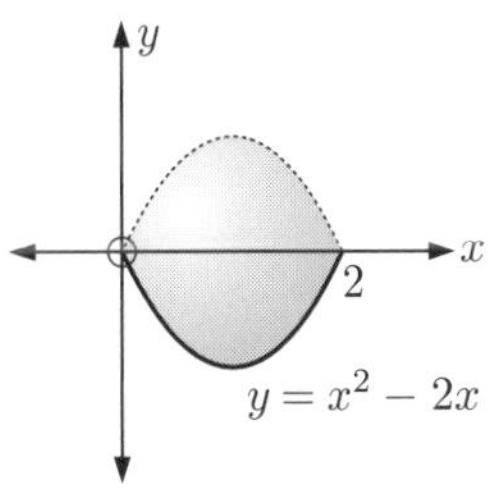


$V = \pi \displaystyle\int_0^2 y^2\,dx$

$= \pi \displaystyle\int_0^2 (x^2 - 2x)^2\,dx$

$= \pi \displaystyle\int_0^2 x^4 - 4x^3 + 4x^2\,dx$

$= \pi \left[\dfrac{x^5}{5} - \dfrac{4x^4}{4} + \dfrac{4x^3}{3}\right]_0^2$

$= \pi(\frac{32}{5} - 16 + \frac{32}{3})$

$= \frac{16}{15}\pi$ units$^3$

**58** $y = 4 - x^2$ cuts the $x$-axis where $y = 0$

$\therefore \quad 4 - x^2 = 0$

$\therefore \quad x^2 = 4$

$\therefore \quad x = \pm 2$

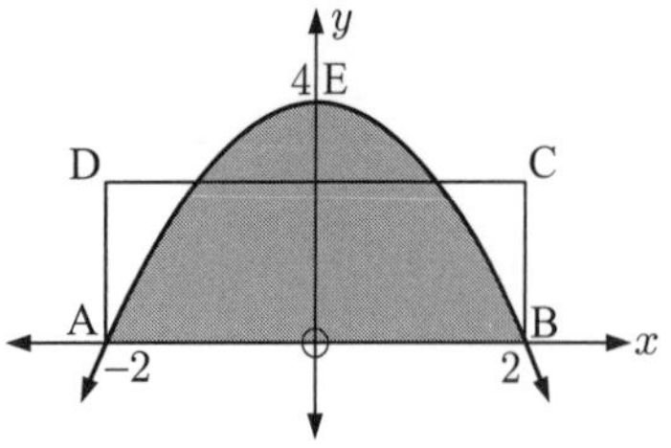


Shaded area $= \int_{-2}^{2} (4 - x^2)dx$

$= 2\int_0^2 (4 - x^2)dx$ {by symmetry}

$= 2\left[4x - \dfrac{x^3}{3}\right]_0^2$

$= 2((8 - \frac{8}{3}) - (0))$

$= 2(\frac{16}{3})$

$= \frac{32}{3}$ units$^2$

Now area of rectangle $= \frac{32}{3} = \text{AB} \times \text{BC}$

$\therefore \quad \frac{32}{3} = 4 \times \text{BC}$

$\therefore \quad \frac{8}{3} = \text{BC}$

$\therefore$ the rectangle is 4 units by $\frac{8}{3}$ units.

**59** **a** $y = x^2 - 3x + 3$ meets $y = x + 3$ where

$x^2 - 3x + 3 = x + 3$

$\therefore \quad x^2 - 4x = 0$

$\therefore \quad x(x - 4) = 0$

$\therefore \quad x = 0$ or $4$

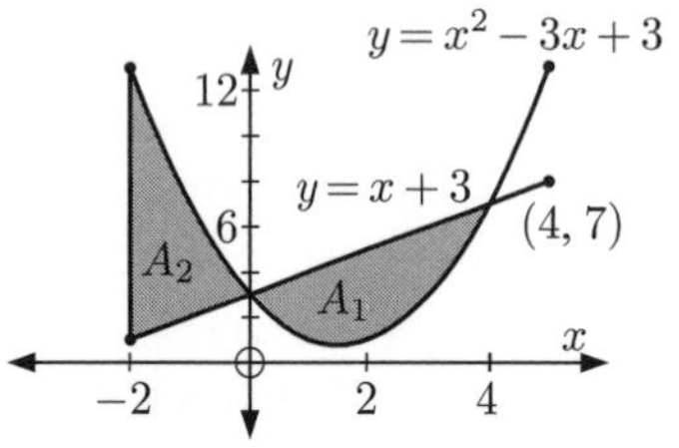


The area contained between the curve and the line is

$A_1 = \int_0^4 (x + 3 - x^2 + 3x - 3)\,dx$

$= \int_0^4 (-x^2 + 4x)\,dx$

$= \left[-\dfrac{x^3}{3} + 2x^2\right]_0^4$

$= \left(-\frac{64}{3} + 32\right) - (0)$

$= \frac{32}{3}$ units$^2$

$\int_{-2}^{4} (4x - x^2)dx = \left[2x^2 - \dfrac{x^3}{3}\right]_{-2}^{4}$

$= \left(32 - \frac{64}{3}\right) - \left(8 + \frac{8}{3}\right) = 0$

But $\int_{-2}^{4} (4x - x^2)\,dx = \int_{-2}^{0} (4x - x^2)\,dx + \int_0^4 (4x - x^2)\,dx$

$\therefore \quad 0 = -A_2 + A_1$

$\therefore \quad A_1 = A_2$

**60** **a** $\int (x^2 + 2)^2\,dx$

$= \int (x^4 + 4x^2 + 4)\,dx$

$= \dfrac{x^5}{5} + \dfrac{4x^3}{3} + 4x + c$

**b** $\int \sqrt{4x + 5}\,dx$

$= \int (4x + 5)^{\frac{1}{2}}\,dx$

$= \frac{1}{4}\,\dfrac{(4x + 5)^{\frac{3}{2}}}{\frac{3}{2}} + c$

$= \frac{1}{6}(4x + 5)^{\frac{3}{2}} + c$

**61** **a** $\displaystyle\int_0^1 \frac{1}{2x + 1}\,dx = \left[\tfrac{1}{2}\ln(2x + 1)\right]_0^1, \quad 2x + 1 > 0$

$= \frac{1}{2}\ln 3 - \frac{1}{2}\ln 1$

$= \frac{1}{2}\ln 3 - 0$

$= \frac{1}{2}\ln 3$

**b** $\int (e^x - 1)^2\,dx = \int (e^{2x} - 2e^x + 1)\,dx$

$= \frac{1}{2}e^{2x} - 2e^x + x + c$

**62** $y = x^2$ meets $y = x$ where $x^2 = x$

$\therefore \quad x(x - 1) = 0$

$\therefore \quad x = 0$ or $1$

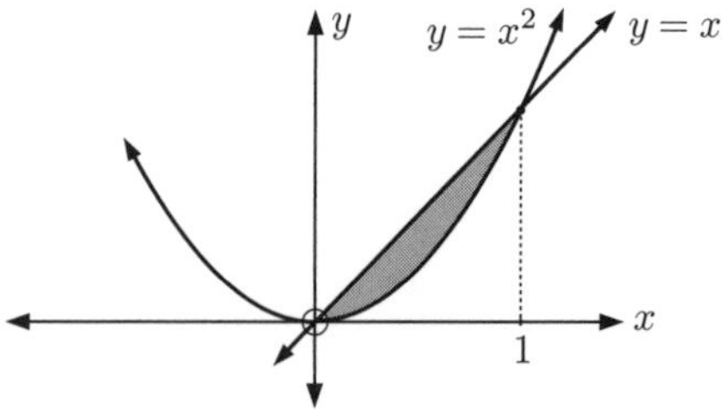


The required area $= \int_0^1 (x - x^2)\,dx$

$= \left[\frac{1}{2}x^2 - \frac{1}{3}x^3\right]_0^1$

$= \frac{1}{2} - \frac{1}{3} - 0 + 0$

$= \frac{1}{6}$ units$^2$

**63** The parabola has $x$-intercepts $\pm\pi$, so its equation is $y = k(x - \pi)(x + \pi)$ for some $k$.

The $y$-intercept is $\alpha$, so $k(-\pi)\pi = \alpha$

$\therefore \quad k = -\dfrac{\alpha}{\pi^2}$

$\therefore \quad y = -\dfrac{\alpha}{\pi^2}(x^2 - \pi^2)$

$= -\dfrac{\alpha}{\pi^2}x^2 + \alpha$

We need to consider two possible cases:

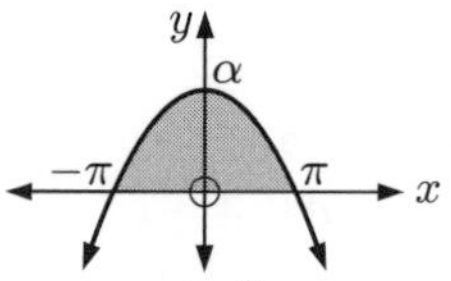


$\alpha > 0$

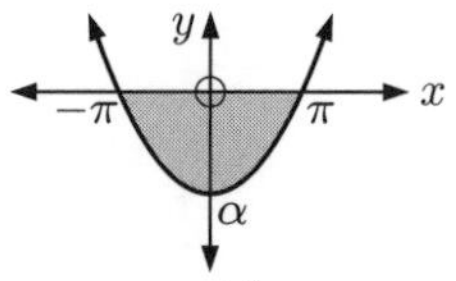


$\alpha < 0$

Consider the case $\alpha > 0$.

Using symmetry, the shaded area is $2\int_0^{\pi} \left(-\dfrac{\alpha}{\pi^2}x^2 + \alpha\right)dx$.

$\therefore \quad 2\displaystyle\int_0^{\pi} \left(-\frac{\alpha}{\pi^2}x^2 + \alpha\right)dx = 4$

$\therefore \quad \left[-\dfrac{\alpha}{3\pi^2}x^3 + \alpha x\right]_0^{\pi} = 2$

$\therefore \quad -\dfrac{\alpha\pi}{3} + \alpha\pi + 0 - 0 = 2$

$\therefore \quad \frac{2}{3}\alpha\pi = 2$

$\therefore \quad \alpha = \frac{3}{\pi}$

By symmetry, the other possible solution is $\alpha = -\frac{3}{\pi}$.

So, $\alpha = \pm\frac{3}{\pi}$.

**64** $v(t) = 1 + 2t - 2t^3$ m s$^{-1}$

$\therefore \quad s(t) = \int (1 + 2t - 2t^3)dt$

$= t + \dfrac{2t^2}{2} - \dfrac{2t^4}{4} + c$

$= t + t^2 - \frac{1}{2}t^4 + c$

But $s(2) = 4$, so $2 + 2^2 - \frac{1}{2}(2^4) + c = 4$

$\therefore \quad 2 + 4 - 8 + c = 4$

$\therefore \quad c = 6$

Thus $s(t) = t + t^2 - \frac{1}{2}t^4 + 6$

$\therefore \quad s(4) = 4 + 16 - 128 + 6 = -102$

$\therefore$ the particle is 102 m left of the origin.

**65** $y = x^2 e^{-x^2}$

$\therefore \quad \dfrac{dy}{dx} = (2x)e^{-x^2} + x^2(e^{-x^2})(-2x)$ {product rule}

$= 2xe^{-x^2} - 2x^3e^{-x^2}$

$= 2xe^{-x^2}(1-x^2)$

$= 2x(1-x^2)e^{-x^2}$

Thus $\int 2x(1-x^2)e^{-x^2}\,dx = x^2e^{-x^2} + c_1$

$\therefore \quad 2\int x(1-x^2)e^{-x^2}\,dx = x^2e^{-x^2} + c_1$

$\therefore \quad \int x(1-x^2)e^{-x^2}\,dx = \frac{1}{2}x^2e^{-x^2} + c$

**66** $y = x^2 + 2x - 3$ meets $y = x - 1$ where

$x^2 + 2x - 3 = x - 1$

$\therefore \quad x^2 + x - 2 = 0$

$\therefore \quad (x+2)(x-1) = 0$

$\therefore \quad x = -2$ or $1$

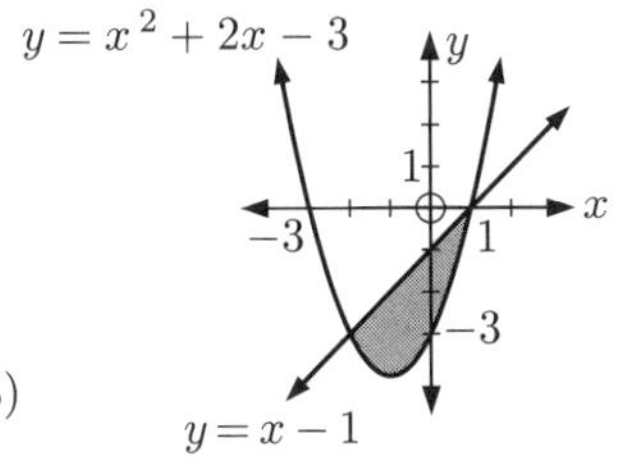


When $x = -2$, $y = -3$.

When $x = 1$, $y = 0$.

$\therefore$ the graphs meet at $(-2, -3)$ and $(1, 0)$.

$\therefore$ the area enclosed

$= \int_{-2}^{1} ((x-1) - (x^2+2x-3))\,dx$

$= \int_{-2}^{1} \left(x - 1 - x^2 - 2x + 3\right)\,dx$

$= \int_{-2}^{1} \left(2 - x - x^2\right)\,dx$

$= \left[2x - \frac{1}{2}x^2 - \frac{1}{3}x^3\right]_{-2}^{1}$

$= 2 - \frac{1}{2} - \frac{1}{3} - \left(2(-2) - \frac{1}{2}(-2)^2 - \frac{1}{3}(-2)^3\right)$

$= 2 - \frac{1}{2} - \frac{1}{3} + 4 + 2 - \frac{8}{3}$

$= 4\frac{1}{2}$ units$^2$

**67** **a** $v(t) = t - 4t^3$

$= t(1 - 4t^2)$

$= t(1+2t)(1-2t)$

$v(t)$ has sign diagram:

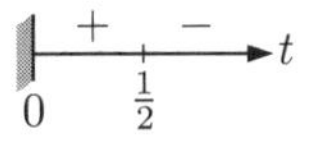


The change of sign at $t = \frac{1}{2}$ indicates a reversal of direction.

Now $s(t) = \int v(t)\,dt = \int (t - 4t^3)\,dt$

$= \dfrac{t^2}{2} - \dfrac{4t^4}{4} + c$

$= \dfrac{t^2}{2} - t^4 + c$

So, $s(0) = c$

$s(\frac{1}{2}) = \frac{1}{8} - \frac{1}{16} + c = c + \frac{1}{16}$

$s(1) = \frac{1}{2} - 1 + c = c - \frac{1}{2}$

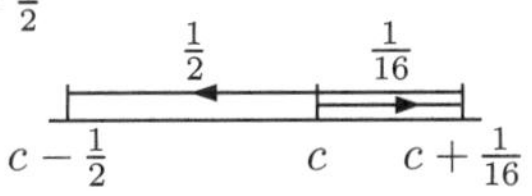


$\therefore$ the total distance travelled is

$\frac{1}{16} + \frac{1}{16} + \frac{1}{2} = \frac{1}{2} + \frac{1}{8} = \frac{5}{8}$ m

**68** **a** Suppose the line and the arc meet at point P where $x = k$.

$\therefore$ P has coordinates $(k, \sqrt{3}k)$.

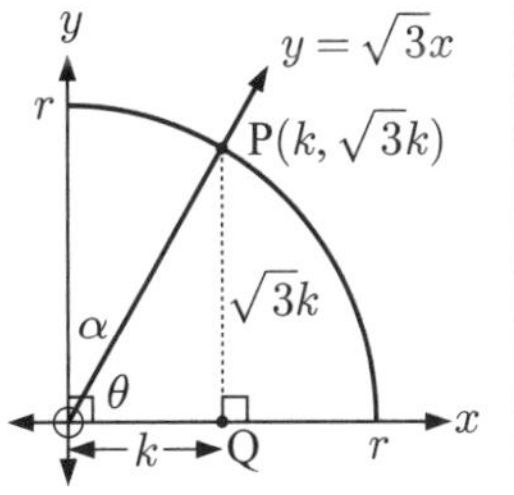


$\tan\theta = \dfrac{\sqrt{3}k}{k} = \sqrt{3}$

$\therefore \quad \theta = \frac{\pi}{3}$ and $\alpha = \frac{\pi}{2} - \theta = \frac{\pi}{6}$

arc length $l = \theta r = \frac{r\pi}{6}$ units

area $A = \frac{1}{2}\alpha r^2 = \frac{1}{2}(\frac{\pi}{6})r^2 = \frac{\pi r^2}{12}$ units$^2$

**b** Using Pythagoras, $k^2 + (\sqrt{3}k)^2 = r^2$

$\therefore \quad k^2(1+3) = r^2$

$\therefore \quad k^2 = \frac{1}{4}r^2$

But $k > 0$, so $k = \frac{1}{2}r$

The equation of the arc is $y^2 = r^2 - x^2$

$\therefore$ since $y > 0$, $y = \sqrt{r^2 - x^2}$

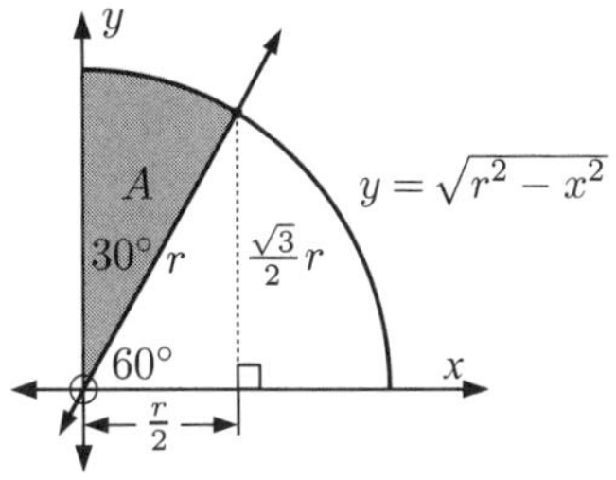


Now $A = \int_0^{\frac{r}{2}} \left(\sqrt{r^2 - x^2} - \sqrt{3}x\right)\,dx$

$= \int_0^{\frac{r}{2}} \sqrt{r^2 - x^2}\,dx - \sqrt{3}\int_0^{\frac{r}{2}} x\,dx$

$= \int_0^{\frac{r}{2}} \sqrt{r^2 - x^2}\,dx - \sqrt{3}\left[\frac{1}{2}x^2\right]_0^{\frac{r}{2}}$

$= \int_0^{\frac{r}{2}} \sqrt{r^2 - x^2}\,dx - \sqrt{3} \times \frac{1}{2}\left(\frac{r}{2}\right)^2$

$= \int_0^{\frac{r}{2}} \sqrt{r^2 - x^2}\,dx - \frac{\sqrt{3}r^2}{8}$ as required.

**c** Using **a** and **b**, $A = \dfrac{\pi r^2}{12} = \displaystyle\int_0^{\frac{r}{2}} \sqrt{r^2 - x^2}\,dx - \dfrac{\sqrt{3}r^2}{8}$

$\therefore \quad \displaystyle\int_0^{\frac{r}{2}} \sqrt{r^2 - x^2}\,dx = \dfrac{\pi r^2}{12} + \dfrac{\sqrt{3}r^2}{8}$

**d** Letting $r = 2$ in **c**,

$\int_0^1 \sqrt{4 - x^2}\,dx = \dfrac{\pi(4)}{12} + \dfrac{\sqrt{3}(4)}{8}$

$= \frac{\pi}{3} + \frac{\sqrt{3}}{2}$

$\therefore \quad 3\int_0^1 \sqrt{4 - x^2}\,dx = \pi + \frac{3\sqrt{3}}{2}$

$\therefore \quad \int_0^1 \sqrt{36 - 9x^2}\,dx = \pi + \frac{3\sqrt{3}}{2}$

**69** $\dfrac{2}{x+1} + \dfrac{1}{1-x}$

$= \left(\dfrac{2}{x+1}\right)\left(\dfrac{x-1}{x-1}\right) + \left(\dfrac{1}{1-x}\right)\left(\dfrac{x+1}{x+1}\right)$

$= \dfrac{2(x-1)}{x^2-1} + \dfrac{1+x}{1-x^2}$

$= \dfrac{2x - 2 - 1 - x}{x^2 - 1}$

$= \dfrac{x-3}{x^2-1}$

So, $\displaystyle\int_0^{\frac{1}{2}} \dfrac{x-3}{x^2-1}\,dx = \int_0^{\frac{1}{2}} \left(\dfrac{2}{x+1} + \dfrac{1}{1-x}\right)\,dx$

$= \left[2\ln(x+1) - \ln(1-x)\right]_0^{\frac{1}{2}}$

{since $x + 1 > 0$ and $1 - x > 0$ on the interval $0 \leqslant x \leqslant \frac{1}{2}$}

$= \left(2\ln\frac{3}{2} - \ln\frac{1}{2} - \cancel{2\ln 1} - \cancel{\ln 1}\right)$

$= 2\ln 3 - 2\ln 2 - \cancel{\ln 1} + \ln 2$

$= 2\ln 3 - \ln 2$ as required.

**70** $V = \int_0^2 \pi y^2\, dx$
$= \pi \int_0^2 x^4\, dx$
$= \pi \left[\dfrac{x^5}{5}\right]_0^2$
$= \pi \left(\dfrac{2^5}{5} - 0\right)$
$= \dfrac{32\pi}{5}$ units$^3$

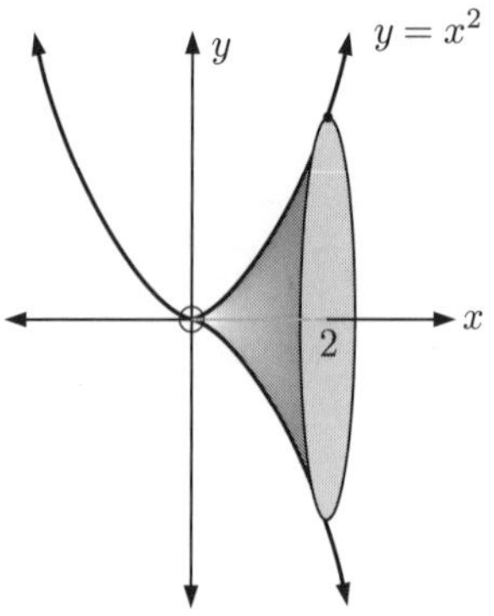


**71** **a** $f(x) = \dfrac{x+2}{\sqrt{x-1}}$ is real if $x - 1 > 0$, so $x > 1$.

**b** $f(x) = \dfrac{x+2}{(x-1)^{\frac{1}{2}}}$

$\therefore\ f'(x) = \dfrac{(1)(x-1)^{\frac{1}{2}} - (x+2)(\frac{1}{2})(x-1)^{-\frac{1}{2}}(1)}{x-1}$

$\therefore\ f'(10) = \dfrac{9^{\frac{1}{2}} - 12(\frac{1}{2})9^{-\frac{1}{2}}}{9} = \dfrac{3 - 6(\frac{1}{3})}{9} = \frac{1}{9}$

$\therefore$ the gradient of the normal at $x = 10$ is $\frac{-9}{1} = -9$

Now $f(10) = \frac{12}{\sqrt{9}} = 4$ so the point of contact is $(10, 4)$.

$\therefore$ the equation of the normal is $\dfrac{y-4}{x-10} = -9$
which is $y - 4 = -9x + 90$
or $9x + y = 94$

**72** **a** $\text{OP} + \text{OQ} + \text{PQ} = 40$ cm
$\therefore\ x + x + s = 40$
$\therefore\ s = 40 - 2x$

**b** $A = \frac{1}{2}\theta x^2$ where $s = \theta x$
$\therefore\ A = \frac{1}{2}\left(\dfrac{s}{x}\right)x^2$
$= \frac{1}{2}xs$
$= \frac{1}{2}x(40 - 2x)$
$\therefore\ A = 20x - x^2$ cm$^2$

**c** $\dfrac{dA}{dx} = 20 - 2x$

$\dfrac{dA}{dx}$ has sign diagram:

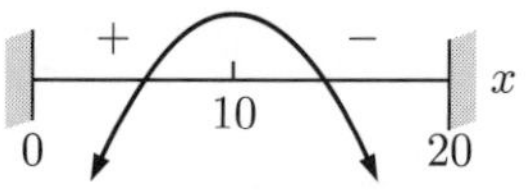


$\therefore$ the area is a maximum when $x = 10$.

**d** When $x = 10$, $s = 40 - 2x = 40 - 20 = 20$
Using $s = \theta x$, $20 = \theta(10)$
$\therefore\ \theta = 2$ radians.

**73** **a** $v(t) = e^{2t} - 3e^t = e^t(e^t - 3)$
$\therefore\ v(0) = e^0 - 3e^0 = 1 - 3 = -2$ m s$^{-1}$
Also, since $e^t > 0$ for all $t$, $v(t) = 0$ when $e^t = 3$
which is when $t = \ln 3$

$\therefore$ the initial velocity is $-2$ m s$^{-1}$ and the particle is stationary at $t = \ln 3$ seconds.

**b** $s(t) = \int v(t)\, dt = \int (e^{2t} - 3e^t)\, dt$
$\therefore\ s(t) = \frac{1}{2}e^{2t} - 3e^t + c$ metres.
But $s(0) = 1$, so $\frac{1}{2}e^0 - 3e^0 + c = 1$
$\therefore\ \frac{1}{2} - 3 + c = 1$
$\therefore\ c = 3\frac{1}{2}$
Thus $s(t) = \frac{1}{2}e^{2t} - 3e^t + \frac{7}{2}$ metres

$\therefore\ s(\ln 5) = \frac{1}{2}e^{2\ln 5} - 3e^{\ln 5} + \frac{7}{2}$
$= \frac{1}{2}e^{\ln 5^2} - 3(5) + \frac{7}{2}$
$= \frac{25}{2} - 15 + \frac{7}{2}$
$= 16 - 15$
$= 1$ m

So, the particle is 1 m to the right of O.

**c** $v(t)$ has sign diagram:

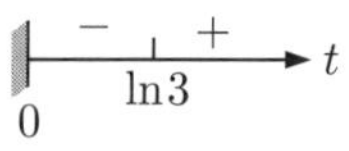


$\therefore$ a reversal of direction occurs at $t = \ln 3$ seconds.
Now $s(0) = \frac{1}{2} - 3 + \frac{7}{2} = 1$
$s(\ln 3) = \frac{1}{2}e^{2\ln 3} - 3e^{\ln 3} + \frac{7}{2}$
$= \frac{1}{2}(9) - 3(3) + \frac{7}{2} = -1$
and $s(\ln 5) = 1$

$\therefore$ the total distance travelled is 4 m.

**d** The velocity is increasing when $v'(t) \geqslant 0$
$\therefore\ e^{2t}(2) - 3e^t \geqslant 0$
$\therefore\ e^t(2e^t - 3) \geqslant 0$
$\therefore\ 2e^t - 3 \geqslant 0$ {as $e^t > 0$ for all $t$}
$\therefore\ e^t \geqslant \frac{3}{2}$
$\therefore\ t \geqslant \ln\left(\frac{3}{2}\right)$ seconds

**74** **a** $f(x) = 3\sin(x - 4)$
$\therefore\ f'(x) = 3\cos(x - 4) \times 1$
$= 3\cos(x - 4)$

**b** $f(x) = 12x - 2\cos\left(\frac{x}{3}\right)$
$\therefore\ f'(x) = 12 - 2(-\sin(\frac{x}{3})) \times \frac{1}{3}$
$= 12 + \frac{2}{3}\sin\left(\frac{x}{3}\right)$

**c** $f(x) = \sin 2x \cos 3x$
$\therefore\ f'(x) = 2\cos 2x \cos 3x + \sin 2x \times -3\sin 3x$
$= 2\cos 2x\cos 3x - 3\sin 2x \sin 3x$

**d** $f(x) = [\sin(2x+1)]^{\frac{1}{2}}$
$\therefore\ f'(x) = \frac{1}{2}[\sin(2x+1)]^{-\frac{1}{2}} \times 2\cos(2x+1)$
$= \dfrac{\cos(2x+1)}{\sqrt{\sin(2x+1)}}$

**e** $f(x) = e^{2\sin x}$
$\therefore\ f'(x) = e^{2\sin x} \times 2\cos x$
$= 2e^{2\sin x}\cos x$

**f** $f(x) = \tan(3x - 4)$
$\therefore\ f'(x) = \dfrac{\frac{d}{dx}(3x-4)}{\cos^2(3x-4)}$
$= \dfrac{3}{\cos^2(3x-4)}$

**75** **a** $V = \int_0^1 \pi(2x+3)^2\, dx$
$= \pi\left[\frac{1}{2}\dfrac{(2x+3)^3}{3}\right]_0^1$
$= \frac{\pi}{6}(5^3 - 3^3)$
$= \frac{98\pi}{6}$ units$^3$

**b** $V = \int_1^3 \pi(e^{2x})^2\, dx$
$= \pi\int_1^3 e^{4x}\, dx$
$= \pi\left[\frac{1}{4}e^{4x}\right]_1^3$
$= \frac{\pi}{4}(e^{12} - e^4)$ units$^3$

**76** $y = \dfrac{\sin 2x}{1+x}$

$\therefore\ \dfrac{dy}{dx} = \dfrac{2\cos 2x \times (1+x) - \sin 2x \times 1}{(1+x)^2}$
$= \dfrac{2(1+x)\cos 2x - \sin 2x}{(1+x)^2}$

**77** $f(x) = \ln(\cos x)$

**a** $f(x)$ is undefined when $\cos x \leqslant 0$.

Sign diagram for $\cos x$ on the domain $0 \leqslant x \leqslant \pi$:

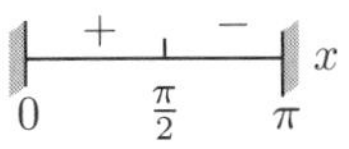


So, $f(x)$ is undefined when $\frac{\pi}{2} \leqslant x \leqslant \pi$.

**b** If $f(x) = \ln g(x)$ then $f'(x) = \dfrac{g'(x)}{g(x)}$.

So, $f'(x) = \dfrac{-\sin x}{\cos x} = -\tan x$

**78** **a** $y = \dfrac{\sin x + \cos x}{\sin x - \cos x}$

$$\therefore \quad \frac{dy}{dx} = \frac{\left(\begin{array}{r}(\cos x - \sin x)(\sin x - \cos x) \\ -(\sin x + \cos x)(\cos x + \sin x)\end{array}\right)}{(\sin x - \cos x)^2}$$

**b** $y = e^{\tan x}$

$$\therefore \quad \frac{dy}{dx} = e^{\tan x} \times \frac{1}{\cos^2 x} = \frac{e^{\tan x}}{\cos^2 x}$$

**c** $y = x^{\frac{7}{2}} \sin 3x$

$$\therefore \quad \frac{dy}{dx} = \tfrac{7}{2}x^{\frac{5}{2}} \sin 3x + 3x^{\frac{7}{2}} \cos 3x$$

**79** **a** $\int_0^{\pi} \sin x \, dx$

$= [-\cos x]_0^{\pi}$

$= (-\cos \pi) - (-\cos 0)$

$= -(-1) + 1$

$= 2$

**b** $\int_0^{8\pi} \sin x \, dx$

$= [-\cos x]_0^{8\pi}$

$= (-\cos 8\pi) - (-\cos 0)$

$= -1 + 1$

$= 0$

**c** $\int_{-\frac{\pi}{4}}^{\frac{\pi}{4}} \cos 2x \, dx = \left[\frac{1}{2} \sin 2x\right]_{-\frac{\pi}{4}}^{\frac{\pi}{4}}$

$= \frac{1}{2}\sin(\frac{\pi}{2}) - \frac{1}{2}\sin(-\frac{\pi}{2})$

$= \frac{1}{2}(1) - \frac{1}{2}(-1)$

$= 1$

**80**

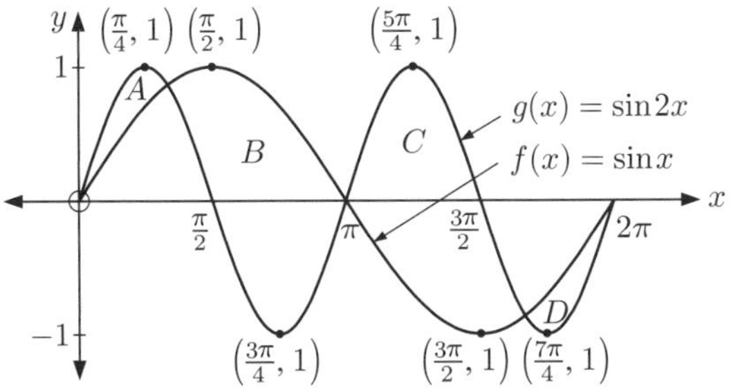


The graphs meet where $\sin 2x = \sin x$

$\therefore \quad 2\sin x \cos x - \sin x = 0$

$\therefore \quad \sin x(2\cos x - 1) = 0$

$\therefore \quad \sin x = 0$ or $\cos x = \frac{1}{2}$

$\therefore \quad x = 0, \frac{\pi}{3}, \pi, \frac{5\pi}{3}, 2\pi$

Area $A$ = Area $D$

$= \int_0^{\frac{\pi}{3}} (\sin 2x - \sin x) \, dx$

$= \left[-\frac{1}{2}\cos 2x + \cos x\right]_0^{\frac{\pi}{3}}$

$= \left(-\frac{1}{2}\cos\left(\frac{2\pi}{3}\right) + \cos\left(\frac{\pi}{3}\right)\right) - \left(-\frac{1}{2}\cos 0 + \cos 0\right)$

$= \left(-\frac{1}{2}(-\frac{1}{2}) + \frac{1}{2}\right) - \left(-\frac{1}{2} + 1\right)$

$= \frac{1}{4}$ unit$^2$

Area $B$ = Area $C$

$= \int_{\frac{\pi}{3}}^{\pi} (\sin x - \sin 2x) \, dx$

$= \left[-\cos x + \frac{1}{2}\cos 2x\right]_{\frac{\pi}{3}}^{\pi}$

$= (-\cos \pi + \frac{1}{2}\cos 2\pi) - (-\cos\left(\frac{\pi}{3}\right) + \frac{1}{2}\cos\left(\frac{2\pi}{3}\right))$

$= (1 + \frac{1}{2}) - \left(-\frac{1}{2} + \frac{1}{2}(-\frac{1}{2})\right)$

$= 2\frac{1}{4}$ units$^2$

**81** **a** Any odd function has rotational symmetry about O.

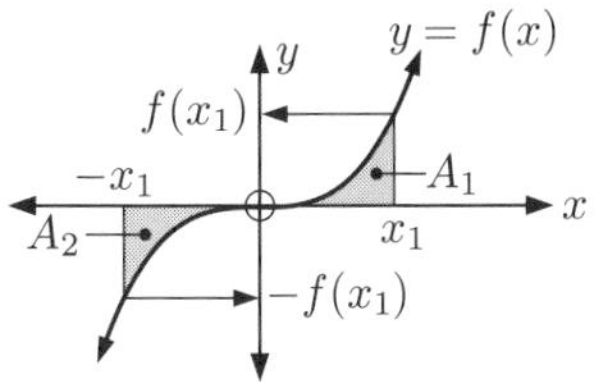


**b** $\int_{-1}^{1} f(x)\, dx = \int_{-1}^{0} f(x)\, dx + \int_0^1 f(x)\, dx$

$= (-A_2) + A_1$

$= A_1 - A_2$

But by symmetry, $A_1 = A_2$ for any odd function.

$\therefore \quad \int_{-1}^{1} f(x) dx = 0$

**c** If $f(x) = x^3 \cos 2x$ then

$f(-x) = (-x)^3 \cos(-2x)$

$= -(x^3 \cos(-2x))$

$= -(x^3 \cos 2x)$ $\quad \{\cos(-\theta) = \cos\theta$ for all $\theta\}$

$= -f(x)$ for all $x$.

$\therefore \quad f(x)$ is an odd function.

**d** $\int_{-1}^{1} (e^{-2x} + x^3 \cos 2x)\, dx$

$= \int_{-1}^{1} e^{-2x}\, dx + \int_{-1}^{1} x^3 \cos 2x \, dx$

$= [\frac{1}{-2}e^{-2x}]_{-1}^{1} + 0$ $\quad$ {using **b**, since $x^3 \cos 2x$ is odd}

$= (-\frac{1}{2}e^{-2}) - (-\frac{1}{2}e^2)$

$= \frac{1}{2}(e^2 - \dfrac{1}{e^2})$

**82** $y = \dfrac{\cos 3x}{2 + x}$

$$\therefore \quad \frac{dy}{dx} = \frac{-3\sin 3x \times (2 + x) - \cos 3x \times (1)}{(2 + x)^2}$$

**83** $x = \sin t + \frac{1}{2}\sin 2t$

Velocity $v = \dfrac{dx}{dt} = \cos t + \frac{1}{2} \times 2\cos 2t$

$= \cos t + \cos 2t$

When $t = 0$, $x = \sin 0 + \frac{1}{2}\sin 0 = 0$ cm

$v = \cos 0 + \cos 0 = 2$ cm s$^{-1}$

When $t = 2\pi$, $x = \sin 2\pi + \frac{1}{2}\sin 4\pi = 0$ cm

$v = \cos 2\pi + \cos 4\pi = 2$ cm s$^{-1}$

The point comes to rest when $v = 0$

$\therefore \quad \cos t + \cos 2t = 0$

$\therefore \quad \cos t + (2\cos^2 t - 1) = 0$

$\therefore \quad 2\cos^2 t + \cos t - 1 = 0$

$\therefore \quad (2\cos t - 1)(\cos t + 1) = 0$

$\cos t = \frac{1}{2}$ or $-1$

$\therefore \quad t = \frac{\pi}{3}, \pi, \frac{5\pi}{3}$

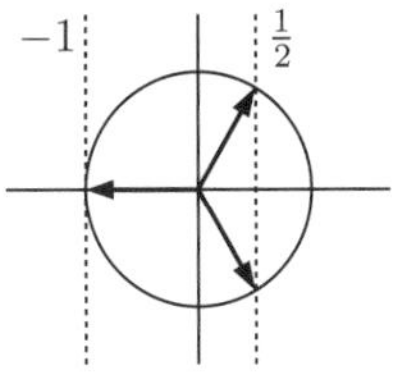


Sign diagram for $v$ is:

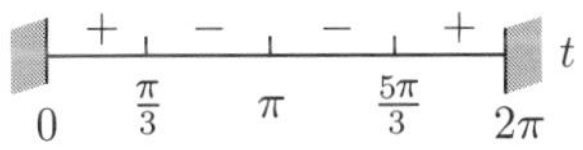


Acceleration $a = \dfrac{dv}{dt} = -\sin t - 2\sin 2t$

$\therefore \quad a(\frac{\pi}{3}) = -\frac{\sqrt{3}}{2} - 2(\frac{\sqrt{3}}{2}) = -\frac{3\sqrt{3}}{2}$ cm s$^{-2}$,

$a(\pi) = 0$ cm s$^{-2}$

and $a(\frac{5\pi}{3}) = \frac{\sqrt{3}}{2} + \frac{2\sqrt{3}}{2} = \frac{3\sqrt{3}}{2}$ cm s$^{-2}$

At the time $t = 0$, the point is moving with velocity 2 cm s$^{-1}$ in the positive direction. It moves in this direction for $\frac{\pi}{3}$ seconds, before coming to rest. It moves back to its initial position, arriving there after $\pi$ seconds. It continues to move in the negative direction until $t = \frac{5\pi}{3}$ seconds, at which time it changes direction and moves back to the initial position, arriving there at $t = 2\pi$ seconds.

**84** $f(\theta) = \dfrac{2 - \cos\theta}{\sin\theta}$

$$f'(\theta) = \frac{\sin\theta \times \sin\theta - (2-\cos\theta)\cos\theta}{\sin^2\theta}$$
$$= \frac{\sin^2\theta - 2\cos\theta + \cos^2\theta}{\sin^2\theta}$$
$$= \frac{1 - 2\cos\theta}{\sin^2\theta}$$

$\therefore$ $f'(\theta) = 0$ when $\cos\theta = \frac{1}{2}$ $\therefore$ $\theta = \frac{\pi}{3}$

Sign diagram for $f'(\theta)$:

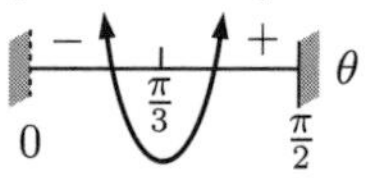


$\therefore$ $f(\theta)$ is a minimum when $\theta = \frac{\pi}{3}$

Now $f(\frac{\pi}{3}) = \dfrac{2 - \frac{1}{2}}{\frac{\sqrt{3}}{2}} = \dfrac{\frac{3}{2}}{\frac{\sqrt{3}}{2}} = \sqrt{3}$

$\therefore$ the minimum value is $\sqrt{3}$ when $\theta = \frac{\pi}{3}$.

**85** $f(\theta) = \cos\theta \times [\sin\theta]^2$

$$\therefore\ f'(\theta) = -\sin\theta[\sin\theta]^2 + \cos\theta \times 2[\sin\theta]^1 \times \cos\theta$$
$$= -\sin^3\theta + 2\sin\theta\cos^2\theta$$
$$= \sin\theta[2\cos^2\theta - \sin^2\theta]$$
$$= \sin\theta[2\cos^2\theta - (1-\cos^2\theta)]$$
$$= \sin\theta[3\cos^2\theta - 1]$$

So, $f'(\theta) = 0$ when $\sin\theta = 0$ or $\cos^2\theta = \frac{1}{3}$

But $0 < \theta \leqslant \frac{\pi}{2}$, so $\cos\theta > 0$ and $\sin\theta > 0$

$\therefore$ $f'(\theta) = 0$ when $\cos\theta = \frac{1}{\sqrt{3}}$

Sign diagram for $f'(\theta)$:

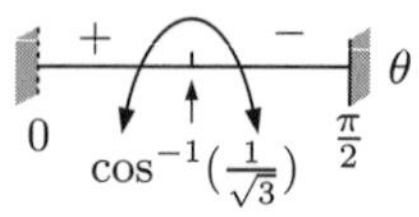


$\therefore$ $f(\theta)$ is a maximum when $\cos\theta = \frac{1}{\sqrt{3}}$

At this time, $\sin^2\theta = 1 - \cos^2\theta = 1 - \frac{1}{3}$
$= \frac{2}{3}$

$\therefore$ the maximum value of $f(\theta)$ is $\frac{1}{\sqrt{3}} \times \frac{2}{3} = \frac{2}{3\sqrt{3}}$

**86** **a** $f(x) = \sin\left(x + \frac{\pi}{6}\right)$ comes from $y = \sin x$ under a translation of $\begin{pmatrix} -\frac{\pi}{6} \\ 0 \end{pmatrix}$.

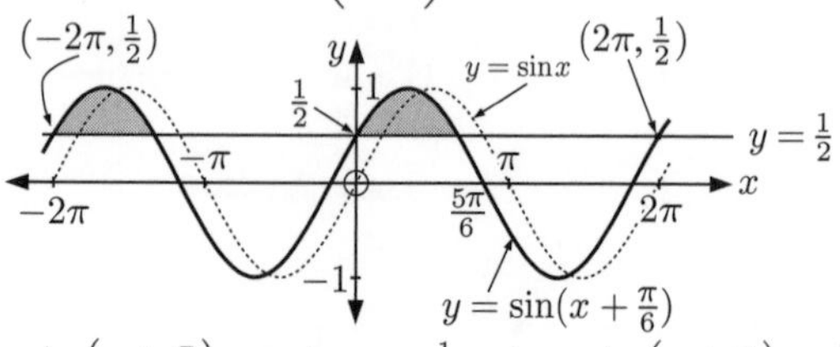


**b** $y = \sin\left(x + \frac{\pi}{6}\right)$ meets $y = \frac{1}{2}$ when $\sin\left(x + \frac{\pi}{6}\right) = \frac{1}{2}$

$$\therefore\ x + \frac{\pi}{6} = \begin{cases} \frac{\pi}{6} + 2k\pi \\ \frac{5\pi}{6} + 2k\pi, \end{cases} \quad k \in \mathbb{Z}$$

$$\therefore\ x = \begin{cases} 2k\pi \\ \frac{2\pi}{3} + 2k\pi, \end{cases} \quad k \in \mathbb{Z}$$

$\therefore$ on the given interval, $x = -2\pi, -\frac{4\pi}{3}, 0, \frac{2\pi}{3}$ and $2\pi$.

The total shaded area $= 2\int_0^{\frac{2\pi}{3}} \left(\sin(x + \frac{\pi}{6}) - \frac{1}{2}\right) dx$

$$= 2\left[-\cos(x + \tfrac{\pi}{6}) - \tfrac{1}{2}x\right]_0^{\frac{2\pi}{3}}$$
$$= 2\left(\left(-\cos\tfrac{5\pi}{6} - \tfrac{\pi}{3}\right) - \left(-\cos\tfrac{\pi}{6}\right)\right)$$
$$= 2\left(\tfrac{\sqrt{3}}{2} - \tfrac{\pi}{3} + \tfrac{\sqrt{3}}{2}\right)$$
$$= 2\sqrt{3} - \tfrac{2\pi}{3} \text{ units}^2$$

**87** $\int_0^{\frac{\pi}{2}} (\sin 3x + 5\cos x)\, dx$

$$= \left[-\tfrac{1}{3}\cos 3x + 5\sin x\right]_0^{\frac{\pi}{2}}$$
$$= \left(-\tfrac{1}{3}\cos(\tfrac{3\pi}{2}) + 5\sin(\tfrac{\pi}{2})\right) - \left(-\tfrac{1}{3}\cos 0 + 5\sin 0\right)$$
$$= (0 + 5) - (-\tfrac{1}{3} + 0) = 5\tfrac{1}{3}$$

**88** **a** $y = \ln(\tan x)$

$$\therefore\ \frac{dy}{dx} = \frac{1}{\tan x} \times \frac{1}{\cos^2 x}$$
$$= \frac{\cos x}{\sin x} \times \frac{1}{\cos^2 x}$$
$$= \frac{1}{\sin x \cos x}$$
$$= \frac{2}{2\sin x \cos x}$$
$$= \frac{2}{\sin 2x}$$

$\therefore$ $k = 2$

**b** Shaded area

$$= \int_{\frac{\pi}{6}}^{\frac{\pi}{3}} \frac{1}{\sin 2x}\, dx$$
$$= \frac{1}{2}\int_{\frac{\pi}{6}}^{\frac{\pi}{3}} \frac{2}{\sin 2x}\, dx$$
$$= \tfrac{1}{2}[\ln(\tan x)]_{\frac{\pi}{6}}^{\frac{\pi}{3}}$$
$$= \tfrac{1}{2}(\ln\sqrt{3} - \ln(\tfrac{1}{\sqrt{3}}))$$
$$= \tfrac{1}{2}(\ln\sqrt{3} + \ln\sqrt{3})$$
$$= \ln\sqrt{3}$$
$$= \ln 3^{\frac{1}{2}}$$
$$= \tfrac{1}{2}\ln 3 \text{ units}^2$$

**89** $\int_a^{a+1} x^2\, dx = \frac{1}{2}$

$$\therefore\ \left[\frac{x^3}{3}\right]_a^{a+1} = \frac{1}{2}$$
$$\therefore\ (a+1)^3 - a^3 = \frac{3}{2}$$
$$\therefore\ a^3 + 3a^2 + 3a + 1 - a^3 = \frac{3}{2}$$
$$\therefore\ 3a^2 + 3a - \frac{1}{2} = 0$$
$$\therefore\ 6a^2 + 6a - 1 = 0$$
$$\therefore\ a = \frac{-6 \pm \sqrt{36 - 4(6)(-1)}}{12}$$
$$\therefore\ a = \frac{-6 \pm \sqrt{60}}{12}$$

But $a > 0$, so $a = \dfrac{\sqrt{60} - 6}{12}$

**90** **a** $S = \pi(1)^2 - \pi(x)^2 = \pi(1 - x^2)$

But in the right angled $\Delta$, $x^2 + y^2 = 1$

$\therefore$ $y^2 = 1 - x^2$

$\therefore$ $S = \pi y^2$

Also, $\sin\theta = \frac{y}{1} = y$, so $S = \pi\sin^2\theta$

**b** The shaded area below [AB] $= \frac{1}{2}r^2(2\theta - \sin 2\theta)$

$$= \tfrac{1}{2}(1)^2(2\theta - \sin 2\theta)$$
$$= \theta - \tfrac{1}{2}\sin 2\theta$$

$\therefore$ the shaded area *between* [AB] and [CD]

$$= S - 2\left(\theta - \tfrac{1}{2}\sin 2\theta\right)$$
$$= \pi\sin^2\theta - 2(\theta - \tfrac{1}{2}\sin 2\theta)$$
$$= \pi\sin^2\theta - 2\theta + \sin 2\theta$$

So, $f(\theta) = \pi\sin^2\theta + \sin 2\theta - 2\theta$

**c** Let $g(\theta) = \pi \sin 2\theta + 2\cos 2\theta$

Now $f'(\theta) = \pi(2)\sin\theta\cos\theta + \cos 2\theta(2) - 2$
$= 2\pi\sin\theta\cos\theta + 2\cos 2\theta - 2$
$= (\pi\sin 2\theta + 2\cos 2\theta) - 2$
$= g(\theta) - 2$

**d** **i** If $f'(\theta) = 0$ then $g(\theta) = 2$
$\therefore$ from the graph, $\theta \approx 1$ $\{0 < \theta < \frac{\pi}{2}\}$

**ii** Sign diagram for $f'(\theta) = g(\theta) - 2$:

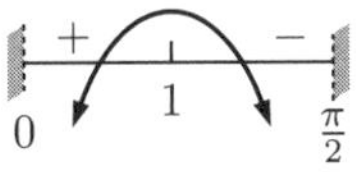


So, the maximum value of $f(\theta)$ is when $\theta \approx 1$.

## CALCULATORS

**1** **a** $(x+h)^3 = x^3 + 3x^2h + 3xh^2 + h^3$ {binomial expansion}

$$\therefore \lim_{h\to 0} \frac{(x+h)^3 - x^3}{h}$$
$$= \lim_{h\to 0} \frac{3x^2h + 3xh^2 + h^3}{h}$$
$$= \lim_{h\to 0} \frac{h(3x^2 + 3xh + h^2)}{h}$$
$$= \lim_{h\to 0} (3x^2 + 3xh + h^2) \quad \{\text{since } h \neq 0\}$$
$$= 3x^2$$

**b** $\dfrac{(5+h)^3 - 5^3}{h} = \dfrac{(5.01)^3 - 5^3}{0.01} = 75.1501$

**c** As $h \to 0$, $\dfrac{(5+h)^3 - 5^3}{h} \to 3 \times 5^2$ {from **a**}

So, $\dfrac{(5+h)^3 - 5^3}{h} \to 75$

**2**

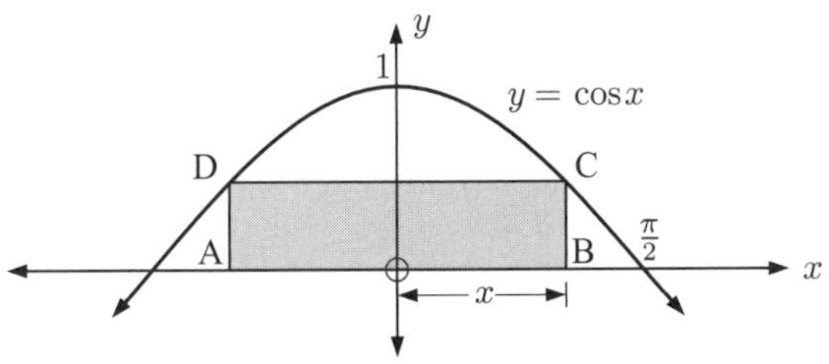

Let $x$ be the $x$-coordinate of C, so C has coordinates $(x, \cos x)$.
Rectangle ABCD has area $A = 2x\cos x$

$\therefore \dfrac{dA}{dx} = 2\cos x + 2x(-\sin x)$ {product rule}

$\therefore \dfrac{dA}{dx} = 0$ when $2x\sin x = 2\cos x$
$\therefore x\tan x = 1$
$\therefore x \approx 0.860$ {using technology}

$\therefore$ C has coordinates $(0.860, 0.652)$.

**3** The bin has capacity 500 litres
$= 500\,000$ mL

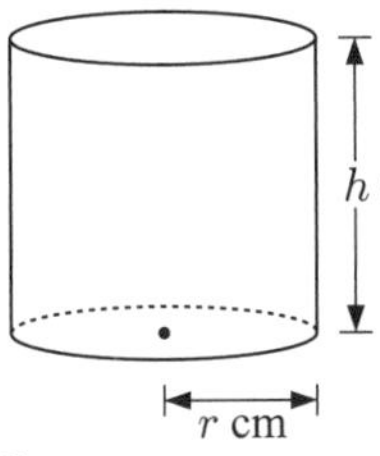


$\therefore \pi r^2 h = 500\,000$

$\therefore h = \dfrac{500\,000}{\pi r^2}$

Surface area $A = 2\pi rh + \pi r^2$
$= 2\pi r\left(\dfrac{500\,000}{\pi r^2}\right) + \pi r^2$
$= 1\,000\,000\, r^{-1} + \pi r^2$

$\therefore \dfrac{dA}{dr} = -\dfrac{1\,000\,000}{r^2} + 2\pi r$

$\therefore \dfrac{dA}{dr} = 0$ when $2\pi r = \dfrac{1\,000\,000}{r^2}$

$\therefore 2\pi r^3 = 1\,000\,000$

$\therefore r = \sqrt[3]{\dfrac{1\,000\,000}{2\pi}} \approx 54.2$

and $h \approx \dfrac{500\,000}{\pi(54.2)^2} \approx 54.2$

So, the surface area of the bin is minimised when the bin has a base radius and height of 54.2 cm.

**4** $f(x) = 3x^3 + 3x^2 - 3x - 1$

**a** $f(0) = -1$, so the $y$-intercept is $-1$.

**b** $f'(x) = 9x^2 + 6x - 3$
$= 3(3x^2 + 2x - 1)$
$= 3(3x - 1)(x + 1)$

$\therefore f'(x) = 0$ when $x = -1$ or $\frac{1}{3}$

Sign diagram for $f'(x)$:

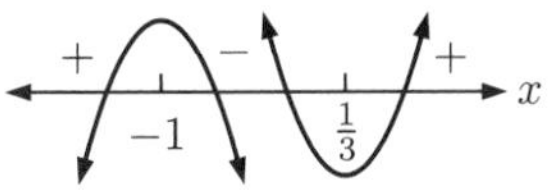


There is a local maximum at $(-1, 2)$ and a local minimum at $(\frac{1}{3}, -1\frac{5}{9})$.

**c**

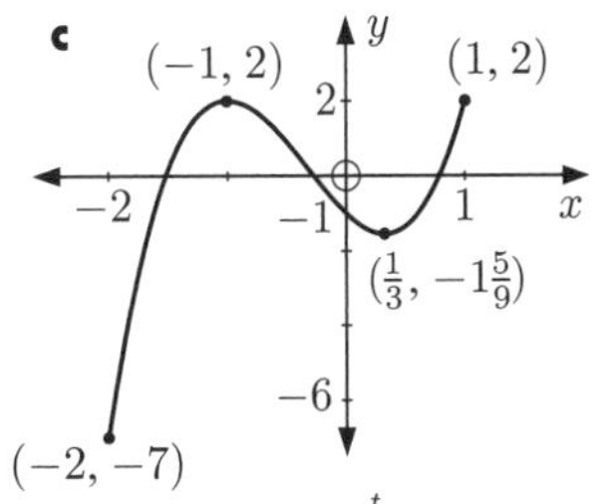


**d** Using technology, the $x$-intercepts are: $x \approx -1.515, -0.278$ and $0.793$.

**5** **a** $W_t = 100e^{-\frac{t}{20}}$

$W_0 = 100e^0 = 100$ g

$W_{10} = 100e^{-\frac{10}{20}} \approx 60.7$ g

$W_{20} = 100e^{-\frac{20}{20}} \approx 36.8$ g

$W_{30} = 100e^{-\frac{30}{20}} \approx 22.3$ g

$W_{40} = 100e^{-\frac{40}{20}} \approx 13.5$ g

**b** If $W = \frac{1}{2}W_0 = 50$ g then $50 = 100e^{-\frac{t}{20}}$

$\therefore e^{-\frac{t}{20}} = \frac{1}{2}$

$\therefore -\frac{t}{20} = \ln\frac{1}{2}$

$\therefore t = -20\ln\frac{1}{2} \approx 13.86$

$\therefore$ it takes about 13.9 days for half of the mass to decay.

**c** $\dfrac{dW}{dt} = 100e^{-\frac{t}{20}}\left(-\frac{1}{20}\right) = -5e^{-\frac{t}{20}}$

As $\dfrac{dW}{dt} < 0$ for all $t$, the weight of radioactive substance is always decreasing.

**d** As $t \to \infty$, $W \to 0$.

**e**

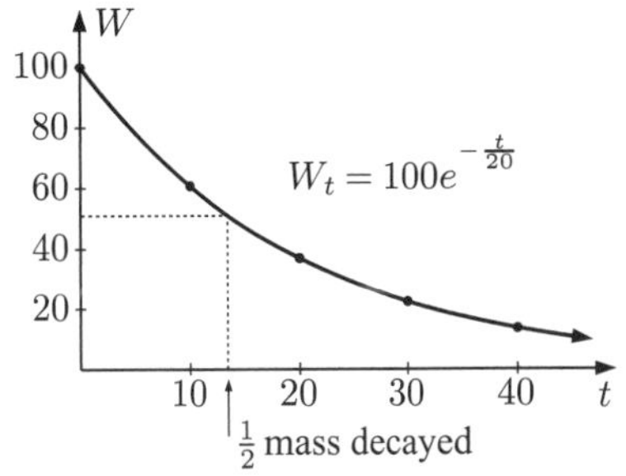


**6** $I(t) = 80(1 - e^{-5t})$, $t \geqslant 0$

**a** **i** $I(0) = 80(1 - e^0) = 80(0) = 0$ amps

**ii** $I(0.2) = 80(1 - e^{-1}) \approx 50.6$ amps

**iii** $I(1) = 80(1 - e^{-5}) \approx 79.5$ amps

**b** As $t \to \infty$, $e^{5t} \to \infty$ $\quad \therefore \quad e^{-5t} \to 0$

$\therefore \quad 1 - e^{-5t} \to 1$

$\therefore \quad I(t) \to 80$ amps.

**c** $I'(t) = 80(0 - e^{-5t}(-5)) = 80(5e^{-5t}) = 400e^{-5t}$

Sign diagram for $I'(t)$:

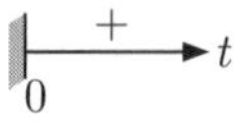


This means that the current is always increasing.

Now $\quad I''(t) = 400e^{-5t}(-5) = -2000\,e^{-5t}$

$\therefore \quad I''(t) < 0 \quad$ for all $t$.

So, although the current is increasing, it increases more slowly as time goes by.

**d**

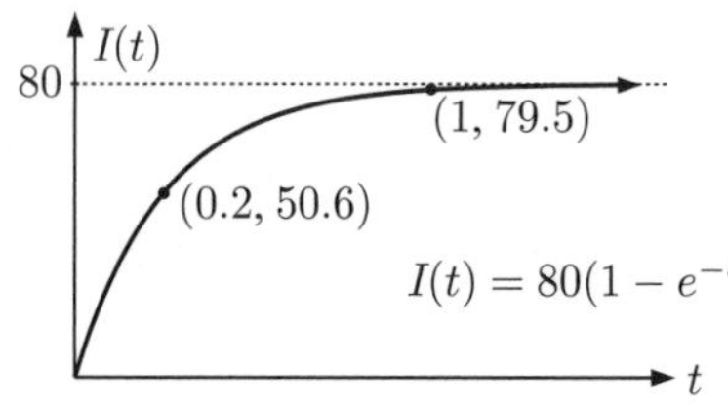


**7** **a** $\quad f(x) = x\ln x + 1, \ 0 < x \leqslant 4$

$\therefore \quad f'(x) = 1\ln x + x\left(\frac{1}{x}\right) + 0 = \ln x + 1$

$\therefore \quad f'(x) = 0$ when $\ln x = -1$, which is when $x = e^{-1}$

Sign diagram for $f'(x)$:

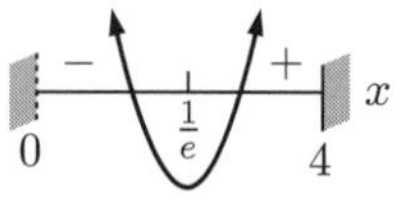


$\therefore$ the minimum ability occurs when the child is

$\frac{1}{e} \approx 0.3679$ years $\approx 4.41$ months

The minimum memorizing ability occurs in the 5th month.

**b** Using technology we graph $y = f(x)$

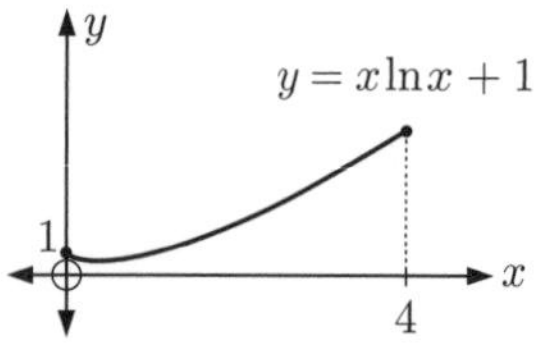


The maximum ability occurs at $x = 4$, or at the end of the 4 year interval.

**8** **a** $\quad f(t) = \dfrac{N}{1 + 2e^{-\frac{t}{2}}}$ where $N > 0$

$= N(1 + 2e^{-\frac{t}{2}})^{-1}$

$\therefore \quad f'(t) = -N(1 + 2e^{-\frac{t}{2}})^{-2}(2e^{-\frac{t}{2}})(-\frac{1}{2})$

$= \dfrac{Ne^{-\frac{t}{2}}}{(1 + 2e^{-\frac{t}{2}})^2}$

$N > 0$ is given and $e^{-\frac{t}{2}} > 0$ and $(1 + 2e^{-\frac{t}{2}})^2 > 0$.

Thus $f'(t) > 0$ for all $t$.

**b** $f''(t) = \dfrac{\left(\begin{array}{l} Ne^{-\frac{t}{2}}(-\frac{1}{2})(1 + 2e^{-\frac{t}{2}})^2 \\ \qquad -Ne^{-\frac{t}{2}}2(1 + 2e^{-\frac{t}{2}})2e^{-\frac{t}{2}}(-\frac{1}{2}) \end{array}\right)}{(1 + 2e^{-\frac{t}{2}})^4}$

$= \dfrac{(1 + 2e^{-\frac{t}{2}})(\frac{1}{2})Ne^{-\frac{t}{2}}[-1 - 2e^{-\frac{t}{2}} + 4e^{-\frac{t}{2}}]}{(1 + 2e^{-\frac{t}{2}})^4}$

$= \dfrac{\frac{1}{2}Ne^{-\frac{t}{2}}[2e^{-\frac{t}{2}} - 1]}{(1 + 2e^{-\frac{t}{2}})^3}$

$\therefore \quad f''(t) = 0$ when $e^{-\frac{t}{2}} = \frac{1}{2}$

$\therefore \quad e^{\frac{t}{2}} = 2$

$\therefore \quad t = \ln 4$

Sign diagram for $f''(t)$:

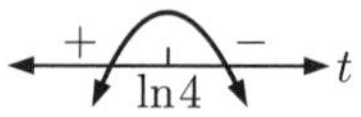


$\therefore \quad f'(t)$ is a maximum when $t = \ln 4$, and this occurs

when $f(t) = \dfrac{N}{1 + 2(\frac{1}{2})} = \dfrac{N}{2}$

**c** Now $f(0) = \dfrac{N}{1+2} = \dfrac{N}{3}$ and as $t \to \infty$, $f(t) \to N$

$f(2) \approx 0.58N, \quad f(4) \approx 0.79N$

$f(6) \approx 0.91N, \quad f(8) \approx 0.96N$

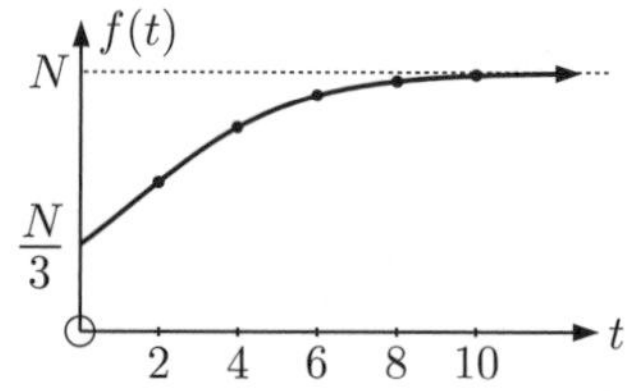


**9** **a** The function is defined for $x > 0$.

**b** $\quad f(x) = x - x^{-\frac{1}{2}}$

$\therefore \quad f'(x) = 1 + \frac{1}{2}x^{-\frac{3}{2}} = 1 + \dfrac{1}{2x\sqrt{x}}$

$\therefore \quad f'(x) > 0 \quad$ for $x > 0$ as each term is positive.

**c** The function cuts the $x$-axis when $y = 0$

$\therefore \quad x - \dfrac{1}{\sqrt{x}} = 0$

$\therefore \quad x = \dfrac{1}{\sqrt{x}}$

$\therefore \quad x^{\frac{3}{2}} = 1$

$\therefore \quad x = 1 \qquad$ So, the $x$-intercept is 1.

The function does not cut the $y$-axis since $x > 0$.

**d** As $x \to 0^+$, $\dfrac{1}{\sqrt{x}} \to \infty \qquad \therefore \ f(x) \to -\infty$

As $x \to \infty$, $\dfrac{1}{\sqrt{x}} \to 0 \qquad \therefore \ f(x) \to \infty$

**e**

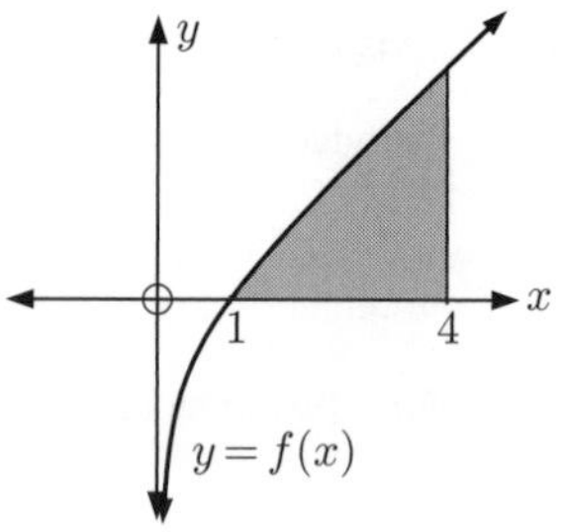


**f** Required area

$= \int_1^4 (x - x^{-\frac{1}{2}})\,dx$

$= 5\frac{1}{2}$ units$^2$

{using technology}

**10** $A(2) = 20e^{2a} = 25$

$\therefore \quad e^{2a} = \frac{25}{20} = \frac{5}{4}$

$\therefore \quad e^a = \left(\frac{5}{4}\right)^{\frac{1}{2}}$

$\therefore \quad a = \ln\left(\frac{5}{4}\right)^{\frac{1}{2}}$

Thus $\ A(t) = 20\left(\frac{5}{4}\right)^{\frac{t}{2}}$

and $\ A(10) = 20(1.25)^5$

$\approx 61.035$

**11** **a** $\quad f(x) = xe^{-2x^2}$

$\therefore \quad f'(x) = 1e^{-2x^2} + xe^{-2x^2}(-4x)$

$= e^{-2x^2}(1 - 4x^2)$

$= e^{-2x^2}(1 + 2x)(1 - 2x)$

where $e^{-2x^2}$ is always positive.

$\therefore$ $f'(x)$ has sign diagram: 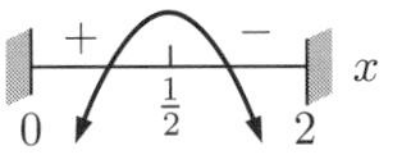


There is a local maximum when $x = \frac{1}{2}$.

This is at $(\frac{1}{2}, \frac{1}{2}e^{-\frac{1}{2}})$ or $(\frac{1}{2}, 0.303)$

**b** $f(0) = 0e^0 = 0$ and $f(2) = 2e^{-8} \approx 0.000\,671$

$\therefore$ the maximum value $\approx 0.303$ and the minimum is 0.

**12** **a** $V =$ area of end $\times$ length

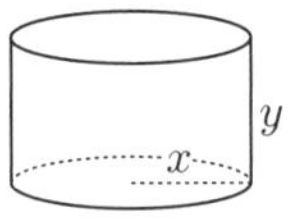


$\therefore \quad 16 = \pi r^2 \times h$

$\therefore \quad 16 = \pi x^2 y$

$\therefore \quad \dfrac{16}{\pi x^2} = y$

Surface area = area of base + area curved surface

$= \pi r^2 + 2\pi r h$

$= \pi x^2 + 2\pi x(y)$

$= \pi x^2 + 2\pi x\left(\dfrac{16}{\pi x^2}\right)$

$= \pi x^2 + \dfrac{32}{x}$ m$^2$

**b** By the theorem of Pythagoras,

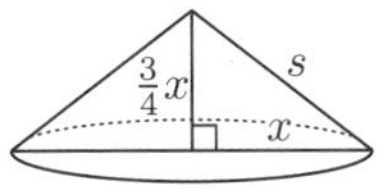


$s^2 = x^2 + (\frac{3}{4}x)^2$

$= x^2 + \frac{9}{16}x^2$

$= \dfrac{16x^2 + 9x^2}{16}$

$= \dfrac{25x^2}{16}$

$\therefore \quad s = \dfrac{5x}{4}$ $\{$as $s > 0\}$

$\therefore$ the surface area $= \pi r s = \pi(x)\dfrac{5x}{4} = \dfrac{5\pi x^2}{4}$ m$^2$

**c** The cost of the base is $k$ \$ m$^{-2}$,

so the cost of cover is $\dfrac{3k}{2}$ \$ m$^{-2}$.

The total cost $C =$ cost of base + cost of cover

$= \left(\pi x^2 + \dfrac{32}{x}\right)k + \left(\dfrac{5\pi x^2}{4}\right)\dfrac{3k}{2}$

$= k\left(\frac{8}{8}\pi x^2 + \dfrac{32}{x} + \dfrac{15\pi x^2}{8}\right)$

$= k\left(\frac{23}{8}\pi x^2 + \dfrac{32}{x}\right)$

**d** Now $C = k\left(\dfrac{23\pi}{8}x^2 + 32x^{-1}\right)$

$\therefore \quad \dfrac{dC}{dx} = k\left(\dfrac{23\pi}{8}(2x) - 32x^{-2}\right)$

$\therefore \quad \dfrac{dC}{dx} = 0$ when $\dfrac{23\pi}{8}(2x) = \dfrac{32}{x^2}$

$\therefore \quad x^3 = \dfrac{128}{23\pi}$

$\therefore \quad x = \sqrt[3]{\dfrac{128}{23\pi}} \approx 1.21$ m

Sign diagram for $\dfrac{dC}{dx}$: 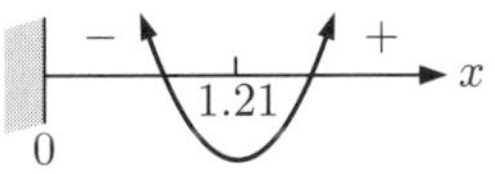


$\therefore$ the minimum cost is when $x \approx 1.21$ m.

**13** **a** $g(x) = \dfrac{\ln x}{x}$ for $0 < x \leqslant 5$

The graph cuts the $x$-axis when $y = 0$. $\quad \therefore \ln x = 0$

$\therefore \quad x = 1$

So, the point is $(1, 0)$.

**b** $g'(x) = \dfrac{\left(\frac{1}{x}\right)x - \ln x\,(1)}{x^2} = \dfrac{1 - \ln x}{x^2}$

$\therefore \quad g'(x) = 0$ when $\ln x = 1$ $\quad \therefore \quad x = e$

Sign diagram for $g'(x)$: 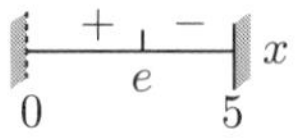


$\therefore$ the stationary point is a local maximum at $\left(e, \frac{1}{e}\right)$.

Also, $g''(x) = \dfrac{\left(-\frac{1}{x}\right)x^2 - (1 - \ln x)2x}{x^4}$

$= \dfrac{-x - 2x + 2x\ln x}{x^4}$

$= \dfrac{2\ln x - 3}{x^3}$

$\therefore \quad g''(x) = 0$ when $\ln x = \frac{3}{2}$

$\therefore \quad x = e^{\frac{3}{2}} \approx 4.482$

Sign diagram for $g''(x)$: 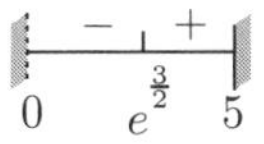


$\therefore$ there is a non-stationary inflection at $(4.48, 0.335)$.

At the point of inflection, the gradient of the graph is

$g'(e^{\frac{3}{2}}) = \dfrac{1 - \ln e^{\frac{3}{2}}}{e^3} = \dfrac{1 - \frac{3}{2}}{e^3} = -\dfrac{1}{2e^3} \approx -0.0249.$

**c** As $x \to 0$ (right), $y \to -\infty$.

**d**

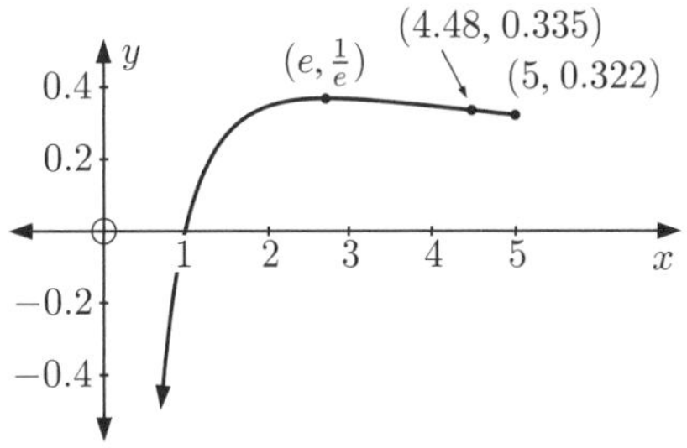


**e** **i** Since there is a local maximum at $\left(e, \frac{1}{e}\right)$,

$g(x) \leqslant \frac{1}{e}$ for all $x > 0$

$\therefore \quad \dfrac{\ln x}{x} \leqslant \frac{1}{e}$ and so $\ln x \leqslant \dfrac{x}{e}$ for $x > 0$

**ii** Now consider the interval $2 \leqslant x \leqslant 4$. There is only a local maximum on this interval, so the minimum is at an endpoint.

$g(2) \approx 0.347$ and $g(4) \approx 0.347$

$\therefore \quad g(x) > 0.347$ for $2 \leqslant x \leqslant 4$

$\therefore \quad \dfrac{\ln x}{x} > 0.347 > \frac{1}{3}$

$\therefore \quad \ln x > \dfrac{x}{3}$ for $2 \leqslant x \leqslant 4$

**14** $f(x) = \ln(x\sqrt{1 - 2x})$

$= \ln x + \ln(1 - 2x)^{\frac{1}{2}}$ $\quad \{\ln ab = \ln a + \ln b\}$

$= \ln x + \frac{1}{2}\ln(1 - 2x)$ $\quad \{\ln a^n = n\ln a\}$

$\therefore \quad f'(x) = \dfrac{1}{x} + \frac{1}{2}\left(\dfrac{-2}{1 - 2x}\right)$

$= \dfrac{1}{x} - \dfrac{1}{1 - 2x}$

$= \dfrac{1 - 2x - x}{x(1 - 2x)}$

$= \dfrac{1 - 3x}{x(1 - 2x)}$

For points where the gradient of the normal is $-\frac{6}{5}$,

$\dfrac{1 - 3x}{x(1 - 2x)} = \frac{5}{6}$

$\therefore \quad 6(1 - 3x) = 5x(1 - 2x)$

$$\therefore \quad 6 - 18x = 5x - 10x^2$$
$$\therefore \quad 10x^2 - 23x + 6 = 0$$
$$\therefore \quad (x-2)(10x-3) = 0$$
$$\therefore \quad x = 2 \text{ or } \tfrac{3}{10}$$

Now $f(2) = \ln(2\sqrt{-3})$ which is undefined and

$f\left(\frac{3}{10}\right) = \ln\left(\frac{3}{10}\sqrt{1-\frac{3}{5}}\right) = \ln\left(\frac{3}{10}\sqrt{\frac{2}{5}}\right) \approx -1.66$

So, the point is $(0.3, -1.66)$.

**15** **a**

$$M = 5e^{-0.1t}$$
$$\therefore \quad M_1 = 5e^{-0.1t_1}$$
$$\text{and } \tfrac{1}{2}M_1 = 5e^{-0.1t_2}$$
$$\therefore \quad \frac{M_1}{\frac{1}{2}M_1} = \frac{5e^{-0.1t_1}}{5e^{-0.1t_2}}$$
$$\therefore \quad 2 = e^{-0.1t_1 + 0.1t_2}$$
$$\therefore \quad 2 = e^{\frac{1}{10}(t_2 - t_1)}$$
$$\therefore \quad \ln 2 = \tfrac{1}{10}(t_2 - t_1)$$
$$\therefore \quad 10 \ln 2 = t_2 - t_1$$

**b** When $t = 0$,
$$M = 5e^0 = 5$$
When $M = \frac{5}{32}$,
$$5e^{-0.1t} = \tfrac{5}{32}$$
$$\therefore \quad e^{-0.1t} = \tfrac{1}{32}$$
$$\therefore \quad e^{0.1t} = 32$$
$$\therefore \quad 0.1t = \ln 32$$
$$\therefore \quad t = 10 \ln 32$$
$$\therefore \quad t \approx 34.7 \text{ years}$$

**16** **a** Consider $f(x) = \left(2 - \frac{1}{x}\right)e^{-x}, \quad x > 0$

$f(x) = 0$ when $2 - \frac{1}{x} = 0 \qquad$ {as $e^{-x} > 0$ for all $x$}
$$\therefore \quad \frac{1}{x} = 2$$
$$\therefore \quad x = \tfrac{1}{2}$$

**b** As $x \to 0$ (right), $\frac{1}{x} \to \infty$ and $e^{-x} \to 1$

$\therefore \quad f(x) \to -\infty$

As $x \to \infty$, $e^{-x} \to 0$ and $2 - \frac{1}{x} \to 2$

$\therefore \quad f(x) \to 0$

**c** Since $f(x) = (2 - x^{-1})e^{-x}$,
$$f'(x) = (x^{-2})e^{-x} + (2 - x^{-1})e^{-x}(-1)$$
$$= e^{-x}\left(x^{-2} - 2 + x^{-1}\right)$$
$$= e^{-x}\left(\frac{1}{x^2} - 2 + \frac{1}{x}\right)$$
$$= \frac{e^{-x}}{x^2}\left(1 - 2x^2 + x\right)$$
$$\therefore \quad f'(x) = 0 \text{ when } -2x^2 + x + 1 = 0$$
$$\therefore \quad 2x^2 - x - 1 = 0$$
$$\therefore \quad (2x+1)(x-1) = 0$$
$$\therefore \quad x = -\tfrac{1}{2} \text{ or } 1$$

Now $f'\left(\frac{1}{2}\right) = 4e^{-\frac{1}{2}} > 0$ and $f'(2) = \dfrac{e^{-2}(-5)}{4} < 0$

So $f'(x)$ has sign diagram:

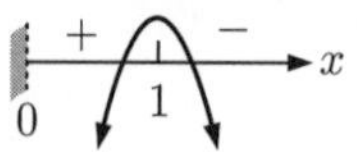


$\therefore$ there is a local maximum at $(1, \frac{1}{e})$.

**d**

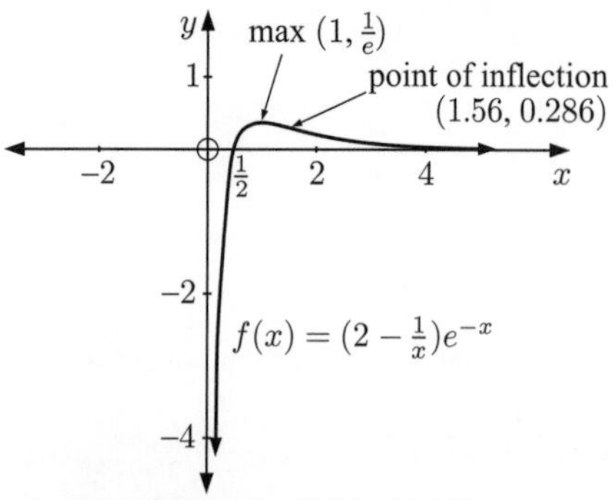


**e** The point of inflection is $(1.56, 0.286)$.

**17** **a** $f(x) = 1 + \dfrac{1}{2x-1} = 1 + (2x-1)^{-1}$

$\therefore \quad f'(x) = -(2x-1)^{-2}(2) = \dfrac{-2}{(2x-1)^2}$

$\therefore \quad f'(x)$ is never zero, and so $f(x)$ has no turning points.

**b**

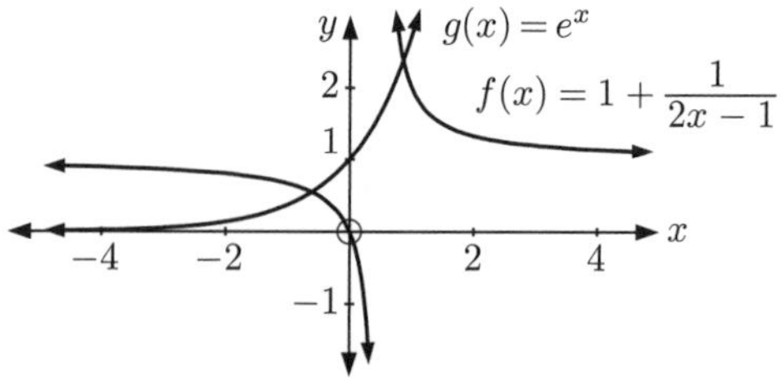


If $(2x-1)e^x - 2x = 0$ then $2x = (2x-1)e^x$
$$\therefore \quad \frac{2x}{2x-1} = e^x$$
$$\therefore \quad \frac{(2x-1)+1}{2x-1} = e^x$$
$$\therefore \quad 1 + \frac{1}{2x-1} = e^x$$

So, the solutions of the equation correspond to the points of intersection of $y = f(x)$ and $y = g(x)$. There are hence two solutions.

**c** Using technology, $x \approx -0.603$ or $0.864$.

**18** **a** $f(x) = \dfrac{1}{x} - \dfrac{4}{x-2} = \dfrac{x-2-4x}{x(x-2)} = \dfrac{-3x-2}{x(x-2)}$

So, $f(x) = 0$ when $-3x - 2 = 0 \qquad \therefore \quad x = -\frac{2}{3}$

**b**
$$f(x) = x^{-1} - 4(x-2)^{-1}$$
$$\therefore \quad f'(x) = -x^{-2} + 4(x-2)^{-2}$$
$$= -\frac{1}{x^2} + \frac{4}{(x-2)^2}$$
$$= \frac{4x^2 - (x-2)^2}{x^2(x-2)^2}$$
$$= \frac{(2x + (x-2))(2x - (x-2))}{x^2(x-2)^2}$$
$$= \frac{(3x-2)(x+2)}{x^2(x-2)^2}$$

$f'(x)$ has sign diagram:

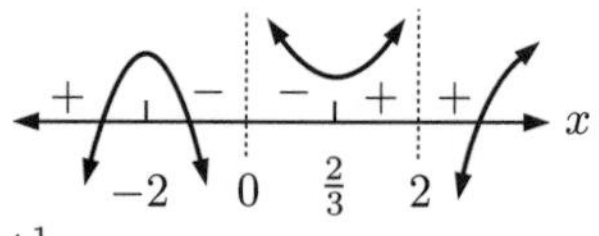


$f(-2) = \frac{1}{2}$ and $f(\frac{2}{3}) = 4\frac{1}{2}$

$\therefore$ there is a local maximum at $(-2, \frac{1}{2})$ and a local minimum at $(\frac{2}{3}, 4\frac{1}{2})$.

**c** $f''(x) = 2x^{-3} - 8(x-2)^{-3} = \dfrac{2}{x^3} - \dfrac{8}{(x-2)^3}$

$\therefore \quad f''(x) = 0$ when $\dfrac{2}{x^3} = \dfrac{8}{(x-2)^3}$ or $(x-2)^3 = 4x^3$

$\therefore \quad x \approx -3.4048 \quad$ {using technology}

$f(-3.4048) \approx -0.2937 + 0.7401 \approx 0.4464$

So, $f''(x) = 0$ at $(-3.40, 0.45)$.

**d**

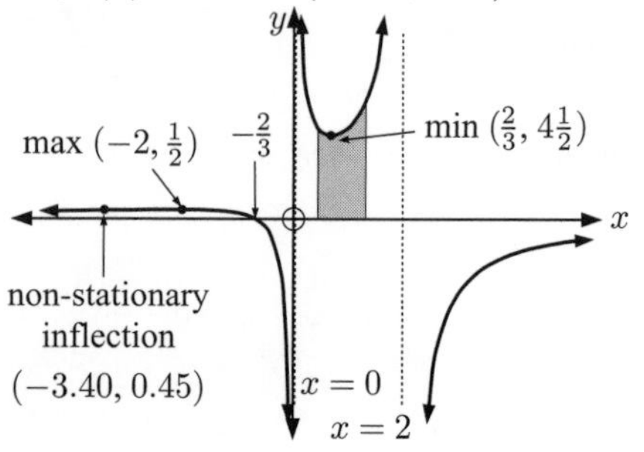

**e** Area $= \int_{\frac{1}{2}}^{1\frac{1}{2}} \left(\frac{1}{x} - \frac{4}{x-2}\right) dx$

$= \int_{\frac{1}{2}}^{1\frac{1}{2}} \left(\frac{1}{x} + \frac{4}{2-x}\right) dx$

$= [\ln x - 4\ln(2-x)]_{\frac{1}{2}}^{\frac{3}{2}}$ $\{2 - x > 0$ for $\frac{1}{2} \leqslant x \leqslant \frac{3}{2}\}$

$= (\ln \frac{3}{2} - 4\ln \frac{1}{2}) - (\ln \frac{1}{2} - 4\ln \frac{3}{2})$

$= \ln \frac{3}{2} - 4\ln \frac{1}{2} - \ln \frac{1}{2} + 4\ln \frac{3}{2}$

$= 5\ln \frac{3}{2} - 5\ln \frac{1}{2}$

$= 5(\ln \frac{3}{2} - \ln \frac{1}{2})$

$= 5\ln 3$ units$^2$

**19** **a** Let $f(x) = \dfrac{2x+6}{1-x}$

**i** A V.A. exists where $1 - x = 0$ $\therefore$ the V.A. is $x = 1$.

$y = \dfrac{-2x-6}{x-1} = \dfrac{-2(x-1)-8}{x-1} = -2 + \dfrac{-8}{x-1}$

$\therefore$ as $x \to \pm\infty$, $y \to -2$

$\therefore$ the H.A. is $y = -2$.

**ii** $f'(x) = \dfrac{2(1-x) - (2x+6)(-1)}{(1-x)^2}$

$= \dfrac{2 - 2x + 2x + 6}{(1-x)^2}$

$= \dfrac{8}{(1-x)^2}$

$\therefore$ $f'(x) > 0$ for all $x$.

Sign diagram of $f'(x)$:

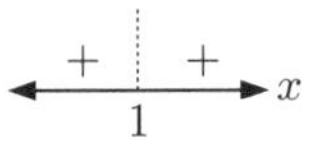


**iii** When $y = 0$, $x = -3$ $\therefore$ the $x$-intercept is $-3$.
When $x = 0$, $y = 6$ $\therefore$ the $y$-intercept is $6$.

**iv**

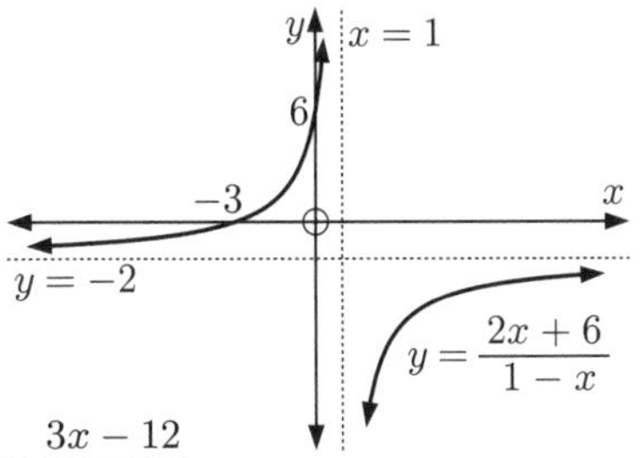


**b** Let $f(x) = \dfrac{3x-12}{x^2-4}$

**i** V.A.s occur when $x^2 - 4 = 0$

$\therefore$ $x = \pm 2$

$\therefore$ the V.A.s are $x = 2$, $x = -2$.

$y = \dfrac{\frac{3}{x} - \frac{12}{x^2}}{1 - \frac{4}{x^2}}$ $\therefore$ as $x \to \pm\infty$, $y \to 0$

$\therefore$ H.A. is $y = 0$.

**ii** $f'(x) = \dfrac{3(x^2-4) - (3x-12)(2x)}{(x^2-4)^2}$

$= \dfrac{3x^2 - 12 - 6x^2 + 24x}{(x+2)^2(x-2)^2}$

$= \dfrac{-3x^2 + 24x - 12}{(x+2)^2(x-2)^2}$

$= \dfrac{-3(x^2 - 8x + 4)}{(x+2)^2(x-2)^2}$

Now $x^2 - 8x + 4 = 0$

when $x = \dfrac{8 \pm \sqrt{64 - 4(1)(4)}}{2}$

$\therefore$ $x = \dfrac{8 \pm \sqrt{48}}{2} = 4 \pm 2\sqrt{3}$

Sign diagram of $f'(x)$:

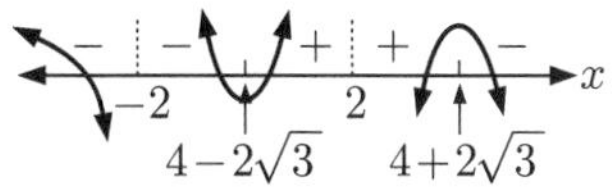


$\therefore$ there is a local maximum at $(4 + 2\sqrt{3}, f(4 + 2\sqrt{3}))$
or $(7.464, 0.201)$
and a local minimum at $(4 - 2\sqrt{3}, f(4 - 2\sqrt{3}))$
or $(0.536, 2.80)$.

**iii** When $y = 0$, $3x - 12 = 0$

$\therefore$ $x = 4$

$\therefore$ the $x$-intercept is 4.

When $x = 0$, $y = 3$ $\therefore$ the $y$-intercept is 3.

**iv**

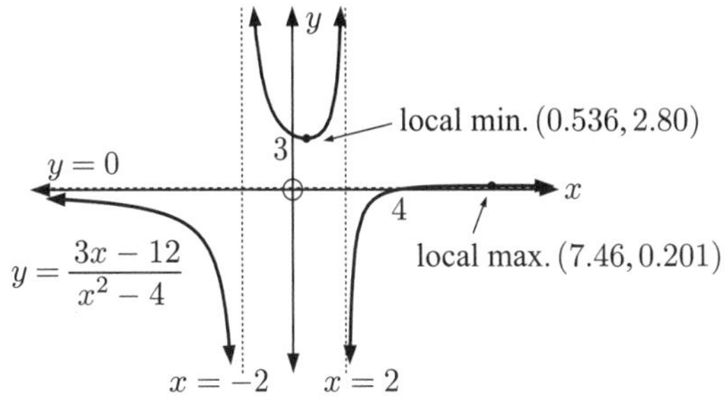


**c** Let $f(x) = \dfrac{5x}{(x+2)^2}$

**i** A V.A. exists where $x + 2 = 0$

$\therefore$ the V.A. is $x = -2$.

As $x \to \pm\infty$, $y \to 0$

$\therefore$ the H.A. is $y = 0$.

**ii** $f'(x) = \dfrac{5(x+2)^2 - 5x \times 2(x+2)(1)}{(x+2)^4}$

$= \dfrac{5(x+2) - 10x}{(x+2)^3}$

$= \dfrac{-5x + 10}{(x+2)^3} = \dfrac{-5(x-2)}{(x+2)^3}$

Sign diagram for $f'(x)$:

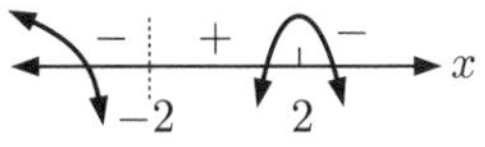


$\therefore$ there is a local maximum at $(2, \frac{5}{8})$.

**iii** When $y = 0$, $x = 0$ $\therefore$ the $x$-intercept is 0
When $x = 0$, $y = 0$ $\therefore$ the $y$-intercept is 0.

**iv**

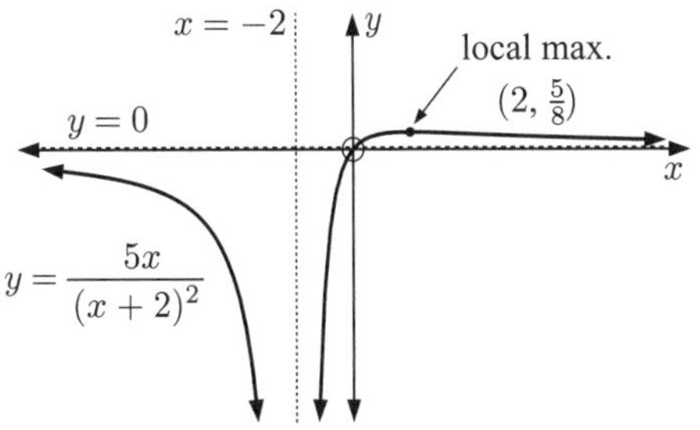


**20** **a** $v = 2t^{\frac{1}{2}} - t = t^{\frac{1}{2}}(2 - t^{\frac{1}{2}})$, $t \geqslant 0$

$\therefore$ $v = 0$ when $t = 0$ or $t^{\frac{1}{2}} = 2$

$\therefore$ $t = 0$ or $t = 4$

Sign diagram of $v$:

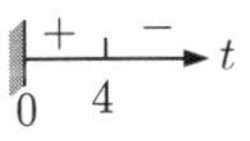


There is a reversal of direction at $t = 4$ s.

**b** $s = \int v \, d(t) = \int (2t^{\frac{1}{2}} - t)\, dt$

$= \dfrac{2t^{\frac{3}{2}}}{\frac{3}{2}} - \dfrac{t^2}{2} + c$

$= \frac{4}{3}t^{\frac{3}{2}} - \frac{1}{2}t^2 + c$

Thus $s(0) = c$,

$s(4) = \frac{4}{3}(4^{\frac{3}{2}}) - \frac{1}{2}(4^2) + c$
$= \frac{32}{3} - 8 + c = \frac{8}{3} + c$

and $s(9) = \frac{4}{3}(9^{\frac{3}{2}}) - \frac{1}{2}(9^2) + c$
$= \frac{4}{3}(27) - 40\frac{1}{2} + c$
$= 36 - 40\frac{1}{2} + c = c - 4\frac{1}{2}$

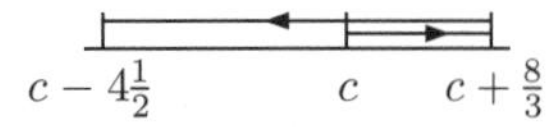


The total distance travelled $= \frac{8}{3} + \frac{8}{3} + 4\frac{1}{2}$ m $= 9\frac{5}{6}$ m.

**21 a** Area $= \int_1^9 x^{-\frac{1}{2}}\, dx$

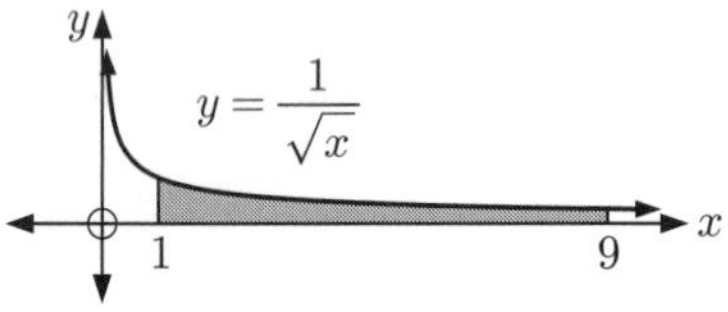


$= \left[\frac{x^{\frac{1}{2}}}{\frac{1}{2}}\right]_1^9$
$= [2\sqrt{x}]_1^9$
$= 6 - 2$
$= 4$ units$^2$

**b** Using technology, area $= \int_{1.3}^{3.5} x^{-\frac{1}{2}}\, dx \approx 1.46$ units$^2$.

**22** $y = 8x - x^2 = x(8-x)$ cuts the $x$-axis at 0 and 8

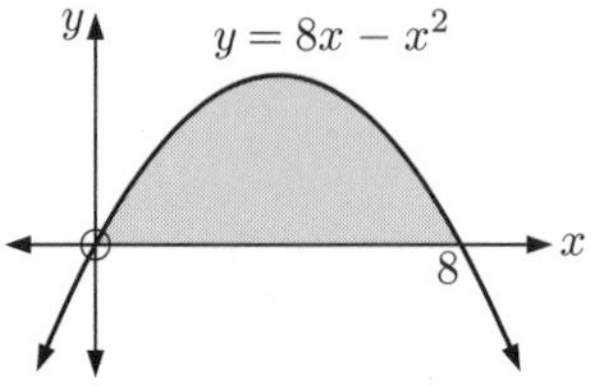


Area $= \int_0^8 \left(8x - x^2\right) dx$
$= \left[\frac{8x^2}{2} - \frac{x^3}{3}\right]_0^8$
$= \left(256 - \frac{512}{3}\right) - 0$
$= \frac{256}{3}$ units$^2$

**23** $y = x^2 - 3x$ meets $y = x$ where
$x^2 - 3x = x$
$\therefore\ x^2 - 4x = 0$
$\therefore\ x(x-4) = 0$
$\therefore\ x = 0$ or $4$

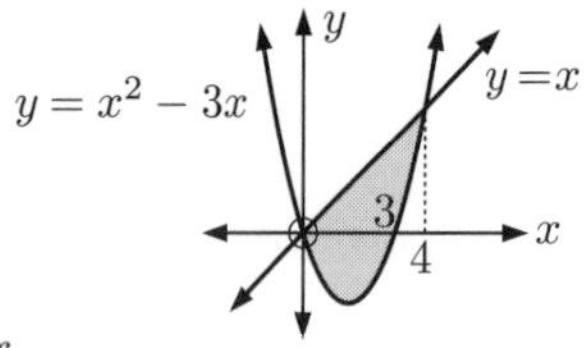


Area $= \int_0^4 \left(x - (x^2 - 3x)\right) dx$
$= \int_0^4 \left(4x - x^2\right) dx$
$= \left[\frac{4x^2}{2} - \frac{x^3}{3}\right]_0^4$
$= 32 - \frac{64}{3}$
$= \frac{32}{3}$ units$^2$

**24** $\int_0^k \sin x\, dx = 0.42$
$\therefore\ [-\cos x]_0^k = 0.42$
$\therefore\ -\cos k + \cos 0 = 0.42$
$\therefore\ \cos k = 0.58$
$\therefore\ k \approx 0.952 \quad \{0 \leqslant k \leqslant \pi\}$

**25 a** Area $= \int_0^3 (3x^2 + 1)\, dx$
$= \left[x^3 + x\right]_0^3$
$= 27 + 3 - (0 + 0)$
$= 30$ units$^2$

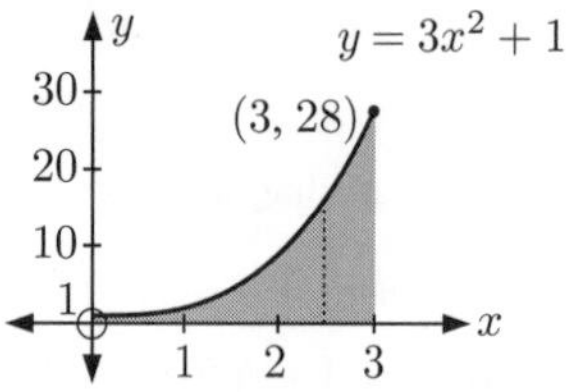


**b** If $\int_0^k (3x^2 + 1)\, dx = 10$
then $\left[x^3 + x\right]_0^k = 10$
$\therefore\ k^3 + k - 10 = 0$
for which the only real solution is $k = 2$
{using technology}

**26** $a = 6t - 30$ cm s$^{-2}$
$\therefore\ v = \int a\, dt = \int (6t - 30)\, dt$
$= 3t^2 - 30t + c$ cm s$^{-1}$

Now when $t = 0$, $v = 27 \quad \therefore\ c = 27$
$\therefore\ v = 3t^2 - 30t + 27$
$\therefore\ s = \int v\, dt = \int (3t^2 - 30t + 27)\, dt$
$= t^3 - 15t^2 + 27t + d$

But when $t = 0$, $s = 0 \quad \therefore\ d = 0$
$\therefore\ s = t^3 - 15t^2 + 27t$
Now $v = 3(t^2 - 10t + 9) = 3(t-1)(t-9)$

So, $v$ has sign diagram:

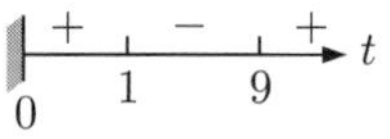


$\therefore$ the particle changes direction at $t = 1$ and $t = 9$ s.
$s(0) = 0$, $s(1) = 13$, $s(9) = 729 - 1215 + 243 = -243$

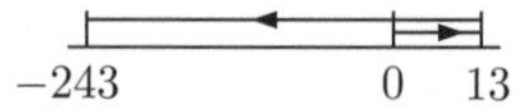


$\therefore$ the total distance travelled $= 13 + 256 = 269$ cm

**27 a** $\int_0^4 (2t+1)^{\frac{1}{2}}\, dt = 8\frac{2}{3}$ {using technology}

**b** $\int (x^3 + 2)^2\, dx = \int (x^6 + 4x^3 + 4)\, dx$
$= \frac{x^7}{7} + x^4 + 4x + c$

**28 a** $f(x) = 3x^4 + 8x^3 + 6x^2 - 8$
$\therefore\ f(-2) = 3(16) + 8(-8) + 6(4) - 8 = 0$
$\therefore\ x = -2$ is a zero of $f(x)$.

$f(0) = -8$ and $f(1) = 3 + 8 + 6 - 8 = 9$
As $f(0) < 0$, $f(1) > 0$, and $f(x)$ is continuous, the graph must cut the $x$-axis between $x = 0$ and $x = 1$. So, there is at least one other zero between $x = 0$ and $x = 1$.

**b** $f'(x) = 12x^3 + 24x^2 + 12x$
$= 12x(x^2 + 2x + 1)$
$= 12x(x+1)^2$

Sign diagram for $f'(x)$:

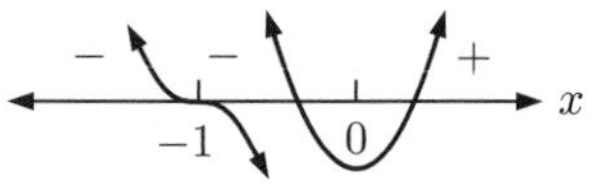


Now $f(-1) = -7$ and $f(0) = -8$.
$\therefore$ there is a local minimum at $(0, -8)$
and a stationary inflection at $(-1, -7)$.

**c**

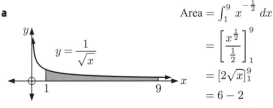

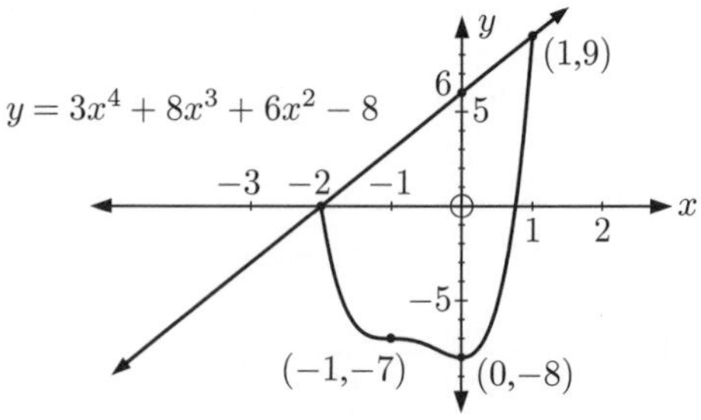


**d** The line cuts graph at $x = -2$ and $x = 1$
$\therefore$ it passes through $(-2, 0)$ and $(1, 9)$.

Its gradient is $\frac{9}{3} = 3$, so its equation is $\frac{y-9}{x-1} = 3$
$\therefore\ y - 9 = 3x - 3$
$\therefore\ 3x - y = -6$ *or* $y = 3x + 6$

**e** Area bounded
$= \int_{-2}^{1} [(3x + 6) - (3x^4 + 8x^3 + 6x^2 - 8)]\, dx$
$= \int_{-2}^{1} (-3x^4 - 8x^3 - 6x^2 + 3x + 14)\, dx$
$= 29.7$ units$^2$ {using technology}

**29** **a** $v(t) = e^{-2t}\ \text{m s}^{-1}$

$a(t) = v'(t) = e^{-2t}(-2)$

$\therefore$ when $a = -\frac{1}{4}$, $e^{-2t}(-2) = -\frac{1}{4}$

$\therefore \quad e^{-2t} = \frac{1}{8}$

$\therefore \quad e^{2t} = 8 \quad$ {reciprocals}

$\therefore \quad 2t = \ln 8$

$\therefore \quad t = \frac{1}{2}\ln 8 \approx 1.04$ s

**b** $s(t) = \int v(t)\,dt = \int e^{-2t}\,dt = -\frac{1}{2}e^{-2t} + c$

When $t = 0$, $s = 2$ $\therefore$ $2 = -\frac{1}{2}e^{0} + c$

$\therefore \quad 2 = -\frac{1}{2} + c$

$\therefore \quad c = 2\frac{1}{2}$

So, $s = -\frac{1}{2}e^{-2t} + 2.5$

$\therefore$ when $t = 1$, $s = -\frac{1}{2}e^{-2} + 2.5 \approx 2.43$ m

The particle is 2.43 m to the right of O.

**30** **a** $v(t) = 30 - 20e^{-0.2t}\ \text{m s}^{-1}$

$\therefore\ v(0) = 30 - 20e^{0} = 30 - 20(1) = 10\ \text{m s}^{-1}$

**b** $v(2) = 30 - 20e^{-0.4} \approx 16.59\ \text{m s}^{-1}$

**c** If $v = 20$ then $20 = 30 - 20e^{-0.2t}$

$\therefore \quad 20e^{-0.2t} = 10$

$\therefore \quad e^{-0.2t} = \frac{1}{2}$

$\therefore \quad e^{0.2t} = 2 \quad$ {reciprocals}

$\therefore \quad 0.2t = \ln 2$

$\therefore \quad t = 5\ln 2 \approx 3.466$

$\therefore \quad t \approx 3.5$ s

**d** As $t \to \infty$, $e^{-0.2t} \to 0$

$\therefore \quad v \to 30\ \text{m s}^{-1}$ (below)

**e** $v'(t) = 0 - 20(e^{-0.2t})(-0.2) = 4e^{-0.2t}$

$\therefore \quad a(t) = \dfrac{4}{e^{0.2t}}\ \text{m s}^{-2}$

Both numerator and denominator are positive so $a(t)$ is positive for all $t \geqslant 0$.

**f**

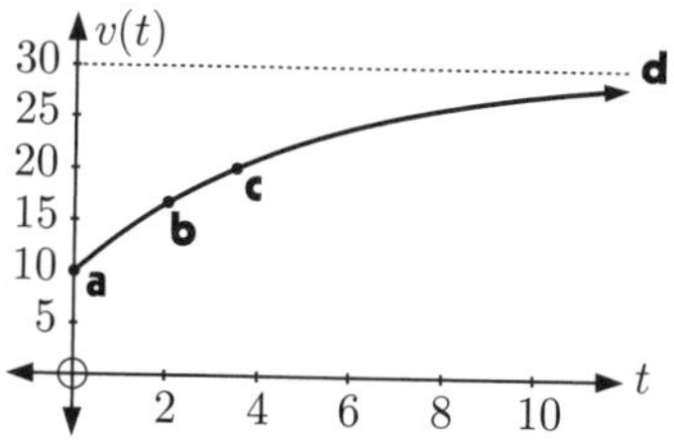


**g** $s(t) = \int v(t)\,dt = \int [30 - 20e^{-0.2t}]\,dt$

$= 30t - \dfrac{20e^{-0.2t}}{-0.2} + c$

$= 30t + 100e^{-0.2t} + c$

But $s(0) = 10$, so $0 + 100 + c = 10$

$\therefore \quad c = -90$

Hence $s(t) = 30t + 100e^{-0.2t} - 90$ m

**31** $\int_a^{2a} \sqrt{x}\,dx = 2$

$\therefore \quad \int_a^{2a} x^{\frac{1}{2}}\,dx = 2$

$\therefore \quad \left[\dfrac{x^{\frac{3}{2}}}{\frac{3}{2}}\right]_a^{2a} = 2$

$\therefore \quad \frac{2}{3}\left((2a)^{\frac{3}{2}} - a^{\frac{3}{2}}\right) = 2$

$\therefore \quad (2a)^{\frac{3}{2}} - a^{\frac{3}{2}} = 3$

Using technology, $a \approx 1.391$

**32** **a** $C(x) = \dfrac{8}{x^2} + \dfrac{1}{(2-x)^2}$

$\therefore \quad C(x) = 8x^{-2} + (2-x)^{-2}$

$\therefore \quad C'(x) = -16x^{-3} - 2(2-x)^{-3}(-1)$

$= -\dfrac{16}{x^3} + \dfrac{2}{(2-x)^3}$

**b** $C'(x) = 0$ when $\dfrac{2}{(2-x)^3} = \dfrac{16}{x^3}$

$\therefore \quad \dfrac{x^3}{(2-x)^3} = 8$

$\therefore \quad \left(\dfrac{x}{2-x}\right)^3 = 8$

**c** Now when $\left(\dfrac{x}{2-x}\right)^3 = 8$, $\quad \dfrac{x}{2-x} = 2$

$\therefore \quad x = 4 - 2x$

$\therefore \quad 3x = 4$

$\therefore \quad x = \frac{4}{3}$

Sign diagram for $C'(x)$:

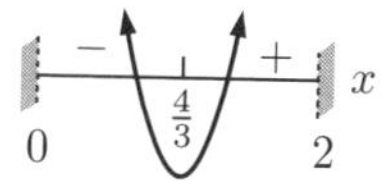


$\therefore$ the pollutants are minimised when $x = \frac{4}{3}$.

**33** **a** $N = (8-t)e^{t-6}, \quad 0 < t \leqslant 8$

$\therefore \quad \dfrac{dN}{dt} = (-1)e^{t-6} + (8-t)e^{t-6}(1)$

$= e^{t-6}(-1 + 8 - t)$

$= (7-t)e^{t-6}$

**b** **i** $\dfrac{dN}{dt} = 0$ when $t = 7$

Sign diagram for $\dfrac{dN}{dt}$:

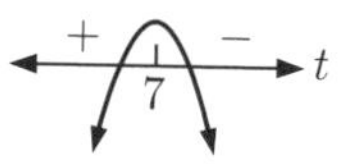


$N(7) = (1)e^1 = e$

$\therefore$ there is a local maximum at $(7, e)$.

**ii** $\dfrac{d^2N}{dt^2} = (-1)e^{t-6} + (7-t)e^{t-6}(1)$

$= e^{t-6}(-1 + 7 - t)$

$= e^{t-6}(6 - t)$

$\therefore \quad \dfrac{d^2N}{dt^2} = 0$ when $t = 6$.

Sign diagram for $\dfrac{d^2N}{dt^2}$:

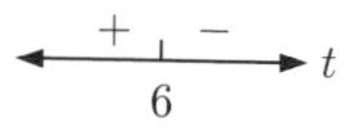


$N(6) = 2e^0 = 2(1) = 2$

$\therefore$ there is a non-stationary inflection point at $(6, 2)$.

**iii** The graph cuts the $t$-axis when $N = 0$

$\therefore \ (8-t)e^{t-6} = 0$

$\therefore \ t = 8$ as $e^{t-6} > 0$ for all $t$.

**c** **i** When all bacteria are dead, $N = 0$ $\therefore$ $t = 8$ hours.

**ii** The maximum number of bacteria in the sample is $e$ million $\approx 2.72 \times 10^6$ bacteria

**iii** The rate of increase is a maximum when $\dfrac{d^2N}{dt^2} = 0$.

This is at $t = 6$ hours.

**d**

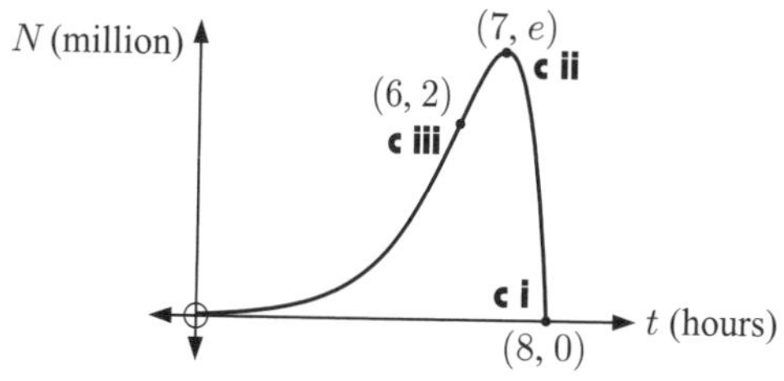

**34** **a** $y=\sin(2x+3)$

$\therefore\ \dfrac{dy}{dx}=2\cos(2x+3)$

$\therefore$ when $x=0.4$, $\dfrac{dy}{dx}=2\cos(3.8)\approx -1.58$

So, the gradient of the tangent $\approx -1.58$

**b** Using technology, $\int_{0.1}^{0.9} e^{\cos^2 x}\,dx \approx 1.71$

**35**

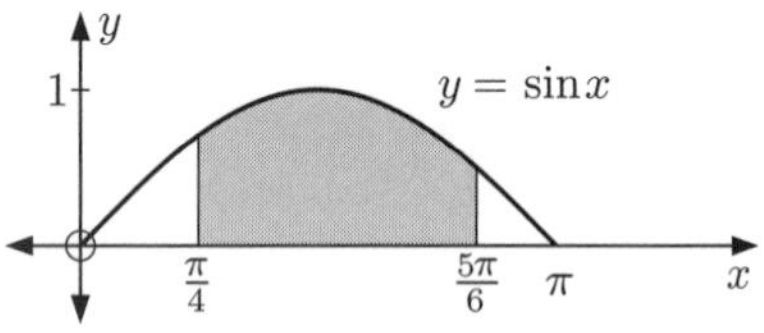


$$\begin{aligned}V&=\pi\int_{\frac{\pi}{4}}^{\frac{5\pi}{6}}(\sin x)^2\,dx\\&=\pi\int_{\frac{\pi}{4}}^{\frac{5\pi}{6}}\left(\tfrac{1}{2}-\tfrac{1}{2}\cos 2x\right)dx\\&=\pi\left[\frac{x}{2}-\tfrac{1}{2}\left(\tfrac{1}{2}\right)\sin 2x\right]_{\frac{\pi}{4}}^{\frac{5\pi}{6}}\\&=\pi\left(\tfrac{5\pi}{12}-\tfrac{1}{4}\sin\left(\tfrac{5\pi}{3}\right)-\tfrac{\pi}{8}+\tfrac{1}{4}\sin\left(\tfrac{\pi}{2}\right)\right)\\&=\pi\left(\tfrac{7\pi}{24}+\tfrac{\sqrt{3}}{8}+\tfrac{1}{4}\right)\\&\approx 4.34\text{ units}^3\end{aligned}$$

**36** **a**

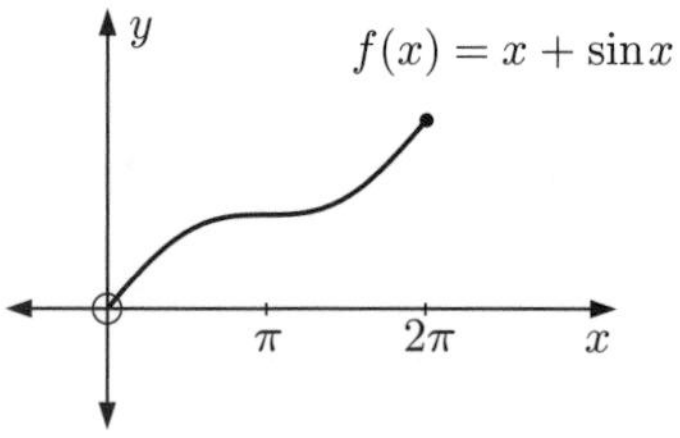


**b** Area $=\int_0^{\frac{\pi}{2}}(x+\sin x)\,dx$

$$\begin{aligned}&=\left[\frac{x^2}{2}-\cos x\right]_0^{\frac{\pi}{2}}\\&=\left(\tfrac{\pi^2}{8}-0\right)-(0-1)\\&=\tfrac{\pi^2}{8}+1\\&\approx 2.23\text{ units}^2\end{aligned}$$

**c** We need to solve $x+\sin x=x^2$

Using technology, $x=0$ or $x\approx 1.618$.

So, $a\approx 1.618$

**d**

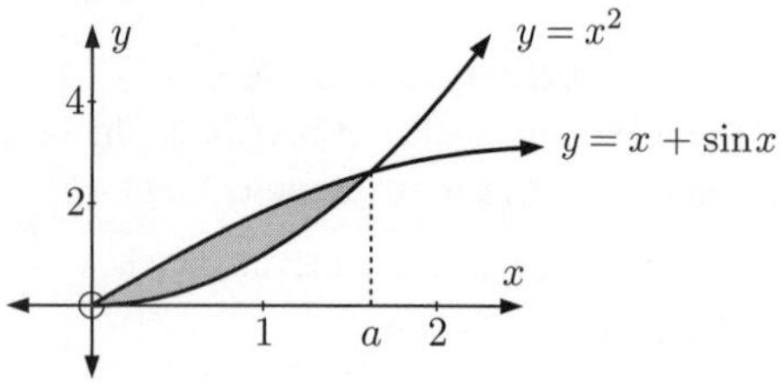


Area $=\int_0^a(x+\sin x-x^2)\,dx$

$$\begin{aligned}&=\left[\frac{x^2}{2}-\cos x-\frac{x^3}{3}\right]_0^a\\&\approx\left(\frac{(1.618)^2}{2}-\cos(1.618)-\frac{(1.618)^3}{3}\right)-(-1)\\&\approx 0.944\text{ units}^2\end{aligned}$$

**37** **a**

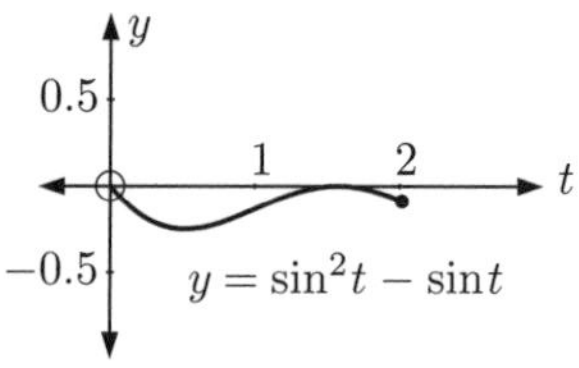


**b** The graph meets the $t$-axis when $y=0$

$\therefore\ \sin^2 t-\sin t=0$

$\therefore\ \sin t(\sin t-1)=0$

$\therefore\ \sin t=0$ or $1$

So, for $0\leqslant t\leqslant 2$, $t=0$ or $\frac{\pi}{2}$.

Area $=\int_0^2\left[0-(\sin^2 t-\sin t)\right]dt$

$\{f(t)$ touches the $t$-axis at $t=\frac{\pi}{2}\}$

$$\begin{aligned}&=\int_0^2\left[\sin t-\sin^2 t\right]dt\\&=\int_0^2\left[\sin t-\left(\tfrac{1}{2}-\tfrac{1}{2}\cos 2t\right)\right]dt\\&=\left[-\cos t-\frac{t}{2}+\tfrac{1}{2}\times\tfrac{1}{2}\sin 2t\right]_0^2\\&=\left(-\cos 2-1+\tfrac{1}{4}\sin 4\right)-(-1-0+0)\\&\approx 0.227\text{ units}^2\end{aligned}$$

**38** Since $y=x^2+1$ is symmetric about the $y$-axis,

$$\begin{aligned}&\int_0^k\left(x^2+1\right)dx=12\\\therefore\ &\left[\frac{x^3}{3}+x\right]_0^k=12\\\therefore\ &\left(\frac{k^3}{3}+k\right)-(0)=12\\\therefore\ &k^3+3k=36\\\therefore\ &k^3+3k-36=0\end{aligned}$$

Using technology, the only real solution is $k=3$.

**39** **a** Acceleration, $a=4\cos t$ m s$^{-2}$

$\therefore\ v=\int 4\cos t\,dt=4\sin t+c$

But when $t=0$, $v=2$ $\therefore\ 2=4(0)+c$

$\therefore\ c=2$

$\therefore\ v=4\sin t+2$ m s$^{-1}$

$\therefore\ v(4)\approx -1.03$ m s$^{-1}$

**b** Now $v=0$ when $\sin t=-\frac{1}{2}$

For the domain $0\leqslant t\leqslant 5$, $t=\frac{7\pi}{6}$

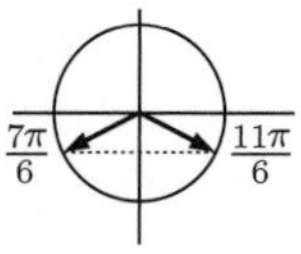


Sign diagram for $v$:

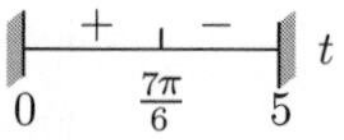


$\therefore$ there is a reversal of direction at $t=\frac{7\pi}{6}$ s

Now $s(t)=\int(4\sin t+2)\,dt$

$=4(-\cos t)+2t+d$

$=2t-4\cos t+d$

$\therefore\ s(0)=d-4$,

$s\left(\frac{7\pi}{6}\right)=2\left(\frac{7\pi}{6}\right)-4\cos\left(\frac{7\pi}{6}\right)+d$

$\approx d+10.794$

and $s(5)=10-4\cos 5+d\approx 8.865+d$

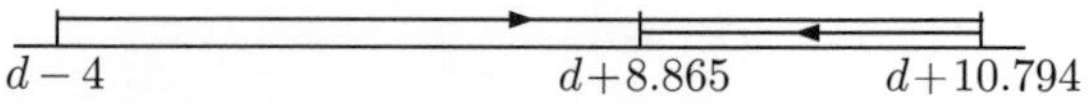


$\therefore$ the total distance travelled

$=(10.794+4)+(10.794-8.865)\approx 16.72$ m

**40** **a** $f(x) = 2\cos x - \sin x + 2x\sin x$

$\therefore \; f'(x) = -2\sin x - \cos x + 2\sin x + 2x\cos x$
$= 2x\cos x - \cos x$
$= (2x-1)\cos x$

**b** $f'(x) = 0$ when $2x - 1 = 0$ or $\cos x = 0$

$\therefore$ for $0 \leqslant x \leqslant 2$, $x = \frac{1}{2}$ or $x = \frac{\pi}{2}$

$f'(\frac{1}{4}) = -\frac{1}{2}\cos\frac{1}{4} < 0$

$f'(1) = \cos 1 > 0$

$f'(1.9) = 2.8 \times \cos 1.9 \approx -0.9052 < 0$

Sign diagram for $f'(x)$:

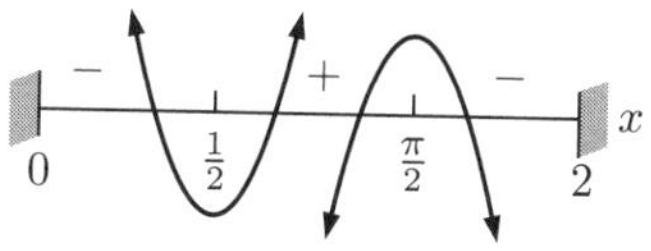


Now $f(\frac{1}{2}) = 2\cos\frac{1}{2} - \sin\frac{1}{2} + \sin\frac{1}{2}$
$\approx 1.755$

and $f(2) = 2\cos 2 - \sin 2 + 4\sin 2$
$= 2\cos 2 + 3\sin 2$
$\approx 1.896$

$\therefore$ the smallest value is $\approx 1.76$ when $x = \frac{1}{2}$.

**41** $\int_a^{a+2} \sin x \, dx = 0.3$

$\therefore \; [-\cos x]_a^{a+2} = 0.3$

$\therefore \; -\cos(a+2) + \cos a = 0.3$

$\therefore \; \cos a - \cos(a+2) = 0.3$

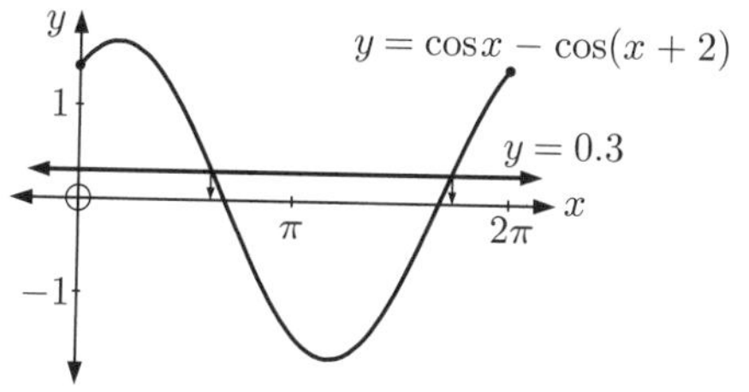


So, $x = a \approx 1.96$ or $5.46$ {using technology}

## SOLUTIONS TO EXAMINATION PRACTICE SET 1

**1** **a** **i** $y = 3e^{x^2} + 3(2-x)$
$= 3e^{x^2} + 6 - 3x$

$\therefore \; \frac{dy}{dx} = 3e^{x^2}(2x) + 0 - 3$
$= 6xe^{x^2} - 3$

**ii** $y = \ln(2x+5)$

$\therefore \; \frac{dy}{dx} = \frac{1}{2x+5} \times 2$

$\therefore \; \frac{dy}{dx} = \frac{2}{2x+5}$

**b** **i** $\int \sin(\pi - x)\,dx$
$= \left(\frac{1}{-1}\right)(-\cos(\pi - x)) + c$
$= \cos(\pi - x) + c$

**ii** $\int x(1+x)\,dx$
$= \int (x + x^2)\,dx$
$= \frac{x^2}{2} + \frac{x^3}{3} + c$

**2**

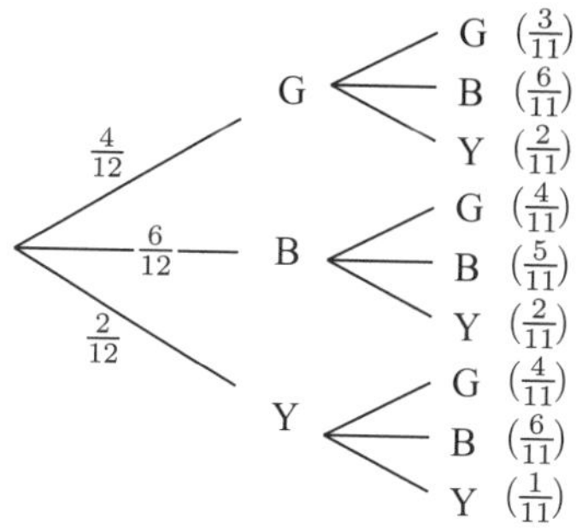


P(different colours)
$= 1 - \text{P(same colours)}$
$= 1 - \left(\frac{4}{12} \times \frac{3}{11} + \frac{6}{12} \times \frac{5}{11} + \frac{2}{12} \times \frac{1}{11}\right)$
$= 1 - \frac{44}{12 \times 11}$
$= 1 - \frac{1}{3}$
$= \frac{2}{3}$

**3** **a** $\log_7 A^3 = 3\log_7 A$
$= 3x$

**b** $\log_7 \frac{1}{\sqrt{A}} = \log_7 A^{-\frac{1}{2}}$
$= -\frac{1}{2}\log_7 A$
$= -\frac{1}{2}x$

**c** Let $\log_{49} A = m$

$\therefore \; A = 49^m = 7^{2m}$

$\therefore \; \log_7 A = 2m$

So, $\log_{49} A = \frac{1}{2}\log_7 A = \frac{1}{2}x$

**4** **a** $\mathbf{r} = \begin{pmatrix} 1 \\ 2 \end{pmatrix} + t\begin{pmatrix} 4 \\ -1 \end{pmatrix}$

$= \begin{pmatrix} 1 \\ 2 \end{pmatrix} + \begin{pmatrix} 4 \\ -1 \end{pmatrix} + (t-1)\begin{pmatrix} 4 \\ -1 \end{pmatrix}$

$= \begin{pmatrix} 5 \\ 1 \end{pmatrix} + s\begin{pmatrix} 4 \\ -1 \end{pmatrix}$ {where $s = t - 1$}

$\therefore$ **A** is the same line.

$\mathbf{r} = \begin{pmatrix} 1 \\ 2 \end{pmatrix} + t\begin{pmatrix} 4 \\ -1 \end{pmatrix}$

$= \begin{pmatrix} 1 \\ 2 \end{pmatrix} - 2\begin{pmatrix} 4 \\ -1 \end{pmatrix} + (t+2)\begin{pmatrix} 4 \\ -1 \end{pmatrix}$

$= \begin{pmatrix} -7 \\ 4 \end{pmatrix} + s\begin{pmatrix} 4 \\ -1 \end{pmatrix}$ {where $s = t + 2$}

$\therefore$ **B** is the same line.

**C** is not the same line as the direction vector is $\begin{pmatrix} -4 \\ -1 \end{pmatrix}$ rather than $\begin{pmatrix} 4 \\ -1 \end{pmatrix}$ or $\begin{pmatrix} -4 \\ 1 \end{pmatrix}$.

$\mathbf{r} = \begin{pmatrix} 1 \\ 2 \end{pmatrix} + t\begin{pmatrix} 4 \\ -1 \end{pmatrix}$

$= \begin{pmatrix} 1 \\ 2 \end{pmatrix} + \frac{1}{3}t\begin{pmatrix} 12 \\ -3 \end{pmatrix}$

$= \begin{pmatrix} 1 \\ 2 \end{pmatrix} + s\begin{pmatrix} 12 \\ -3 \end{pmatrix}$ {where $s = \frac{1}{3}t$}

$\therefore$ **D** is the same line.

**b** $\begin{pmatrix} 0 \\ 3 \\ 4 \end{pmatrix}$ has length $\sqrt{0+9+16} = \sqrt{25} = 5$

So, the velocity vector is $800 \times \frac{1}{5}\begin{pmatrix} 0 \\ 3 \\ 4 \end{pmatrix} = 160\begin{pmatrix} 0 \\ 3 \\ 4 \end{pmatrix}$.

The position vector is $\mathbf{r} = \begin{pmatrix} 2 \\ 5 \\ 0.05 \end{pmatrix} + 160t\begin{pmatrix} 0 \\ 3 \\ 4 \end{pmatrix}$.

**5** **a** Vertical asymptotes occur when $4 - x^2 = 0$

$\therefore \; x^2 = 4$

$\therefore$ the vertical asymptotes are $x = -2$ and $x = 2$.

**b** $f(x) = \frac{4}{\sqrt{4 - x^2}} = 4(4 - x^2)^{-\frac{1}{2}}$

$\therefore \; f'(x) = 4\left(-\frac{1}{2}\right)\left(4 - x^2\right)^{-\frac{3}{2}}(-2x)$
$= 4x(4 - x^2)^{-\frac{3}{2}}$

$f'(x)$ has sign diagram:

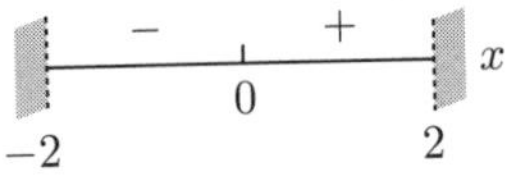


Now $f(0) = \frac{4}{\sqrt{4}} = 2$

$\therefore$ there is a local minimum at $(0, 2)$.

**c**

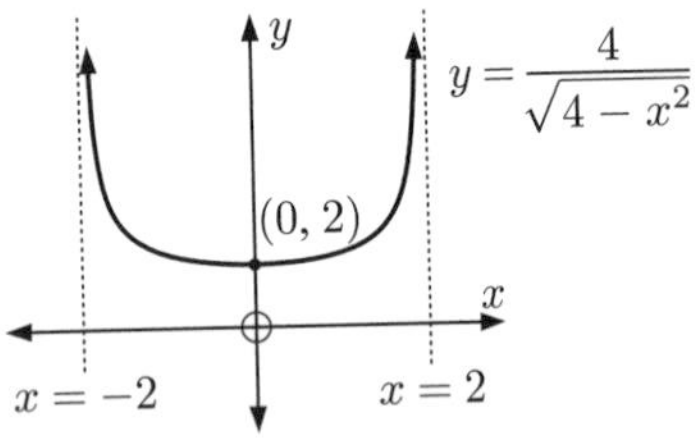


**6** To obtain $y = 2f(x-1) - 3$ we stretch vertically with dilation factor 2, then translate through $\begin{pmatrix} 1 \\ -3 \end{pmatrix}$.

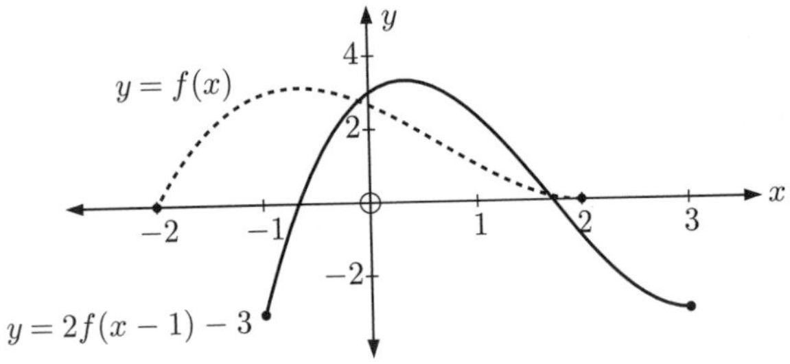


**7**
- $a > 0$ as the parabola opens upwards
- $c$ is the $y$-intercept, so $c > 0$
- The axis of symmetry is $x = \frac{-b}{2a}$ and so $\frac{-b}{2a} < 0$

  $\therefore$ since $a > 0$, $-b < 0$

  $\therefore$ $b > 0$
- $b^2 - 4ac = 0$ as the graph touches the $x$-axis

| *expression* | *positive* | *negative* | *zero* |
|---|---|---|---|
| $a$ | yes | no | no |
| $b$ | yes | no | no |
| $c$ | yes | no | no |
| $b^2 - 4ac$ | no | no | yes |

**8** **a** $g$ is $y = e^{-x}$

$\therefore$ $g^{-1}$ is $x = e^{-y}$

$\therefore$ $-y = \ln x$

$\therefore$ $y = -\ln x$

$\therefore$ $g^{-1}(x) = -\ln x$

**b** $(f \circ g)(x) = f(g(x))$

$= f(e^{-x})$

$= e^{-x} + \frac{1}{e^{-x}}$

$= e^{-x} + e^{x}$

**9** At $x = -5$, $\frac{dy}{dx} \approx -6$ At $x = 3$, $\frac{dy}{dx} = 0$

At $x = -2$, $\frac{dy}{dx} = 0$ At $x = 5$, $\frac{dy}{dx} \approx -4$

At $x = 0$, $\frac{dy}{dx} \approx 1$ At $x = 6$, $\frac{dy}{dx} \approx -9$

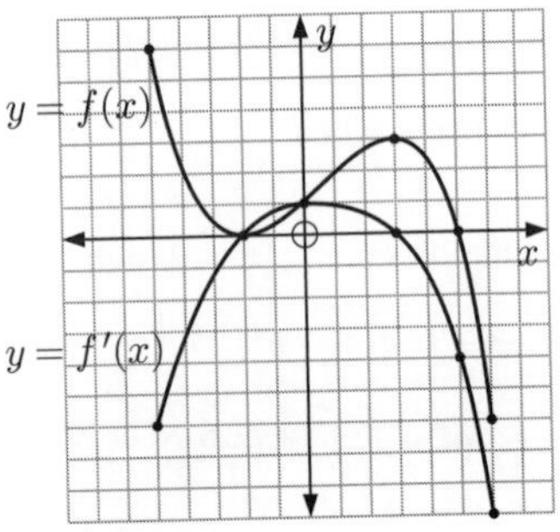


**10** **a** $kx^2 - 7x + 4 = 0$ has $\Delta = b^2 - 4ac$

$= 49 - 4(k)(4)$

$= 49 - 16k$

There is exactly one solution if $\Delta = 0$

$\therefore$ $49 - 16k = 0$

$\therefore$ $16k = 49$

$\therefore$ $k = \frac{49}{16}$

**b** $-1 \leqslant \sin(2x - \pi) \leqslant 1$

$\therefore$ $-3 \leqslant 3\sin(2x - \pi) \leqslant 3$

$\therefore$ $3\sin(2x - \pi) = n$ has no solutions if $n < -3$ or $n > 3$

**c** $y = 2\cos(4x + \pi)$

$\therefore$ $\frac{dy}{dx} = -2\sin(4x + \pi) \times 4$

$= -8\sin(4x + \pi)$

When $x = \frac{\pi}{8}$, $\frac{dy}{dx} = -8\sin(\frac{3\pi}{2}) = -8(-1) = 8$

So, the tangent has equation $y - 0 = 8(x - \frac{\pi}{8})$

which is $y = 8x - \pi$.

**11** **a** $|\mathbf{a}| = \sqrt{(-2)^2 + 6^2} = \sqrt{4 + 36} = \sqrt{40}$

**b** $2\mathbf{a} - 3\mathbf{b} = \begin{pmatrix} -4 \\ 12 \end{pmatrix} - \begin{pmatrix} 12 \\ -15 \end{pmatrix} = \begin{pmatrix} -16 \\ 27 \end{pmatrix}$

**c** $\mathbf{a} \bullet \mathbf{b} = (-8) + (-30) = -38$

**d** $\mathbf{r} = \begin{pmatrix} 1 \\ 5 \end{pmatrix} + t\begin{pmatrix} 4 \\ -5 \end{pmatrix}$, $t \in \mathbb{R}$

**12** **a** $2x^2 - 3mx + 8 = 0$ has exactly one solution for $x$ if $\Delta = 0$

$\therefore$ $(-3m)^2 - 4(2)(8) = 0$

$\therefore$ $9m^2 = 64$

$\therefore$ $m^2 = \frac{64}{9}$

$\therefore$ $m = \pm\frac{8}{3}$

But $m > 0$, so $m = \frac{8}{3}$

**b** Consider $h : x \mapsto \sqrt{4x + 9}$ where $x \geqslant -2\frac{1}{4}$, $y \geqslant 0$

$h^{-1}$ is given by $x = \sqrt{4y + 9}$ where $x \geqslant 0$, $y \geqslant -2\frac{1}{4}$

Rearranging, $x^2 = 4y + 9$

$\therefore$ $y = \frac{x^2 - 9}{4}$

So, $h^{-1}(x) = \frac{x^2 - 9}{4}$ for $x \geqslant 0$

and $h^{-1}(10) = \frac{10^2 - 9}{4} = \frac{91}{4}$

**13**

| | *Girls* | *Boys* | *Total* |
|---|---|---|---|
| *Computer Games* | 10 | 12 | 22 |
| *Sport* | 34 | 24 | 58 |
| *Total* | 44 | 36 | 80 |

**a** P(prefers sport) $= \frac{58}{80} = \frac{29}{40}$

**b** P(prefers sport | a girl) $= \frac{34}{44} = \frac{17}{22}$

**14** $(ax - 3)^4$

$= (ax)^4 + 4(ax)^3(-3) + 6(ax)^2(-3)^2 + 4(ax)(-3)^3 + (-3)^4$

$= a^4x^4 - 12a^3x^3 + 54a^2x^2 - 108ax + 81$

**15 a** $\mathbf{A} = \begin{pmatrix} 2 & 4 \\ 3 & 2 \\ -1 & 2 \end{pmatrix}$ and $\mathbf{AB} = \mathbf{C}$

$3 \times 2 \quad 2 \times n \quad 3 \times n$

**i** $\mathbf{B}$ is $2 \times n$ and $\mathbf{C}$ is $3 \times n$, for $n = 1, 2, 3, 4, ....$

**ii** If $\mathbf{B} = \begin{pmatrix} -2 \\ 3 \end{pmatrix}$ then

$$\mathbf{C} = \begin{pmatrix} 2 & 4 \\ 3 & 2 \\ -1 & 2 \end{pmatrix}\begin{pmatrix} -2 \\ 3 \end{pmatrix} = \begin{pmatrix} 8 \\ 0 \\ 8 \end{pmatrix}$$

**b**
$$\begin{aligned}(\mathbf{A}+2\mathbf{I})(\mathbf{A}-3\mathbf{I}) &= \mathbf{A}^2 + 2\mathbf{IA} - 3\mathbf{AI} - 6\mathbf{I}^2 \\ &= \mathbf{A}^2 + 2\mathbf{A} - 3\mathbf{A} - 6\mathbf{I} \\ &= \mathbf{A}^2 - \mathbf{A} - 6\mathbf{I}\end{aligned}$$

If $(\mathbf{A}+2\mathbf{I})(\mathbf{A}-3\mathbf{I}) = \mathbf{O}$

then $\mathbf{A}^2 - \mathbf{A} - 6\mathbf{I} = \mathbf{O}$

$\therefore \mathbf{A}(\mathbf{A}-\mathbf{I}) = 6\mathbf{I}$ {form $\mathbf{AB} = 6\mathbf{I}$}

$\therefore \mathbf{A}\frac{1}{6}(\mathbf{A}-\mathbf{I}) = \mathbf{I}$

$\therefore \mathbf{A}^{-1} = \frac{1}{6}(\mathbf{A}-\mathbf{I})$

**16 a i** Volume = length × breadth × depth
$= 2x(x)y$
$= 2x^2y$

$\therefore 2x^2y = 9$ and so $y = \dfrac{9}{2x^2}$ .... $(*)$

**ii** Total surface area, $A = 2(2xx + xy + 2xy)$

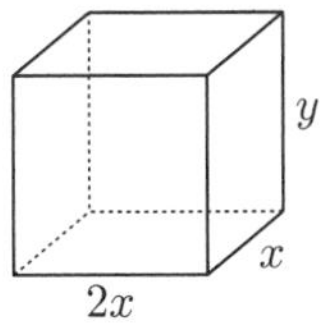


$\therefore A = 2(2x^2 + 3xy)$

$\therefore A = 4x^2 + 6xy$

$\therefore A = 4x^2 + 6x\left(\dfrac{9}{2x^2}\right)$ {from $(*)$}

$\therefore A = \left(4x^2 + \dfrac{27}{x}\right)$ m$^2$

**iii** Now $A = 4x^2 + 27x^{-1}$

$\therefore \dfrac{dA}{dx} = 8x - 27x^{-2} = 8x - \dfrac{27}{x^2} = \dfrac{8x^3 - 27}{x^2}$

$\therefore \dfrac{dA}{dx} = 0$ when $8x^3 - 27 = 0$

$\therefore x^3 = \frac{27}{8}$

$\therefore x = \frac{3}{2}$

Now $\dfrac{d^2A}{dx^2} = 8 + 54x^{-3} = 8 + \dfrac{54}{x^3}$

$\therefore \dfrac{d^2A}{dx^2} > 0$ for all $x > 0$

is the shape of $A$ against $x$.

$\therefore$ the minimum of $A$ occurs when $x = 1\frac{1}{2}$

and $y = \dfrac{9}{2(\frac{3}{2})^2} = \dfrac{9}{\frac{9}{2}} = 2$

$\therefore$ the tank is $1\frac{1}{2}$ m by 3 m by 2 m.

**b i** $f(x) = 1 - \dfrac{1}{1+x^2} = 1 - (1+x^2)^{-1}$

$\therefore f'(x) = 0 + (1+x^2)^{-2}(2x) = \dfrac{2x}{(1+x^2)^2}$

$f'(x)$ has sign diagram:

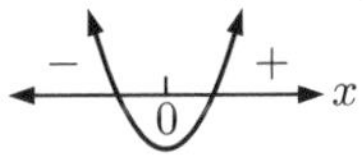


Now $f(0) = 1 - \frac{1}{1} = 1 - 1 = 0$

$\therefore$ there is a local minimum at $(0, 0)$.

**ii**
$$\begin{aligned}f''(x) &= \frac{2(1+x^2)^2 - 2x(2)(1+x^2)^1(2x)}{(1+x^2)^4} \\ &= \frac{2(1+x^2) - 8x^2}{(1+x^2)^3}\end{aligned}$$

$$\begin{aligned}\therefore f''(x) &= \frac{2-6x^2}{(1+x^2)^3} \\ &= \frac{2(1-3x^2)}{(1+x^2)^3} \\ &= \frac{2(1+\sqrt{3}x)(1-\sqrt{3}x)}{(1+x^2)^3}\end{aligned}$$

$f''(x)$ has sign diagram:

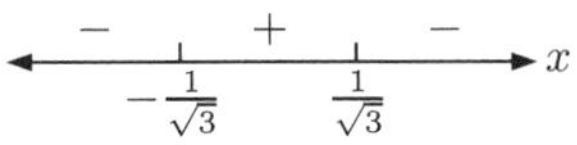


Now $f\left(-\frac{1}{\sqrt{3}}\right) = 1 - \dfrac{1}{1+\frac{1}{3}} = \frac{1}{4}$

and $f\left(\frac{1}{\sqrt{3}}\right) = 1 - \dfrac{1}{1+\frac{1}{3}} = \frac{1}{4}$

$\therefore$ there are points of inflection at $(-\frac{1}{\sqrt{3}}, \frac{1}{4})$ and $(\frac{1}{\sqrt{3}}, \frac{1}{4})$.

**iii** $f(x) = 1 - \dfrac{1}{1+x^2} = \dfrac{1+x^2}{1+x^2} - \dfrac{1}{1+x^2} = \dfrac{x^2}{1+x^2}$

$f(x)$ has sign diagram:

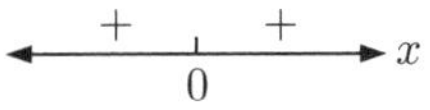


$\therefore f(x) \geqslant 0$ for all $x$.

**iv**

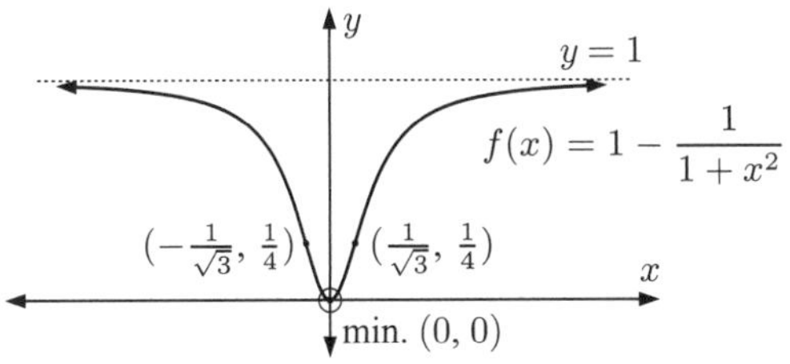


**17 a**

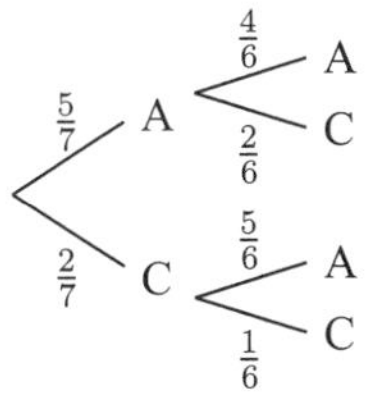


P(both same author)
$= \text{P(AA or CC)}$
$= \frac{5}{7} \times \frac{4}{6} + \frac{2}{7} \times \frac{1}{6}$
$= \frac{22}{42}$
$= \frac{11}{21}$

**b**

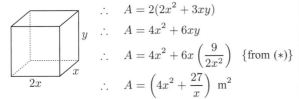

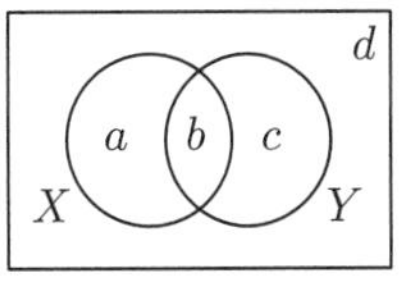


We are given
$$\begin{cases} a+b+c+d = 100 \\ a+b = 60 \\ b+c = 70 \\ b = 42 \end{cases}$$

$\therefore c = 28,\ a = 18$ and $d = 12$

**i (1)** $n(X \cup Y) = a + b + c = 88$

**(2)** $\text{P}(X') = \dfrac{28+12}{100} = 0.4$

**(3)** $\text{P}(Y \mid X') = \dfrac{c}{c+d} = \frac{28}{40} = 0.7$

**ii** $\text{P}(X \cap Y) = \dfrac{b}{a+b+c+d} = \dfrac{42}{100} = 0.42$

$\text{P}(X)\,\text{P}(Y) = \frac{60}{100} \times \frac{70}{100} = 0.42$

Since $\text{P}(X \cap Y) = \text{P}(X)\,\text{P}(Y)$, $X$ and $Y$ are independent.

**18 a i** $y = 10 - 3x$ cuts the $x$-axis when $y = 0$

$\therefore 10 - 3x = 0$

$\therefore x = 3\frac{1}{3}$

$\therefore$ P is at $(3\frac{1}{3}, 0)$.

$y = 10 - 3x$ cuts the $y$-axis when $x = 0,\ y = 10$

$\therefore$ Q is at $(0, 10)$.

**ii** Area $= \frac{1}{2} \times \text{base} \times \text{altitude}$
$= \frac{1}{2} \times 3\frac{1}{3} \times 10$
$= \frac{1}{2} \times \frac{10}{3} \times 10$
$= \frac{50}{3}$ units$^2$

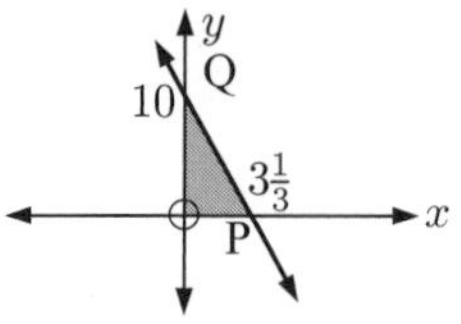


**b** The gradient of [AB] is $\dfrac{2 - -4}{6 - -2} = \frac{6}{8} = \frac{3}{4}$

$\therefore$ the gradient of the perpendicular is $-\frac{4}{3}$.

M is $\left(\dfrac{-2+6}{2}, \dfrac{-4+2}{2}\right)$ or $(2, -1)$.

So, the perpendicular has equation

$$y - -1 = -\tfrac{4}{3}(x - 2)$$
$$\therefore \quad 3(y + 1) = -4(x - 2)$$
$$\therefore \quad 3y + 3 = -4x + 8$$
$$\therefore \quad 4x + 3y = 5$$

**c** Area $= \displaystyle\int_1^2 \left(x + \frac{2}{x-3}\right) dx$

$= \displaystyle\int_1^2 \left(x - \frac{2}{3-x}\right) dx$

$= \left[\dfrac{x^2}{2} + 2\ln(3 - x)\right]_1^2 \quad \left\{\begin{array}{l}\text{since } 3 - x > 0 \\ \text{on } 1 \leqslant x \leqslant 2\end{array}\right\}$

$= (2 + 2\ln 1) - (\frac{1}{2} + 2\ln 2)$

$= 2 - \frac{1}{2} - 2\ln 2$

$= \frac{3}{2} - 2\ln 2$ units$^2 \qquad (a = \frac{3}{2},\ b = -2)$

**19 a i** $\mathbf{v} + 2\mathbf{w} = 3\mathbf{i} - 7\mathbf{j} + 2(5\mathbf{i} + 2\mathbf{j})$
$= 3\mathbf{i} - 7\mathbf{j} + 10\mathbf{i} + 4\mathbf{j}$
$= 13\mathbf{i} - 3\mathbf{j}$

**ii** $\mathbf{v} = \begin{pmatrix} 3 \\ -7 \end{pmatrix}$ and $|\mathbf{v}| = \sqrt{9 + 49}$
$= \sqrt{58}$ units

$\therefore$ a unit vector is $\frac{1}{\sqrt{58}}\begin{pmatrix} 7 \\ 3 \end{pmatrix}$. $\left\{\begin{pmatrix} 3 \\ -7 \end{pmatrix} \bullet \begin{pmatrix} 7 \\ 3 \end{pmatrix} = 0\right\}$

**iii** $(\mathbf{v} + \mathbf{w}) \bullet (\mathbf{v} - \mathbf{w})$
$= \mathbf{v} \bullet \mathbf{v} + \mathbf{w} \bullet \mathbf{v} - \mathbf{v} \bullet \mathbf{w} - \mathbf{w} \bullet \mathbf{w}$
$= |\mathbf{v}|^2 - |\mathbf{w}|^2 \quad \{\mathbf{x} \bullet \mathbf{y} = \mathbf{y} \bullet \mathbf{x}$ and $\mathbf{x} \bullet \mathbf{x} = |\mathbf{x}|^2\}$
$= (\sqrt{58})^2 - (\sqrt{25 + 4})^2$
$= 58 - 29$
$= 29$

**iv** $|3\mathbf{w}| = |3||\mathbf{w}| = 3\sqrt{29}$ units

**b i** $L_1$ is $\begin{pmatrix} x \\ y \\ z \end{pmatrix} = \begin{pmatrix} 4 \\ -11 \\ 5 \end{pmatrix} + t\begin{pmatrix} 1 \\ 2 \\ -1 \end{pmatrix}, \quad t \in \mathbb{R}$.

$L_2$ has direction vector $\begin{pmatrix} 10 - -2 \\ -4 - 2 \\ -2 - 16 \end{pmatrix} = \begin{pmatrix} 12 \\ -6 \\ -18 \end{pmatrix}$

$\therefore$ $L_2$ is $\begin{pmatrix} x \\ y \\ z \end{pmatrix} = \begin{pmatrix} 10 \\ -4 \\ -2 \end{pmatrix} + s\begin{pmatrix} 12 \\ -6 \\ -18 \end{pmatrix}, \quad s \in \mathbb{R}$.

**ii** $L_1$ meets $L_2$ where

$$\begin{pmatrix} 4 \\ -11 \\ 5 \end{pmatrix} + t\begin{pmatrix} 1 \\ 2 \\ -1 \end{pmatrix} = \begin{pmatrix} 10 \\ -4 \\ -2 \end{pmatrix} + s\begin{pmatrix} 12 \\ -6 \\ -18 \end{pmatrix}$$

$$\therefore \quad t\begin{pmatrix} 1 \\ 2 \\ -1 \end{pmatrix} - s\begin{pmatrix} 12 \\ -6 \\ -18 \end{pmatrix} = \begin{pmatrix} 6 \\ 7 \\ -7 \end{pmatrix}$$

$\therefore$ $t - 12s = 6$, (1) $\quad 2t + 6s = 7$, (2) $\quad -t + 18s = -7$ (3)

Adding (1) and (3), $6s = -1$ and so $s = -\frac{1}{6}$

$\therefore$ using (1), $t = 12s + 6 = -2 + 6 = 4$

In (2), $2t + 6s = 8 + (-1) = 7$ ✓

So, the lines meet at

$$\begin{pmatrix} x \\ y \\ z \end{pmatrix} = \begin{pmatrix} 4 \\ -11 \\ 5 \end{pmatrix} + 4\begin{pmatrix} 1 \\ 2 \\ -1 \end{pmatrix} = \begin{pmatrix} 8 \\ -3 \\ 1 \end{pmatrix}$$

which is the point $(8, -3, 1)$.

**iii** $L_1$ has direction vector $\begin{pmatrix} 1 \\ 2 \\ -1 \end{pmatrix}$.

$L_2$ has direction vector $\begin{pmatrix} 12 \\ -6 \\ -18 \end{pmatrix} = 6\begin{pmatrix} 2 \\ -1 \\ -3 \end{pmatrix}$.

If $\theta$ is the acute angle between $L_1$ and $L_2$, then

$$\cos\theta = \frac{|\mathbf{l}_1 \bullet \mathbf{l}_2|}{|\mathbf{l}_1|\,|\mathbf{l}_2|} = \frac{|2 - 2 + 3|}{\sqrt{1 + 4 + 1}\sqrt{4 + 1 + 9}} = \frac{3}{\sqrt{6}\sqrt{14}} = \frac{3}{\sqrt{84}}$$

**20 a**

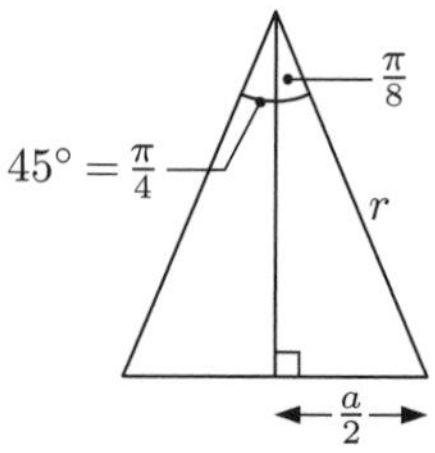


$\sin\frac{\pi}{8} = \dfrac{\frac{a}{2}}{r}$

$\therefore \quad \dfrac{a}{2} = r\sin\frac{\pi}{8}$

$\therefore \quad a = 2r\sin\frac{\pi}{8}$

**b** Area of octagon $= 8 \times$ area of one triangle
$= 8 \times \frac{1}{2}r^2\sin\frac{\pi}{4}$
$= 4r^2(2\sin\frac{\pi}{8}\cos\frac{\pi}{8})$
$= 8r^2\sin\frac{\pi}{8}\cos\frac{\pi}{8}$

**c i** $A$ = area of base + area of sides
$= 8r^2\sin\frac{\pi}{8}\cos\frac{\pi}{8} + 8 \times a \times h$
$= 8r^2\sin\frac{\pi}{8}\cos\frac{\pi}{8} + 8(2r\sin\frac{\pi}{8})h$

$\therefore \quad A = 8r(r\cos\frac{\pi}{8} + 2h)\sin\frac{\pi}{8}$ .... (1)

and $V$ = area of base × height

$\therefore \quad V = 8r^2h\sin\frac{\pi}{8}\cos\frac{\pi}{8}$ .... (2)

**ii** From (2), $h = \dfrac{V}{8r^2\sin\frac{\pi}{8}\cos\frac{\pi}{8}}$

Substituting into (1),

$$A = 8r\sin\tfrac{\pi}{8}\left(r\cos\tfrac{\pi}{8} + \frac{V}{4r^2\sin\frac{\pi}{8}\cos\frac{\pi}{8}}\right)$$

$$\therefore \quad A = 8r^2\sin\tfrac{\pi}{8}\cos\tfrac{\pi}{8} + \frac{2V}{r\cos\frac{\pi}{8}}$$

**iii** $A = 8r^2\sin\frac{\pi}{8}\cos\frac{\pi}{8} + \dfrac{2V}{\cos\frac{\pi}{8}}r^{-1}$

$\therefore \quad \dfrac{dA}{dr} = 16r\sin\frac{\pi}{8}\cos\frac{\pi}{8} - \dfrac{2V}{\cos\frac{\pi}{8}}r^{-2}$

$\therefore \quad \dfrac{dA}{dr} = 0$ when $16r\sin\frac{\pi}{8}\cos\frac{\pi}{8} = \dfrac{2V}{r^2\cos\frac{\pi}{8}}$

$\therefore \quad r^3 = \dfrac{2V}{16\sin\frac{\pi}{8}\cos^2\frac{\pi}{8}}$

$\therefore \quad r = \left(\dfrac{V}{8\sin\frac{\pi}{8}\cos^2\frac{\pi}{8}}\right)^{\frac{1}{3}}$

Now $\dfrac{d^2A}{dr^2} = 16\sin\frac{\pi}{8}\cos\frac{\pi}{8} + \dfrac{4V}{\cos\frac{\pi}{8}}r^{-3}$

$= 16\sin\frac{\pi}{8}\cos\frac{\pi}{8} + \dfrac{4V}{r^3\cos\frac{\pi}{8}}$

$\therefore\ \dfrac{d^2A}{dr^2} > 0$ for all $r > 0$

$\therefore$ the graph has shape

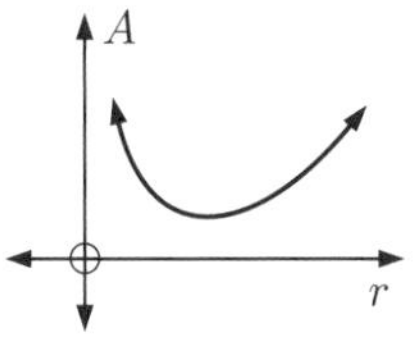


$\therefore$ the minimum value of $A$ occurs when

$r = \left(\dfrac{V}{8\sin\frac{\pi}{8}\cos^2\frac{\pi}{8}}\right)^{\frac{1}{3}}$.

## SOLUTIONS TO EXAMINATION PRACTICE SET 2

**1** **a** $u_1 = 8$ and $u_{30} = u_1 + 29d = 124$

$\therefore\ 8 + 29d = 124$

$\therefore\ 29d = 116$

$\therefore\ d = \frac{116}{29} = 4$

So, $u_{12} = u_1 + 11d$

$= 8 + 11 \times 4$

$= 52$

**b** $S_n = \dfrac{n}{2}(u_1 + u_n)$

$\therefore\ S_{12} = \frac{12}{2}(u_1 + u_{12})$

$= 6(8 + 52)$

$= 360$

**2** **a** $\mathbf{A} - \mathbf{B} = \begin{pmatrix} 2 & 7 & 6 \\ -1 & 3 & 2 \\ 4 & -2 & 0 \end{pmatrix} - \begin{pmatrix} -3 & 1 & 2 \\ 2 & 1 & -5 \\ -2 & 4 & 3 \end{pmatrix}$

$= \begin{pmatrix} 5 & 6 & 4 \\ -3 & 2 & 7 \\ 6 & -6 & -3 \end{pmatrix}$

**b** $\mathbf{AB} = \begin{pmatrix} 2 & 7 & 6 \\ -1 & 3 & 2 \\ 4 & -2 & 0 \end{pmatrix}\begin{pmatrix} -3 & 1 & 2 \\ 2 & 1 & -5 \\ -2 & 4 & 3 \end{pmatrix}$

$= \begin{pmatrix} -4 & 33 & -13 \\ 5 & 10 & -11 \\ -16 & 2 & 18 \end{pmatrix}$

**c** $|\mathbf{A}| = 2\begin{vmatrix} 3 & 2 \\ -2 & 0 \end{vmatrix} - 7\begin{vmatrix} -1 & 2 \\ 4 & 0 \end{vmatrix} + 6\begin{vmatrix} -1 & 3 \\ 4 & -2 \end{vmatrix}$

$= 2(4) - 7(-8) + 6(-10)$

$= 4$

**d** $\mathbf{B}^{-1} = \frac{1}{45}\begin{pmatrix} -23 & -5 & 7 \\ -4 & 5 & 11 \\ -10 & -10 & 5 \end{pmatrix}$ {using technology}

**3** **a** $A = 180^o - 43^o - 18^o = 119^o$

Using the sine rule, $\dfrac{a}{\sin 119^o} = \dfrac{35.6}{\sin 43^o}$

$\therefore\ a = \dfrac{35.6 \times \sin 119^o}{\sin 43^o}$

$\therefore\ a \approx 45.7$

So, the distance is about 45.7 cm.

**b** Area $= \frac{1}{2}ab\sin C$

$\approx \frac{1}{2} \times 45.6547 \times 35.6 \times \sin 18^o$

$\approx 251\ \text{cm}^2$

**4** $T_{r+1} = \binom{10}{r}(2x)^{10-r}5^r$

$= \binom{10}{r}2^{10-r}x^{10-r}5^r, \quad r = 0, 1, 2, ...., 10$

The power of $x$ is 6 when $10 - r = 6$

$\therefore\ r = 4$

When $r = 4$, $T_5 = \binom{10}{4}2^6 5^4 x^6$

So, the coefficient of $x^6$ is $\binom{10}{4}2^6 5^4$ or $8\,400\,000$.

**5** **a** $\begin{pmatrix} 1 & -3 \\ -2 & 1 \end{pmatrix}\begin{pmatrix} x \\ y \end{pmatrix} = \begin{pmatrix} -3 \\ -4 \end{pmatrix}$

$\therefore\ \begin{pmatrix} x \\ y \end{pmatrix} = \begin{pmatrix} 1 & -3 \\ -2 & 1 \end{pmatrix}^{-1}\begin{pmatrix} -3 \\ -4 \end{pmatrix}$

$\therefore\ \begin{pmatrix} x \\ y \end{pmatrix} = \begin{pmatrix} 3 \\ 2 \end{pmatrix}$ {using technology}

$\therefore\ x = 3,\ y = 2$

**b** **i** If an inverse exists then $\begin{vmatrix} 1 & p-2 \\ 2p & p^2 \end{vmatrix} \neq 0$

$\therefore\ p^2 - 2p^2 + 4p \neq 0$

$\therefore\ 4p - p^2 \neq 0$

$\therefore\ p(4-p) \neq 0$

$\therefore\ p \neq 0$ or 4

**ii** The inverse is $\dfrac{1}{4p - p^2}\begin{pmatrix} p^2 & 2-p \\ -2p & 1 \end{pmatrix}$

$= \begin{pmatrix} \dfrac{p^2}{4p-p^2} & \dfrac{2-p}{4p-p^2} \\ \dfrac{-2p}{4p-p^2} & \dfrac{1}{4p-p^2} \end{pmatrix}$

**6** $\mu = 3.18$, $\sigma = 0.195$, and let $X$ be the height of a randomly selected tree.

**a** **i** $\text{P}(X > 3) \approx 0.822$

**ii** $\text{P}(2.8 < X < 3.3) \approx 0.705$

**b** We need to find $k$ such that $\text{P}(X \geqslant k) = 0.2$ or $\text{P}(X \leqslant k) = 0.8$.

$\therefore\ \text{P}\left(\dfrac{X - 3.18}{0.195} \leqslant \dfrac{k - 3.18}{0.195}\right) = 0.8$

$\therefore\ \text{P}\left(Z \leqslant \dfrac{k - 3.18}{0.195}\right) = 0.8$

$\therefore\ \dfrac{k - 3.18}{0.195} = 0.841\,621$

$\therefore\ k - 3.18 = 0.164\,116$

$\therefore\ k \approx 3.344$

So, a tree must be about 3.34 m high to be in the tallest 20%.

**7** **a** $f(x) = 3\sin(2x+1)$

**i** $f'(x) = 3\cos(2x+1) \times 2$

$= 6\cos(2x+1)$

**ii** $\int f(x)\,dx = \int 3\sin(2x+1)\,dx$

$= 3(\frac{1}{2})(-\cos(2x+1)) + c$

$= -\frac{3}{2}\cos(2x+1) + c$

**b** $\int e^x(1 - e^{2x})\,dx = \int (e^x - e^{3x})\,dx$

$= e^x - \frac{1}{3}e^{3x} + c$

**8** **a** E is (0, 0, 6), M is (5, 4, 0), and G is (5, 8, 6).

**b** **i** $\overrightarrow{ME} = \begin{pmatrix} 0-5 \\ 0-4 \\ 6-0 \end{pmatrix} = \begin{pmatrix} -5 \\ -4 \\ 6 \end{pmatrix}$

**ii** $\overrightarrow{MG} = \begin{pmatrix} 5-5 \\ 8-4 \\ 6-0 \end{pmatrix} = \begin{pmatrix} 0 \\ 4 \\ 6 \end{pmatrix}$

**c**

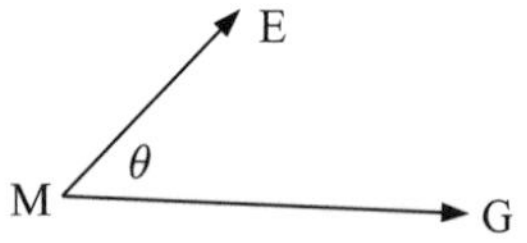


$\overrightarrow{ME} \bullet \overrightarrow{MG} = |\overrightarrow{ME}||\overrightarrow{MG}|\cos\theta$

$\therefore \quad 0 + (-16) + 36 = \sqrt{25+16+36}\sqrt{16+36}\cos\theta$

$\therefore \quad 20 = \sqrt{77}\sqrt{52}\cos\theta$

$\therefore \quad \cos\theta = \dfrac{20}{\sqrt{77 \times 52}}$

$\therefore \quad \theta \approx 71.6^o$

**9** **a**

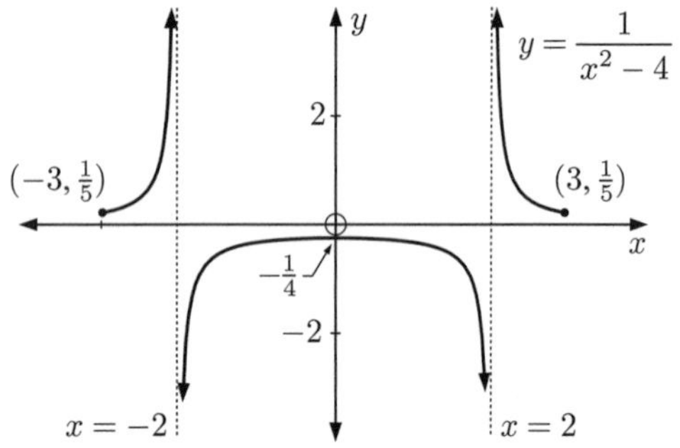


**b** The vertical asymptotes occur when $x^2 - 4 = 0$

$\therefore \quad x^2 = 4$

$\therefore$ the vertical asymptotes are $x = 2$ and $x = -2$.

**c** Range is $\{y \mid y \leqslant -\frac{1}{4} \text{ or } y \geqslant \frac{1}{5}\}$.

**10** **a**

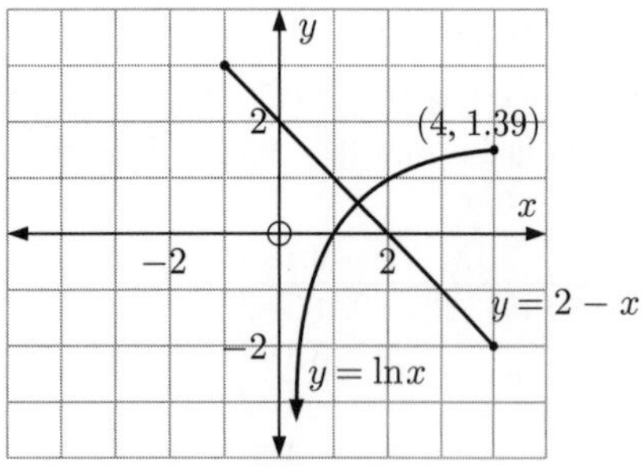


**b** $\ln x = 2 - x$ has solution $x \approx 1.56$ {using technology}

**11** **a** $3\cos^2\theta - 10\cos\theta + 3 = (3\cos\theta - 1)(\cos\theta - 3)$

**b** $3\cos^2\theta - 10\cos\theta + 3 = 0$

$\therefore \quad (3\cos\theta - 1)(\cos\theta - 3) = 0$

$\therefore \quad \cos\theta = \frac{1}{3}$ or 3

But all values of $\cos\theta$ lie between $-1$ and 1

$\therefore \quad \cos\theta = \frac{1}{3}$

$\therefore \quad \theta = \cos^{-1}(\frac{1}{3})$

or $360^o - \cos^{-1}(\frac{1}{3})$

$\therefore \quad \theta \approx 71^o$ or $289^o$

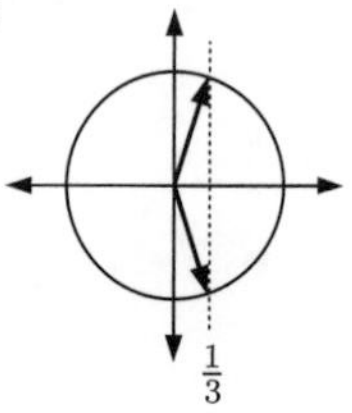


**12** **a** $u_0 = 12\,000$ euros

$u_1 = 12\,000 \times 1.072$

$u_2 = 12\,000 \times (1.072)^2$

$\vdots$

$u_t = 12\,000 \times (1.072)^t$ euros

**b** $u_4 = 12\,000 \times (1.072)^4$

$\approx 15\,847.49$ euros

**c** If $u_t = 25\,000$, $12\,000 \times (1.072)^t = 25\,000$

$\therefore \quad (1.072)^t = \frac{25}{12}$

$\therefore \quad \log(1.072)^t = \log(\frac{25}{12})$

$\therefore \quad t\log(1.072) = \log(\frac{25}{12})$

$t = \dfrac{\log(\frac{25}{12})}{\log(1.072)}$

$t \approx 10.557$

So, it will take 11 years as interest is paid annually.

**13** **a** $\overrightarrow{AC} = \begin{pmatrix} 7--2 \\ 2-0 \\ -1-3 \end{pmatrix} = \begin{pmatrix} 9 \\ 2 \\ -4 \end{pmatrix}$

$\therefore \quad |\overrightarrow{AC}| = \sqrt{81+4+16} = \sqrt{101}$ units

**b** $\overrightarrow{AB} = \begin{pmatrix} 1--2 \\ -3-0 \\ 5-3 \end{pmatrix} = \begin{pmatrix} 3 \\ -3 \\ 2 \end{pmatrix}$

$\therefore \quad |\overrightarrow{AB}| = \sqrt{9+9+4} = \sqrt{22}$ units

$\therefore$ a unit vector is $\frac{1}{\sqrt{22}}\begin{pmatrix} 3 \\ -3 \\ 2 \end{pmatrix}$.

**c** $\overrightarrow{AC} = \begin{pmatrix} 9 \\ 2 \\ -4 \end{pmatrix}$ and $\overrightarrow{AB} = \begin{pmatrix} 3 \\ -3 \\ 2 \end{pmatrix}$.

If the measure of $\widehat{CAB}$ is $\theta$ then

$\overrightarrow{AC} \bullet \overrightarrow{AB} = |\overrightarrow{AC}||\overrightarrow{AB}|\cos\theta$

$\therefore \quad 27 - 6 - 8 = \sqrt{101}\sqrt{22}\cos\theta$

$\therefore \quad 13 = \sqrt{101 \times 22}\cos\theta$

$\therefore \quad \cos\theta = \dfrac{13}{\sqrt{101 \times 22}}$

$\therefore \quad \theta \approx 74.0^o$

$\therefore \quad \widehat{CAB}$ has measure $\approx 74.0^o$.

**14** **a** Using the cosine rule,

$(AB)^2 = 16^2 + 16^2 - 2(16)(16)\cos 110^o$

$\therefore \quad AB = \sqrt{16^2 + 16^2 - 2(16)(16)\cos 110^o}$

$\therefore \quad AB \approx 26.2$ cm

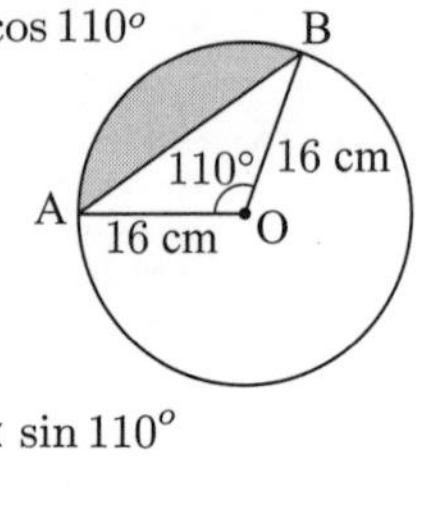


**b** Shaded area

$=$ area of sector $-$ area of $\Delta$

$= (\frac{110}{360}) \times \pi \times 16^2 - \frac{1}{2} \times 16 \times 16 \times \sin 110^o$

$\approx 125$ cm$^2$

**15** **a**

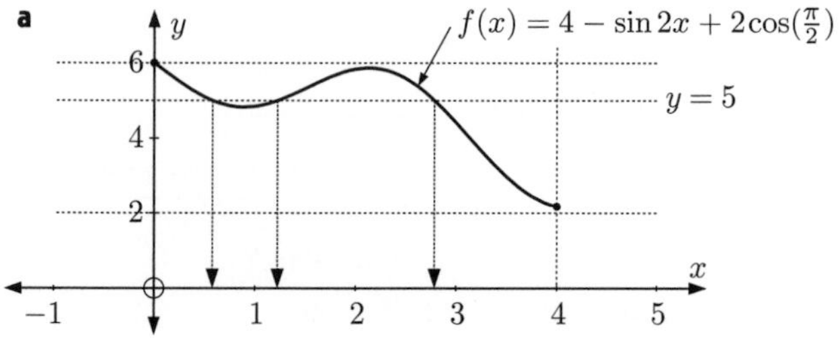

**b** If $f(x) = 5$ then $4 - \sin 2x + 2\cos(\frac{x}{2}) = 5$
Using technology, $x \approx 0.580,\ 1.226,$ or $2.789$

**c** The minimum value is $f(4) = 4 - \sin 8 + 2\cos 2$
$\approx 2.18$

**16 a** $\begin{vmatrix} 1 & 2 & -1 \\ 1 & k & 2 \\ 2 & -1 & 1 \end{vmatrix} = 0$

$\therefore\ 1\begin{vmatrix} k & 2 \\ -1 & 1 \end{vmatrix} - 2\begin{vmatrix} 1 & 2 \\ 2 & 1 \end{vmatrix} - 1\begin{vmatrix} 1 & k \\ 2 & -1 \end{vmatrix} = 0$

$\therefore\ k + 2 - 2(-3) - 1(-1 - 2k) = 0$

$\therefore\ k + 2 + 6 + 1 + 2k = 0$

$\therefore\ 3k = -9$

$\therefore\ k = -3$

**b i** (1, 0) lies on the circle if
$1^2 + 0^2 + p + 0 + s = 0$
$\therefore\ p + s = -1$ .... (1)
(2, 3) lies on the circle if
$2^2 + 3^2 + 2p + 3q + s = 0$
$\therefore\ 2p + 3q + s = -13$ .... (2)
(1, 6) lies on the circle if
$1^2 + 6^2 + p + 6q + s = 0$
$\therefore\ 37 + p + 6q + s = 0$
$\therefore\ p + 6q + s = -37$ .... (3)

**ii** Solving (1), (2) and (3) simultaneously using technology, $p = 6,\ q = -6,\ s = -7$.

**17 a i** When $t = 60,\ N \approx 50$. So, about 50 students took less than 60 seconds.

**ii** $\frac{1}{2}(200) = 100$ and when $N = 100,\ t = 65$
So, the median is 65 seconds.
$\frac{3}{4}(200) = 150$, so $Q_3 = 70$
$\frac{1}{4}(200) = 50$, so $Q_1 = 60$
$\text{IQR} = Q_3 - Q_1 = 70 - 60 = 10$ s

**iii** 90% of 200 = 180 $\therefore$ the 90th percentile is 80 s.

**b i** The random variable is the number of sponsorships obtained.

**ii** The possible outcomes are:

| | |
|---|---|
| 0 sponsorships, 9 failures | 5 sponsorships, 4 failures |
| 1 sponsorship, 8 failures | 6 sponsorships, 3 failures |
| 2 sponsorships, 7 failures | 7 sponsorships, 2 failures |
| 3 sponsorships, 6 failures | 8 sponsorships, 1 failure |
| 4 sponsorships, 5 failures | 9 sponsorships, 0 failures |

**iii** $X \sim B(9, 0.3)$

**(1)** $P(X = 4)$
$= \binom{9}{4}(0.3)^4(0.7)^5$
$\approx 0.172$

**(2)** P(at least 3)
$= P(X \geqslant 3)$
$= 1 - P(X \leqslant 2)$
$\approx 1 - 0.463$
$\approx 0.537$

**iv** The commission is $2.5\% = \$250$ per sponsorship plus $1\% = \$100$ per sponsorship after the first. The costs are \$150.
If $X$ is the number of sponsorships then the
profit $= \$(250X + 100(X - 1) - 150)$
$= \$(350X - 250)$
So, the profit $\geqslant \$1150$ when $X \geqslant 4$.
We need $P(X \geqslant 4) = 1 - P(X \leqslant 3)$
$\approx 1 - 0.730$
$\approx 0.270$

So, the probability she makes a profit of \$1150 or greater is 0.270.

**v** $n = 40$ and the costs have increased to \$300
$\therefore$ the profit $= \$(350X - 400)$
$\therefore$ the profit $= \$6600$ when $X = \dfrac{7000}{350} = 20$
$P(X < 20) = P(X \leqslant 19)$
$\approx 0.994$
So, the probability she makes a profit less than \$6600 is 0.994.

**18 a** $f(x) = e^{3x} \sin 2x$
$\therefore\ f'(x) = e^{3x}(3)\sin 2x + e^{3x}\cos 2x(2)$
$= e^{3x}(3\sin 2x + 2\cos 2x)$
$\therefore\ f'(x) = 0$ when $3\sin 2x + 2\cos 2x = 0$
{as $e^{3x} > 0$ for all $x$}
$\therefore\ 3\sin 2x = -2\cos 2x$
$\therefore\ \dfrac{\sin 2x}{\cos 2x} = -\frac{2}{3}$
$\therefore\ \tan 2x = -\frac{2}{3}$

**b i** The graph cuts the $x$-axis when $y = 0$

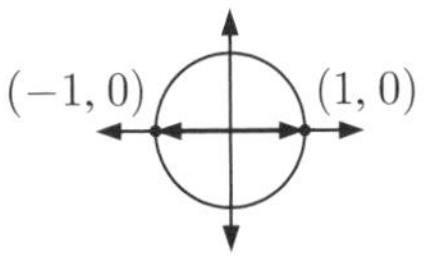


$\therefore\ e^{3x}\sin 2x = 0$
$\therefore\ \sin 2x = 0$
$\therefore\ 2x = 0 + k\pi$
$\therefore\ x = k(\frac{\pi}{2}),\quad k \in \mathbb{Z}$
The $x$-coordinate of B is $\frac{\pi}{2}$ when $k = 1$
and the $x$-coordinate of C is $\pi$ when $k = 2$.

**ii** A is a local maximum, so $f'(x) = 0$ at A.
$\tan 2x = -\frac{2}{3}$
$\therefore\ 2x = \tan^{-1}(-\frac{2}{3})$
$\therefore\ 2x = \pi - \tan^{-1}(\frac{2}{3})$
$\therefore\ 2x \approx 2.5536$
$\therefore\ x \approx 1.28$

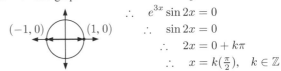

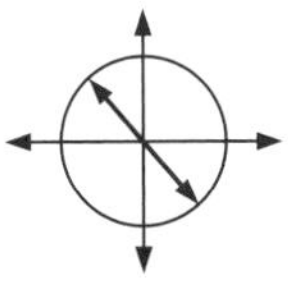

So, the $x$-coordinate of A $\approx 1.28$.

**c i** $g(x) = \frac{1}{13}(3e^{3x}\sin 2x - 2e^{3x}\cos 2x)$
$= \frac{3}{13}e^{3x}\sin 2x - \frac{2}{13}e^{3x}\cos 2x$
$\therefore\ g'(x) = \frac{3}{13}\left[e^{3x}(3)\sin 2x + e^{3x}\cos 2x(2)\right]$
$- \frac{2}{13}\left[e^{3x}(3)\cos 2x + e^{3x}(-\sin 2x)(2)\right]$
$= e^{3x}\left(\frac{9}{13}\sin 2x + \frac{6}{13}\cos 2x\right.$
$\left.- \frac{6}{13}\cos 2x + \frac{4}{13}\sin 2x\right)$
$= e^{3x}\left(\frac{13}{13}\sin 2x\right)$
$= e^{3x}\sin 2x$

**ii** Area $= \int_0^{\frac{\pi}{2}} e^{3x}\sin 2x\, dx$
$\approx 17.3$ units$^2$ {using technology}

**19 a**

| | | |
|---|---|---|
| A(4, 0, 0) | K(5, 6, 3) | P(5, 0, 3) |
| B(4, 6, 0) | L(−1, 6, 3) | Q(−1, 0, 3) |
| C(0, 6, 0) | M(2, 6, 5) | R(2, 0, 5) |

**b** $\overrightarrow{MK} = \begin{pmatrix} 5-2 \\ 6-6 \\ 3-5 \end{pmatrix} = \begin{pmatrix} 3 \\ 0 \\ -2 \end{pmatrix}$

$\therefore$ the line (MK) has equation
$\begin{pmatrix} x \\ y \\ z \end{pmatrix} = \begin{pmatrix} 2 \\ 6 \\ 5 \end{pmatrix} + t\begin{pmatrix} 3 \\ 0 \\ -2 \end{pmatrix},\quad t \in \mathbb{R}$

When $t = 0$ we are at M and when $t = 1$ we are at K

$\therefore$ the edge [MK] has equation

$$\begin{pmatrix} x \\ y \\ z \end{pmatrix} = \begin{pmatrix} 2 \\ 6 \\ 5 \end{pmatrix} + t \begin{pmatrix} 3 \\ 0 \\ -2 \end{pmatrix}, \quad 0 \leqslant t \leqslant 1.$$

**c** $\overrightarrow{MK} = \begin{pmatrix} 3 \\ 0 \\ -2 \end{pmatrix}$, $\overrightarrow{AC} = \begin{pmatrix} -4 \\ 6 \\ 0 \end{pmatrix}$

If the acute angle is $\theta$ then

$$\cos\theta = \frac{\left|\begin{pmatrix} 3 \\ 0 \\ -2 \end{pmatrix} \bullet \begin{pmatrix} -4 \\ 6 \\ 0 \end{pmatrix}\right|}{\sqrt{9+0+4}\sqrt{16+36+0}}$$

$$= \frac{|-12|}{\sqrt{13}\sqrt{52}}$$

$$= \tfrac{12}{26} = \tfrac{6}{13}$$

$$\therefore \theta = \cos^{-1}\left(\tfrac{6}{13}\right) \approx 62.5^o$$

So, the acute angle is about $62.5^o$.

**d** Let the top of the pole be T, so T is $(6, 2, 5)$.

A general point on [MK] is $(2+3t, 6, 5-2t)$, $0 \leqslant t \leqslant 1$

Using the distance formula,

$$\sqrt{(2+3t-6)^2 + (6-2)^2 + (5-2t-5)^2} = 5.05$$

$$\therefore (3t-4)^2 + 4^2 + (-2t)^2 = 25.5025$$

$$\therefore 9t^2 - 24t + 16 + 16 + 4t^2 - 25.5025 = 0$$

$$\therefore 13t^2 - 24t + 6.4975 = 0$$

$\therefore t \approx 0.3296$ or $1.5166$ {using technology}

But $0 \leqslant t \leqslant 1$, so $t \approx 0.3296$.

So, the point is $(2.99, 6, 4.34)$.

**20 a i**

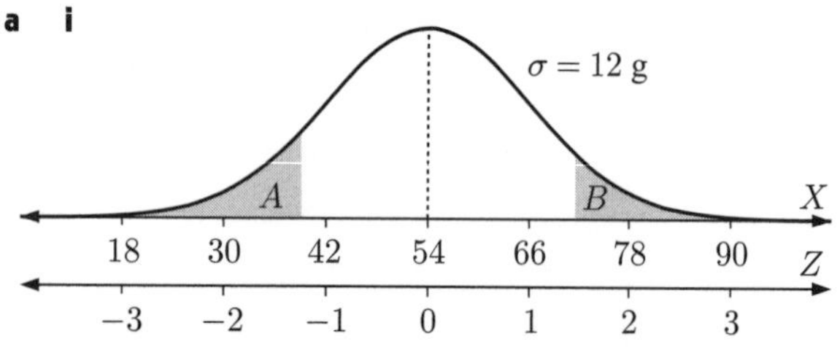


**ii** $\mu = 54$, $\sigma = 12$

We need to find $k$ such that $P(X \leqslant k) = 0.12$

Now $P(X \leqslant k) = 0.12$ means that

$$P\left(Z \leqslant \frac{k-54}{12}\right) = 0.12$$

$$\therefore \frac{k-54}{12} \approx -1.1750$$

$$\therefore k \approx 12 \times (-1.1750) + 54$$

$$\therefore k \approx 39.9$$

So, the greatest weight of any mouse in the lightest 12% of the population $\approx$ 39.9 grams.

**iii** We need to find $k$ such that $P(X \leqslant k) = 0.92$

$$\therefore P\left(Z \leqslant \frac{k-54}{12}\right) = 0.92$$

$$\therefore \frac{k-54}{12} \approx 1.4051$$

$$\therefore k \approx 12 \times 1.4051 + 54$$

$$\therefore k \approx 70.9$$

So, the lowest weight of a mouse in the top 8% of the population $\approx$ 70.9 grams.

**b**

$$P(X < 6) = 0.2$$

$$\therefore P\left(\frac{X-9}{\sigma} < \frac{6-9}{\sigma}\right) = 0.2$$

$$\therefore P\left(Z < -\frac{3}{\sigma}\right) = 0.2$$

$$\therefore -\frac{3}{\sigma} \approx -0.841\,62$$

$$\therefore \sigma \approx \frac{-3}{-0.841\,62} \approx 3.56$$

**c** Let X be the number of times Pele scores.

$X \sim B(20, 0.8)$.

**i** $E(X) = np = 20 \times 0.8 = 16$

So, he expects success on 16 occasions.

**ii** $P(X = 18) = \binom{20}{18}(0.8)^{18}(0.2)^2$

$\approx 0.137$

**iii** $P(X \geqslant 18) = 1 - P(X \leqslant 17)$

$\approx 1 - 0.794$

$\approx 0.206$

## SOLUTIONS TO EXAMINATION PRACTICE SET 3

**1 a**

$$f(x) = 2\cos(3x+1)$$

$$\therefore f'(x) = 2(-\sin(3x+1)) \times 3$$

$$= -6\sin(3x+1)$$

$$\therefore f''(x) = -6(\cos(3x+1)) \times 3$$

$$= -18\cos(3x+1)$$

**b** $\int 2\cos(3x+1)\,dx = 2(\tfrac{1}{3})\sin(3x+1) + c$

$= \tfrac{2}{3}\sin(3x+1) + c$

**2 a** $\sqrt{x-4}$ is defined when $x - 4 \geqslant 0$

or $x \geqslant 4$

So, the domain is $\{x \mid x \geqslant 4\}$.

**b** $\sqrt{\dfrac{1}{x-4}}$ is defined when $x - 4 > 0$

or $x > 4$

So, the domain is $\{x \mid x > 4\}$.

**c** $\sqrt{\ln(x-4)}$ is defined when $\ln(x-4) \geqslant 0$

$\therefore x - 4 \geqslant 1$

$\therefore x \geqslant 5$

So, the domain is $\{x \mid x \geqslant 5\}$.

**3 a** $p = -2$, $q = 6$ or vice versa

**b** $y = a(x+2)(x-6)$

When $x = 4$, $y = 3$, so $3 = a(6)(-2)$

$\therefore 3 = -12a$

$\therefore a = -\tfrac{1}{4}$

**c**

$$y = -\tfrac{1}{4}(x+2)(x-6)$$

$$= -\tfrac{1}{4}(x^2 - 4x - 12)$$

$$\therefore y = -\tfrac{1}{4}x^2 + x + 3$$

**4** $\cos^2 A + \sin^2 A = 1$

$\therefore \cos^2 A + \tfrac{64}{225} = 1$

$\therefore \cos^2 A = \tfrac{161}{225}$

$\therefore \cos A = \pm\tfrac{\sqrt{161}}{15}$

$\therefore \cos A = -\tfrac{\sqrt{161}}{15}$

{$A$ is obtuse}

$\therefore \sin 2A = 2\sin A\cos A$

$= 2\left(\tfrac{8}{15}\right)\left(-\tfrac{\sqrt{161}}{15}\right)$

$= \tfrac{-16\sqrt{161}}{225}$

**5** $f(x) = 6 - 2x, \; g(x) = x^2 + 3$

**a** $f$ has inverse given by $x = 6 - 2y$

$$\therefore \; 2y = 6 - x$$

$$\therefore \; y = \frac{6-x}{2}$$

$$\text{So, } \; f^{-1}(x) = \frac{6-x}{2}$$

$$\therefore \; f^{-1}(4) = \frac{6-4}{2} = 1$$

**b**
$$\begin{aligned}(g \circ f)(x) &= g(f(x)) \\ &= g(6-2x) \\ &= (6-2x)^2 + 3 \\ \therefore \; (g \circ f)(-2) &= (6+4)^2 + 3 \\ &= 103\end{aligned}$$

**6** **a** $3x^2 + 12x - 5 = 0$

$$\begin{aligned}\therefore \; x &= \frac{-12 \pm \sqrt{144 - 4(3)(-5)}}{6} \\ &= \frac{-12 \pm \sqrt{144+60}}{6} \\ &= \frac{-12 \pm \sqrt{204}}{6} \\ &= \frac{-12 \pm 2\sqrt{51}}{6} \\ &= -2 \pm \tfrac{1}{3}\sqrt{51}\end{aligned}$$

**b** $2\sin x + \sqrt{3} = 0, \quad 0 \leqslant x \leqslant 2\pi$

$$\therefore \; \sin x = -\tfrac{\sqrt{3}}{2}$$

$$\therefore \; x = \tfrac{4\pi}{3} \text{ or } \tfrac{5\pi}{3}$$

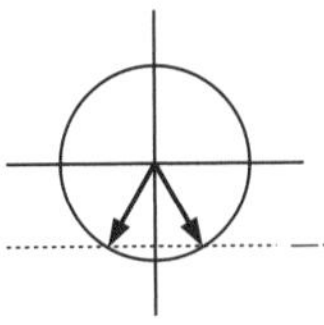


**7** **a** $\overrightarrow{AB} = \begin{pmatrix} 4-2 \\ -2--1 \\ 5-2 \end{pmatrix} = \begin{pmatrix} 2 \\ -1 \\ 3 \end{pmatrix}$

**b** $\overrightarrow{AC} = \begin{pmatrix} 5-2 \\ 2--1 \\ 1-2 \end{pmatrix} = \begin{pmatrix} 3 \\ 3 \\ -1 \end{pmatrix}$

$\therefore \; \overrightarrow{AB} \bullet \overrightarrow{AC} = 6 - 3 - 3 = 0$

$\therefore \; \overrightarrow{AB} \perp \overrightarrow{AC}$, and $B\widehat{A}C$ is a right angle.

**8**
$$\begin{aligned}&\log_b \frac{N^3}{M\sqrt{P}} \\ &= \log_b N^3 - \log_b MP^{\frac{1}{2}} \\ &= 3\log_b N - \left(\log_b M + \log_b P^{\frac{1}{2}}\right) \quad \{\text{logarithm laws}\} \\ &= 3\log_b N - \log_b M - \tfrac{1}{2}\log_b P \\ &= 3y - x - \tfrac{1}{2}z\end{aligned}$$

**9** **a** $v(t) = 30 - 6t^2 \text{ m s}^{-1}$

$$\therefore \; a(t) = \frac{dv}{dt} = -12t \text{ m s}^{-2}$$

$$\therefore \; a(5) = -60 \text{ m s}^{-2}$$

**b**
$$\begin{aligned}s(t) = \int v(t)\,dt &= \int (30 - 6t^2)dt \\ &= 30t - \frac{6t^3}{3} + c \\ &= 30t - 2t^3 + c \text{ m}\end{aligned}$$

But $s(0) = 15$, so $c = 15$

Hence $s(t) = 30t - 2t^3 + 15$ m

**10** When $x = 0, \; y = 70$

$\therefore \; a\cos 0 + c = 70$

$\therefore \; a + c = 70$

The amplitude is 20, so $a = 20$

$\therefore \; c = 50$

Now the period $= \dfrac{2\pi}{b} = \pi$

$\therefore \; b = 2$

$\therefore \; y = 20\cos 2x + 50$

*Check:* When $x = \frac{\pi}{2}, \; y = 20\cos\pi + 50$
$= 20(-1) + 50 = 30$ ✓

So, $a = 20, \; b = 2, \; c = 50$

**11** **a** **i** $\mathbf{M} + \mathbf{N} = \begin{pmatrix} 1 & a \\ b & c \end{pmatrix} + \begin{pmatrix} a & 2 \\ d & 0 \end{pmatrix} = \begin{pmatrix} 1+a & a+2 \\ b+d & c \end{pmatrix}$

**ii** $\mathbf{MN} = \begin{pmatrix} 1 & a \\ b & c \end{pmatrix}\begin{pmatrix} a & 2 \\ d & 0 \end{pmatrix} = \begin{pmatrix} a+ad & 2 \\ ab+cd & 2b \end{pmatrix}$

**b** **i** $\mathbf{A} - \mathbf{B} = \begin{pmatrix} 1 & 2 & a \\ b & 1 & c \\ 3 & 0 & 1 \end{pmatrix} - \begin{pmatrix} a & 0 & b \\ 1 & b & c \\ a & 1 & 1 \end{pmatrix}$

$= \begin{pmatrix} 1-a & 2 & a-b \\ b-1 & 1-b & 0 \\ 3-a & -1 & 0 \end{pmatrix}$

**ii** $\mathbf{AB} = \begin{pmatrix} 1 & 2 & a \\ b & 1 & c \\ 3 & 0 & 1 \end{pmatrix}\begin{pmatrix} a & 0 & b \\ 1 & b & c \\ a & 1 & 1 \end{pmatrix}$

which has 3rd column: $\begin{pmatrix} b+2c+a \\ b^2+2c \\ 3b+1 \end{pmatrix}$

**12** **a** **i** $\overrightarrow{BA} = \begin{pmatrix} -3-6 \\ 4--1 \end{pmatrix} = \begin{pmatrix} -9 \\ 5 \end{pmatrix}$

**ii** $\overrightarrow{BC} = \begin{pmatrix} -1-6 \\ 12--1 \end{pmatrix} = \begin{pmatrix} -7 \\ 13 \end{pmatrix}$

**b** $\overrightarrow{BA} \bullet \overrightarrow{BC} = 63 + 65 = 128$

**c** $\overrightarrow{AC} = \begin{pmatrix} -1--3 \\ 12-4 \end{pmatrix} = \begin{pmatrix} 2 \\ 8 \end{pmatrix}$

$\therefore \; |\overrightarrow{AC}| = \sqrt{4+64} = \sqrt{68}$ units

**d**

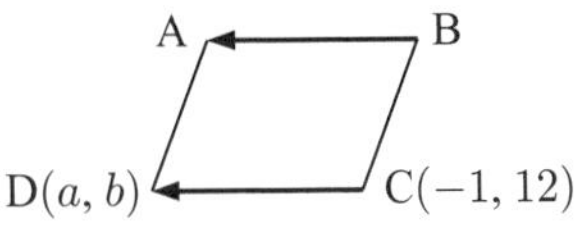


$\overrightarrow{CD} = \overrightarrow{BA}$

$\therefore \; \begin{pmatrix} a--1 \\ b-12 \end{pmatrix} = \begin{pmatrix} -9 \\ 5 \end{pmatrix}$

$\therefore \; a + 1 = -9$ and $b - 12 = 5$

$\therefore \; a = -10$ and $b = 17$

$\therefore$ D is at $(-10, 17)$.

**13** $(8, 4)$ lies on $ax + by = 32$

so $8a + 4b = 32$

$\therefore \; 2a + b = 8 \quad .... \; (1)$

Now $ax + by = 32$ has gradient $-\dfrac{a}{b}$

and $2x - 3y = 4$ has gradient $\frac{2}{3}$

Since the lines are perpendicular, $\left(-\frac{a}{b}\right)\left(\frac{2}{3}\right) = -1$

$\therefore \; 2a = 3b \quad .... \; (2)$

Substituting (2) into (1), $3b + b = 8$

$\therefore \; 4b = 8$

$\therefore \; b = 2$

Using (2), $2a = 6$, so $a = 3$

So, $a = 3, \; b = 2$

**14**

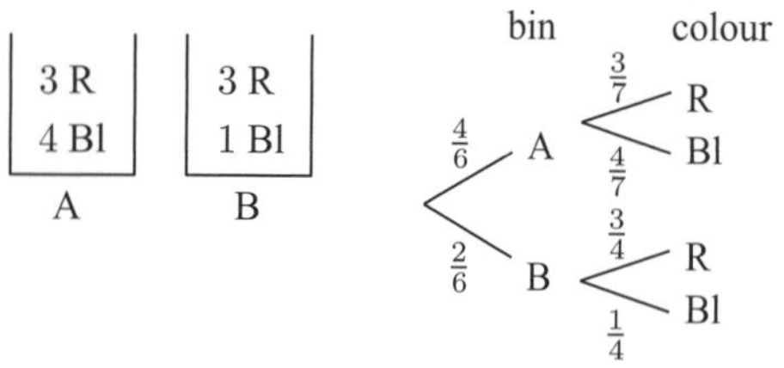


**a** P(Bl)

$= \text{P(A and BL or B and Bl)}$

$= (\frac{4}{6})(\frac{4}{7}) + (\frac{2}{6})(\frac{1}{4})$

$= \frac{13}{28}$

**b** P(B | Bl)

$= \dfrac{\text{P}(\text{B} \cap \text{Bl})}{\text{P(Bl)}}$

$= \dfrac{(\frac{2}{6})(\frac{1}{4})}{\frac{13}{28}}$

$= \frac{7}{39}$

**15** The lines meet when

$$\begin{pmatrix} 2 \\ 3 \\ -1 \end{pmatrix} + t\begin{pmatrix} -1 \\ 2 \\ 1 \end{pmatrix} = \begin{pmatrix} -3 \\ 1 \\ 4 \end{pmatrix} + s\begin{pmatrix} 1 \\ 2 \\ -1 \end{pmatrix}$$

$$\therefore \quad t\begin{pmatrix} -1 \\ 2 \\ 1 \end{pmatrix} - s\begin{pmatrix} 1 \\ 2 \\ -1 \end{pmatrix} = \begin{pmatrix} -5 \\ -2 \\ 5 \end{pmatrix}$$

So, $\begin{cases} -t - s = -5 \\ 2t - 2s = -2 \\ t + s = 5 \end{cases}$

$t + s = 5$
$t - s = -1$
adding, $2t = 4$

$\therefore \quad t = 2$ and $s = 3$

These values check in all three equations.

When $t = 2$, $\begin{pmatrix} x \\ y \\ z \end{pmatrix} = \begin{pmatrix} 2 \\ 3 \\ -1 \end{pmatrix} + 2\begin{pmatrix} -1 \\ 2 \\ 1 \end{pmatrix} = \begin{pmatrix} 0 \\ 7 \\ 1 \end{pmatrix}$

So, the lines meet at $(0, 7, 1)$.

**16** **a** $y = a + bx + x^2$ passes through B(1, 3),

so $3 = a + b + 1$ .... (1)

and also through C(4, 9), so $9 = a + 4b + 16$ .... (2)

So, $a + 4b = -7$ {from (2)}

$-a - b = -2$ {from (1)}

adding, $3b = -9$

$\therefore \quad b = -3$

Using (1), $a - 3 = 2$ and so $a = 5$

So, $a = 5$ and $b = -3$.

**b** The first parabola is $y = 5 - 3x + x^2$

$\therefore$ A is (0, 5) and so $p = 5$.

**c** For the first parabola, $\dfrac{dy}{dx} = -3 + 2x$

$\therefore$ at A(0, 5), $\dfrac{dy}{dx} = -3$

**d** For the second parabola, $\dfrac{dy}{dx} = q - 2x$

$\therefore$ at A(0, 5), $\dfrac{dy}{dx} = q$

**e** Comparing **c** and **d**, $q = -3$.

**17** **a** The first maximum is when $x = 1$

$\therefore \quad a = \frac{\pi}{2}$

**b** (AB) passes through (1, 1) and (2, 0)

Its gradient is $\dfrac{0-1}{2-1} = -1$

so its equation is $x + y = 2$

$\therefore \quad y = 2 - x$

**c** On the interval from A to B, $\sin\left(\frac{\pi}{2}x\right) \geqslant 2 - x$

$\therefore$ the shaded area

$= \int_1^2 \left(\sin(\frac{\pi}{2}x) - (2 - x)\right) dx$

$= \int_1^2 \left(\sin(\frac{\pi}{2}x) + x - 2\right) dx$

$= \left[-\frac{2}{\pi}\cos(\frac{\pi}{2}x) + \frac{1}{2}x^2 - 2x\right]_1^2$

$= \left[-\frac{2}{\pi}\cos\pi + \frac{1}{2}(4) - 4\right] - \left[-\frac{2}{\pi}\cos\frac{\pi}{2} + \frac{1}{2} - 2\right]$

$= \frac{2}{\pi} + 2 - 4 - \frac{1}{2} + 2$

$= \frac{2}{\pi} - \frac{1}{2}$ units$^2$

**18** **a** Let BD $= x$ cm.

Using the cosine rule in $\Delta$ABD,

$x^2 = 3^2 + 4^2 - 2(3)(4)\cos\alpha$

$\therefore \quad \cos\alpha = \dfrac{25 - x^2}{24}$

Using the cosine rule in $\Delta$BCD,

$x^2 = 1^2 + 5^2 - 2(1)(5)\cos\beta$

$\therefore \quad \cos\beta = \dfrac{26 - x^2}{10}$

If $\alpha = \beta$ then $\cos\alpha = \cos\beta$

$\therefore \quad \dfrac{25 - x^2}{\cancel{24}\,12} = \dfrac{26 - x^2}{\cancel{10}\,5}$

$\therefore \quad 5(25 - x^2) = 12(26 - x^2)$

$\therefore \quad 125 - 5x^2 = 312 - 12x^2$

$\therefore \quad 7x^2 = 187$

$\therefore \quad x^2 = \frac{187}{7}$

$\therefore$ since $x > 0$, $x = \sqrt{\frac{187}{7}}$

$\therefore \quad \text{BD} = \sqrt{\frac{187}{7}}$ cm

**b** Since the area of $\Delta$ABD = the area of $\Delta$BCD,

$\cancel{\tfrac{1}{2}} \times 3 \times 4 \times \sin\alpha = \cancel{\tfrac{1}{2}} \times 1 \times 5 \times \sin\beta$

$\therefore \quad 12\sin\alpha = 5\sin\beta$

$\therefore \quad \dfrac{\sin\alpha}{\sin\beta} = \frac{5}{12}$

**19** **a** $\log_x 2 = -\frac{1}{3}$

$\therefore \quad 2 = x^{-\frac{1}{3}}$

$\therefore \quad x^{\frac{1}{3}} = \frac{1}{2}$

$\therefore \quad x = \left(\frac{1}{2}\right)^3$

$\therefore \quad x = \frac{1}{8}$

**b** $\log_2 5 = 3\log_x 5$

$\therefore \quad \log_2 5 = \dfrac{3\log_2 5}{\log_2 x}$

$\therefore \quad \log_2 x = 3$

$\therefore \quad x = 2^3$

$\therefore \quad x = 8$

**c** $e^x = \dfrac{2}{e^x + 1}$

$\therefore \quad e^x(e^x + 1) = 2$

$\therefore \quad e^{2x} + e^x - 2 = 0$

$\therefore \quad (e^x + 2)(e^x - 1) = 0$

$\therefore \quad e^x = -2$ or $1$

But $e^x > 0$ for all $x$, so $e^x = 1$

$\therefore \quad x = 0$

**d** $\displaystyle\int_0^x \frac{1}{2t + 1}\,dt = 2$

$\therefore \quad \left[\frac{1}{2}\ln(2t + 1)\right]_0^x = 2$

$\therefore \quad \frac{1}{2}\ln(2x + 1) - \cancel{\tfrac{1}{2}\ln 1} = 2$

$\therefore \quad \ln(2x + 1) = 4$

$\therefore \quad 2x + 1 = e^4$

$\therefore \quad 2x = e^4 - 1$

$\therefore \quad x = \dfrac{e^4 - 1}{2}$

**20** **a** $f(x) = 3x^4 - 8x^3 - 6x^2 + 24x$

$f(0) = 0$, so $x = 0$ is a zero of the function.

**b**
$$f'(x) = 12x^3 - 24x^2 - 12x + 24$$
$$= 12(x^3 - 2x^2 - x + 2)$$
$$\therefore\ f'(2) = 12(8 - 8 - 2 + 2) = 0$$
$$\therefore\ f'(x) = 12(x-2)(x^2-1)$$
$$= 12(x-2)(x-1)(x+1)$$

$\therefore$ $f'(x)$ has sign diagram:

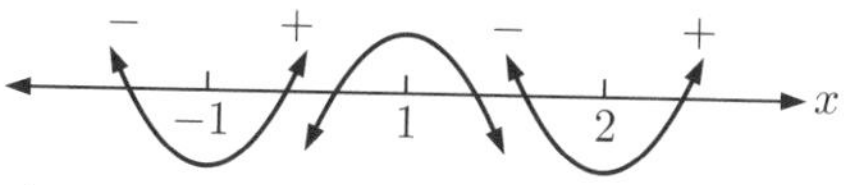


Now $f(-1) = 3 + 8 - 6 - 24 = -19$

$f(1) = 3 - 8 - 6 + 24 = 13$

$f(2) = 48 - 64 - 24 + 48 = 8$

So, there are local minima at $(-1, -19)$ and $(2, 8)$, and a local maximum at $(1, 13)$.

**c**
$$f''(x) = 36x^2 - 48x - 12$$
$$= 12(3x^2 - 4x - 1)$$
$$\therefore\ f''(x) = 0 \text{ when } x = \frac{4 \pm \sqrt{16 - 4(3)(-1)}}{2(3)}$$
$$= \frac{4 \pm \sqrt{28}}{6} = \frac{2 \pm \sqrt{7}}{3}$$

$\therefore$ $f''(x)$ has sign diagram:

$\therefore$ $f(x)$ is concave up on the intervals $x \leqslant \frac{2-\sqrt{7}}{3}$ and $x \geqslant \frac{2+\sqrt{7}}{3}$, and concave down on the interval $\frac{2-\sqrt{7}}{3} \leqslant x \leqslant \frac{2+\sqrt{7}}{3}$.

**d**

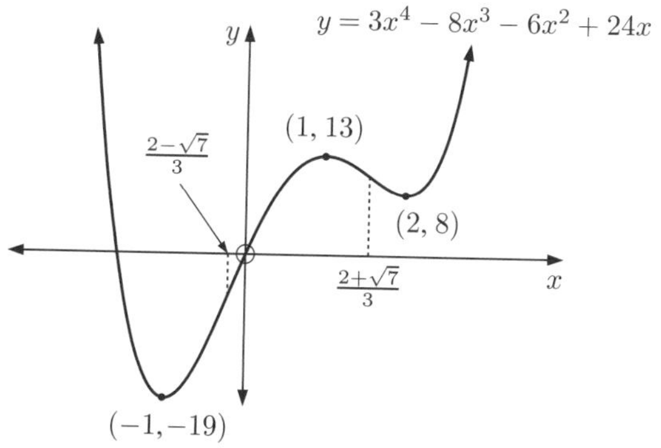


## SOLUTIONS TO EXAMINATION PRACTICE SET 4

**1** **a**
$$y = (x^2+9)^{\frac{1}{2}}$$
$$\therefore\ \frac{dy}{dx} = \tfrac{1}{2}(x^2+9)^{-\frac{1}{2}}(2x) = \frac{x}{\sqrt{x^2+9}}$$

**b** **i**
$$\int \left(x - \frac{4}{x}\right)^2 dx = \int \left(x^2 - 8 + \frac{16}{x^2}\right) dx$$
$$= \int (x^2 - 8 + 16x^{-2})\, dx$$
$$= \frac{x^3}{3} - 8x + \frac{16x^{-1}}{-1} + c$$
$$= \tfrac{1}{3}x^3 - 8x - \frac{16}{x} + c$$

**ii**
$$\int \frac{3}{2x+4}\, dx = 3(\tfrac{1}{2})\ln(2x+4) + c, \quad 2x+4 > 0$$
$$= \tfrac{3}{2}\ln(2x+4) + c, \quad x > -2$$

**c** $\int_0^2 e^{-x^2}\, dx \approx 0.8821$ {using technology}

**2**
$$\cos\theta = \frac{100^2 + 100^2 - 120^2}{2 \times 100 \times 100}$$
$$= 0.28$$
$$\therefore\ \theta \approx 73.74^o$$

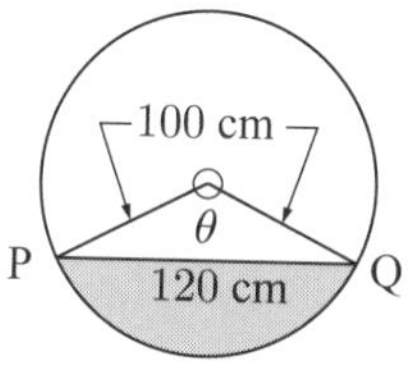


Shaded area

$= \text{area of sector} - \text{area of } \Delta\text{OPQ}$

$$= \left(\frac{\theta}{360}\right)\pi\, 100^2 - \tfrac{1}{2} \times 100 \times 100 \times \sin\theta$$
$$\approx \frac{73.74}{360} \times \pi \times 100^2 - \tfrac{1}{2} \times 100^2 \times \sin 73.74^o$$
$$\approx 1635 \text{ cm}^2 \approx 1640 \text{ cm}^2$$

**3** **a**
$$2\sin x = 6\cos x, \quad 0 \leqslant x \leqslant 2\pi$$
$$\therefore\ \frac{\sin x}{\cos x} = \tfrac{6}{2}$$
$$\therefore\ \tan x = 3$$
$$\therefore\ x = \tan^{-1}(3)$$
$$\therefore\ x \approx 1.2490 \text{ or } \pi + 1.2490$$
$$\therefore\ x \approx 1.25 \text{ or } 4.39$$

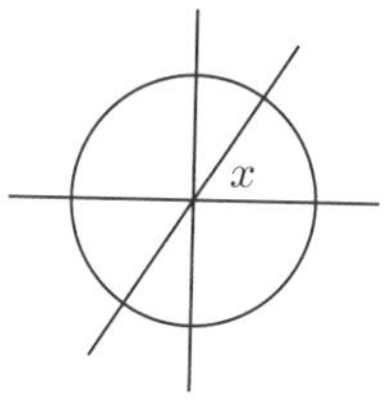


**b** $3\sin 2\theta = 4\cos\theta, \quad 0 \leqslant x \leqslant 360^o$
$$\therefore\ 3(2\sin\theta\cos\theta) - 4\cos\theta = 0$$
$$\therefore\ 2\cos\theta(3\sin\theta - 2) = 0$$
$$\therefore\ \cos\theta = 0 \text{ or } \sin\theta = \tfrac{2}{3}$$
$$\therefore\ \theta = 90^o \text{ or } 270^o,$$
$$\text{or } \theta \approx 41.8^o \text{ or } 138.2^o.$$

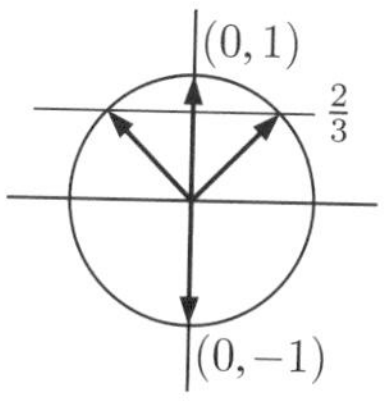


**4** **a** If the variable $D$ denotes the diameter of optical fibre produced, then $D \sim \text{N}(0.502, 0.0025^2)$.

$\text{P}(0.5 - 0.005 < D < 0.5 + 0.005)$

$= \text{P}(0.495 < D < 0.505)$

$\approx 0.882$

$1 - 0.882 \approx 0.118$, so the proportion failing to meet specifications is $11.8\%$.

**b** **i** The possible outcomes are: 0 heads, 6 tails
1 head, 5 tails
2 heads, 4 tails
3 heads, 3 tails
4 heads, 2 tails
5 heads, 1 tail
6 heads, 0 tails

**ii** $X \sim \text{B}(6, 0.2)$

**(1)** $\text{P}(X = 3) = \binom{6}{3}(0.2)^3(0.8)^3$

$\approx 0.0819$

**(2)** $\text{P}(X = 2 \text{ or fewer}) = \text{P}(X \leqslant 2)$

$\approx 0.901$

**(3)** $\text{P(H on first toss only)} = \text{P(HTTTTT)}$

$= (0.2) \times (0.8)^5$

$\approx 0.0655$

**5** $\mathbf{M}^{-1} = \frac{1}{39}\begin{pmatrix} 13 & 26 & 13 \\ 2 & 16 & 11 \\ 7 & 17 & 19 \end{pmatrix}$ {using technology}

In matrix form, the system is
$$\begin{pmatrix} 3 & -7 & 2 \\ 1 & 4 & -3 \\ -2 & -1 & 4 \end{pmatrix}\begin{pmatrix} a \\ b \\ c \end{pmatrix} = \begin{pmatrix} 25 \\ -20 \\ 21 \end{pmatrix}$$
which has the form $\mathbf{MX} = \mathbf{A}$

So, $\mathbf{X} = \mathbf{M}^{-1}\mathbf{A}$

$$\therefore \begin{pmatrix} a \\ b \\ c \end{pmatrix} = \tfrac{1}{39}\begin{pmatrix} 13 & 26 & 13 \\ 2 & 16 & 11 \\ 7 & 17 & 19 \end{pmatrix}\begin{pmatrix} 25 \\ -20 \\ 21 \end{pmatrix}$$

$$= \begin{pmatrix} 2 \\ -1 \\ 6 \end{pmatrix} \quad \text{\{using technology\}}$$

$\therefore \quad a = 2, \; b = -1, \; c = 6$

**6** **a** $6 - 3 + 1\frac{1}{2} - \frac{3}{4} + ....$ is geometric with $u_1 = 6$ and $r = -\frac{1}{2}$

As $-1 < r < 1$, the series has sum

$$\frac{u_1}{1-r} = \frac{6}{1-(-\frac{1}{2})} = 4$$

**b** If the population was $x$ students two years ago, then

$$x \times (1.052)^2 = 1250$$

$$\therefore \quad x = \frac{1250}{(1.052)^2} \approx 1129.47$$

So, there were about 1130 students.

**7** **a** **i** For $f(x)$ to be defined, $3x - 2 \neq 0$

$\therefore \quad x \neq \frac{2}{3}$

$\therefore$ the domain is $\{x \,|\, x \neq \frac{2}{3}\}$.

**ii** For $g(x)$ to be defined, $2x + 16 \geqslant 0 \quad \therefore \quad 2x \geqslant -16$

$\therefore \quad x \geqslant -8$

$\therefore$ the domain is $\{x \,|\, x \geqslant -8\}$.

**b** **i**

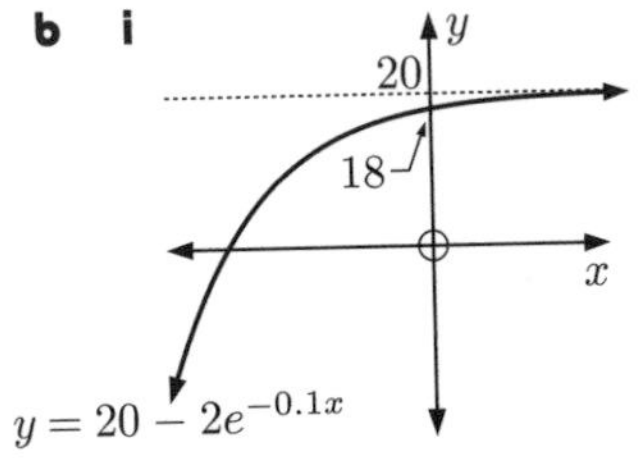


The range is $\{y \,|\, y < 20\}$.

**ii**

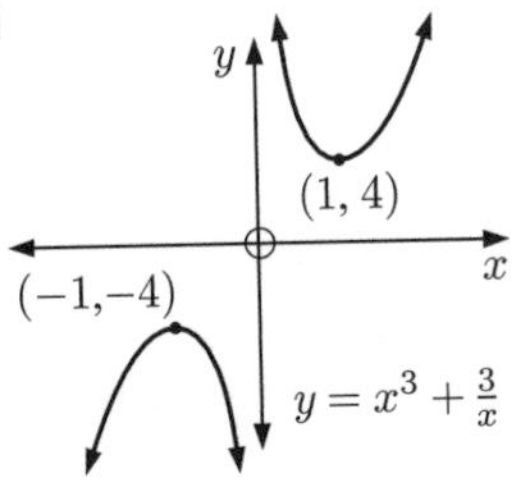


The range is $\{y \,|\, y \leqslant -4 \text{ or } y \geqslant 4\}$.

**8** **a**

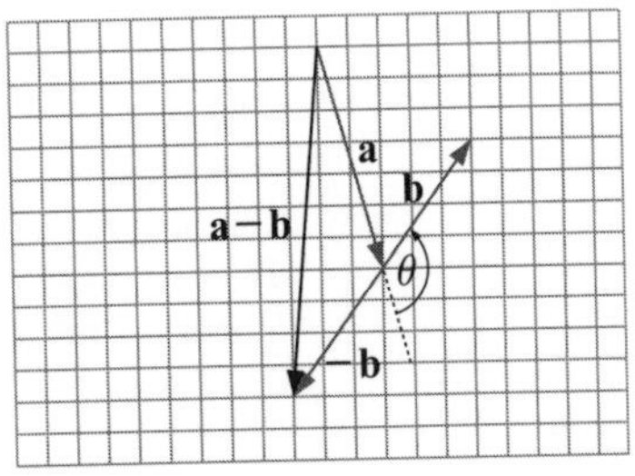


$$\mathbf{a} - \mathbf{b} = \begin{pmatrix} -1 \\ -11 \end{pmatrix}$$

**b** $\mathbf{a} \bullet \mathbf{b} = \begin{pmatrix} 2 \\ -7 \end{pmatrix} \bullet \begin{pmatrix} 3 \\ 4 \end{pmatrix} = 6 + (-28) = -22$

But $\mathbf{a} \bullet \mathbf{b} = |\mathbf{a}|\,|\mathbf{b}| \cos\theta$

$$\therefore \quad -22 = \sqrt{4+49}\,\sqrt{9+16}\,\cos\theta$$

$$\therefore \quad \cos\theta = \frac{-22}{\sqrt{53 \times 25}}$$

$$\therefore \quad \theta = \cos^{-1}\left(\frac{-22}{5\sqrt{53}}\right) \approx 127^\circ$$

**9** **a** $D = 4.7 + 3.4\cos nt$ has period $\dfrac{2\pi}{n}$

$$\therefore \quad \frac{2\pi}{n} = 12.6$$

$$\therefore \quad n = \frac{2\pi}{12.6} = \frac{\pi}{6.3}$$

**b** The rock is exposed when $D < 3$

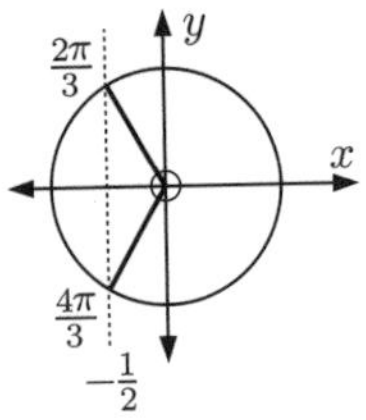


$$\therefore \quad 4.7 + 3.4\cos\left(\frac{\pi t}{6.3}\right) < 3$$

$$\therefore \quad 3.4\cos\left(\frac{\pi t}{6.3}\right) < -1.7$$

$$\therefore \quad \cos\left(\frac{\pi t}{6.3}\right) < -\tfrac{1}{2}$$

$\therefore \quad \dfrac{2\pi}{3} < \dfrac{\pi t}{6.3} < \dfrac{4\pi}{3}$ is one time interval, and it repeats 12.6 hours later.

So, $4.2 < t < 8.4$ or $16.8 < t < 21.0$

The rock will be exposed between 4:12 am and 8:24 am, and between 4:48 pm and 9:00 pm.

**10** There are 60 scores.

**a** $\text{median} = \dfrac{30\text{th} + 31\text{st}}{2} = \dfrac{13+13}{2}$

$= 13$

**b** $\text{mode} = 13$ {most frequently occurring score}

**c** $\text{mean} \approx 12.9$ {using technology}

**11** **a** $h(x) = x^2 + 8x - 2$

$$\therefore \quad h(x) = x^2 + 8x + 4^2 - 2 - 4^2$$

$$= (x+4)^2 - 18$$

**b** From **a**, the vertex of $h(x)$ is $(-4, -18)$.

**c** The graph of $h(x)$ cuts the $x$-axis

when $h(x) = 0$

$$\therefore \quad (x+4)^2 - 18 = 0$$

$$\therefore \quad (x+4)^2 = 18$$

$$\therefore \quad x + 4 = \pm 3\sqrt{2}$$

$$\therefore \quad x = -4 \pm 3\sqrt{2}$$

So, the $x$-intercepts are $-4 + 3\sqrt{2}$ and $-4 - 3\sqrt{2}$.

**12** $T = T_0 e^{-0.02t}$

**a** If the temperature reduces by 30% then

$$T = 70\% \text{ of } T_0$$

$$\therefore \quad 0.7T_0 = T_0 e^{-0.02t}$$

$$\therefore \quad e^{-0.02t} = 0.7$$

$$\therefore \quad -0.02t = \ln 0.7$$

$$\therefore \quad t = \frac{\ln(0.7)}{-0.02} \approx 17.83$$

So, it has reduced by 30% after $t = 18$ mins (to the nearest minute)

**b** $\dfrac{dT}{dt} = T_0 e^{-0.02t} \times -0.02$

$= -0.02T$

So, when $T = 20$, $\dfrac{dT}{dt} = -0.02 \times 20$

$= -0.4\ ^\circ\text{C min}^{-1}$

**13** **a** Area, $A$ = area of rectangle − area of circle radius $\dfrac{x}{2}$ − area of circle radius $x$

$$\therefore \quad A = 10 \times 2x - \pi\left(\frac{x}{2}\right)^2 - \pi x^2$$

$$= 20x - \frac{\pi x^2}{4} - \pi x^2$$

$$= 20x - \frac{\pi x^2}{4} - \frac{4\pi x^2}{4}$$

$$\therefore \quad A = 20x - \frac{5\pi}{4}x^2 \text{ cm}^2$$

$\therefore \quad \dfrac{dA}{dx} = 20 - \dfrac{5\pi}{4} \times 2x = 20 - \dfrac{5\pi x}{2}$

$\therefore \quad \dfrac{dA}{dx} = 0$ when $\dfrac{5\pi x}{2} = 20$, which is when $x = \dfrac{8}{\pi}$

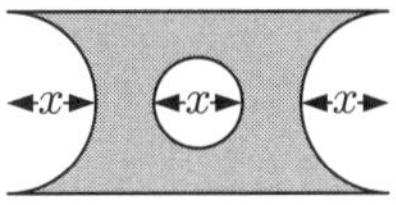


We note that $3x \leqslant 10$ and $x > 0$

$\therefore \quad 0 < x \leqslant 3\frac{1}{3}$

Sign diagram of $\dfrac{dA}{dx}$:

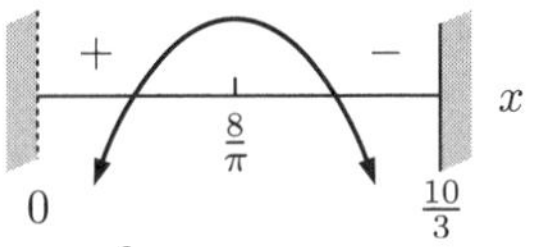


$\therefore$ A is a maximum when $x = \dfrac{8}{\pi}$.

**b** The largest value that $x$ can have is $3\frac{1}{3}$.

**14** **a**
$$\begin{aligned}&(f \circ g)(x)\\ &= f(x-2)\\ &= 2(x-2)+1\\ &= 2x-4+1\\ &= 2x-3\end{aligned}$$

**b**
$$\begin{aligned}&(f \circ f)(x)\\ &= f(2x+1)\\ &= 2(2x+1)+1\\ &= 4x+2+1\\ &= 4x+3\end{aligned}$$

**c** $f(x) = 2x+1 \quad \therefore \ f^{-1}(x)$ is given by $x = 2y+1$

$\therefore \ 2y = x - 1$

$\therefore \ y = \frac{1}{2}x - \frac{1}{2}$

$g(x) = x - 2$

$\therefore \ g^{-1}(x)$ is given by $x = y - 2$

$\therefore \ y = x + 2$

So, $f^{-1}(x)$ and $g^{-1}(x)$ meet when $\frac{1}{2}x - \frac{1}{2} = x + 2$

$\therefore \ \frac{1}{2}x = -\frac{5}{2}$

$\therefore \ x = -5$

**15** The expansion of $\left(2x - \dfrac{1}{2x}\right)^5$ has general term

$$\begin{aligned}T_{r+1} &= \tbinom{5}{r}(2x)^{5-r}\left(-\frac{1}{2x}\right)^r\\ &= \tbinom{5}{r}2^{5-r}x^{5-r}(-1)^r 2^{-r}x^{-r}\\ &= \tbinom{5}{r}2^{5-2r}(-1)^r x^{5-2r}\end{aligned}$$

The term corresponding to $x$ occurs when $5 - 2r = 1$

$\therefore \ r = 2$

So, the coefficient of $x$ is $\binom{5}{2}2^1(-1)^2 = 20$.

**16** **a**

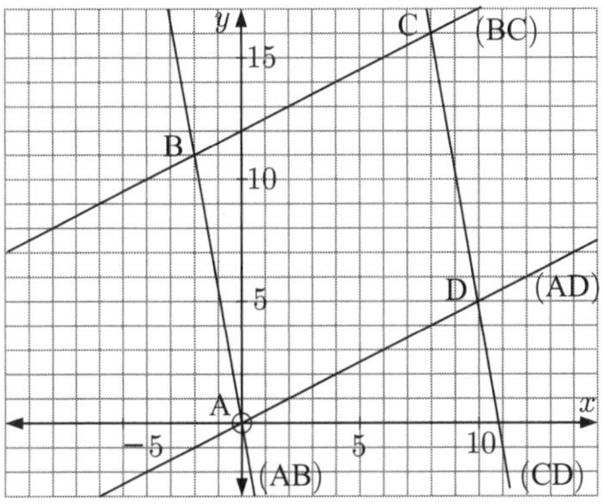


B is $(-2, 11)$, C is $(8, 16)$, and D is $(10, 5)$.

**b** **i** $\overrightarrow{AC} = \begin{pmatrix} 8-0 \\ 16-0 \end{pmatrix} = \begin{pmatrix} 8 \\ 16 \end{pmatrix}$

**ii** $\overrightarrow{DB} = \begin{pmatrix} -2-10 \\ 11-5 \end{pmatrix} = \begin{pmatrix} -12 \\ 6 \end{pmatrix}$

**iii** $\overrightarrow{AC} \bullet \overrightarrow{DB} = \begin{pmatrix} 8 \\ 16 \end{pmatrix} \bullet \begin{pmatrix} -12 \\ 6 \end{pmatrix} = -96 + 96 = 0$

**c** **i** $\overrightarrow{BC} = \begin{pmatrix} 8--2 \\ 16-11 \end{pmatrix} = \begin{pmatrix} 10 \\ 5 \end{pmatrix}$

$\therefore \ |\overrightarrow{BC}| = \sqrt{100+25} = \sqrt{125} = 5\sqrt{5}$ units

**ii** $\overrightarrow{BA} = \begin{pmatrix} 0--2 \\ 0-11 \end{pmatrix} = \begin{pmatrix} 2 \\ -11 \end{pmatrix}$

$\therefore \ |\overrightarrow{BA}| = \sqrt{4+121} = \sqrt{125} = 5\sqrt{5}$ units

**iii** $\overrightarrow{BC} \bullet \overrightarrow{BA} = |\overrightarrow{BC}||\overrightarrow{BA}|\cos\theta$

$\therefore \ \begin{pmatrix} 10 \\ 5 \end{pmatrix} \bullet \begin{pmatrix} 2 \\ -11 \end{pmatrix} = 5\sqrt{5} \times 5\sqrt{5} \times \cos\theta$

$\therefore \ 20 - 55 = 125\cos\theta$

$\therefore \ -35 = 125\cos\theta$

$\therefore \ \cos\theta = \frac{-35}{125} = -\frac{7}{25}$

$\therefore \ \theta = \cos^{-1}(-\frac{7}{25}) \approx 106.3^o$

$\therefore \ \widehat{CBA} \approx 106^o$

**d** **i** $\overrightarrow{AB} = -\overrightarrow{BA} = \begin{pmatrix} -2 \\ 11 \end{pmatrix}$

**ii** $\overrightarrow{DC} = \begin{pmatrix} 8-10 \\ 16-5 \end{pmatrix} = \begin{pmatrix} -2 \\ 11 \end{pmatrix}$

**e** From **b**, (AC) $\perp$ (DB)

From **c**, BC = BA

From **d**, $\overrightarrow{AB} = \overrightarrow{DC}$ and so (AB) || (CD)

So, ABCD is a rhombus.

**17** **a** $R(0) = 8.4 + 6.1\sin\left[\frac{\pi}{12}(0-1)\right]$

$= 8.4 + 6.1\sin(-\frac{\pi}{12})$

$\approx 6.821$

So, the UV radiation rate at sunrise was 6.82 units.

**b** The maximum UV radiation rate occurs when $\sin\left[\frac{\pi}{12}(t-1)\right] = 1$, which is when $\frac{\pi}{12}(t-1) = \frac{\pi}{2} = \frac{6\pi}{12}$

$\therefore \ t - 1 = 6$

$\therefore \ t = 7$

So, the maximum rate occurs 7 hours after sunrise.

At this time, the radiation rate is $8.4 + 6.1 = 14.5$

**c**

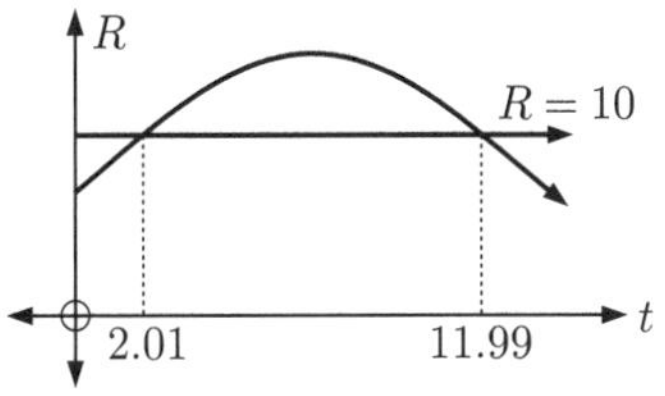


Using technology, the curves $y = 8.4 + 6.1\sin\left[\frac{\pi}{12}(t-1)\right]$ and $y = 10$ intersect at $t \approx 2.01$ and $11.99$ for $0 \leqslant t \leqslant 12$.

$\therefore$ the UV radiation rate is 10 at 2.01 hours and 11.99 hours after sunrise.

**d** Noon is 5 hours and 47 minutes $\approx 5.783$ hours after sunrise.

$\therefore$ the UV radiation rate $\approx R(5.783) \approx 14.2$

**e**

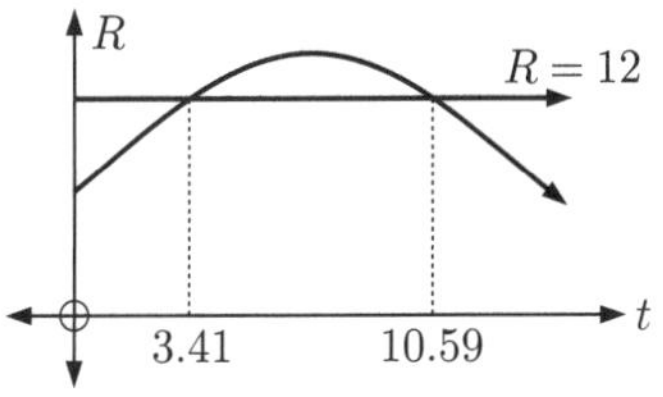

Using technology, the curves $y = 8.4 + 6.1\sin\left(\frac{\pi}{12}(t-1)\right)$ and $y = 12$ intersect at $t \approx 3.41$ and $10.59$ for $0 \leqslant t \leqslant 12$.

The UV radiation rate equals or exceeds 12 when $3.41 \leqslant t \leqslant 10.59$.

Now $3.41$ hours $\approx 3$ h 25 min

and $10.59$ hours $\approx 10$ h 35 min

so this level is reached betweeen 9:38 am and 4:48 pm.

**18** **a** Using technology, $\mu \approx 14.5$, $\sigma \approx 2.58$.

**b** If $X$ mm is the diameter of an orange then $X$ is normally distributed with mean $\mu$ and standard deviation 7 mm.

$$\text{Now } \text{P}(X > 68) = 0.98$$
$$\therefore\ \text{P}(X \leqslant 68) = 0.02$$
$$\therefore\ \text{P}\left(\frac{X-\mu}{7} \leqslant \frac{68-\mu}{7}\right) = 0.02$$
$$\therefore\ \text{P}\left(Z \leqslant \frac{68-\mu}{7}\right) = 0.02$$
$$\therefore\ \frac{68-\mu}{7} \approx -2.053\,75$$
$$\therefore\ \mu \approx 68 - 7(-2.053\,75)$$
$$\therefore\ \mu \approx 82.4 \text{ mm}$$

**c** Since the students are selected with replacement, a binomially distributed variable $X$ can be used to find the answers using $n = 20$ and $p = \frac{160}{800} = 0.2$.

**i** P(7 or fewer)
$= \text{P}(X \leqslant 7)$
$\approx 0.968$

**ii** P(3 or more)
$= 1 - \text{P}(X \leqslant 2)$
$\approx 1 - 0.206$
$\approx 0.794$

**d** $\mu = 6.72$, $\sigma = 2.31$

**i** Let $X$ be the number of minutes by which a randomly chosen bus is late.

P(bus arriving more than 15 minutes late)
$= \text{P}(X > 15)$
$\approx 0.000\,169$

So, less than 1 bus in every 5000 will arrive more than 15 minutes late.

**ii** P(bus arriving between 2 and 5 minutes late)
$= \text{P}(2 < X < 5)$
$\approx 0.208$

**19** **a** 2000, 2200, 2400, .... is arithmetic with $u_1 = 2000$, $d = 200$

$$\therefore\ u_5 = u_1 + 4d = 2000 + 4(200) = 2800 \text{ m}$$

Raymond swims 2800 m in the fifth week.

**b** 5000, 5500, 6000, .... is arithmetic with $u_1 = 5000$, $d = 500$

$$\therefore\ u_{10} = u_1 + 9d = 5000 + 9(500) = 9500 \text{ m}$$

Raymond cycles 9500 m in the tenth week.

**c** 4000, $4000 \times 1.1$, $4000 \times 1.1^2$, .... is geometric with $u_1 = 4000$, $r = 1.1$

$$\therefore\ u_4 = u_1 \times r^3 = 4000 \times 1.1^3 = 5324 \text{ m}$$

Raymond runs about 5.32 km in the fourth week.

**d** $S_{10} = 5000 + 5500 + .... + 9500$ is arithmetic with $u_1 = 5000$, $n = 10$, $u_{10} = 9500$

$$\therefore\ S_{10} = \tfrac{10}{2}(u_1 + u_{10}) = 5 \times (5000 + 9500) = 72\,500 \text{ metres}$$

After 10 weeks Raymond has cycled 72.5 km.

**e** $S_{10} = 4000 + 4000 \times 1.1 + 4000 \times 1.1^2 + ....$ is geometric with $u_1 = 4000$, $r = 1.1$, $n = 10$

$$\therefore\ S_{10} = \frac{4000(1.1^{10} - 1)}{1.1 - 1} \approx 63\,749.7 \text{ metres}$$

After 10 weeks Raymond has run about 63.7 km.

**20** **a** **i**
$$f(x) = x + 1 + 4(x-1)^{-1}$$
$$\therefore\ f'(x) = 1 - 4(x-1)^{-2}(1)$$
$$= 1 - \frac{4}{(x-1)^2}$$
$$= \frac{(x-1)^2 - 4}{(x-1)^2}$$
$$= \frac{(x-1+2)(x-1-2)}{(x-1)^2}$$
$$= \frac{(x+1)(x-3)}{(x-1)^2}$$

$f'(x)$ has sign diagram:

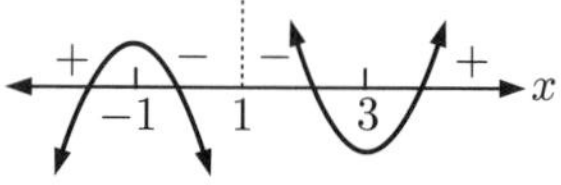


Now $f(-1) = 0 - 2 = -2$
and $f(3) = 4 + 2 = 6$
$\therefore$ there is a local maximum at $(-1, -2)$ and a local minimum at $(3, 6)$.

**ii** $f(0) = 1 + \frac{4}{-1} = 1 - 4 = -3$
$\therefore$ the $y$-intercept is $-3$.

**iii**

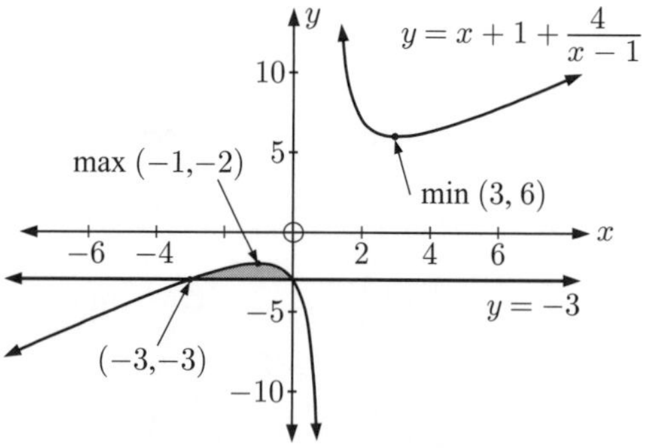


**iv** $y = -3$ meets $y = x + 1 + \dfrac{4}{x-1}$ where

$$x + 1 + \frac{4}{x-1} = -3$$
$$\therefore\ \frac{4}{x-1} = -4 - x$$
$$\therefore\ (x-1)(-4-x) = 4$$
$$\therefore\ -4x + 4 - x^2 + x = 4$$
$$\therefore\ x^2 + 3x = 0$$
$$\therefore\ x(x+3) = 0$$
$$\therefore\ x = 0 \text{ or } x = -3$$
$$\therefore\ \text{area} = \int_{-3}^{0}\left(\left(x + 1 + \frac{4}{x-1}\right) - (-3)\right) dx$$
$$\approx 1.95 \text{ units}^2 \quad \{\text{using technology}\}$$

**b**

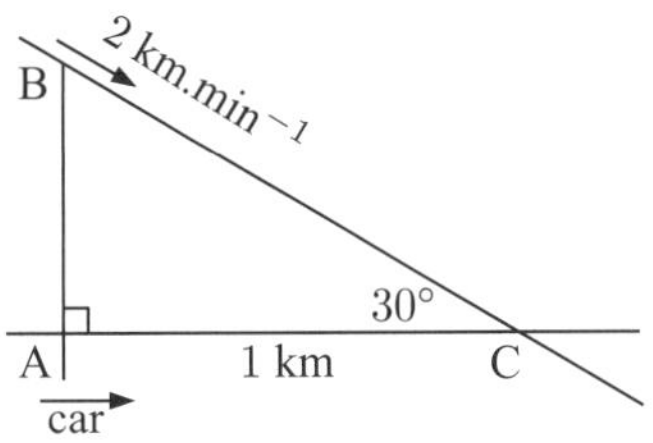


**i** $a(t) = 2e^{-2t}$

$\therefore \quad v(t) = \int a\,dt = \int 2e^{-2t}\,dt$

$= 2 \times -\frac{1}{2}e^{-2t} + c$

$= -e^{-2t} + c$

When $t = 0,\ v = 1$ $\quad \therefore \quad 1 = -e^{0} + c$

$\therefore \quad 1 = -1 + c$

$\therefore \quad c = 2$

$\therefore \quad v = -e^{-2t} + 2$

$\therefore \quad v = 2 - e^{-2t}$ km min$^{-1}$

As $t \to \infty,\ e^{-2t} \to 0$, so $v \to 2$ km min$^{-1}$

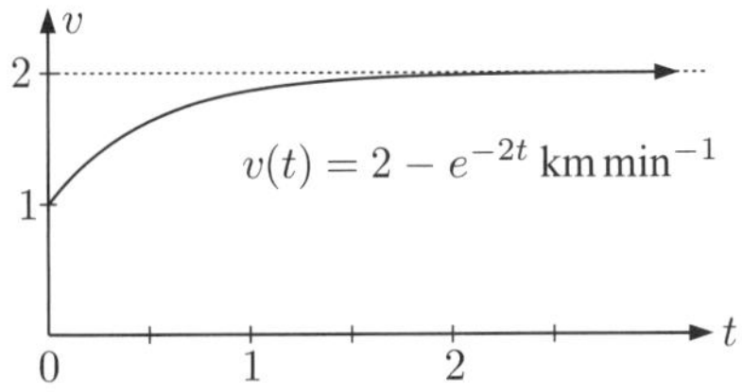


**ii** $\cos 30^{o} = \dfrac{1}{x}$

$\therefore \quad \dfrac{\sqrt{3}}{2} = \dfrac{1}{x}$

$\therefore \quad x = \frac{2}{\sqrt{3}}$

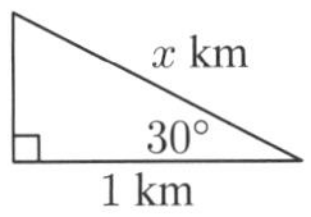


speed $= \dfrac{\text{distance}}{\text{time}}$, so time $= \dfrac{\text{distance}}{\text{speed}}$

$\therefore \quad \text{time} = \dfrac{\frac{2}{\sqrt{3}}\text{ km}}{2\text{ km min}^{-1}} = \frac{1}{\sqrt{3}}\text{ min} \approx 34.64\text{ s}$

It will take about 34.6 seconds.

**iii** $s = \int v\,dt = \int (2 - e^{-2t})\,dt$

$= 2t - (\frac{1}{-2})e^{-2t} + d$

$= 2t + \frac{1}{2}e^{-2t} + d$

When $t = 0,\ s = 0$ $\quad \therefore \quad 0 = 0 + \frac{1}{2} + d$

$\therefore \quad d = -\frac{1}{2}$

$\therefore \quad s = 2t + \frac{1}{2}e^{-2t} - \frac{1}{2}$ km

$s\left(\frac{1}{\sqrt{3}}\right) = 2\left(\frac{1}{\sqrt{3}}\right) + \frac{1}{2}e^{-\frac{2}{\sqrt{3}}} - \frac{1}{2}$

$\approx 1.1547 + 0.1576 - 0.5000$

$\approx 0.8123$ km, which is $< 1$ km

$\therefore$ the train reaches C before the car.

## SOLUTIONS TO EXAMINATION PRACTICE SET 5

**1**

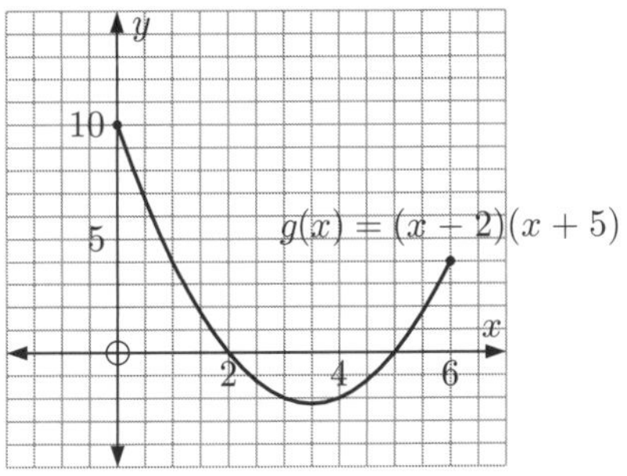


**2** $f(x) = \dfrac{5}{1-x} = 5(1-x)^{-1}$

**a** $f'(x) = -5(1-x)^{-2} \times (-1)$

$= 5(1-x)^{-2}$

$\therefore \quad f''(x) = -10(1-x)^{-3}(-1)$

$= \dfrac{10}{(1-x)^3}$

**b** $\displaystyle\int f(x)\,dx = \int \frac{5}{1-x}\,dx$

$= \displaystyle\int \frac{-5}{x-1}\,dx$

$= -5\ln(x-1) + c, \quad x - 1 > 0$

**3** **a** $\mathbf{A} = \begin{pmatrix} -1 & -1 \\ 3 & 3 \end{pmatrix}$

$\therefore \quad \mathbf{A}^2 = \begin{pmatrix} -1 & -1 \\ 3 & 3 \end{pmatrix}\begin{pmatrix} -1 & -1 \\ 3 & 3 \end{pmatrix}$

$= \begin{pmatrix} -2 & -2 \\ 6 & 6 \end{pmatrix}$

$= 2\mathbf{A}$

$\therefore \quad \frac{1}{8}\mathbf{A}^4 = \frac{1}{8}\mathbf{A}^2\mathbf{A}^2$

$= \frac{1}{8}(2\mathbf{A})(2\mathbf{A})$

$= \frac{1}{8}(4\mathbf{A}^2)$

$= \frac{1}{8}(8\mathbf{A})$

$= \mathbf{A}$

**b** $\frac{1}{8}\mathbf{A}^4 + 2\mathbf{I} = \mathbf{A} + 2\mathbf{I}$ $\quad$ {using **a**}

$= \begin{pmatrix} -1 & -1 \\ 3 & 3 \end{pmatrix} + \begin{pmatrix} 2 & 0 \\ 0 & 2 \end{pmatrix}$

$= \begin{pmatrix} 1 & -1 \\ 3 & 5 \end{pmatrix}$

So, the equation is $\begin{pmatrix} 1 & -1 \\ 3 & 5 \end{pmatrix}\begin{pmatrix} x \\ y \end{pmatrix} = \begin{pmatrix} 2 \\ 7 \end{pmatrix}$

Now $\begin{vmatrix} 1 & -1 \\ 3 & 5 \end{vmatrix} = 5 - (-3) = 8 \neq 0$,

so $\begin{pmatrix} 1 & -1 \\ 3 & 5 \end{pmatrix}^{-1}$ exists.

$\therefore \quad \begin{pmatrix} x \\ y \end{pmatrix} = \begin{pmatrix} 1 & -1 \\ 3 & 5 \end{pmatrix}^{-1}\begin{pmatrix} 2 \\ 7 \end{pmatrix}$

$= \frac{1}{8}\begin{pmatrix} 5 & 1 \\ -3 & 1 \end{pmatrix}\begin{pmatrix} 2 \\ 7 \end{pmatrix}$

$= \frac{1}{8}\begin{pmatrix} 10+7 \\ -6+7 \end{pmatrix}$

$= \begin{pmatrix} \frac{17}{8} \\ \frac{1}{8} \end{pmatrix}$

$\therefore \quad x = \frac{17}{8},\ y = \frac{1}{8}$

**4** **a**

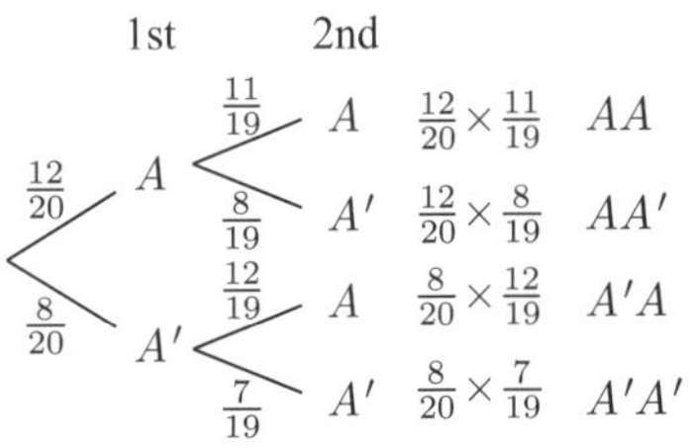


**b** $P(A'A') = \frac{8}{20} \times \frac{7}{19} = \frac{14}{95}$

**c** $P(A_1' \mid A_2) = \dfrac{P(A_1' \cap A_2)}{P(A_2)} = \dfrac{\frac{8}{20} \times \frac{12}{19}}{\frac{12}{20} \times \frac{11}{19} + \frac{8}{20} \times \frac{12}{19}}$

$= \dfrac{8 \times 12}{12 \times 11 + 8 \times 12}$

$= \frac{8}{19}$

**5** **a** $\log_2 x = 8 \quad \therefore \quad x = 2^8$

$\therefore \quad x = 256$

**b** $\log_6 x + \log_6 (x+6) = \log_6 16$

$\therefore \quad \log_6 [x(x+6)] = \log_6 16$

$\therefore \quad x^2 + 6x = 16$

$\therefore \quad x^2 + 6x - 16 = 0$

$\therefore \quad (x+8)(x-2) = 0$

$\therefore \quad x = -8 \text{ or } 2$

But $x > 0$, so $x = 2$

**c** $\log_8 64 + \log_8 2 + \log_8(\frac{1}{4}) = \log_8 x$

$\therefore \quad \log_8(64 \times 2 \times \frac{1}{4}) = \log_8 x$

$\therefore \quad x = 64 \times \frac{1}{2} = 32$

**6** **a** $f(x) = a(x+5)(x-2), \quad a \neq 0$

But $f(0) = 10$, so $a(5)(-2) = 10$

$\therefore \quad a = -1$

So, $f(x) = -1(x^2 + 3x - 10)$

$= -x^2 - 3x + 10$

$\therefore \quad a = -1, \ b = -3$ and $c = 10$.

**b** $g(x) = 2(x+3)(x-7)$ has $x$-intercepts $-3$ and $7$

$\therefore$ A is at $(-3, 0)$ and D is at $(7, 0)$.

$g(0) = 2(3)(-7) = -42$

$\therefore$ B is at $(0, -42)$.

The $x$-coordinate of the vertex is midway between those of A and D.

So, $x_D = \dfrac{-3+7}{2} = 2$

Now $g(2) = 2(5)(-5) = -50$

$\therefore$ D is at $(2, -50)$.

**7** $f(x) = 2^x$ and $g(x) = x + 2$

$g^{-1}$ is given by $x = y + 2$

$\therefore \quad y = x - 2$

$\therefore \quad g^{-1}(x) = x - 2$

So, $(g^{-1} \circ f)(x) = g^{-1}(f(x))$

$= g^{-1}(2^x)$

$= 2^x - 2$

We need to solve $2^x - 2 = 6$

$\therefore \quad 2^x = 8$

$\therefore \quad x = 3$

**8** **a** $4\sin^2 x = 1, \quad 0 < x < 2\pi$

$\therefore \quad \sin^2 x = \frac{1}{4}$

$\therefore \quad \sin x = \pm\frac{1}{2}$

$\therefore \quad x = \frac{\pi}{6}, \frac{5\pi}{6}, \frac{7\pi}{6}, \frac{11\pi}{6}$

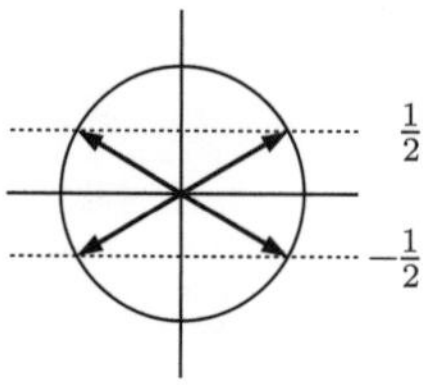


**b** $e^{2x} = 4e^x$

$\therefore \quad e^{2x} - 4e^x = 0$

$\therefore \quad e^x(e^x - 4) = 0$

$\therefore \quad e^x = 0 \text{ or } 4$

$\therefore \quad e^x = 4 \quad \{\text{as } e^x > 0 \text{ for all } x\}$

$\therefore \quad x = \ln 4$

**9** **a** In matrix form the system is

$$\underset{\mathbf{B}}{\begin{pmatrix} 2 & -3 \\ 5 & -2 \end{pmatrix}} \underset{\mathbf{X}}{\begin{pmatrix} x \\ y \end{pmatrix}} = \underset{\mathbf{C}}{\begin{pmatrix} -2 \\ 5 \end{pmatrix}}$$

$|\mathbf{B}| = \begin{vmatrix} 2 & -3 \\ 5 & -2 \end{vmatrix} = 2(-2) - (-3)5$

$= -4 + 15$

$= 11$

$\therefore \quad \mathbf{B}^{-1} = \frac{1}{11}\begin{pmatrix} -2 & 3 \\ -5 & 2 \end{pmatrix}$

Now $\mathbf{X} = \mathbf{B}^{-1}\mathbf{C}$

$\therefore \quad \begin{pmatrix} x \\ y \end{pmatrix} = \begin{pmatrix} 2 & -3 \\ 5 & -2 \end{pmatrix}^{-1} \begin{pmatrix} -2 \\ 5 \end{pmatrix}$

$= \frac{1}{11}\begin{pmatrix} -2 & 3 \\ -5 & 2 \end{pmatrix}\begin{pmatrix} -2 \\ 5 \end{pmatrix}$

$= \frac{1}{11}\begin{pmatrix} 19 \\ 20 \end{pmatrix}$

$\therefore \quad x = \frac{19}{11}, \quad y = \frac{20}{11}$

**10** **a** $y = (x+1)^2$ **b** $y = -(x+1)^2$

**c** $y = -2(x+1)^2$ **d** $y = -2(x+1)^2 + 5$

**11** **a** $a = c - \frac{1}{10}t \text{ m s}^{-2}$

$\therefore \quad v(t) = \int a(t)\,dt = \int \left(c - \frac{1}{10}t\right) dt$

$= ct - \frac{1}{10}\left(\dfrac{t^2}{2}\right) + d$

$= ct - \dfrac{t^2}{20} + d$

When $t = 0$, $v = 0$, so $d = 0$.

$\therefore \quad v(t) = ct - \dfrac{t^2}{20} \text{ m s}^{-1}$

Now when $t = 60$, $v = 30 \text{ m s}^{-1}$.

$\therefore \quad 30 = 60c - \dfrac{3600}{20}$

$\therefore \quad 30 = 60c - 180$

$\therefore \quad 210 = 60c$

$\therefore \quad c = \frac{7}{2}$

So, $v(t) = \frac{7}{2}t - \dfrac{t^2}{20}$

$= \dfrac{70t - t^2}{20}$

$= \dfrac{t(70-t)}{20}$

$v(t)$ has sign diagram:

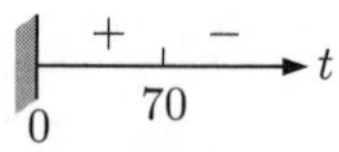


There are no sign changes for $v$ in the first 60 seconds, so there are no direction changes.

Now $s(t) = \int v(t)\,dt = \displaystyle\int \left(\frac{7}{2}t - \frac{t^2}{20}\right) dt$

$= \frac{7}{2}\left(\dfrac{t^2}{2}\right) - \dfrac{t^3}{60} + k$

$\therefore$ the total distance travelled $= s(60) - s(0)$

$= \frac{7}{4}(60)^2 - \dfrac{(60)^3}{60} + k - k$

$= (60)^2\left(\frac{7}{4} - 1\right)$

$= 2700$ m

**b** **i** $y = 12 - x - x^2$ meets $y = x + 4$ where

$12 - x - x^2 = x + 4$

$\therefore \quad 0 = x^2 + 2x - 8$

$\therefore \quad (x+4)(x-2)=0$

$\therefore \quad x=-4$ or $2$

$\therefore$ they meet at $(-4, 0)$ and $(2, 6)$.

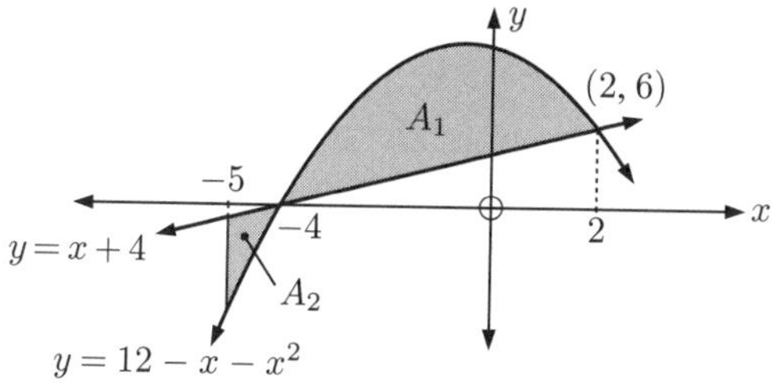


The shaded area $A_1$

$= \int_{-4}^{2} [(12-x-x^2)-(x+4)]dx$

$= \int_{-4}^{2} (-x^2-2x+8)dx$

$= \left[-\dfrac{x^3}{3}-x^2+8x\right]_{-4}^{2}$

$= \left(-\frac{8}{3}-4+16\right)-\left(\frac{64}{3}-16-32\right)$

$= 36$ units$^2$

**ii** $\int_{-5}^{2} (8-2x-x^2)\,dx$

$= \int_{-5}^{-4} (8-2x-x^2)\,dx + \int_{-4}^{2} (8-2x-x^2)\,dx$

$= -A_2 + A_1$

$= A_1 - A_2$

**12** **a** $\mathbf{A}^2 = \begin{pmatrix} 3 & 2 \\ -2 & -1 \end{pmatrix}\begin{pmatrix} 3 & 2 \\ -2 & -1 \end{pmatrix} = \begin{pmatrix} 5 & 4 \\ -4 & -3 \end{pmatrix}$

**b** If $\mathbf{A}^2 = a\mathbf{A} + b\mathbf{I}$, then

$\begin{pmatrix} 5 & 4 \\ -4 & -3 \end{pmatrix} = \begin{pmatrix} 3a & 2a \\ -2a & -a \end{pmatrix} + \begin{pmatrix} b & 0 \\ 0 & b \end{pmatrix}$

$\therefore \quad 3a+b=5,\ 2a=4,\ -2a=-4$ and $-a+b=-3$

Thus $a=2,\ b=-1$ which check in all 4 equations.

**c** $|\mathbf{A}| = -3 - -4 = 1$ which is $\neq 0$ $\quad \therefore\ \mathbf{A}^{-1}$ exists.

**d** From **b**, $\quad \mathbf{A}^2 = 2\mathbf{A} - \mathbf{I}$

$\therefore \quad \mathbf{A}^{-1}\mathbf{A}^2 = \mathbf{A}^{-1}(2\mathbf{A}-\mathbf{I})$

$\therefore \quad \mathbf{A} = 2\mathbf{I} - \mathbf{A}^{-1}$

$\therefore \quad \mathbf{A}^{-1} = 2\mathbf{I} - \mathbf{A}$

**13** **a**

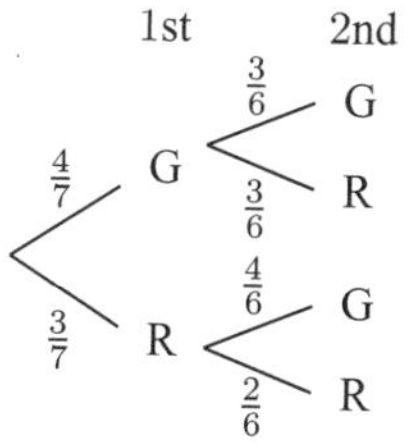


P(0 greens) $=$ P(RR) $= \frac{3}{7}\times\frac{2}{6} = \frac{1}{7}$

P(1 green) $=$ P(GR or RG)

$= \frac{4}{7}\times\frac{3}{6} + \frac{3}{7}\times\frac{4}{6} = \frac{4}{7}$

P(2 green) $=$ P(GG) $= \frac{4}{7}\times\frac{3}{6} = \frac{2}{7}$

| $x$ | 0 | 1 | 2 |
|---|---|---|---|
| $P(X=x)$ | $\frac{1}{7}$ | $\frac{4}{7}$ | $\frac{2}{7}$ |

**b** $E(X) = \sum x\,P(X=x) = 0(\frac{1}{7}) + 1(\frac{4}{7}) + 2(\frac{2}{7})$

$= \frac{8}{7}$

**14** $3x-6y=10$ has gradient $-\frac{3}{-6} = \frac{1}{2}$

$x+ky=4$ has gradient $-\dfrac{1}{k}$

**a** If the lines are parallel then $\quad \frac{1}{2} = -\dfrac{1}{k}$

$\therefore\ k=-2$

**b** If the lines are perpendicular then $\quad -\dfrac{1}{k} = -\frac{2}{1}$

$\therefore\ k=\frac{1}{2}$

**15**

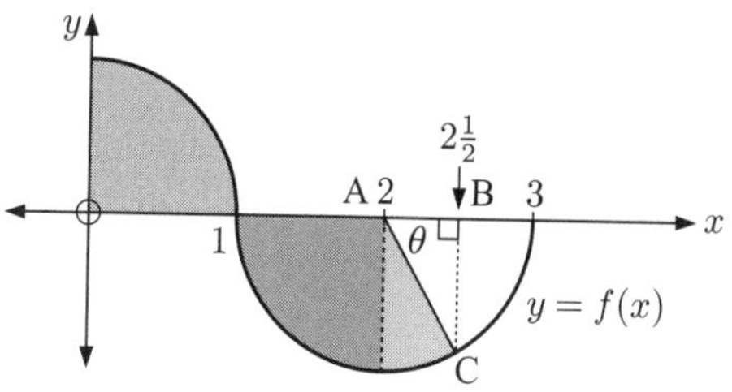


$\cos\theta = \frac{0.5}{1} = 0.5$, so $\theta = 60^o$

**a** $\int_1^{2\frac{1}{2}} f(x)\,dx = -$ area below $x$-axis

$= -$ (area of sector with $120^o$

$+$ area of triangle ABC)

$= -\left(\frac{120}{360}\pi 1^2 + \frac{1}{2}\times\frac{1}{2}\times\frac{\sqrt{3}}{2}\right)$

$= -\left(\frac{\pi}{3} + \frac{\sqrt{3}}{8}\right)$

**b** $\int_0^{2\frac{1}{2}} f(x)\,dx = \int_0^1 f(x)\,dx + \int_1^{2\frac{1}{2}} f(x)\,dx$

$= \frac{1}{4}\pi 1^2 - \left(\frac{\pi}{3} + \frac{\sqrt{3}}{8}\right)$

$= \frac{\pi}{4} - \frac{\pi}{3} - \frac{\sqrt{3}}{8}$

$= -\left(\frac{\pi}{12} + \frac{\sqrt{3}}{8}\right)$

**16** **a** $f(x) = 3+2x-x^2$

$\therefore\ f(0)=3$, and so the $y$-intercept is 3.

$f(x)=0$ when $x^2-2x-3=0$

$\therefore\ (x-3)(x+1)=0$

$\therefore\ x=-1$ or $3$

$\therefore$ the $x$-intercepts are $-1$ and 3.

**b** $f(x) = -x^2+2x+3$

$= -(x^2-2x)+3$

$= -(x^2-2x+1)+3+1$

$= -(x-1)^2+4$

$\therefore$ the vertex is at $(1, 4)$.

**c** $f(2) = 3+4-4 = 3$, so the point is $(2, 3)$.

$f'(x) = -2x+2$

$\therefore\ f'(2) = -4+2 = -2$

$\therefore$ the tangent at $(2, 3)$ has gradient $-2$.

Its equation is $\dfrac{y-3}{x-2} = -2$

$\therefore\ y-3 = -2x+4$

$\therefore\ y = -2x+7$

**d**

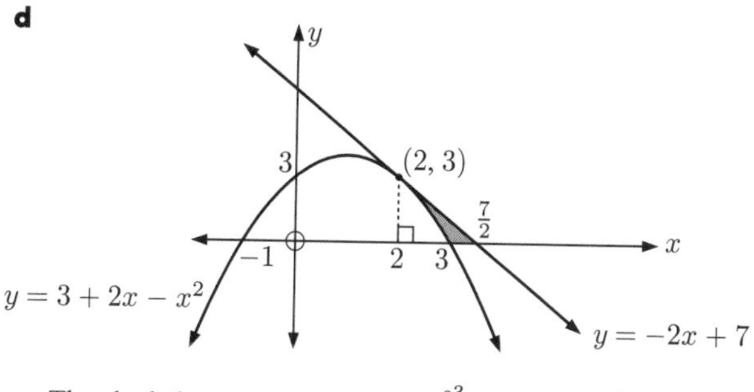


The shaded area $=$ area of $\Delta - \int_2^3 (3+2x-x^2)\,dx$

$= \frac{1}{2}\times\left(\frac{7}{2}-2\right)\times 3 - \left[3x+x^2-\frac{1}{3}x^3\right]_2^3$

$= \frac{9}{4} - \left(9+9-9-\left(6+4-\frac{8}{3}\right)\right)$

$= \frac{9}{4} - \left(9-10+\frac{8}{3}\right)$

$= \frac{9}{4} - \frac{5}{3} = \frac{7}{12}$ units$^2$

**17** **a** $\int_0^1 (2x+1)^3\,dx$

$= \left[\frac{1}{2} \times \frac{(2x+1)^4}{4}\right]_0^1$

$= \left[\frac{1}{8}(2x+1)^4\right]_0^1$

$= \frac{1}{8} \times 3^4 - \frac{1}{8} \times 1$

$= \frac{81}{8} - \frac{1}{8}$

$= 10$

**b** $\int_0^7 \sqrt{3x+4}\,dx$

$= \int_0^7 (3x+4)^{\frac{1}{2}}\,dx$

$= \left[\frac{1}{3} \times \frac{2}{3}(3x+4)^{\frac{3}{2}}\right]_0^7$

$= \frac{2}{9} \times 25^{\frac{3}{2}} - \frac{2}{9} \times 4^{\frac{3}{2}}$

$= \frac{250}{9} - \frac{16}{9}$

$= \frac{234}{9}$

$= 26$

**c** $\int_e^{2e} \frac{1}{2x+e}\,dx$

$= \left[\frac{1}{2}\ln(2x+e)\right]_e^{2e}$

$= \frac{1}{2}\ln 5e - \frac{1}{2}\ln 3e$

$= \frac{1}{2}\ln\frac{5}{3}$

**d** $\int_{\frac{\pi}{6}}^{\frac{\pi}{3}} \sin 2x\,dx$

$= \left[-\frac{1}{2}\cos 2x\right]_{\frac{\pi}{6}}^{\frac{\pi}{3}}$

$= -\frac{1}{2}\cos\frac{2\pi}{3} + \frac{1}{2}\cos\frac{\pi}{3}$

$= -\frac{1}{2}\left(-\frac{1}{2}\right) + \frac{1}{2}\left(\frac{1}{2}\right)$

$= \frac{1}{2}$

**18** **a** $f(x) = \sqrt{\ln x}$ is defined provided $\ln x \geqslant 0$

$\therefore\ x \geqslant 1$

$\therefore$ the domain is $\{x \mid x \geqslant 1\}$.

As $x \to \infty$, $\ln x \to \infty$

$\therefore$ the range is $\{y \mid y \geqslant 0\}$.

**b** $f'(x) = \frac{1}{2}(\ln x)^{-\frac{1}{2}} \times \frac{1}{x} = \frac{1}{2x\sqrt{\ln x}}$

$\therefore\ f'(e) = \frac{1}{2e\sqrt{\ln e}} = \frac{1}{2e}$

So, the tangent has gradient $\frac{1}{2e}$.

**c** $\frac{d}{dx}(x\ln x) = \ln x + \frac{x}{x}$

$= \ln x + 1$

$\int \ln x\,dx = \int(\ln x + 1 - 1)\,dx$

$= \int(\ln x + 1)\,dx - \int 1\,dx$

$= x\ln x - x + c$

**d** Volume

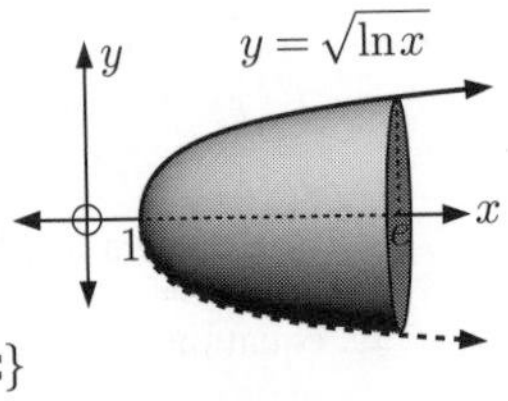


$= \int_1^e \pi y^2\,dx$

$= \int_1^e \pi \ln x\,dx$

$= \pi\left[x\ln x - x\right]_1^e$ {using **c**}

$= \pi(e\ln e - e - (\ln 1 - 1))$

$= \pi(e - e + 1)$

$= \pi$ units$^3$

**19** **a**

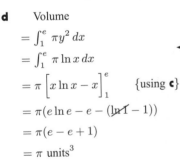

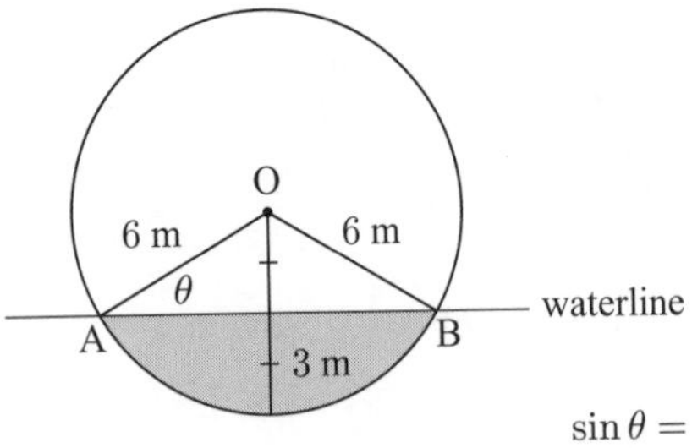


$\sin\theta = \frac{3}{6} = \frac{1}{2}$

$\therefore\ \theta = \frac{\pi}{6}$

$\therefore\ \widehat{AOB} = \frac{2\pi}{3}$

$\therefore$ Sammy is under water $\frac{1}{3}$ of the hour, or 20 minutes.

**b** Area submerged $=$ area of sector $-$ area of triangle AOB

$= \frac{1}{3} \times \pi \times 6^2 - \frac{1}{2} \times 6 \times 6 \times \sin\frac{2\pi}{3}$

$= 12\pi - 18 \times \frac{\sqrt{3}}{2}$

$= 12\pi - 9\sqrt{3}$ m$^2$

**c** $h(t) = a + b\sin ct$ m

The amplitude $= 6$, so $b = 6$.

O is 3 m above the water level, so $a = 3$.

The wheel does 3 revolutions per minute, so the period is 20 s.

$\therefore\ \frac{2\pi}{c} = 20$

$\therefore\ c = \frac{\pi}{10}$

So, $a = 3$, $b = 6$ and $c = \frac{\pi}{10}$.

**20** **a** $\mathbf{r}_A = \begin{pmatrix}1\\0\\0\end{pmatrix} + s\begin{pmatrix}1\\3\\5\end{pmatrix}$, $s \geqslant 0$

**b** $\mathbf{r}_A = \begin{pmatrix}1+s\\3s\\5s\end{pmatrix}$ and $\mathbf{r}_B = \begin{pmatrix}3+t\\4+t\\-5t\end{pmatrix}$

$\therefore$ the beams meet when $\begin{cases} 1+s = 3+t & \text{.... (1)} \\ 3s = 4+t & \text{.... (2)} \\ 5s = -5t & \text{.... (3)} \end{cases}$

Using (3), $t = -s$

Substituting into (2), $3s = 4 - s$

$\therefore\ 4s = 4$

$\therefore\ s = 1$ and $t = -1$

and this checks in (1).

So, the beams meet when $\mathbf{r}_A = \begin{pmatrix}2\\3\\5\end{pmatrix}$ which is the point (2, 3, 5).

**c** The distance travelled from (2, 3, 5) to (4, 7, 9)

$= \sqrt{(4-2)^2 + (7-3)^2 + (9-5)^2}$

$= \sqrt{2^2 + 4^2 + 4^2}$

$= 6$ units on the grid

$= 60$ m

$\therefore$ the speed is $\frac{60 \text{ m}}{2 \text{ s}} = 30$ m s$^{-1}$

**d** If $\theta$ is the angle between the beams then

$\cos\theta = \frac{\begin{pmatrix}1\\3\\5\end{pmatrix} \bullet \begin{pmatrix}1\\1\\-5\end{pmatrix}}{\sqrt{1^2+3^2+5^2}\sqrt{1^2+1^2+(-5)^2}}$

$= \frac{1+3-25}{\sqrt{35}\sqrt{27}}$

$= -\frac{21}{\sqrt{105 \times 9}}$

$= -\frac{21}{3\sqrt{105}}$ or $-\frac{7}{\sqrt{105}}$

## SOLUTIONS TO EXAMINATION PRACTICE SET 6

**1** **a** 20, 23, 26, 29, .... is arithmetic with $u_1 = 20$, $d = 3$

$\therefore\ u_{30} = u_1 + 29d$

$= 20 + 29 \times 3$

$= 20 + 87$

$= 107$

$\therefore$ there are 107 seats in the 30th row.

**b** The total number of seats is $S_{30} = \frac{30}{2}(u_1 + u_{30})$
$= 15(20 + 107)$
$= 15 \times 127$
$= 1905$ seats

**2** **a** $\log_b 45$
$= \log_b(3^2 \times 5)$
$= 2\log_b 3 + \log_b 5$
$= 2p + q$

**b** $\log_b(0.6)$
$= \log_b(\frac{3}{5})$
$= \log_b 3 - \log_b 5$
$= p - q$

**c** $\log_5 3 = \dfrac{\log_b 3}{\log_b 5} = \dfrac{p}{q}$

**3**

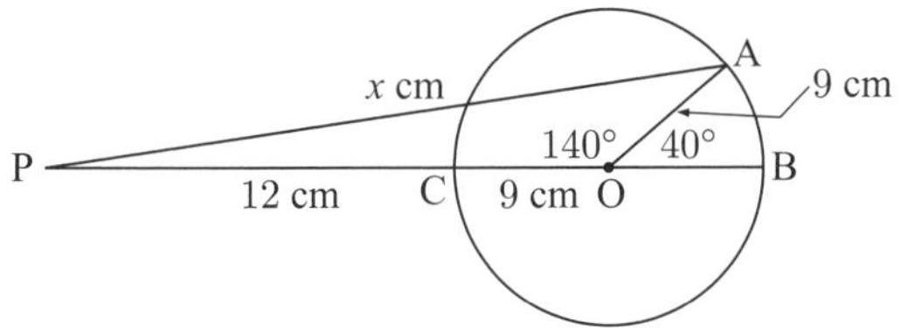


Using the cosine rule,
$x^2 = 9^2 + 21^2 - 2 \times 9 \times 21 \times \cos 140^o$
$\therefore \quad x = \sqrt{9^2 + 21^2 - 2 \times 9 \times 21 \times \cos 140^o}$
$\therefore \quad x \approx 28.5$
So, AP $\approx 28.5$ cm

**4** **a** **i**

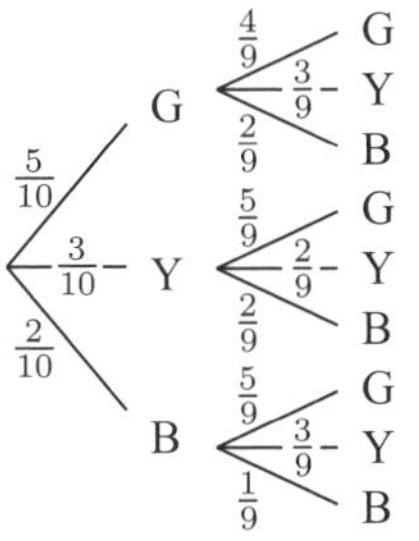


**ii** P(2 Blues) $= \frac{2}{10} \times \frac{1}{9} = \frac{2}{90} = \frac{1}{45}$
P(1 Blue) $= \frac{2}{10} \times \frac{5}{9} + \frac{2}{10} \times \frac{3}{9} + \frac{3}{10} \times \frac{2}{9} + \frac{5}{10} \times \frac{2}{9}$
$= \frac{16}{45}$
P(0 Blues) $= 1 - \frac{16}{45} - \frac{1}{45} = \frac{28}{45}$

| $x$ | 0 | 1 | 2 |
|---|---|---|---|
| $P(X = x)$ | $\frac{28}{45}$ | $\frac{16}{45}$ | $\frac{1}{45}$ |

where $X$ is the number of blue tickets chosen.

**iii** P(2 different colours)
$= 1 - $ P(2 the same colour)
$= 1 - (\frac{5}{10} \times \frac{4}{9} + \frac{3}{10} \times \frac{2}{9} + \frac{2}{10} \times \frac{1}{9})$
$= 1 - \frac{28}{90}$
$= \frac{62}{90}$
$= \frac{31}{45}$

**b** $X \sim B(25, 0.07)$
**i** $P(X = 3) \approx 0.160$
**ii** P(at least 3) $= 1 - P(X \leqslant 2)$
$\approx 1 - 0.747$
$\approx 0.253$

**5** **a** The initial investment, $u_1 = 20\,000$
So, $u_2 = 20\,000 \times 1.067$
$u_3 = 20\,000 \times (1.067)^2$
$\vdots$
$u_9 = 20\,000 \times (1.067)^8$
$\approx \$33\,600.47$
After 8 years the investment will be worth about \$33 600.

**b** The total interest earned is about \$13 600.

**6** **a** There are $x$ students in class A, $y$ students in class B, and $z$ students in class C.
$\therefore \quad x + y + z = 82$ .... (1)
$\frac{1}{6}$ of class A, $\frac{1}{3}$ of class B, and $\frac{1}{2}$ of class C study Physics.
$\therefore \quad \dfrac{x}{6} + \dfrac{y}{3} + \dfrac{z}{2} = 27$
$\therefore \quad x + 2y + 3z = 162$ .... (2)
$\frac{1}{10}$ of class A, $\frac{3}{8}$ of class B, and $\frac{1}{4}$ of class C study Chinese.
$\therefore \quad \dfrac{x}{10} + \dfrac{3y}{8} + \dfrac{z}{4} = 19$
$\therefore \quad 4x + 15y + 10z = 760$ .... (3)

**b** In matrix form, the system can be written as
$$\begin{pmatrix} 1 & 1 & 1 \\ 1 & 2 & 3 \\ 4 & 15 & 10 \end{pmatrix} \begin{pmatrix} x \\ y \\ z \end{pmatrix} = \begin{pmatrix} 82 \\ 162 \\ 760 \end{pmatrix}$$
Solving using technology, $x = 30$, $y = 24$, $z = 28$
$\therefore$ there are 30 students in class A, 24 students in class B, and 28 students in class C.

**7** **a** $f(x) = 2x^2 - 12x + 25$
$= 2(x^2 - 6x + 3^2) + 25 - 2 \times 3^2$
$= 2(x-3)^2 + 7$

**b** $g(x) = -f(x - 5)$
$= -\left[2(x-8)^2 + 7\right]$
$= -2(x-8)^2 - 7$

**8** **a** There have been $345 + 138 + 1623 + 1215$
$= 3321$ tickets sold.

**b** **i** There are $345 + 1623 = 1968$ adults.
$\therefore$ P(adult) $= \frac{1968}{3321} \approx 0.593$
**ii** There are $1623 + 1215 = 2838$ people in category B seats.
$\therefore$ P(category B) $= \frac{2838}{3321} \approx 0.855$
**iii** There are $138 + 1215 = 1353$ concession ticket holders.
$\therefore$ P(category A | concession ticket holder) $= \frac{138}{1353}$
$\approx 0.102$

**9** Let the unknown mean and standard deviation be $\mu$ and $\sigma$ respectively.
Now $P(X < 20) = 0.08$
$\therefore \quad P\left(\dfrac{X - \mu}{\sigma} < \dfrac{20 - \mu}{\sigma}\right) = 0.08$
$\therefore \quad P\left(Z < \dfrac{20 - \mu}{\sigma}\right) = 0.08$
$\therefore \quad \dfrac{20 - \mu}{\sigma} \approx -1.4051$
$\therefore \quad 20 - \mu \approx -1.4051\sigma$ .... (1)

Also, $P(X > 35) = 0.23$

$\therefore\ P(X \leqslant 35) = 0.77$

$\therefore\ P\left(\frac{X-\mu}{\sigma} \leqslant \frac{35-\mu}{\sigma}\right) = 0.77$

$\therefore\ P\left(Z \leqslant \frac{35-\mu}{\sigma}\right) = 0.77$

$\therefore\ \frac{35-\mu}{\sigma} \approx 0.7388$

$\therefore\ 35-\mu \approx 0.7388\sigma$ .... (2)

Solving (1) and (2) simultaneously, we find $\sigma \approx 7.00$ and $\mu \approx 29.8$.

So, the average age is about 30 years with standard deviation 7 years.

**10** The expansion of $\left(\frac{2}{x}+x^2\right)^6$ has general term

$$T_{r+1} = \binom{6}{r}\left(\frac{2}{x}\right)^{6-r}(x^2)^r$$
$$= \binom{6}{r}2^{6-r}x^{r-6+2r}$$
$$= \binom{6}{r}2^{6-r}x^{3r-6}$$

For the constant term, $3r-6=0$

$\therefore\ r = 2$

So, the constant term is $\binom{6}{2}2^4 = 240$

**11** $f(x) = a\ln x + b$

$\therefore\ f'(x) = \frac{a}{x}$

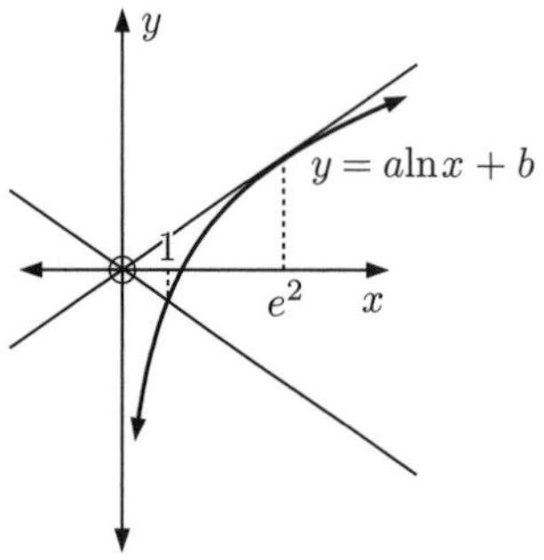


Now $f(1) = a\ln 1 + b = b$

and $f'(1) = a$

The normal at $(1, b)$ has gradient $-\frac{1}{a}$, so its equation is

$x + ay = 1 + ab$

But this normal passes through O, so $1 + ab = 0$

$\therefore\ ab = -1$ .... $(*)$

Also, $f(e^2) = a\ln e^2 + b = 2a + b$

and $f'(e^2) = \frac{a}{e^2}$

The tangent at $(e^2, 2a+b)$ has gradient $\frac{a}{e^2}$, so its equation is

$$ax - e^2y = ae^2 - e^2(2a+b)$$
$$= -e^2(a+b)$$

This tangent also passes through O, so $-e^2(a+b) = 0$

$\therefore\ b = -a$

Using $(*)$, $-a^2 = -1$

$\therefore\ a^2 = 1$

We are given $a > 0$, so $a = 1$ and $b = -1$

**12** **a** Let $S$ represent sport and $M$ represent movies.

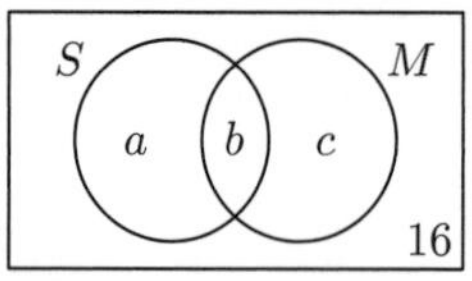


We are given that $a + b = 35$

$b + c = 28$

and $a + b + c = 44$

$\therefore\ c = 9,\ b = 19,\ a = 16$

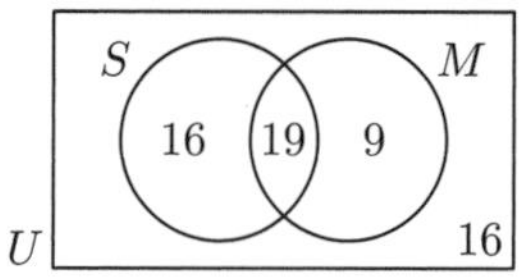


**b** **i** P(watches movies) $\approx \frac{28}{60} \approx 0.467$

**ii** P(not interested in sport) $\approx \frac{9+16}{60} \approx 0.417$

**iii** P(likes sport and movies) $\approx \frac{19}{60} \approx 0.317$

**iv** P(likes movies but not sport) $\approx \frac{9}{60} \approx 0.15$

**13** **a** $25^x - 5^{x+1} + 6 = 0$

$\therefore\ (5^x)^2 - 5(5^x) + 6 = 0$

$\therefore\ (5^x - 3)(5^x - 2) = 0$

$\therefore\ 5^x = 2$ or $3$

$\therefore\ x = \log_5 2$ or $\log_5 3$

$\therefore\ x \approx 0.431$ or $0.683$

**b** $\ln\sqrt{x} - \ln x^2 = (\ln x)^2$

$\therefore\ \frac{1}{2}\ln x - 2\ln x = (\ln x)^2$

$\therefore\ -\frac{3}{2}\ln x = (\ln x)^2$

$\therefore\ \ln x\left(\ln x + \frac{3}{2}\right) = 0$

$\therefore\ \ln x = 0$ or $-\frac{3}{2}$

$\therefore\ x = 1$ or $e^{-\frac{3}{2}}$

$\therefore\ x = 1$ or $x \approx 0.223$

**14** $\tan\theta = -2$

and $\frac{\pi}{2} < \theta < \frac{3\pi}{2}$

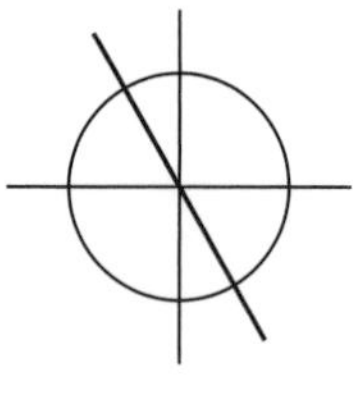

So $\cos\theta < 0$ and $\sin\theta > 0$.

Now $\frac{\sin\theta}{\cos\theta} = -2$

$\therefore\ \sin^2\theta = 4\cos^2\theta$

$\therefore\ \sin^2\theta = 4(1 - \sin^2\theta)$

$\therefore\ 5\sin^2\theta = 4$

$\therefore\ \sin^2\theta = \frac{4}{5}$

Since $\sin\theta > 0$, $\sin\theta = \frac{2}{\sqrt{5}}$ and $\cos\theta = -\frac{1}{\sqrt{5}}$

**15** **a** $P(t) = 15 + t + 2\sin t$

$\therefore\ P'(t) = 1 + 2\cos t$

$\therefore\ P'(t) = 0$ when $\cos t = -\frac{1}{2}$

$\therefore\ t = \frac{2\pi}{3}$ or $\frac{4\pi}{3}$

↑ A    ↑ B

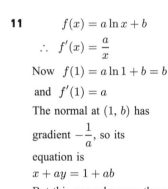

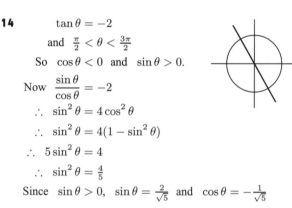

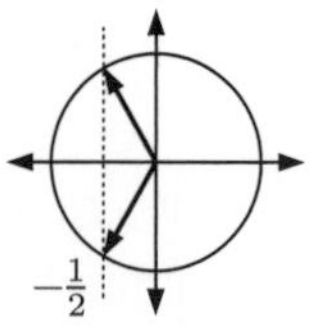


Now $P\left(\frac{2\pi}{3}\right) = 15 + \frac{2\pi}{3} + 2\left(\frac{\sqrt{3}}{2}\right) \approx 18.83$

$\therefore$ A is $(2.09, 18.8)$.

**b** $P\left(\frac{4\pi}{3}\right) = 15 + \frac{4\pi}{3} + 2\left(-\frac{\sqrt{3}}{2}\right) \approx 17.46$

The price fall is $P\left(\frac{2\pi}{3}\right) - P\left(\frac{4\pi}{3}\right) \approx 18.83 - 17.46$

$\approx \$1.37$

**16** A is at $(-2, 24)$, B is at $(18, 9)$, C is at $(8, -15)$.

**a** $\begin{pmatrix} p \\ q \end{pmatrix}$ is the position vector of A.

$\therefore\ p = -2,\ q = 24.$

**b** $\overrightarrow{AB} = \begin{pmatrix} 18 - -2 \\ 9 - 24 \end{pmatrix} = \begin{pmatrix} 20 \\ -15 \end{pmatrix}$

**c** $\overrightarrow{AB}$ has length $\sqrt{20^2 + (-15)^2}$

$= \sqrt{625}$

$= 25$

The yacht has speed 10 km h$^{-1}$, so its velocity vector is $\frac{10}{25} \times \begin{pmatrix} 20 \\ -15 \end{pmatrix} = \begin{pmatrix} 8 \\ -6 \end{pmatrix}$.

**d** At 10:30 am, $t = 1\frac{1}{2}$

$$\text{So, } \begin{pmatrix} x \\ y \end{pmatrix} = \begin{pmatrix} -2 \\ 24 \end{pmatrix} + \tfrac{3}{2}\begin{pmatrix} 8 \\ -6 \end{pmatrix} = \begin{pmatrix} -2 \\ 24 \end{pmatrix} + \begin{pmatrix} 12 \\ -9 \end{pmatrix} = \begin{pmatrix} 10 \\ 15 \end{pmatrix}$$

$\therefore$ the yacht is 10 km east and 15 km north of O.

**e** We need to solve $\begin{pmatrix} -2 \\ 24 \end{pmatrix} + t\begin{pmatrix} 8 \\ -6 \end{pmatrix} = \begin{pmatrix} 18 \\ 9 \end{pmatrix}$

$\therefore$ $-2 + 8t = 18$ and $24 - 6t = 9$

$\therefore$ $8t = 20$ and $6t = 15$

We see that $t = 2\frac{1}{2}$ satisfies both equations.

$2\frac{1}{2}$ hours past 9:00 am is 11:30 am, so the time is 11:30 am.

**f** $\overrightarrow{BC} = \begin{pmatrix} 8-18 \\ -15-9 \end{pmatrix} = \begin{pmatrix} -10 \\ -24 \end{pmatrix} = 2\begin{pmatrix} -5 \\ -12 \end{pmatrix}$

So, $|\overrightarrow{BC}| = 2 \times \sqrt{25+144} = 2 \times 13 = 26$

$\therefore$ C is 26 km from B.

$\therefore$ the yacht, travelling at 13 km h$^{-1}$, will take 2 hours to reach C.

$\therefore$ the yacht will reach C 2 hours after 11:30 am, which is 1:30 pm.

**g** The velocity vector of the yacht from B to C is $\begin{pmatrix} -5 \\ -12 \end{pmatrix}$.

$\therefore$ the position vector of the yacht from B to C is

$$\begin{pmatrix} x \\ y \end{pmatrix} = \begin{pmatrix} 18 \\ 9 \end{pmatrix} + s\begin{pmatrix} -5 \\ -12 \end{pmatrix}, \quad 0 \leqslant s \leqslant 2$$

where $s$ is the time in hours after 11:30 am.

Now $s = t - 2.5$, so the coordinates are

$(18 + (t-2.5)(-5),\ 9 + (t-2.5)(-12))$

or $(30.5 - 5t,\ 39 - 12t)$, $2.5 \leqslant t \leqslant 4.5$.

**h** If X is $(30.5 - 5t, 39 - 12t)$,

$\overrightarrow{OX} = \begin{pmatrix} 30.5 - 5t \\ 39 - 12t \end{pmatrix}$ and $\overrightarrow{BC} = 2\begin{pmatrix} -5 \\ -12 \end{pmatrix}$

At the closest point, $\overrightarrow{OX} \perp \overrightarrow{BC}$

$\therefore$ $\overrightarrow{OX} \bullet \overrightarrow{BC} = 0$

$\therefore$ $-5(30.5 - 5t) - 12(39 - 12t) = 0$

$\therefore$ $-152.5 + 25t - 468 + 144t = 0$

$\therefore$ $169t = 620.5$

$\therefore$ $t \approx 3.6716$

$\therefore$ the yacht was closest at 9 am + 3 h 40.3 min which is 12:40:18 pm.

**17** $N = b + cT + \dfrac{a}{T+1}$

**a** When $T = 1$, $N = 4$ thousand

$\therefore$ $\dfrac{a}{2} + b + c = 4$

$\therefore$ $a + 2b + 2c = 8$ .... (1)

When $T = 2$, $N = 5$ thousand

$\therefore$ $\dfrac{a}{3} + b + 2c = 5$

$\therefore$ $a + 3b + 6c = 15$ .... (2)

When $T = 3$, $N = 6.5$ thousand

$\therefore$ $\dfrac{a}{4} + b + 3c = 6.5$

$\therefore$ $a + 4b + 12c = 26$ .... (3)

We thus have the system $\begin{cases} a + 2b + 2c = 8 \\ a + 3b + 6c = 15 \\ a + 4b + 12c = 26 \end{cases}$

**b** The system can be written in matrix form as

$$\begin{pmatrix} 1 & 2 & 2 \\ 1 & 3 & 6 \\ 1 & 4 & 12 \end{pmatrix}\begin{pmatrix} a \\ b \\ c \end{pmatrix} = \begin{pmatrix} 8 \\ 15 \\ 26 \end{pmatrix}.$$

Using technology, the solution is: $a = 6$, $b = -1$, $c = 2$.

**c** Using **b**, $N = -1 + 2T + \dfrac{6}{T+1}$

When $N = 10$ thousand, $10 = -1 + 2T + \dfrac{6}{T+1}$

$\therefore$ $2T + \dfrac{6}{T+1} - 11 = 0$

$\therefore$ $2T(T+1) + 6 - 11(T+1) = 0$

$\therefore$ $2T^2 - 9T - 5 = 0$

$\therefore$ $(2T+1)(T-5) = 0$

But $T > 0$, so $T = 5$.

$\therefore$ the population reached 10 000 at the beginning of 2005.

**18** **a**

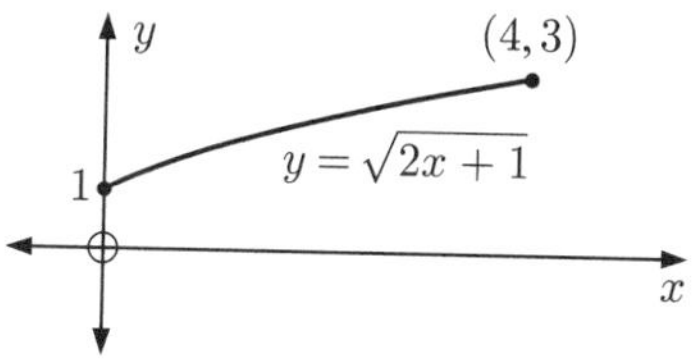


**b** Volume

$= \pi \int_0^4 \left(\sqrt{2x+1}\right)^2 dx$

$= \pi \int_0^4 (2x+1)\, dx$

$= \pi \left[\dfrac{2x^2}{2} + x\right]_0^4$

$= \pi[(16+4) - (0)]$

$= 20\pi$ units$^3$

**c** We need to find $k$ such that

$\pi \int_k^{2k} (2x+1)\, dx = 30$ units$^3$

$\therefore$ $\left[x^2 + x\right]_k^{2k} = \dfrac{30}{\pi}$

$\therefore$ $\left(4k^2 + 2k\right) - \left(k^2 + k\right) = \dfrac{30}{\pi}$

$\therefore$ $3k^2 + k = \dfrac{30}{\pi}$

Using technology, $k \approx -1.959$ or $1.625$

But $k > 0$, so $k \approx 1.63$

**d** **i** The line has gradient $= \dfrac{0 - r}{h - 0} = \dfrac{-r}{h}$

$\therefore$ its equation is $y = -\dfrac{r}{h}x + r$

**ii**

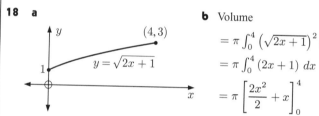

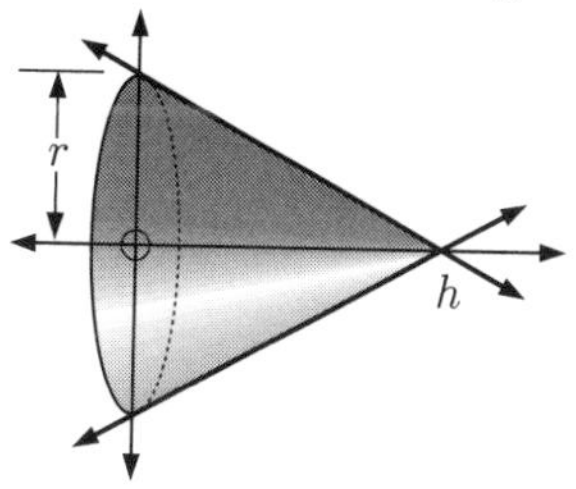


The solid of revolution is a cone of base radius $r$ and height $h$.

**iii** $\text{Volume} = \pi \int_0^h \left(-\frac{r}{h}x + r\right)^2 dx$

$= \pi r^2 \int_0^h \left(1 - \frac{x}{h}\right)^2 dx$

$= \pi r^2 \left[ \frac{1}{-\frac{1}{h}} \frac{\left(1-\frac{x}{h}\right)^3}{3} \right]_0^h$

$= \pi r^2 \left(-\frac{h}{3}(0) - \frac{-h}{3}(1)\right)$

$= \pi r^2 \times \frac{h}{3}$

$= \frac{1}{3}\pi r^2 h$

**19** **a** **i** $y(t) = 8 - 4\cos(\frac{\pi t}{4})$ has period $\frac{2\pi}{\frac{\pi}{4}} = 8$

**ii** $y(t)$ is a minimum when $\cos(\frac{\pi t}{4}) = 1$

$\therefore \quad \frac{\pi t}{4} = 0 + k\,2\pi, \quad k \in \mathbb{Z}$

$\therefore \quad t = 8k, \quad k \in \mathbb{Z}$

On the given domain, this is at $t = 0$ and $t = 8$.

The minimum value is $8 - 4 = 4$.

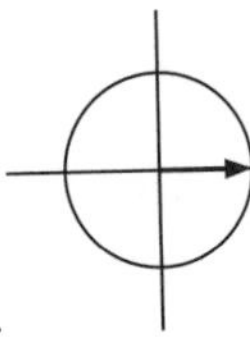


**iii** $y(t)$ has a maximum value of $8 - 4(-1) = 12$ when $\cos(\frac{\pi t}{4}) = -1$, which is when $t = 4$

**iv**

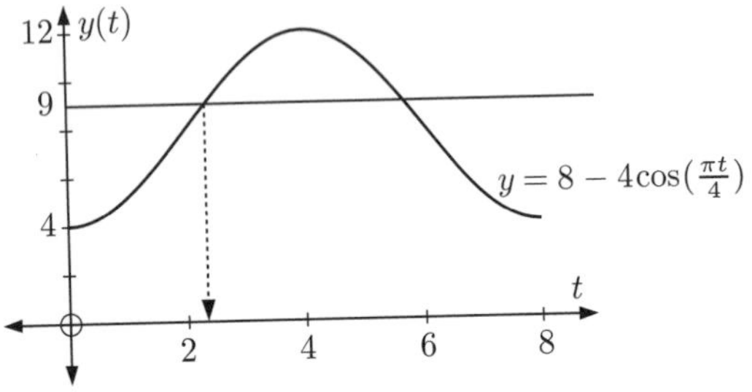


**b** **i** At low tide the depth is 4 m, and at high tide the depth is 12 m.

**ii** The next high tide is 4 hours later, which is at 3:30 pm.

**iii** When $y(t) = 9$,

$9 = 8 - 4\cos(\frac{\pi t}{4})$

$\therefore \quad 4\cos(\frac{\pi t}{4}) = -1$

$\therefore \quad \cos(\frac{\pi t}{4}) = -\frac{1}{4}$

$\therefore \quad \frac{\pi t}{4} \approx 1.8234$ or $4.4597$

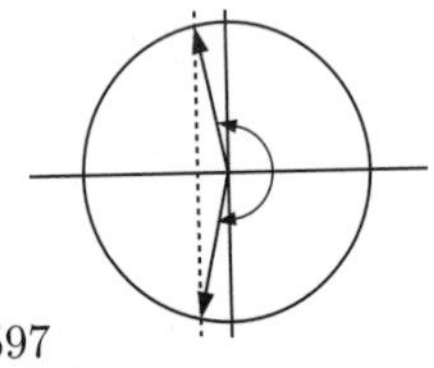

Using technology, the smallest positive solution is $t \approx 2.32$ hours $\approx 2$ hours 19 minutes

$\therefore$ the earliest time the ship can enter the harbour is 1:49 pm.

**20** **a** A(2, −1, 0), B(−10, 50, 1)

$\therefore \quad \overrightarrow{AB} = \begin{pmatrix} -10-2 \\ 50--1 \\ 1-0 \end{pmatrix} = \begin{pmatrix} -12 \\ 51 \\ 1 \end{pmatrix}$

and $|\overrightarrow{AB}| = \sqrt{144 + 2601 + 1} \approx 52.4$

So, the aircraft is about 52.4 km away.

**b** The aircraft has direction vector $= \begin{pmatrix} 4 \\ -3 \\ 0 \end{pmatrix}$

which has length $\sqrt{16+9+0} = \sqrt{25} = 5$ km

Its speed is 200 $\text{km h}^{-1}$, so its velocity vector

$= 40\begin{pmatrix} 4 \\ -3 \\ 0 \end{pmatrix} = \begin{pmatrix} 160 \\ -120 \\ 0 \end{pmatrix}.$

So, the position vector is

$\mathbf{r} = \begin{pmatrix} x \\ y \\ z \end{pmatrix} = \begin{pmatrix} -10 \\ 50 \\ 1 \end{pmatrix} + t\begin{pmatrix} 160 \\ -120 \\ 0 \end{pmatrix}$

(position at 10:00 am; velocity vector)

**c** At 10:30 am, $t = \frac{1}{2}$

$\therefore \quad \begin{pmatrix} x \\ y \\ z \end{pmatrix} = \begin{pmatrix} -10 \\ 50 \\ 1 \end{pmatrix} + \begin{pmatrix} 80 \\ -60 \\ 0 \end{pmatrix} = \begin{pmatrix} 70 \\ -10 \\ 1 \end{pmatrix}$

$\therefore$ the aircraft is at $(70, -10, 1)$.

**d** When $t = 0$, the helicopter has $z$-coordinate $= 0.5$

$\therefore$ it is flying at 500 m.

**e** The velocity vector $= \begin{pmatrix} -120 \\ -50 \\ 0.5 \end{pmatrix}$

$\therefore$ its speed $= \sqrt{14\,400 + 2500 + 0.25}$

$\approx 130 \text{ km h}^{-1}$

**f** **i** The helicopter is directly below the airplane when

$\begin{pmatrix} -10 \\ 50 \end{pmatrix} + t\begin{pmatrix} 160 \\ -120 \end{pmatrix} = \begin{pmatrix} 74 \\ 29 \end{pmatrix} + t\begin{pmatrix} -120 \\ -50 \end{pmatrix}$

$\therefore \quad -10 + 160t = 74 - 120t$ and

$50 - 120t = 29 - 50t$

$\therefore \quad 280t = 84$ and $70t = 21$

Both equations are satisfied by $t = 0.3$ and so the time is 10:18 am.

**ii** $\mathbf{h} = \begin{pmatrix} x \\ y \\ z \end{pmatrix} = \begin{pmatrix} 74 \\ 29 \\ 0.5 \end{pmatrix} + 0.3\begin{pmatrix} -120 \\ -50 \\ 0.5 \end{pmatrix} = \begin{pmatrix} 38 \\ 14 \\ 0.65 \end{pmatrix}$

So, the helicopter is at $(38, 14, 0.65)$.

**iii** The distance from the helicopter to the airport

$= \sqrt{(38-2)^2 + (14--1)^2 + (0.65-0)^2}$

$\approx 39.0$ km

So the helicopter, travelling at $\approx 130 \text{ km h}^{-1}$, will arrive at the airport $\approx \frac{39.0}{130} \approx 0.3$ hours after 10:18 am.

So, the helicopter will arrive at 10:36 am.